NANOMATERIALS: NEW RESEARCH

NANOMATERIALS: NEW RESEARCH

B.M. CARUTA
EDITOR

Nova Science Publishers, Inc.
New York

For permission to use material from this book please contact us:
Telephone 631-231-7269; Fax 631-231-8175
Web Site: http://www.novapublishers.com

NOTICE TO THE READER

Library of Congress Cataloging-in-Publication Data
Available upon request

ISBN: 1-59454-369-0

Published by Nova Science Publishers, Inc. ✢ New York

Contents

PREFACE

Materials science includes those parts of chemistry and physics that deal with the properties of materials.

It encompasses four classes of materials, the study of each of which may be considered a separate field: metals; ceramics; polymers and composites. Materials science is often referred to as materials science and engineering because it has many applications. Industrial applications of materials science include processing techniques (casting, rolling, welding, ion implantation, crystal growth, thin-film deposition, sintering, glassblowing, etc.), analytical techniques (electron microscopy, x-ray diffraction, calorimetry, nuclear microscopy (HEFIB) etc.), materials design, and cost/benefit tradeoffs in industrial production of materials. This book presents new research directions in the very new field of nanomaterials.

In: Nanomaterials: New Research
Editor: B.M. Caruta, pp. 1-79
ISBN: 1-59454-369-0

Chapter 1

WEAR RESISTANT THERMOSETTING POLYMER BASED NANOCOMPOSITES

Ming Qiu Zhang[1*], Min Zhi Rong[1], Bernd Wetzel[2] and Klaus Friedrich[2]

[1]Materials Science Institute, Key Laboratory for Polymeric Composite and Functional Materials of Ministry of Education, Zhongshan University, Guangzhou 510275, P. R. China

[2]Institute for Composite Materials (IVW), University of Kaiserslautern, D-67663 Kaiserslautern, Germany

ABSTRACT

Thermosetting resins are finding increasing use in a wide range of engineering applications because of their on-the-spot processing characteristics, good affinity to heterogeneous materials, considerable creep and solvent resistance, and higher operating temperature. For example, they have been frequently incorporated with various inorganic particles as the binder to formulate wear resistant composite materials. The tribological properties of these composites, however, are factually far from the specifications demanded by consumers for various working conditions, especially in the case of protective coatings that should shield the substrates against mechanical wear. This is due to both the poor interfacial adhesion around the particle boundaries and the heterogeneous dispersion of the particles.

Since the predominant feature of nanoparticles lies in their ultra-fine dimension, a large fraction of the filler atoms can reside at the interface and can lead to a strong interfacial interaction when the nanoparticles are well dispersed on a nanometer level in the surrounding polymer matrix. As the interfacial structure plays a critical role in determining the composites' properties, nanocomposites coupled with a great number of interfaces are expected to provide unusual properties, and the shortcomings induced by

---

* Prof. Ming Qiu ZHANG; Materials Science Institute; Zhongshan University; Guangzhou 510275; P. R. China; Tel./Fax: +86-20-84036576; E-mail: ceszmq@zsu.edu.cn

the heterogeneity of conventional particles filled composites would also be avoided. On the other hand, the wear mechanisms involved in the nanocomposites are different from those of conventional composites because the fillers have the same size as the segments of the surrounding polymer chains. Severe wear caused by abrasion and particle pull-out associated with the accumulation of detached harder bulk particulate fillers adherent to the frictional surface is replaced by rather mild wear resulting from the fine individual debris which acts as a lubricant and contributes to material removal by polishing.
This chapter gives a brief but thorough review of the state of the art in the area of wear resistant nanocomposites and then carefully describes the progress made by the authors, which is focused on the surface pre-treatment of the nanoparticles and its effect on the trobological performance improvement of thermosetting nanocomposites.

1. INTRODUCTION

1.1. Particulate Filled Polymeric Composites Used for Tribological Applications

Composite materials have been employed in a vast range of applications because they offer combinations of properties unattainable with metals, ceramics or polymers alone. Especially particulate filled polymers form an interesting class of composites associated with specific microstructures, a viscoelastic nature, more preferable damage tolerance, chemical inertness, a better wear resistance, and, as a result, lower costs of routine maintenance. In this way, they can substitute traditional metallic components as self-lubricating materials employed in unlubricated, corrosive, low velocity and high loading circumstances.

Over the years, many species of inorganic particles have been used as fillers for polymers, such as solid lubricants, metal powders and oxides, and inorganic compounds. They not only act as a reinforcing agent for the bulk properties of the composites, but also impart specific properties. Regarding the effectiveness of these fillers in the modification of the wear and friction performance, hypotheses and mechanisms have been proposed by a number of researchers [1, 2], but until now, the tribological behavior of particulate filled polymers is still clouded with mysteries. In the case of thermoplastic composites, effects of fillers were mainly attributed to the following objectives:

I. modifying counterpart surface and supporting the applied load during wearing [3, 4];
II. increasing the shear strength of matrix, preventing the occurrence of large-scale destruction of polymer [5];
III. improving the adhesion of the transfer film into the counterface [6-12].

For thermosetting composites, relatively little works have been presented; recent studies were focused on fabric reinforced poly (vinyl butyral)-modified phenolic resin composites [13], unidirectionally oriented E-glass fiber reinforced epoxy composites [14], and silica filled epoxy-based coatings [15]. Nevertheless, some valuable findings are still available. For example, the adhesion between thermosetting binder and fillers should be strong enough because not only disintegration of the fillers but also detached particles were frequently observed to be torn out of both the phenolic and epoxy resin composites when an indentor moved over the systems, resulting in sharp fluctuations in the measured coefficient of friction [16]. Yamaguchi et al [17] found that the wear rates of unsaturated polyesters and epoxy resins filled with different proportions of SiO_2 decreased significantly only at a high loading of 40 wt%, which is factually detrimental to the coating applications. Sekiguchi et al [18] studied the effects of species of conventional solid lubricants (PTFE, MoS_2, and graphite) on the tribological properties of newly synthesized thermosetting resins, i.e. condensed polycyclic aromatic (COPNA) resin. The results indicated that the most effective filler for wear reduction is graphite, while the friction coefficient is 0.35-0.8 times that of the unfilled version. Symonds and Mellor [15] stated that the silica particles in an epoxy matrix, exposed to wear loading, support a large fraction of the load. Since the particles fracture before they plastically deform, the true contact area and hence the frictional coefficient remain constant. Besides, the silica particles also reduced the wear of the coating by blocking the penetration of the steel asperity tips.

As known from short fiber reinforced composites, the fiber/polymer interfacial adhesion is greatly responsible for the wear resistance of polymer composite materials [19]. Since the weakest link of a fiber reinforced system lies at the interface, disintegration of filled materials generally takes place along interfacial boundaries. To solve this problem, chemical modifications of the fiber surfaces are used to essentially improve the wettability of the filler particles with the binder. Other approaches have overcome this problem by the creation of a self-reinforcement in the original polymers, and this was especially introduced by Song and Ehrenstein for wear resistant systems [20, 21]. Regarding the particulate filled systems, however, self-reinforcement mechanisms for improving the filler/matrix adhesion are not possible. Other results showed that the conventional filler treatments usually did not perform as outstandingly as expected because the composites were distinctly characterized by a heterogeneity on a micron scale of their structure, so that crack initiation and coalescence became much easier in the particulate-rich phase. Therefore, not only filler/matrix bonding but also the dispersion and geometry of fillers should be carefully considered. On the basis of this analysis, it can be concluded that the inhomogeneous distribution of micron size particles inevitably resulting from the conventional compounding process provides the composites with a fatal weak side, which accounts for the common three-body abrasive wear caused by the entrapped hard grits removed from the rubbing composites.

Nevertheless, incorporation of particulates was proved to be an effective way to modify polymers for tribological applications, because the latter mostly could not be used alone due to their higher coefficient of linear expansion, low thermal conductivity and unsatisfactory mechanical properties. Considering the above-stated inherent defects imparted by micron size particles, utilization of nanoparticles as fillers could be an optimum alternative to make the most of the technique based on the addition of particles.

1.2. Polymer Based Nanocomposites

Since the predominant feature of nanoparticles lies in their ultra-fine dimension, a large fraction of the filler atoms can reside at the interface and can lead to a strong interfacial interaction, but only if the nanoparticles are well dispersed on a nanometer level in the surrounding polymer matrix. As the interfacial structure plays a critical role in determining the composites' properties, nanocomposites coupled with a great number of interfaces could be expected to provide unusual properties, and the shortcomings induced by the heterogeneity of conventional particles filled composites would also be avoided. On the other hand, the wear mechanisms involved in the nanocomposites would be different from those of conventional composites because the fillers have the same size as the segments of the surrounding polymer chains. Severe wear caused by abrasion and particle pull-out associated with the accumulation of detached harder bulk particulate fillers adherent to the frictional surface might be replaced by rather mild wear resulting from the fine individual debris which acts as a lubricant and contributes to material removal by polishing.

Recent progress indicated that polymer based nanocomposites acquired mechanical properties much higher than the usual systems at a rather low filler loading [22]. Although there are very few reports concerning the effect of nanoparticles on the tribological behavior of polymer composites, some scientists have made pilot investigations on nanoparticle/thermoplastics and nanoparticle/thermosetting composites. Wang et al [23, 24] investigated PEEK filled with nanometer-sized Si_3N_4 and SiO_2 particles by sliding the PEEK composite block against a carbon steel ring. It was found that the nanocomposites exhibited much lower wear rates and frictional coefficients than the neat PEEK matrix. Moreover, a thin, uniform and tenacious transfer film was formed on the ring surface, improving the tribological behavior of the composites. In addition, Wang et al [25] reported that the incorporation of nano-ZrO_2 (7wt %) into PEEK caused a considerable improvement in the tribological characteristics. It was found that the dominant wear mechanism changed from melting adhesive transfer wear to slight transfer wear, and finally to abrasive wear with increasing nano-ZrO_2 content. He et al [26] prepared nanoscale ceramic (TiC, Si_3N_4, B_4C)/PTFE multilayers by ion beam sputtering deposition at room temperature. Ball-on-disk tribological tests showed that the multilayers with optimized layer thickness arrangement had good performance in wear resistance. There was no obvious periodic variation in the friction coefficient. Schadler et al [27] produced silica/PA nanocomposite coatings using high-speed oxyfuel thermal spray processing; they found that the surface chemistry of the nano-silica affected the final coating properties. Silica particles with a hydrophobic surface resulted in higher scratch resistance than those with a hydrophilic surface.

It should be noticed that the smaller the size of filler particles is, the larger becomes their specific surface area, and the more likely the aggregation of the particles. Consequently, the so-called nanoparticle filled polymers sometimes contain a number of loosened clusters of particles (Fig.1), where the polymer binder is impoverished. This may exhibit properties even worse than conventional particle/polymer systems. Extensive material loss would thus occur as a result of disintegration and crumbling of the particle agglomerates under tribological conditions. It is therefore necessary to break down these nanoparticle agglomerates and to produce nanostructured composites. Some approaches have been developed in this direction as follows [22, 28-34]:

I. in-situ polymerization of metal alkoxides in organic matrices via sol-gel technique;
II. intercalation polymerization by inserting polymer chains into the sheets of smectite clay and other layered inorganic materials;
III. addition of organically modified nanoparticles to a polymer solution;
IV. in-situ polymerization of monomers at the presence of nanoparticles.

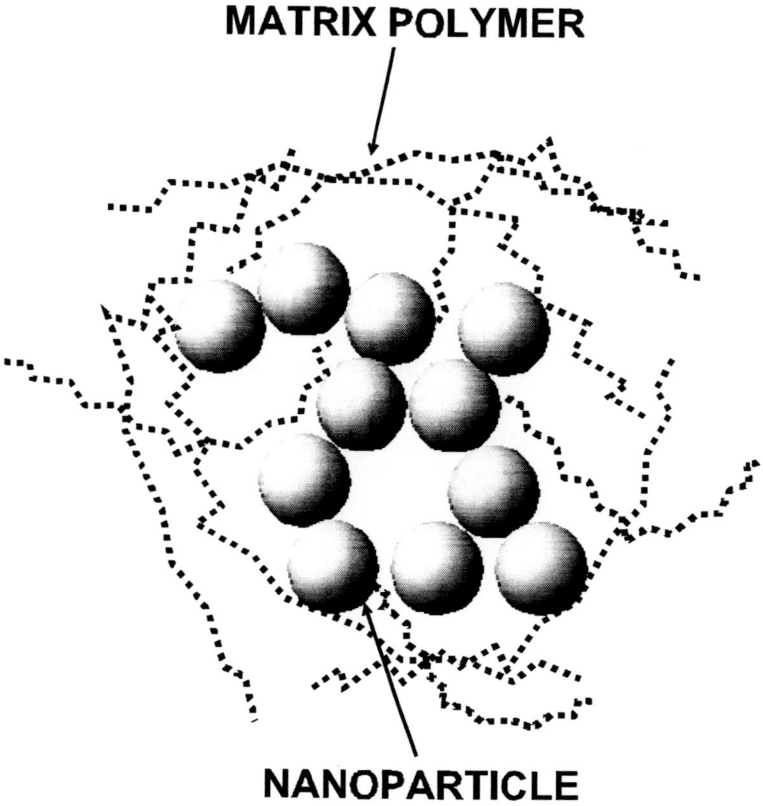

Figure1. Aggregated nanopaticles dispersed in a polymer matrix.

Since the above techniques are characterized by complex polymerization procedures and special conditions, and since they require polymerization equipment and solvent recovery, evidently a mass production of nanocomposites with cost effectiveness and applicability should better follow another route.

By examining the current technical level and the feasibility of the available processing methods, it can be concluded that the widely used compounding techniques (characterized by a direct mixing of the components) for the preparation of conventionally filled polymers is still the most convenient way. The problem is that nanoparticle agglomerates are also hard to be disconnected by the limited shear force during mixing. This is true even when a coupling agent is used [35]. Since the latter can only react with the exterior nanoparticles, the agglomerates will maintain their friable structure in the composite and can hardly provide properties improvement at all [36].

1.3. New Solutions

As convinced by the previous scientific achievements, the development of a new technique is always the most important methodology to overcome the difficulties. With respect to the above-mentioned strong tendency for nanoparticles to agglomerate, the particles should be effectively modified before being incorporated with polymer so as to obtain a uniform dispersion state. According to our idea, nanoparticles are pretreated by irradiation to introduce grafting polymers onto the surface of the tiny particles not only outside but also inside the particle agglomerates. Owing to the low molecular weight nature, the monomers can penetrate into the agglomerated nanoparticles easily and react with the activated sites of the nanoparticles. In the course of grafting polymerization, the gap between the nanoparticles will be filled with grafting macromolecular chains, and the agglomerated nanoparticles will be separated further as a result (Fig.2). Besides, the surface of the nanoparticles will also become "hydrocarbon" due to an increased hydrophobicity resulting from the grafting polymer. This is beneficial for the filler/matrix miscibility and hence for the ultimate properties, as revealed in ref.[27]. When the pre-grafted nanoparticles are mechanically mixed with a thermosetting polymer, the former will keep their more stationary suspension state due to the interaction between the grafting polymer and the matrix. After curing of the mixture, filler/matrix adhesion would be substantially enhanced by the entanglement between the grafting polymer and the matrix polymer. This is different from composites filled with conventionally treated nanoparticle agglomerates, because direct contacts between the fillers would no longer appear due to the uniform coverage of grafting polymers on the surface of each nanoparticles even through the particles could not be dispersed completely in the form of primary nanoparticles.

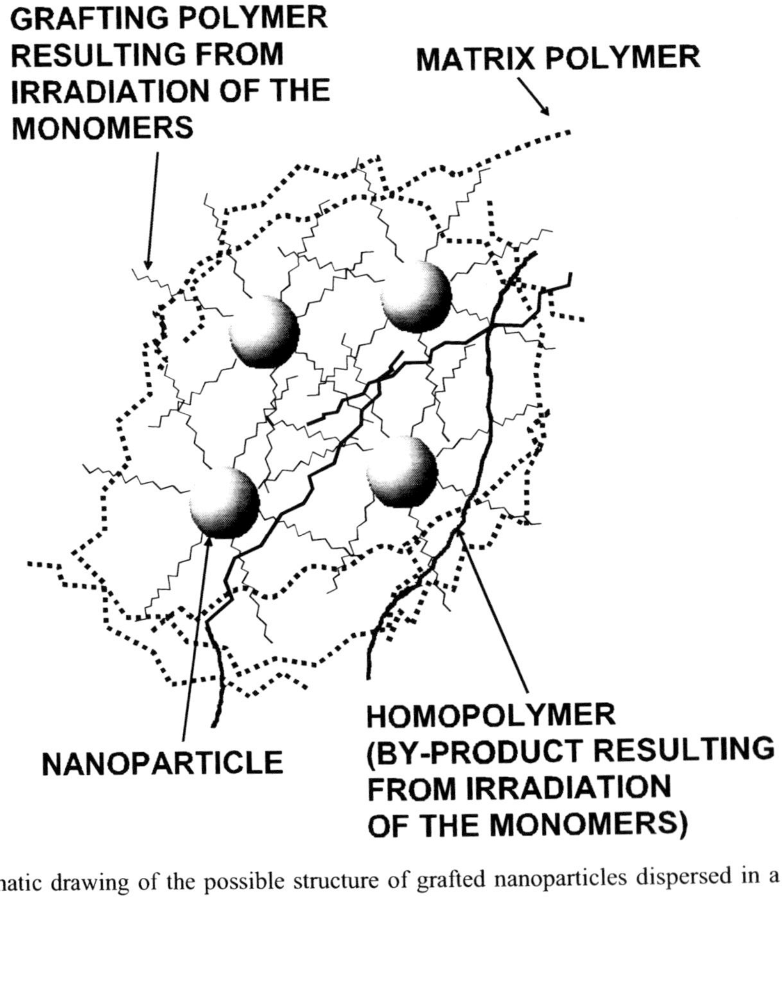

Figure 2. Schematic drawing of the possible structure of grafted nanoparticles dispersed in a polymer matrix.

In our preliminary work, polymerization by irradiation was applied to induce the grafting polystyrene, polymethyl methacrylate, polyethyl acrylate and polybutyl acrylate onto the surface of nanometer SiO_2 and $CaCO_3$ [37]. The experimental results showed that these grafting polymers were chemically bonded on the surface of the nanoparticles rather than physically coating them. When the grafted nanoparticles were incorporated with polypropylene by extrusion mixing, the dispersion homogeneity of the particles were improved remarkably, leading to a significant increase in the mechanical properties of the composites, and toughness in particular, at a filler concentration lower than 2% by volume [38].

The current chapter is concentrated on the development of inorganic nanoparticles/thermosetting polymer composites with remarkable tribological performance, which can be used e.g. as a candidate for coatings on hard composite rollers. A viable surface treatment of nanoparticles through grafting polymerization will be explored to break up the commercially available nanoparticle agglomerates and to improve the interfacial adhesion between the particles and the matrix resin. The proposed graft technique should make it possible to control the molecular structure of the grafting polymers so that the performance of the target composite materials can be tailored. Knowledge for an optimum formulation and preparation will be provided from a careful investigation of the effects of the nanoparticles on the wear reduction of the thermosetting polymer. Further conclusions can be drawn from the relationship between particle dispersion status and mixing process, as well as from an understanding of the friction and wear mechanisms involved in the nanocomposites. It can therefore be expected that the results of this project will be of certain universal significance and thus applicable for many inorganic nanoparticles/thermosetting composites in consideration of their potential use in various industrial applications.

2. Pretreatment of Inorganic Nanoparticles and the Correlated Characterization

In the following work, Al_2O_3 and SiC nanoparticles were chosen as the fillers due to the fact that the bulk materials of these inorganic substances are known to be of high wear resistance. Considering the agglomeration of these nanoparticles, grafting pretreatment has to be carried out as stated above.

Grafting polymer onto the surface of inorganic nanoparticles is a field of growing interests. Several works have been done with respect to improving the dispersibility of these particles in solvents and to their compatibility in polymer matrices [39-44]. Mostly, the grafting polymerization was conducted via two routes: (i) monomers were polymerized from the active compounds (initiators or comonomers) and then covalently attached to the inorganic particle surfaces; and (ii) ready-made polymers with reactive end-groups reacted with the functional groups on the particle surfaces. Various kinds of polymerization processes have been tried in the grafting investigations, including radical, anionic and cationic polymerizations. In our previous studies [38,45,46], the necessity of surface modification of nanoparticles in making polymer nanocomposites was elucidated. To develop an effective and versatile approach, an irradiation grafting technique was proposed to introduce polymers onto nano-silica. However, it was found that the molecular weight and the density of the grafted macromolecules are quite difficult to be controlled, in addition to the complexity of the reaction details. A fine adjustment of the interfacial interaction in the subsequent composites is therefore restricted.

To solve this problem, the authors tried to graft polymers onto the surface of nanoparticles by a simple chemical reaction, which would make it possible to control the grafting polymer chains more easily. Considering that some kinds of coupling agents contain polymerizable groups, a surface treatment using these coupling agents followed by radical grafting polymerization should be feasible. In this work, polyacrylamide (PAAM) and polystyrene (PS) were introduced onto the surface of silane coupling agent pre-treated Al_2O_3 and SiC nanoparticles by aqueous and non-aqueous radical polymerization processes, respectively. The amide groups of PAAM would take part in the curing of epoxy resin and the encapsulation with PS is believed to be able to greatly increase the hydrophobicity of the particles and hence the compatibility with the polymer matrix. That is, these treatment approaches are selected for purposes of facilitating nanoparticles/matrix interfacial adhesion.

2.1. Materials and Nanoparticles Pretreatment

The nanosized alumina (γ-phase) was provided by Hua-Tai Co. Ltd., China, and possesses a specific surface area of $146.3m^2/g$ and an averaged diameter of 10.4nm. The SiC nanoparticles (α-phase) were also produced by Hua-Tai Co. Ltd., China, and provide a specific surface area of $15.3m^2/g$, whereas the averaged diameter counts to 61nm. Prior to use, the particles were dried in an oven at 110°C under vacuum for 24h in order to get rid of the physically absorbed and weakly chemically bonded species.

A KH570 silane coupling agent (γ-methacryloxypropyl trimethoxy silane), provided by Liao Ning Gazhou Chemical Industry Co. Ltd., China, was employed to introduce the reactive functional groups on the surface of the nanoparticles. Styrene was obtained from Shanghai Guanghua Chemical Agent Factory, China, and acrylamide was supplied by Guangzhou Chemical Agent Factory, China. The two types of monomers were identified as being a reagent grade. In non-aqueous systems, the azobis(isobutyronitrile, AIBN) was used as an initiator, and toluene, tetrahydrofunan (THF) and cyclohexane were chosen as solvents. For aqueous systems, a mixture of ammonium persulfate and sodium hydrogen sulfite (1:1 in mole) was used as the initiator, and deionized water was taken as a solvent. All the components of the recipes were used as received from the suppliers without further purification.

The introduction of reactive groups onto the surface of nanoparticles was achieved by the reaction of silane with the hydroxyl groups of the particles (Fig.3). A typical example can be given as follows: 2.0g alumina nanoparticles and 2.0g KH570 in 100 ml of 95% alcohol solution were charged into a 300ml flask equipped with a reflux condenser. The mixture was refluxed at the boiling temperature of the solution over different stirring times. After that, the alumina was centrifuged, and the precipitate was extracted with alcohol for 16h to remove the excess silane absorbed on the alumina. Then the treated alumina was air-dried and allowed to react at 80°C under vacuum for 24h. The content of the double bonds introduced onto the alumina surfaces by the above treatment was detected according to the method stated in ref.[47].

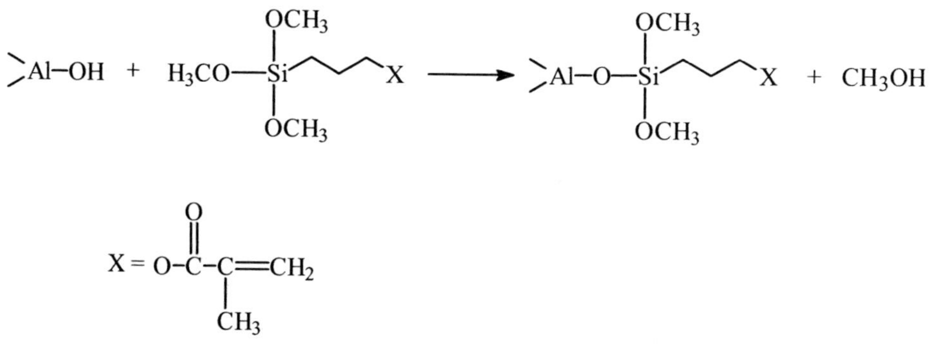

Figure 3. Schematic illustration of the reaction of KH570 silane coupling agent with the hydroxyl groups of alumina.

2.2. Graft Polymerization of Vinyl Monomers onto Nano-Al_2O_3

The graft polymerization reactions for both styrene and acrylamide monomers were performed in air environment in a flask equipped with a condenser at 70°C and 50°C, respectively. Firstly, the modified alumina and the solvent were put in the temperature-controlled reactor with stirring. When the reactant reached the desired temperature, the initiator and the monomer were added in four ways of feeding: (i) both the initiator and the monomer were added simultaneously in one batch; (ii) the initiator was charged alone, and then the monomer was added in one batch after 30min of reaction; (iii) similar to (ii), but the monomer was added by drip feeding; (iv) one third of the total dosage of the initiator was added, and then the monomer and the rest initiator were added in two equal batches after the alumina reacted with the first batch of initiator for a while. In all the cases, the concentration of the monomers and the initiators, as well as the reaction time, were changed in order to study their influence on the reaction processes and the degrees of reaction.

Compared with the untreated version, the infrared spectrum of the modified alumina exhibits absorptions at 1731, 1457 and 1409cm^{-1}, which are characteristic for the silane coupling agent (Fig.4). Correspondingly, a quantitative analysis indicates that the amount of double bonds introduced onto the particles increases with treating time (Fig.5). Having been treated for 4h, the double bonds reach a level of 0.77mmol/g, implying that about 66% hydroxyl groups on the surfaces of nano-alumina particles have been consumed for the introduction of these reactive groups. It can thus be deduced that the treatment employed in the present study resulted in a monolayer coverage of silane. Therefore, the nanoparticles with 0.77mmol/g of double bonds were used in the subsequent grafting reactions.

Graft polymerization of styrene and acrylamide was carried out at the presence of modified alumina in different solvents (Table 1). The data of percent grafting indicate that the monomers were successfully grafted onto the surface of alumina through covalent bonding. The formation of grafted polymers can be confirmed by the typical FTIR peaks in Fig.4. For PS-grafted alumina (Al_2O_3-g-PS), a series of absorptions at 1634, 1601, 1492 and 1452cm^{-1} evidence the existence of PS. For PAAM-grafted alumina (Al_2O_3-g-PAAM) a strong absorption of carboxyl groups in PAAM at 1666cm^{-1} occurs.

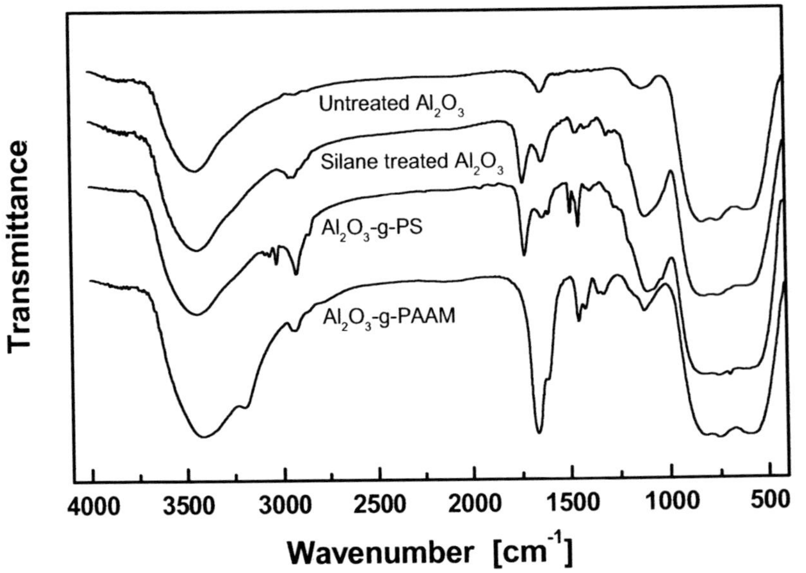

Figure 4. FTIR spectra of nanosized alumina before and after surface modification. Prior to the test, the non-grafted polymers were extracted from both Al_2O_3-g-PS and Al_2O_3-g-PAAM.

Table 1 Graft polymerization of styrene and acrylamide on the surface of silane modified alumina [a]

Grafted polymer on Al_2O_3	Monomer concentration (mol/L)	Initiator concentration (mol/L)	Solvent	Reaction temperature (°C)	Reaction time (h)	γ_c [b] (%)	γ_g [c] (%)	γ_e [d] (%)
PS	0.5	0.001	Toluene	70	2	9.2	10.6	17.7
PS	0.5	0.001	THF	70	2	9.7	9.9	17.8
PS	0.5	0.001	Cyclohexane	70	2	9.6	10.9	18.5
PAAM	1.0	0.02	Deionized water	50	3	85.7	29.1	6.0

[a] The initiator and the monomer were added into the reaction system simultaneously.
[b] γ_c = monomer conversion.
[c] γ_g = percentage of grafting.
[d] γ_e = grafting efficiency.

On the other hand, Table 1 reveals that the reaction systems of Al_2O_3-g-PS with different solvents have nearly the same monomer conversion, percentage of grafting and grafting efficiency. This phenomenon may be related to the fact that all of these solvents are good solvents for PS. Under this circumstance, the grafted polymer exists in an extended conformation and hence has no blocking effect on the diffusion of the monomers towards the alumina surface. Based on this finding, the following reactions use toluene as the solvent because of its higher boiling point and convenience of temperature control.

Table 2 shows the number average molecular weight (M_n) and mass average molecular weight (M_w) of PS grafted onto alumina. It is interesting to note that the molecular weights of grafted PS change with the percentage of grafting. The higher values of γ_g (i.e. 33.9 and 39.7) correspond to higher molecular weights, as compared to the case of lower γ_g (i.e. 12.1). In fact, the polymerization conditions for these samples were different. The molecular weights of the grafted PS should be a function of the concentrations of the monomer and the initiator. In general, the degree of polymerization (kinetic chain length) during a radical polymerization increases with increasing polymerization rate and monomer concentration, while it decreases with increasing initiator concentration [48]. However, this relationship seems not to be completely adapted in the present graft polymerization on alumina.

Table 2. Molecular weights of PS grafted onto alumina [a]

γ_g (%)	Monomer concentration (mol/L)	Initiator concentration (mol/L)	M_n (x10^4)	M_w (x10^4)	M_w/M_n	Grafted number µmol/g µmol/m^2	f_g [b] (%)
39.7	2.0	0.04	2.51	3.86	1.54	15.82 0.108	2.06
33.9	6.0	0.04	3.10	3.95	1.28	10.96 0.075	1.42
12.1	2.0	0.01	1.42	2.43	1.71	8.54 0.058	1.11

[a] The initiator and the monomer were added into the reaction system simultaneously. Toluene served as solvent.

b fg = (amount of double bonds consumed during polymerization)/(initial amount of double bonds)

The number of PS chains grafted onto alumina surfaces was calculated from the number average molecular weight (Table 2). Accordingly, the percentage of double bonds used for the grafting of PS onto the alumina surfaces, i.e. the reaction efficiency of the double bonds attached to the surfaces (f_g), can be obtained. The results reveal that only a few double bonds on the particle surfaces were utilized during the polymerization. For PAAM grafted nanoparticles, the molecular weight of the grafted polymer is not available due to the difficulty in separating the grafted PAAM from the particles as stated in the experimental part. Further efforts are needed in this aspect.

To check the effect of surface treatment, the dispersibility of polymer grafted alumina in a solvent (Al_2O_3-g-PS in THF and Al_2O_3-g-PAAM in acetone) was compared with the untreated alumina (Fig.6). The results show a remarkable improvement of dispersibility resulting from the surface grafting. Untreated alumina completely precipitates after a few hours. On the contrary, PS-grafted and PAAM-grafted alumina give a stable colloidal dispersion in the solvent. In addition, the alumina with a higher percentage of grafting tends to be more stable than that with a lower amount of grafting, indicating that the grafting polymer chains interfere with the agglomeration of alumina nanoparticles.

As different ways of feeding monomer and initiator were used in the course of graft polymerization, it is worth examining the effect of different ways of monomer feeding on the grafting reaction. It was found that these reaction procedures strongly influence especially the acrylamide grafting reaction (Table 3). In comparison with the results corresponding to the first way of feeding, the second feeding route hereby leads to a higher grafting percentage and grafting efficiency, but also to a lower monomer conversion. In the case of the third way of feeding, γ_c, γ_g and γ_e showed the lowest values.

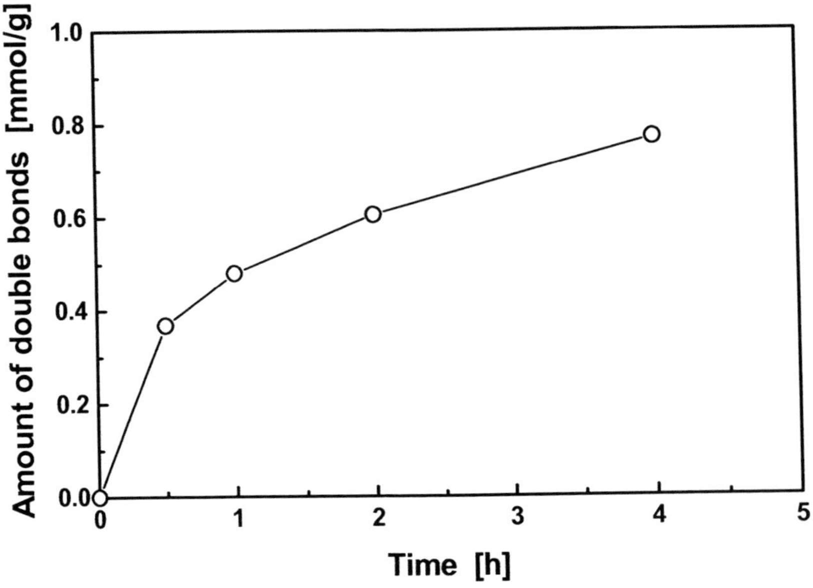

Figure 5. Amount of double bonds introduced onto the alumina surface as a function of reaction time.

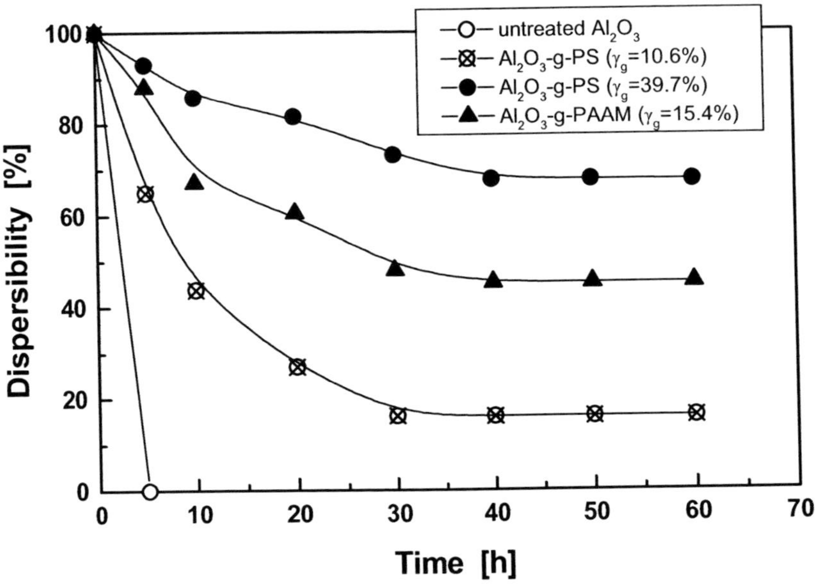

Figure 6. Dispersibility of Al_2O_3-g-PS in THF and Al_2O_3-g-PAAM in acetone at room temperature.

Table 3. Effect of feeding ways of monomer and initiator on the grafting reaction of PAAM [a]

Feeding way [b]	Monomer concentration (mol/L)	Initiator concentration (mol/L)	Reaction temperature (°C)	Reaction time (h)	γ_c (%)	γ_g (%)	γ_e (%)
1	1.0	0.01	50	3	78.6	25.0	20.5
2	1.0	0.01	50	3	49.2	52.0	30.0
3	1.0	0.01	50	3	22.8	16.6	9.3

[a] Deionized water served as solvent.

[b] Details of the ways of feeding monomer and initiator are given in the experimental part.

In a radical polymerization, decomposition of the initiator is usually considered to proceed gradually (non-instantaneously). When both the monomer and the initiator were mixed together, radicals can be formed freely on the surface of the alumina at the beginning of the polymerization. Unfortunately, the surface double bonds can not be initiated at a latter stage of the polymerization because growing polymer radicals and/or grafted polymer chains block the diffusion of radicals towards the particle surface (Fig.7). When the modified alumina was allowed to react with the initiator firstly (i.e. the second way of feeding), more double bonds could be initiated, leading to both a higher percentage of grafting and grafting efficiency. For the third feeding way, the monomer was in a starved condition. The initiated double bonds on the alumina surfaces had to be terminated more seriously. In addition, the initiator was remarkably consumed even before all the monomer dripped into the reactor. This caused the reaction time for the monomers to be relatively insufficient, as indicated by the lowest γ_c, γ_g and γ_e values observed.

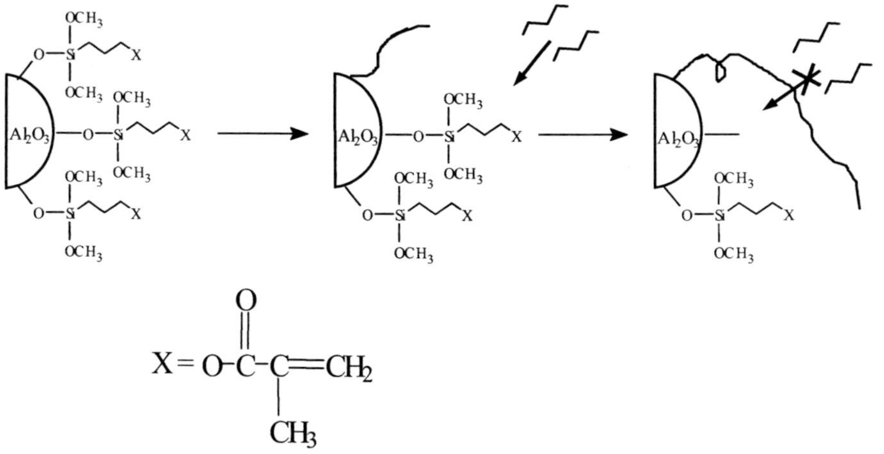

Figure 7. Schematic drawing of the blocking effect of the growing polymeric radicals and/or grafted polymer chains on the diffusion of radicals towards the alumina surface.

In contrast to the case of PAAM, the monomer feeding procedure scarcely influenced the styrene grafting reaction (Table 4). This may be due to the different solvent effect. Toluene is such a good solvent for PS that the blocking effect of grafted PS becomes no longer significant. Comparatively, water is not a very good solvent for PAAM, so that the monomer feeding manner became a controlling factor for the grafting reaction. On the other hand, the initiator might have a longer life in the PS system. That is, the system had enough initiator even if the third feeding way was used. These resulted in an independence of the grafting polymerization of PS onto the alumina particles.

Table 4. Effect of feeding ways of monomer and initiator on the grafting reaction of PS [a]

Feeding way [b]	Monomer concentration (mol/L)	Initiator concentration (mol/L)	Reaction temperature (°C)	Reaction time (h)	γ_c (%)	γ_g (%)	γ_e (%)
1	1.0	0.005	70	3	8.8	12.3	26.8
2	1.0	0.005	70	3	11.1	12.1	21.3
3	1.0	0.005	70	3	10.9	12.1	21.4

[a] Toluene served as solvent.

b Details of the ways of feeding monomer and initiator are given in the experimental part.

2.3. Graft Polymerization of Vinyl Monomers onto Nano-SiC

The grafting polymerization of styrene and acrylamide monomers onto SiC nanoparticles was conducted in slightly different ways. For producing PAAM grafted SiC (SiC-g-PAAM), the silane treated particles were put into a flask filled with water. After a sonication of 30min, the initiator (mixture of $NH_4S_2O_8$ and $NaHSO_3$ at a mole ratio of 1:1) was incorporated into the system at 30°C in N_2 atmosphere. Having been stirred for 30min, acrylamide was added to the mixture with stirring to carry out the grafting polymerization. Then the resultant suspension was centrifuged and washed. The sludge represented the grafted nanoparticles.

To obtain PS grafted SiC (PS-g-SiC), the pretreated particles were mixed with toluene under sonication. When the reactor was kept at 80°C and filled with N_2, AIBN was added with stirring. After one hour, styrene monomer was incorporated into the system. Similarly, the PS-g-SiC can be received from the precipitation of the resultant suspension.

Fig.8 illustrates the infrared spectra of untreated and treated particles. Due to the strong absorption of SiC as-received over a broad wavenumber range, many characteristic peaks of the treated nanoparticles are no longer perceivable. Nevertheless, the stretching mode of SiC at 890cm^{-1} can be seen in the spectrum of silane treated SiC, suggesting that KH570 silane coupling agent has been reacted with the hydroxyl groups on the SiC nanoparticles. In the case of SiC-g-PAAM, although the absorption due to amide at 1659cm^{-1} is unclear, the peaks at 801 and 1258cm^{-1} represent N-H and C-N vibrations, respectively. For SiC-g-PS, the peaks of phenyl rings at 1500~1480$cm^{-1}$and 1600cm^{-1} are hidden by the wide band of SiC, but the two peaks at 700~900cm^{-1}characterize C-H absorption of benzene rings. The above results prove that PAAM and PS have been chemically connected to the surface of SiC particles, respectively.

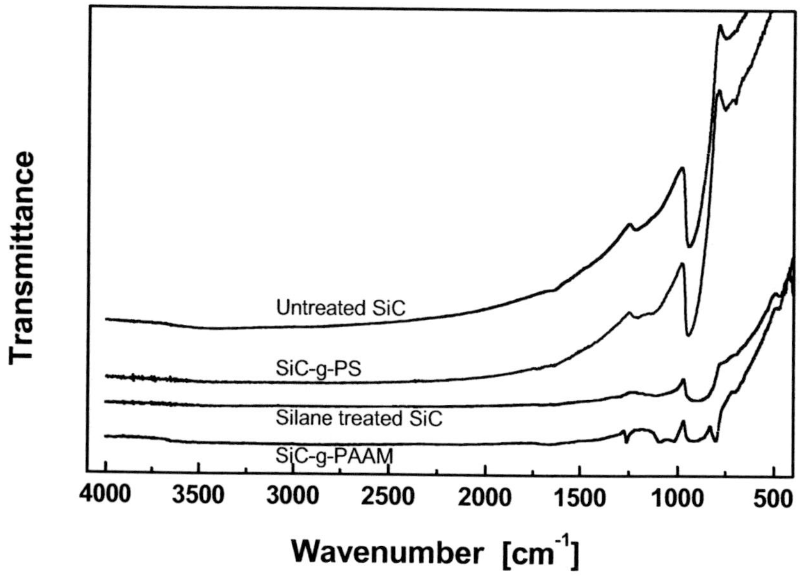

Figure 8. FTIR spectra of nanosized SiC before and after surface modification. Prior to the measurement, the non-grafted polymers were extracted from both SiC-g-PS and SiC-g-PAAM.

The experimental data of grafting polymerization of acrylamide monomer onto SiC nanoparticles are plotted in Fig.9. It is seen that the monomer conversion reaches the maximum of about 75% when the concentration of initiator approaches 3mmol/g. A comparatively lower or higher initiator concentration would result in a decreased monomer conversion. In the case of low initiator concentration, the fraction of free radicals generated in the solution is relatively low. As a result, the conversion rate of the monomers had to be low at a given monomer concentration. When the concentration of the initiator is rather high, the redox effect accompanied with the chain initiation would intensify the decomposition of PAAM chains and lead to a lower conversion of the monomers. With respect to the percentage of grafting, an increase in the concentration of the initiator always facilitates the initiation of the double bonds on the particles surface. This accounts for the continuous increase in the percentage of grafting. However, it should be noted that an unduly high initiator concentration would also increase the probability of radical termination between the growing chains. In this context, a proper selection of concentration of the initiator is necessary.

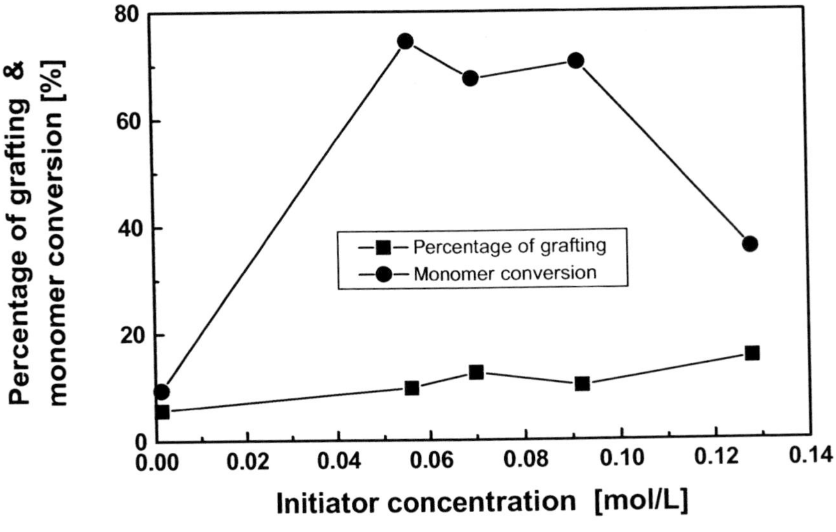

Figure 9. Grafting of acrylamide onto nano-SiC: effect of the initiator concentration on the monomer conversion and percentage of grafting (monomer concentration: 0.67mol/L, reaction time: 4h).

Fig.10 shows the effect of monomer concentration on the percentage of grafting. An approximately linear dependence can be found, implying that the percentage of grafting is closely related to the rate of chain growth. In the case of radical polymerization, the kinetic chain length is generally proportional to the monomer concentration. If the monomer concentration increases, the polymerization rate rises too, and in the same way, the molecular weight of the grafting polymer expands. This directly coincides with the findings of Lin et al. [49]: the molecular weight of PAAM increases with increasing monomer content if the polymerization of acrylamide is carried out in aqueous solution. Because the polymerization of acrylamide completes within a relatively short period of time, the percentage of grafting has to be significantly influenced by the content of the monomer.

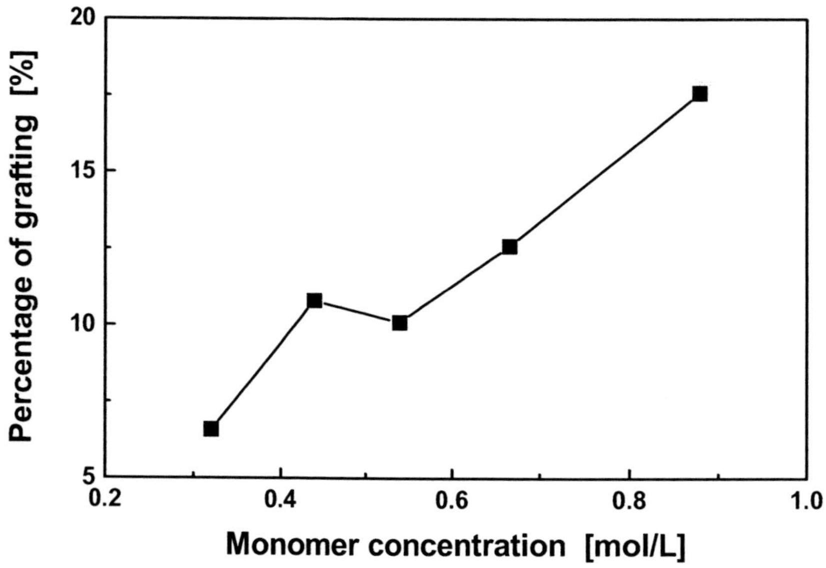

Figure 10. Effect of monomer concentration on the percentage of grafting of acrylamide onto nano-SiC (initiator concentration: 0.076mol/L, reaction time: 4h).

The effect of reaction time is an important factor of grafting polymerization (Fig.11). It is found that a reaction time longer than 2h is somewhat detrimental to the increase of monomer conversion and percentage of grafting. This is due to the degradation of PAAM molecules in the redox system. At the beginning of the polymerization, chain growth plays the leading role. Then, when the polymerization proceeds to a certain extent, the effect of molecular decomposition emerges. With the lapse of time molecular decomposition counteracts the chain growth remarkably. A further increase in the reaction time results therefore in the increased amount of low molecular weight PAAM, and these molecules can easily be lost during the isolation of the homopolymerized PAAM. The measured monomer conversion is thus reduced apparently, when the reaction time is extended. On the other hand, if the short PAAM segments carrying radicals slip through to the surface of the SiC nanoparticles, an increase in the percentage of grafting can be observed as the case of a reaction time of 7h (Fig.11). In summary, the time dependence of monomer conversion and percentage of grafting is a joint result of both competitive effects: chain growth and chain degradation.

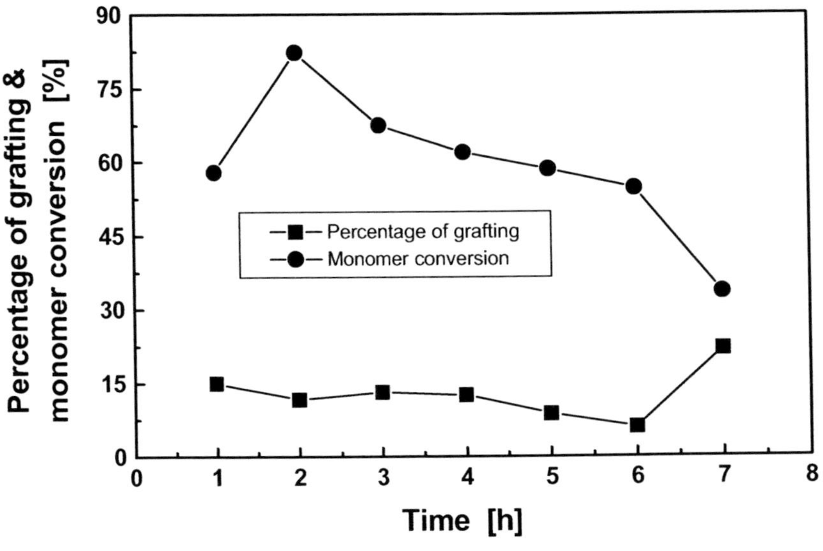

Figure 11. Grafting of acrylamide onto nano-SiC: effect of reaction time on the monomer conversion and percentage of grafting (monomer concentration: 0.67mol/L, initiator concentration: 0.076mol/L).

Grafting polymerization of styrene onto SiC nanoparticles is characterized in Fig.12. When the reaction time is shorter than 6h, the percentage of grafting is rather low. Afterwards, a linear increase in the percentage of grafting with rising time can be seen. In comparison to the data of PAAM grafting, the current percentage of grafting is quite low. This should be attributed to the morphology of the surface reactive groups on the SiC particles and the steric hindrance of the monomers. Since SiC contains C elements, the interaction between SiC particles and organics (i.e. the silane coupling agent and the growing chains) should be stronger than that between other inorganic particles and organics. In case the SiC particle-solvent interactions are weaker, the molecular chains containing reactive double bonds or radicals cannot take the extended form in the solution; they tightly wrap the particles. The attack on the particles launched by the monomers becomes rather difficult. Probably this effect is much severe in toluene. In addition, the steric hindrance of styrene is greater than acrylamide. At the early stage of polymerization it is more difficult for styrene monomers to get access to the reactive chain ends and start the chain growth. With increasing reaction time, some chain radicals are produced at the terminals of the coupling agent and the amount of the chain radicals in the solution keeps on increasing. The termination between the above two types of chain radicals results in the rise in percentage of grafting as shown in Fig.12.

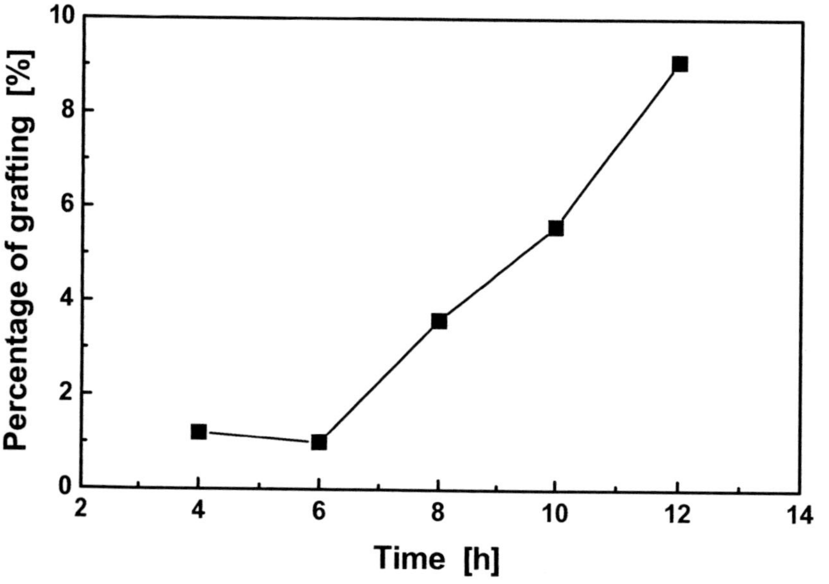

Figure 12. Effect of reaction time on the percentage of grafting of styrene onto nano-SiC (monomer concentration: 1.0mol/L, initiator concentration: 0.01mol/L).

The effect of initiator concentration on the percentage of grafting of styrene onto SiC nanoparticles is illustrated in Fig.13. Although there is an increasing trend in the percentage of grafting with the fraction of the initiator, the variation is not obvious enough. Within the entire range of initiator concentration, the percentage of grafting changes between 4.5~6.5%. As analyzed above, due to the steric hindrance effect between the monomers and the growing chains, an increase in the initiator concentration increases the quantity of the radicals in the solution but cannot effectively improve the ability of chain growth. Only when the probability of termination between the chain radicals on the nanoparticles and those in the solution is increased as a result of a rise in initiator concentration, the percentage of grafting can be increased accordingly.

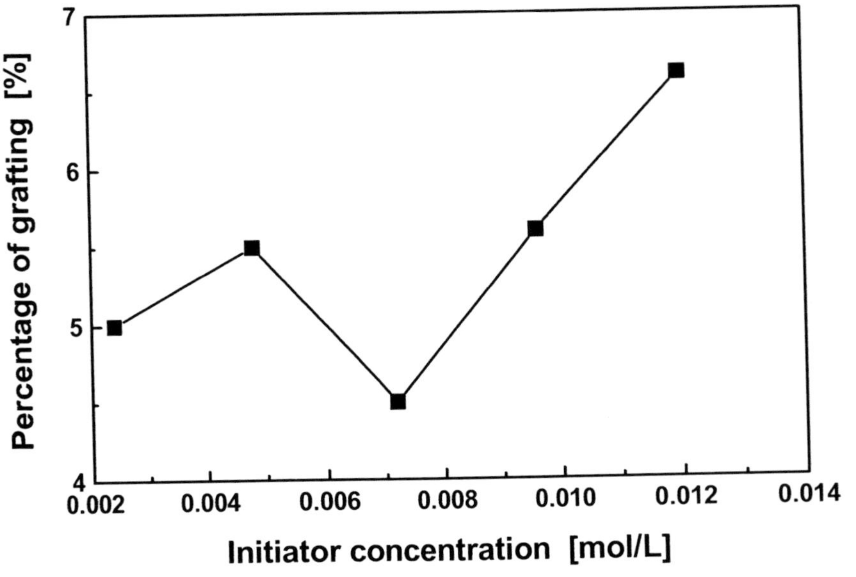

Figure 13. Effect of initiator concentration on the percentage of grafting of styrene onto nano-SiC (monomer concentration: 1.0mol/L, reaction time: 4h).

To check the quality of grafting polymerization on the nanoparticles, the dispersibility of the particles are compared in Fig.14. The untreated particles cannot give a stable dispersion in the solvent. Although the suspension was stirred by sonication, the particles completely precipitated within 15h. In contrast, the grafted particles exhibit good dispersibility in the solvent. About 40% of the particles remained in the suspension after 40h. Fig.14 shows furthermore that the dispersibility of SiC-g-PS is better than that of SiC-g-PAAM owing to the fact that the solvent THF possesses a better miscibility with PS than with PAAM. Based on these results it can be deduced that the grafted nanoparticles would also have a much better miscibility with other polymers when preparing polymer composites. The properties of the composites would thus be effectively enhanced.

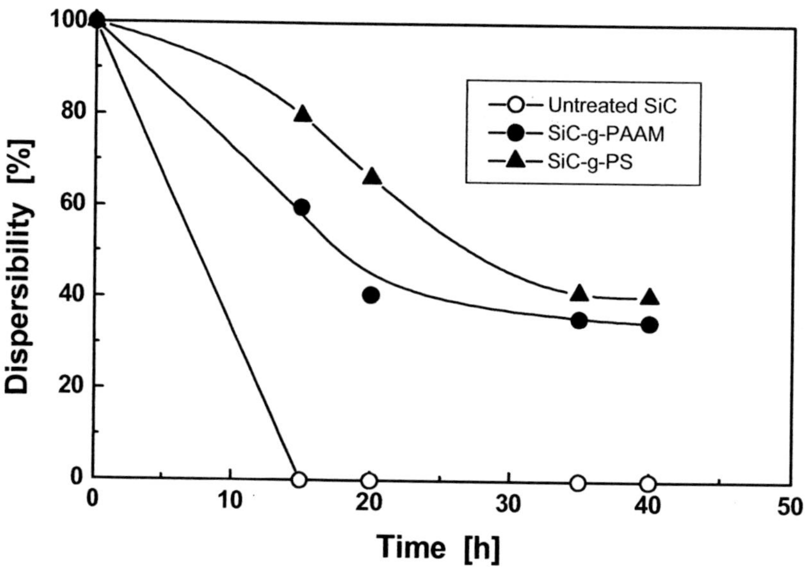

Figure 14. Dispersibility of SiC nanoparticles in THF at room temperature.

2.4. Treatment of SiO_2 and Si_3N_4 Nanoparticles

To make comparative investigations, nano-SiO_2 and nano-Si_3N_4 particles were also involved in our work. The nano-SiO_2 with an average primary particle size of 9nm was purchased from Zhoushan Nanomaterials Co., China. The nano-Si_3N_4 with a specific surface area of $52m^2/g$ and an average primary particle size of 16.8nm were provided by Hua-Tai Co. Ltd., China

The typical grafting of SiO_2 proceeded as follows. The nanoparticles were preheated at 120^oC in vacuum for 24h to eliminate possible absorbed water on the surface of the particles. Then the particles were mixed with acetone solution of acrylamide by sonication. The mixture was irradiated by ^{60}Co γ-ray at a dose rate of 1Mrad/h at room temperature. After exposure to a dose of 4Mrad, the solvent was recovered and the dried residual powder could be compounded with epoxy directly. To obtain homopolomerized PAAM individually, certain amounts of the irradiation products were extracted with water in a Soxhlet's apparatus at room temperature. The residual material (i.e. SiO_2 with the unextractable grafting PAAM) was immersed in 10~20% HF solution to remove the inorganic particles so that the grafting PAAM could be recovered. By using thermogravimetric analysis (TGA), it was known that percent grafting and grafting efficiency of the irradiation products are 10.3% and 53.7%, respectively.

To confirm that PAAM has been grafted onto nano-silica, FTIR study of the particles and the products of graft treatment was conducted. As shown by the infrared spectrum of PAAM grafted SiO_2 (SiO_2-g-PAAM) in Fig.15, the stretching modes of carbonyl in amide and CN in amide appear at 1665 and $1454cm^{-1}$, respectively. The two peaks can also be observed in the spectra of homopolymerized PAAM and grafting PAAM, but the CN peak appears at a lower wave number of 1427cm^{-1} in the spectra of grafting PAAM, suggesting the chemical environment of grafting PAAM is slightly different from that of homopolymerized PAAM. For the grafting PAAM isolated from SiO_2-g-PAAM, the absorption due to inter-molecular hydrogen bonds at 2900~3700cm^{-1} is much broader than that of homopolymerized PAAM. In addition, there is a twin-peak at 3341 and 3413cm^{-1} that is absent in the spectrum of PAAM homopolymer. This can be attributed to the hydroxyl on PAAM generated when silica in SiO_2-g-PAAM was removed by HF solution. That is, during the grafting polymerization, PAAM had been covalently connected with SiO_2 besides physical absorption.

Treatment of Si_3N_4 with coupling agent proceeded as follows. 2.0g Si_3N_4 nanoparticles was charged into the mixture of 8.0g KH550 (γ-aminopropyl trimethoxy silane) in 200ml of 95% alcohol solution, and the reaction was kept for 8h under refluxing condition. Then, the particles were centrifuged, extracted with alcohol for 24hr, and dried in vacuum (60°C, 24h). The content of the attached silane is 6.5wt% as detected by element analysis.

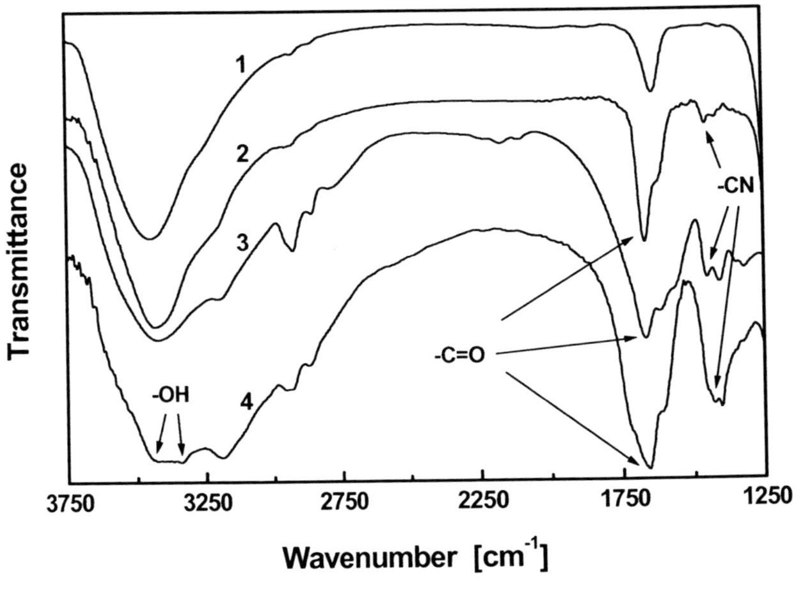

Figure 15. FTIR spectra of (1) SiO_2, (2) SiO_2-g-PAAM, (3) homopolymerized PAAM, and (4) grafting PAAM.

2.5. Manufacturing of Nanoparticles/Epoxy Composites

Bisphenol-A epoxy resin (type E-51) and 4, 4'-diaminodiphenylsulfone (DDS) were provided by Guangzhou Dongfeng Chemical Co., China. The composite materials were prepared by compounding the fillers (unmodified or modified) with preweighted quantities of epoxy at 80°C with stirring for 3h and sonication for 1h, respectively, to distribute the particles homogeneously within the matrix. Then the blends were heated to 130°C and the curing agent DDS was added with stirring for 10min. Finally, the mixture was filled into a mould and placed in vacuum for 50min to get rid of air bubbles. For curing the composites, the procedures listed below were followed step by step: 3h at 100°C, 2h at 140°C, 2h at 180°C and 2h at 200°C.

2.6. Curing Kinetics

Study of the curing kinetics is essential for understanding and designing the curing process of thermosetting composites. As shown in Fig.16, the peak exothermic temperature of nano-Al_2O_3/epoxy composites increases with a rise in the heating rate of the differential scanning calorimetric (DSC) measurement. In addition, species and content of nanoparticles also have important influence on the composites curing reaction. At given heating rate, the peak exothermic temperatures of nano-Al_2O_3/epoxyand nano-Si_3N_4/epoxy composites shift towards low temperature regime as filler loading is increased (Fig.17(a) and (b)). Similar phenomena have been reported in other epoxy based composites [50]. In contrast, the peak exothermic temperature of nano-SiC/epoxy composites increased slightly with increasing the particles fraction (Fig.17(c)). Clearly, nano-Al_2O_3 and nano-Si_3N_4 accelerate the curing of epoxy, while nano-SiC decelerates the reaction.

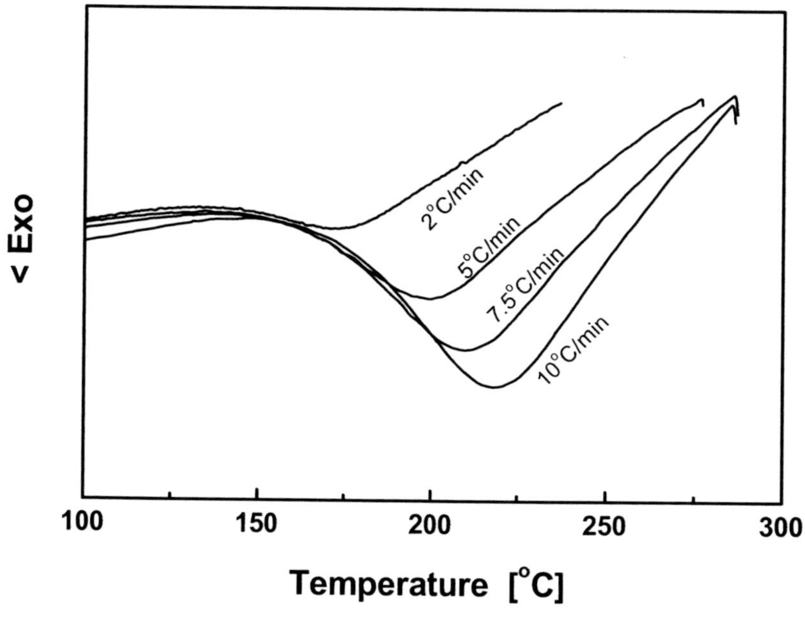

Figure 16. DSC scans of nonisothermal curing processes of nano-Al_2O_3/epoxy composites at different heating rates (Content of nano-Al_2O_3: 1.92vol%).

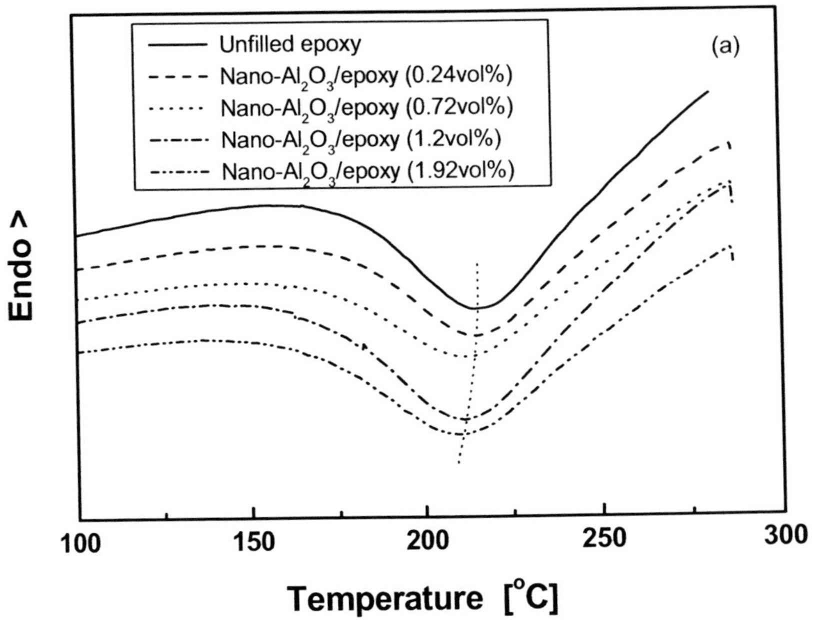
Unfilled epoxy
Nano-Al_2O_3/epoxy (0.24vol%)
Nano-Al_2O_3/epoxy (0.72vol%)
Nano-Al_2O_3/epoxy (1.2vol%)
Nano-Al_2O_3/epoxy (1.92vol%)
(a)
Endo >
100
150
200
250
300
Temperature [°C]

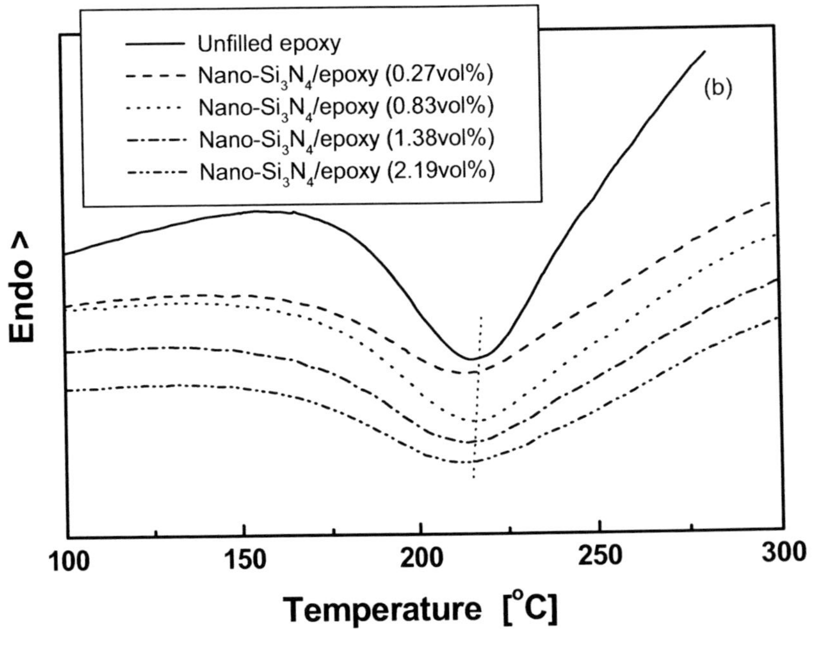
Unfilled epoxy
Nano-Si_3N_4/epoxy (0.27vol%)
Nano-Si_3N_4/epoxy (0.83vol%)
Nano-Si_3N_4/epoxy (1.38vol%)
Nano-Si_3N_4/epoxy (2.19vol%)
(b)
Endo >
100
150
200
250
300
Temperature [°C]

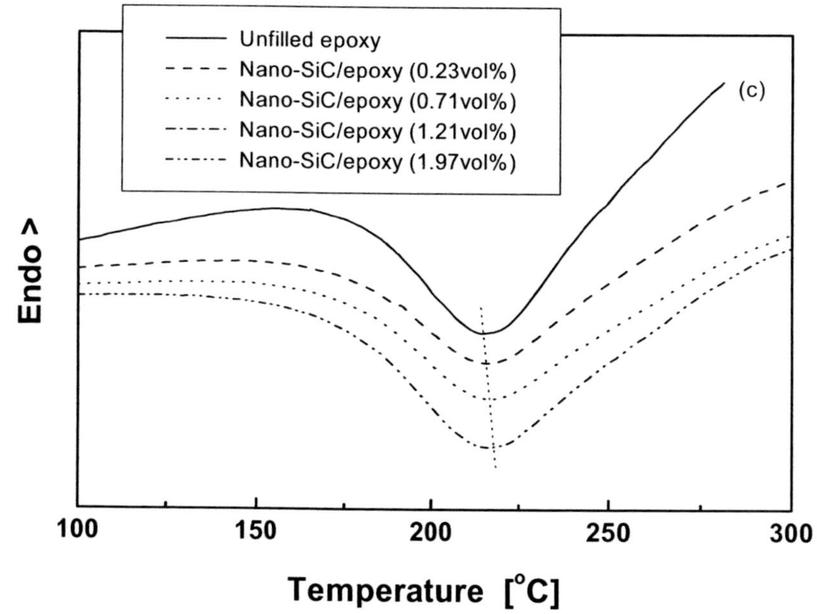

Figure 17. DSC scans of nonisothermal curing processes of (a) nano-Al_2O_3/epoxy, (b) nano-Si_3N_4/epoxy, and (c) nano-SiC/epoxy composites at a heating rate of 7.5°C/min.

To quantify the above effects, Kissinger equation [51], Crane equation [52] and Arrhenius equation are used and the corresponding results are listed in Table 5.

Table 5. Activation energy, E, pre-exponential factor, A, reaction order, n, and rate constant, K, of curing reaction of different nanoparticles/epoxy composites

Composites	Nanoparticles (vol%)	E (kJ/mol)	n	K (s^{-1})
Epoxy	0	62.1	0.89	7.0×10^{-4}
Nano-Al_2O_3/epoxy	0.24	62.4	0.93	8.5×10^{-4}
	0.72	67.9	0.93	5.0×10^{-2}
	1.20	58.8	0.91	6.3×10^{-2}
	1.92	53.8	0.90	5.1×10^{-2}
Nano-Si_3N_4/epoxy	0.27	67.1	0.91	4.4×10^{-3}
	0.83	65.0	0.90	2.0×10^{-3}
	1.38	57.7	0.88	2.1×10^{-3}
	2.19	50.7	0.93	2.1×10^{-3}
Nano-SiC/epoxy	0.23	55.6	0.89	8.0×10^{-4}
	0.71	65.0	0.90	7.1×10^{-4}
	1.21	57.8	0.89	7.4×10^{-4}
	1.97	68.0	0.91	6.6×10^{-4}

* K represents the rate constant of curing at 180°C.

As shown in Table 5, the activation energy of curing reaction of nano-Al_2O_3/epoxy decreases with increasing the filler content and the rate constant is greatly increased. Nano-Si_3N_4 composites also exhibit similar dependence, but less as significant as the former system. These coincide with the results illustrated in Fig.17. For nano-SiC/epoxy composites, however, the changes in both E and K are marginal and the value of E becomes higher at higher filler loading.

Basically, due to the strong interaction between the nanoparticles and the epoxy resin resulting from the specific surface feature of nanoparticles, the curing reaction kinetics of the nanocomposites might be different from neat epoxy resin. The above-observed accelerating effect results from the hydroxyl groups on the nanoparticles' surfaces (donors of hydrogen bonding). The more the surface hydroxyl groups, the higher the activity of the particles. Since nano-Al_2O_3 particles possess much higher amount of hydroxyl groups than nano-SiC [53, 54], it is reasonable to understand the evident acceleration perceived in nano-Al_2O_3/epoxy system. On the other hand, the incorporation of the nanoparticles must raise the viscosity of the composite system (before curing) and/or the strong interaction between the nanoparticles and the matrix polymer would hinder the molecular motion of epoxy, which disfavor the curing of epoxy. Therefore, the effect exerted by the nanoparticles is a competition of the two opposite factors. In the case of nano-Al_2O_3 and nano-Si_3N_4 particles, the effect of acceleration is measured because of the higher amount of their surface hydroxyl groups. For nano-SiC, the hindrance effect plays the leading role as a result of the fewer surface hydroxyl groups. From Table 5, it is known that the curing reaction orders of the three composites are almost the same, suggesting that the nanoparticles don't change the curing mechanism of epoxy.

To look into the influence of graft treatment of nanoparticles, grafted nano-SiO_2 particles are used. Similarly, when the particles are incorporated into epoxy, the curing kinetics of the resin is changed significantly (Fig.18). Evidently, the unmodified silica nanoparticles hinder the curing reaction to a certain extent and lead to a shift of the temperature dependence of conversion towards higher temperature. In contrast, the addition of grafted silica nanoparticles accelerates curing of epoxy, probably due to the catalytic effect of the active hydrogen atoms in amide of PAAM. This behavior is indicative of an improved processability of the system in practice.

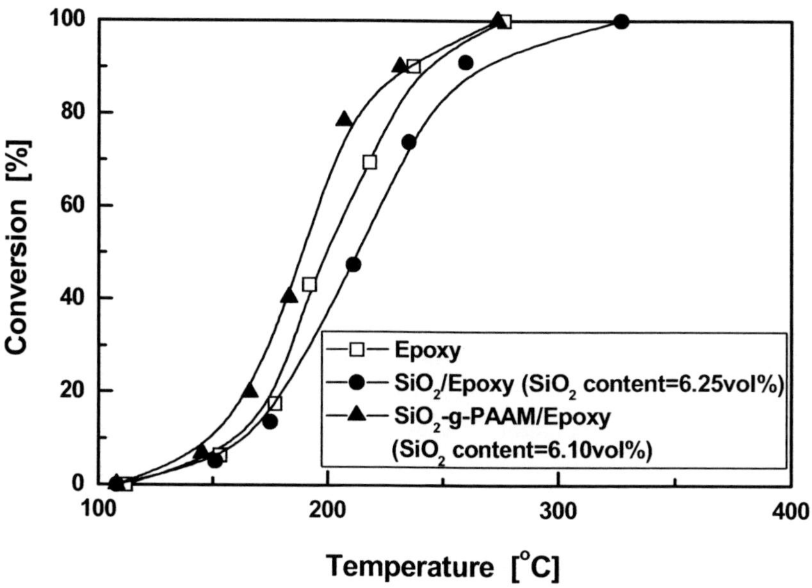

Figure 18. Nonisothermal curing behavior of epoxy and its composites at a heating rate of 2°C/min.

To further understand the curing reaction kinetics of the composites, the results of non-isothermal DSC measurements are used to determine the activation energy, the pre-exponential factor, and the reaction order of curing kinetics of the materials once more (Table 6).

Table 6. Curing characteristics of epoxy and its composites at 2.17vol% nanosilica content

Materials	Epoxy	SiO_2/Epoxy	SiO_2-g-PAAM/Epoxy
E (kJ/mol)	68.9	69.4	57.8
LnA	8.4	8.6	5.6
n	1.25	1.35	1.23

By comparing the kinetic data, it can be seen that the presence of the nanoparticles in epoxy does not change the overall reaction mechanism. In comparison with the neat epoxy resin, the increase in the activation energy of the SiO_2/epoxy system suggests that the unmodified nanoparticles slightly decelerate the curing reaction. In contrast, the grafted nanoparticles tends to have a promotive effect on the curing of epoxy, as revealed by the decreased activation energy. Considering the fact that the pre-exponential factor of SiO_2-g-PAAM/epoxy composites is significantly reduced, probably due to the steric hindrance generated by the grafting polymers adhering to the nanoparticles, a comprehensive evaluation of the influence of the nanoparticles on the curing behavior of epoxy has to be made by examining the reaction rate constants.

Fig.19 illustrates Arrhenius plots of rate constant lnK of the materials as a function of the reciprocal temperature. The results demonstrate that SiO_2/epoxy has almost the same rate constant as epoxy. For SiO_2-g-PAAM/epoxy, the rate constant is higher than that of the former two systems at a temperature below 205°C, but it becomes lower when the temperature exceeds 205°C. It is generally agreed that the reaction mechanism for the addition of amine to epoxy takes into account the phenomenon of catalysis by hydrogen bond donors. Such a catalytic effect is via hydrogen bonding of the hydroxyl group to the oxygen of the glycidyl ether in the transition state [55]. Therefore, the appearance of the active hydrogen atoms in amide of PAAM grafted nanosilica favors the curing reaction. Since hydrogen bond formation and dissociation in a polymer are thermally reversible, a large portion of hydrogen bonds has to be dissociated at elevated temperature. As a result, diffusion control plays the leading role in SiO_2-g-PAAM/epoxy composites at a temperature higher than 205°C (Fig.19).

In fact, the composites used in this work were cured below 205°C (refer to the experimental part). It means that the grafted nanosilica accelerates the curing reaction of epoxy over the entire curing temperature range and thus improves the processability of the system in practice.

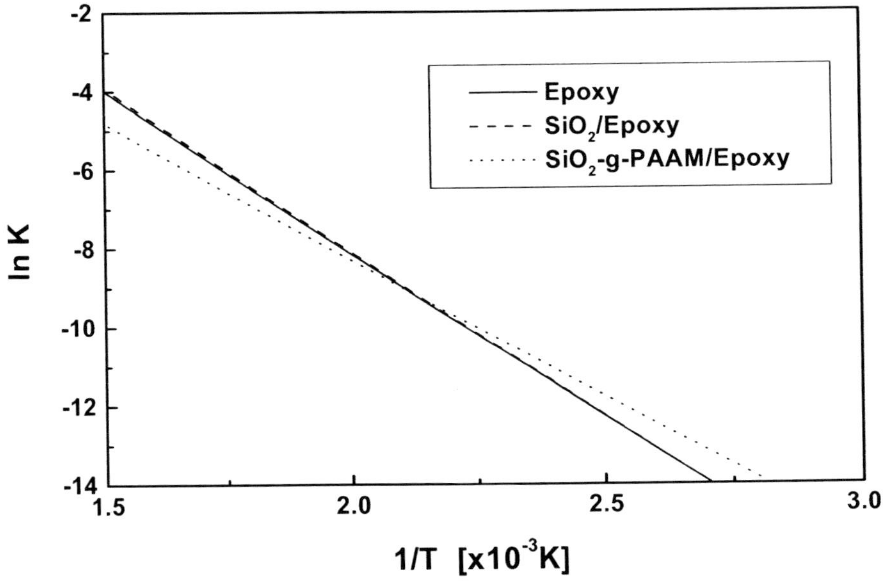

Figure 19. Temperature dependence of rate constant characterizing curing processes of epoxy and its composites at 2.17vol% nanosilica content.

2.7. Interfacial Interaction

To examine the possible interaction between the nanoparticles and epoxy, a series of tests were carried out. For nano-Al_2O_3 and nano-Si_3N_4, the particles were mixed with epoxy, and then the blends were cured in the absence of any curing agent following the aforesaid composites curing procedures. Afterwards, the blends were extracted by acetone to remove the uncured epoxy, and Fourier transform infrared spectroscopy (FTIR) was adopted to check the changes in the chemical structures of the related materials. Due to the strong absorbability of SiC particles, their FTIR spectrum were not collected. As shown in Fig.20, on the spectrum of epoxy one can find the peak corresponding to the stretching mode of C-H of arylene at 3060cm^{-1}, the vibration modes of phenyl rings at 1510 and 1606.7cm^{-1}, the stretching mode of C-O-C of Ar-O-R at 1247.8cm^{-1}. All these characteristic absorptions are not perceivable on the spectrum of either nano-Al_2O_3 or nano-Si_3N_4, but appear on the spectra of the blends with the nanoparticles. It means epoxy has been covalently adhered to the both the untreated and grafted nanoparticles.

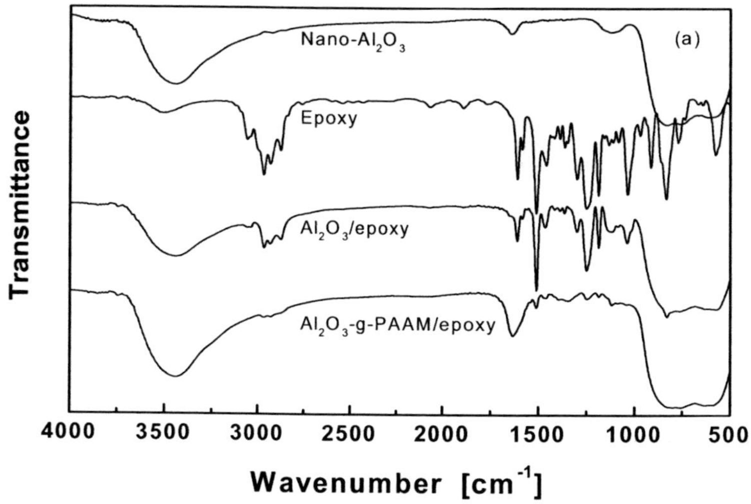

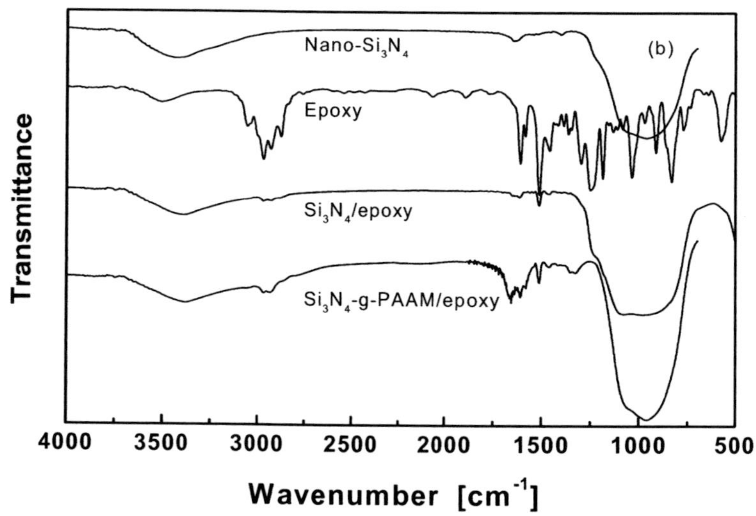

Figure 20. FTIR spectra of epoxy and its composites filled with (a) nano-Al_2O_3 and (b) nano-Si_3N_4. In all the materials there is no curing agent.

For purposes of revealing the reaction details between the grafting PAAM onto the nanoparticles and epoxy, a model system consists of PAAM homopolymer and epoxy (1/2 by weight) excluding other curing agents was thermally treated following the same curing sequence as that applied for producing the composites. Visual inspection indicated that the blends of PAAM and epoxy became consolidated after curing and the resultant product can only be swollen by acetone instead of dissolve in the solvent. In addition, comparison of the infrared spectra of the materials can also yield interesting information. As illustrated by the spectrum of PAAM in Fig.21, the C=O peak at 1665cm^{-1}, the NH_2 peak at 1616cm^{-1} and the CN peak at 1454cm^{-1} correspond to the primary amide. In the case of PAAM/epoxy blends, however, the spectrum profile has been changed as a result of transformation of partial primary amide groups and band overlap due to the incorporation of epoxy. Since the CNH peak at 1530~1550cm^{-1}, a characteristic peak of secondary amide, is not perceived, and the carbonyl peak appears at 1656cm^{-1} instead, it can be deduced that this carbonyl peak in association with the low wavenumber shift (compared with the carbonyl peak position of primary amide) represents the existence of tertiary amide connected with donor group. This evidences the reaction between PAAM and epoxy during curing. It can thus be concluded from the above visual observation and spectral analyses that PAAM is able to take part in the curing reaction of epoxy. Such a chemical bonding between the PAAM chains grafted onto the nanoparticles and surrounding epoxy networks would certainly enhance the filler/matrix adhesion in the composites.

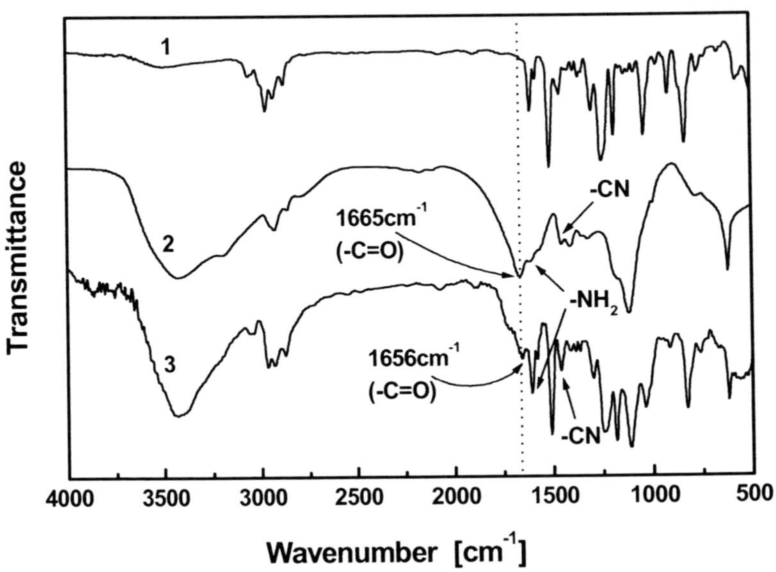

Figure 21. FTIR spectra of (1) epoxy without any curing agent, (2) PAAM, and (3) cured blends of PAAM and epoxy (1/2 w/w).

Dynamic mechanical analysis is a useful tool to monitor interfacial interaction in composite materials Fig.22 illustrates the mechanical loss spectra of mamo-Si_3N_4/epoxy composites. In contrast to the conventional composites [56], whose damping factor at glass transition, Tan δ_{T_g}, is lower than that of the matrix, the internal friction peak intensity of epoxy shown in Fig.22 is weaker than the filled versions. Besides, the glass transition temperature characterized by the α-peak temperature of epoxy is also higher than those of the composites. This phenomenon might result from (i) a weak interfacial interaction in the case of stiff interphase [57] or (ii) a strong interfacial interaction in the case of ductile interphase [58]. Considering that impact tests reveal the ability of the particles to induce plastic deformation, it can be deduced that the latter factor plays the leading role. In fact, this estimation is supported by the calculation of Kubat parameter B [59]:

$$B = \frac{Tan\delta_c}{(1-V_f)Tan\delta_m} - 1 \qquad (1)$$

where Tan δ_c and Tan δ_m denote the damping factors of the composites and the matrix, respectively, and V_f is the filler volume fraction. By using the Tan δ_{T_g} data of the materials shown in Fig.22, the values of B for the composites are yielded: 0.04 (V_f=0.27vol%), 0.51 (V_f=0.83vol%), 0.40 (V_f=1.38vol%), and 0.36 (V_f=2.19vol%). As B approaching 0 corresponds to strong interfacial bonding in the composites, it is known that the nanocomposites at the lowest filler fraction (V_f=0.27vol%) has the highest filler/matrix adhesion.

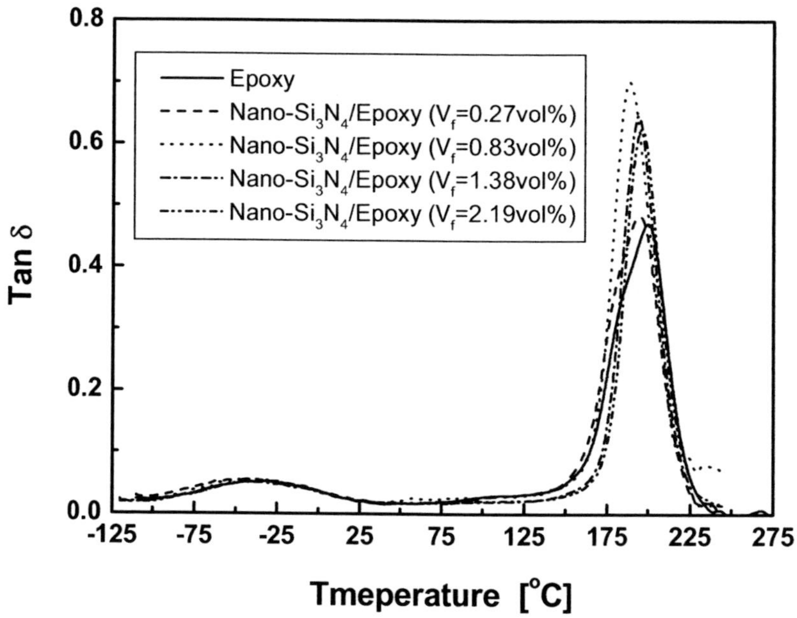

Figure 22. Temperature dependence of internal friction, Tanδ, of nano-Si_3N_4/epoxy composites measured at 1Hz.

Table 7 further lists the peak temperatures and activation enthalpies of the β relaxation, ΔH_β, of the composites. The values of the latter parameters were obtained from Arrhenius regression. β relaxation has been assigned to motions of the O-CH_2-CHOH-CH_2 hydroxypropylether units and cooperative motions involving hydroxypropylether units and amine crosslinking points that are present in all these systems [60, 61]. The greater ΔH_β values of the composites than that of unfilled epoxy induced by the addition of nano-Si_3N_4 means that the particles/matrix interaction is so strong that the motion of alcohol ether in epoxy is greatly obstructed and the crosslinking density is changed to a certain extent as well.

The results of dynamic mechanical analysis of nano-SiO2/epoxy composites are given in Table 8. Activation enthalpies of the β relaxation are ranked in the order: epoxy < SiO_2/epoxy < SiO_2-g-PAAM/epoxy. According to the above discussion, it is known that the strong interactions between the particles and the matrix have been established. This is particular true when grafted nanosilica appears. With respect to the glass transition temperature, the composites filled with treated and untreated nanoparticles have almost the same values. The increase in T_g can be attributed to the decreased mobility of chain segments of epoxy resin as a result of the filler/matrix interaction. Considering molecular mechanisms, it is evident that the additional chemical bonding between grafting PAAM and epoxy exerts a more significant influence on the secondary relaxation of epoxy than on the primary transition.

Table 7. Characterization of β relaxation of nano-Si_3N_4/epoxy composites

V_f (vol%)	Peak temperature of β relaxation (°C)				ΔH_β (kJ/mol)
	30Hz	10Hz	3Hz	1Hz	
0	-13.8	-22.8	-31.4	-35.9	56.6
0.27	-16.8	-25.2	-33.6	-41.3	75.8
0.83	-19.5	-26.2	-33.2	-41.0	103.6
1.38	-16.4	-22.34	-29.8	-37.6	80.7
2.19	-16.2	-23.8	-30.4	-36.6	78.7

Table 8. Characteristic parameters of dynamic mechanical performance of epoxy and its composites at 2.17vol% nanosilica content

Materials	Epoxy	SiO_2/Epoxy	SiO_2-g-PAAM/Epoxy
ΔH_β (kJ/mol)	48.3	54.0	73.9
T_g* (°C)	217.5	225.1	225.8

* T_g: glass transition temperature determined from the peak temperature of the α transition at 10Hz

3. Friction and Wear Properties

3.1. Friction and Wear Properties of Nano-Al_2O_3/Epoxy Composites

The sliding wear rate of nano-Al_2O_3/epoxy composites is illustrated in Fig.23 as a function of nano-alumina particle content. The degrees of the particles pretreatments are listed in Table 9. From Fig.23, it is seen that the high wear rate of unfilled epoxy due to the three-dimensional crosslinking network is greatly decreased by adding nano-Al_2O_3 particles. As compared to the composites with untreated nanoparticles, the low wear rates of the composites filled with treated nano-Al_2O_3 particles keep almost unchanged with filler content up to ~2vol%. The phenomenon is similar to what is reported in ref.[62] in spite of the fact that the testing configurations and conditions are different. Figs.24 and 25 give the results of other composites and clearly show that the wear resistance of unfilled epoxy is decreased by one order of magnitude when treated nano-Al_2O_3 is incorporated.

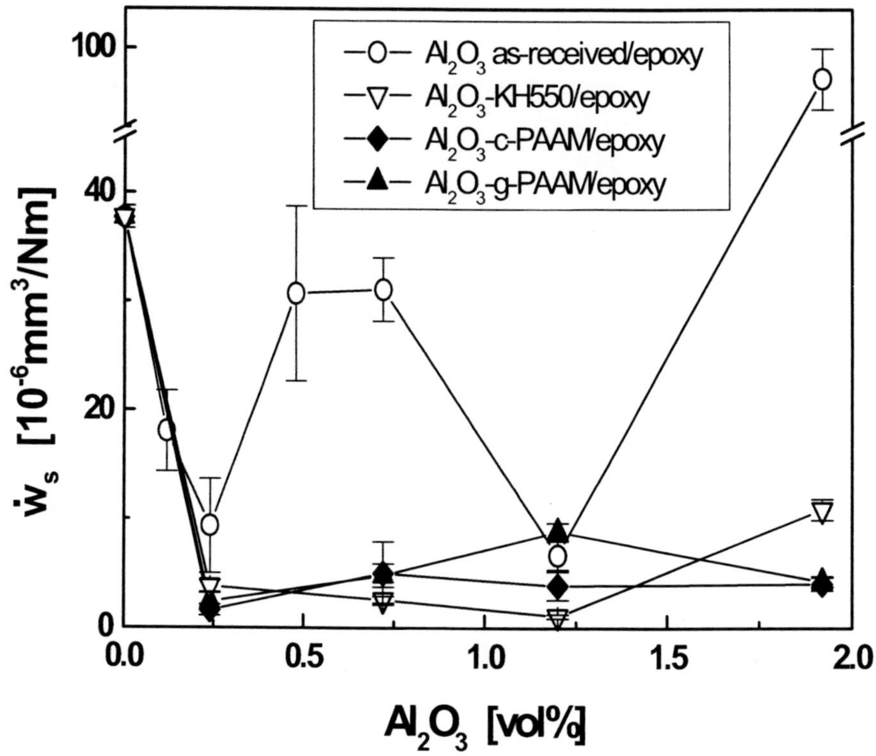

Figure 23. Specific wear rate, $\dot{w}_s$, of nano-Al_2O_3/epoxy composites as a function of volume fraction of nano-Al_2O_3. Test conditions: p=3MPa, v=0.4m/s.

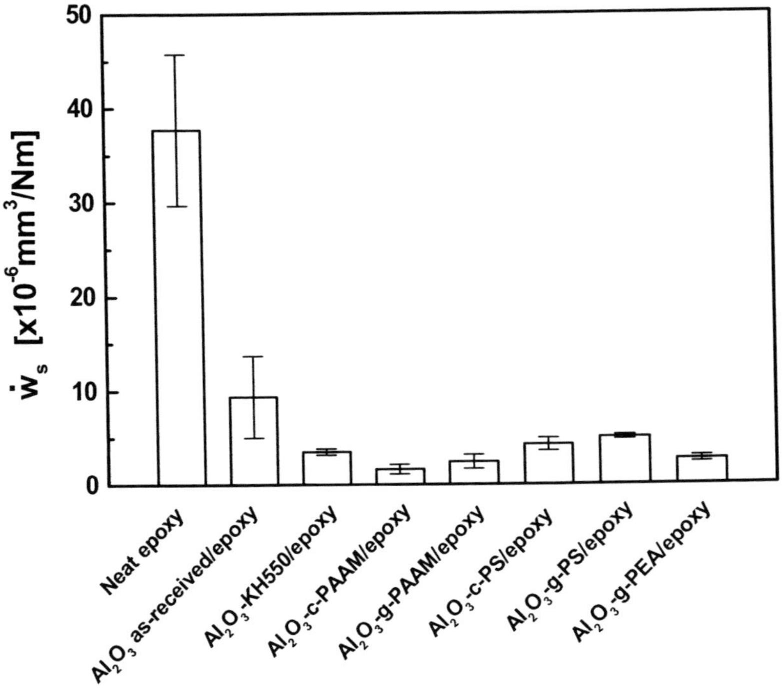

Figure 24. Specific wear rate, $\dot{w}_s$, of nano-Al_2O_3/epoxy composites at a volume fraction of nano-Al_2O_3 of 0.24vol%. Test conditions: p=3MPa, v=0.4m/s.

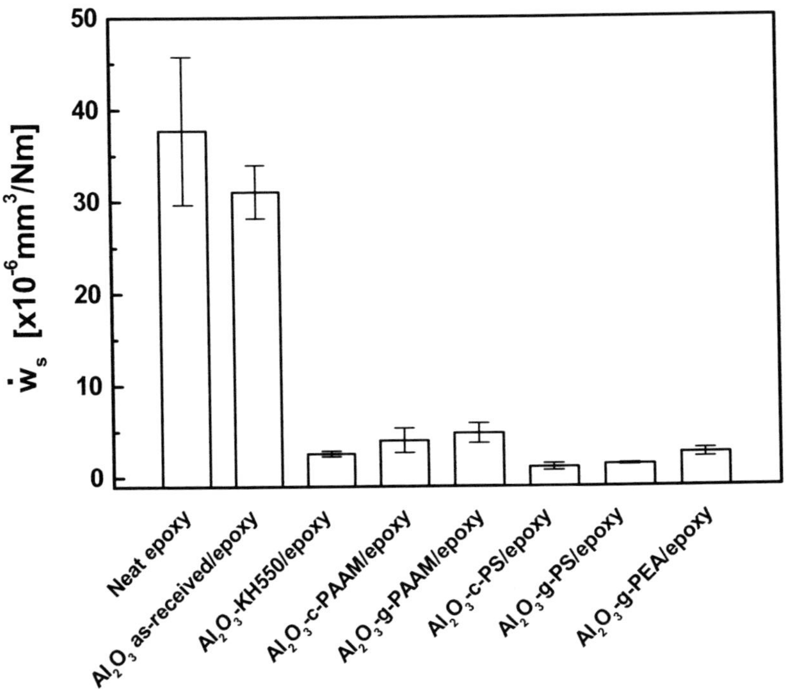

Figure 25. Specific wear rate, $\dot{w}_s$, of nano-Al_2O_3/epoxy composites at a volume fraction of nano-Al_2O_3 of 0.72vol%. Test conditions: p=3MPa, v=0.4m/s.

Table 9. Amounts of the chemicals adhered to Al_2O_3 nanoparticles

Treated particles	Al_2O_3-KH550	Al_2O_3-c-PAAM	Al_2O_3-c-PS	Al_2O_3-c-PEA	Al_2O_3-g-PAAM	Al_2O_3-g-PS	Al_2O_3-g-PEA
$W_{chem/alumina}$* (%)	2.2	15	15.5	20.5	10	9.1	14.6

*$W_{chem/alumina}$: relative amount of the chemical adhered to the particles = weight of the chemical adhered to the particles / weight of Al_2O_3. Al_2O_3-KH550 means the nanosized alumina particles have been treated by KH550 silane. Al_2O_3-c-PAAM, Al_2O_3-c-PS and Al_2O_3-c-PEA denote that the particles are grafted by polyacrylamide, polystyrene and polyethyl acrylate without removing the homopolymers generated during the graft polymerization. Having experienced extraction with proper solvents, the grafted nanoparticles are symbolized by Al_2O_3-g-PAAM, Al_2O_3-g-PS and Al_2O_3-g-PEA, respectively, meaning the particles are accompanied only with the unextractable grafting polymers.

For untreated nano-Al_2O_3 filled epoxy composites, the decrement of wear rate is marginal especially when filler content is greater than 0.24vol%. It resembles the case of untreated nano-Al_2O_3/ultra-high-molecular-weight-polyethylene [63], meaning that the composites cannot effectively entrap the particles and prevent substantial material removal.

Besides improving the wear resistance, the nanoparticles also reduce frictional coefficient of epoxy as shown in Figs.26, 27 and 28. Evidently, the composites with treated nanoparticles have lower frictional coefficients than those with untreated ones. At a content of nano-Al_2O_3 of 0.24vol%, for example, the frictional coefficient of Al_2O_3-c-PAAM/epoxy is 0.35 that amounts to 61% of the value of unfilled epoxy and 69% of the value of untreated nano-Al_2O_3/epoxy. Meanwhile, the specific wear rate of Al_2O_3-c-PAAM/epoxy with the same filler concentration is decreased by 97% and 88% respectively, as compared with the values of unfilled epoxy and untreated nano-Al_2O_3/epoxy.

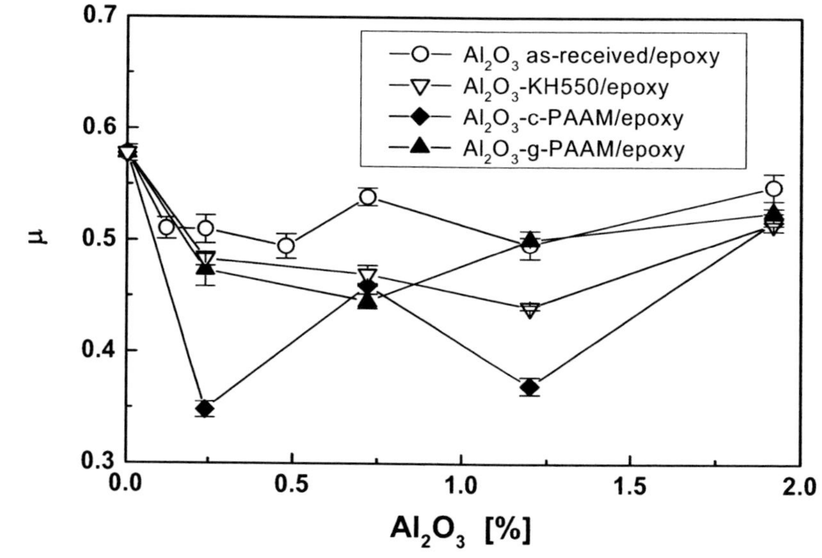

Figure 26. Frictional coefficient, μ, of nano-Al_2O_3/epoxy composites as a function of volume fraction of nano-Al_2O_3. Test conditions: p=3MPa, v=0.4m/s.

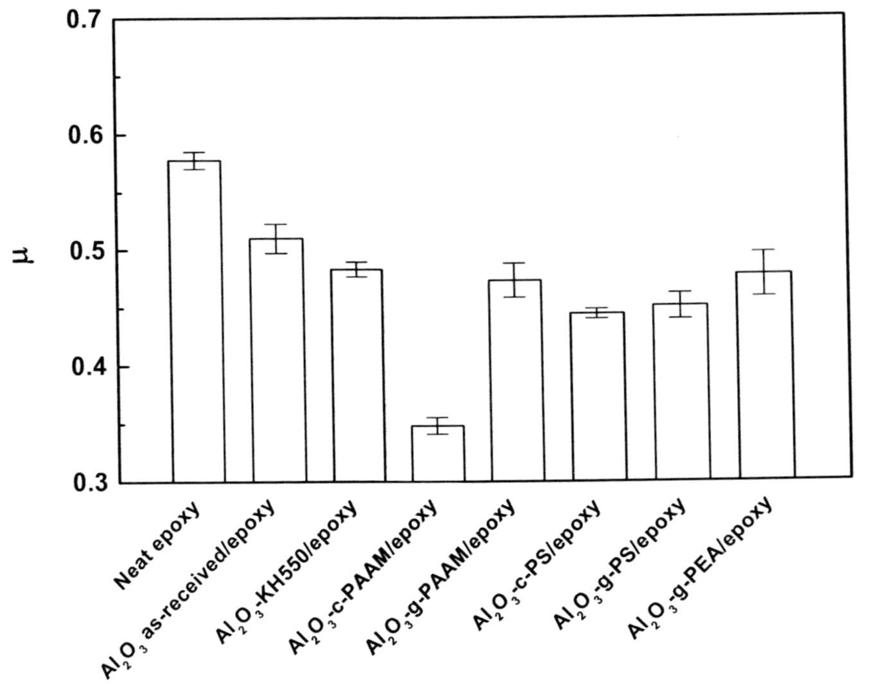

Figure 27. Frictional coefficient, μ, of nano-Al_2O_3/epoxy composites at a volume fraction of nano-Al_2O_3 of 0.24vol%. Test conditions: p=3MPa, v=0.4m/s.

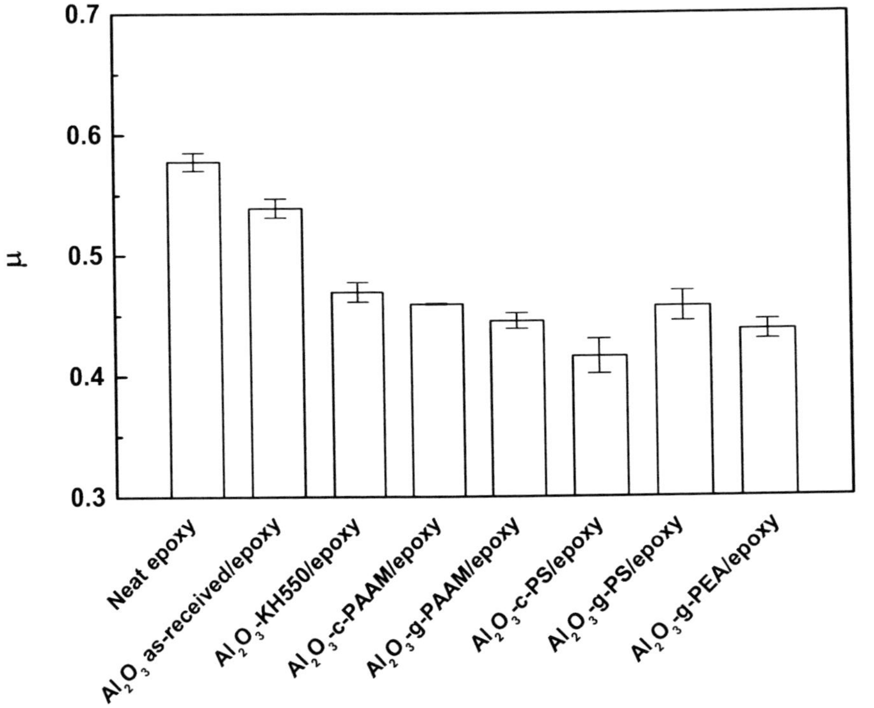

Figure 28. Frictional coefficient, μ, of nano-Al_2O_3/epoxy composites at a volume fraction of nano-Al_2O_3 of 0.72vol%. Test conditions: p=3MPa, v=0.4m/s.

The difference in improving the friction reducing and wear resisting ability of epoxy between the composites with untreated and treated nano-alumina should result mainly from the filler/filler adhesion strength. The treatments employed in the present work can either build up chemical bonding between the nanoparticles and epoxy (for the composites with KH550 treated nano-Al_2O_3 and PAAM grafted nano-Al_2O_3), or improving the interfacial miscibility (for epoxy reinforced by PS grafted nano-Al_2O_3 and PEA grafted nano-Al_2O_3). With respect to the untreated nanoparticles, they have to present themselves in the composites in the form of agglomerates because of the hydrophilic nature of the particles and the limited dispersion force during blending with epoxy. Inside the nanoparticle agglomerates, the particles are bound only by hydrogen bonds and van der Waals bonds. When the composites with the untreated nanoparticles are subjected to wearing, damage induced by localized shear stress concentration at the loosened nanoparticle agglomerates would occur on a relatively large scale and produce bigger blocks of wear debris. These are disadvantageous to the improvement of tribological performance of the matrix. In the case of the composites with enhanced interaction inside and outside the nanoparticle agglomerates, the resistance to periodic frictional stress is greatly increased. Detachment of nanoparticles and small amount of the surrounding matrix plays the leading role in material removal due to wear. The detached nanoparticles might also act as solid lubricants. These account for the low wear rates and frictional coefficients of the composites.

On the other hand, the effect of homopolymers (generated during graft polymerization) on the grafted nanoparticles/epoxy composites is also revealed in Figs.24, 25, 27 and 28. In most cases, the presence of the homopolymers helps to further improve the wear and friction performance of the composites. For example, the wear rate of Al_2O_3-c-PAAM/epoxy is lower than that of Al_2O_3-g-PAAM/epoxy (Figs.24 and 25), and frictional coefficient of Al_2O_3-c-PS/epoxy is lower than Al_2O_3-g-PS/epoxy (Figs.27 and 28). It is believed that the filler/matrix interaction is partially shielded by the homopolymers in the case of Al_2O_3-c-PAAM/epoxy and Al_2O_3-c-PS/epoxy composites. When the composites rub against the steel counterface, the nano-Al_2O_3 particles in Al_2O_3-c-PAAM/epoxy and Al_2O_3-c-PS/epoxy might break away from the binding of the matrix more easily than those in Al_2O_3-g-PAAM/epoxy and Al_2O_3-g-PS/epoxy composites, providing solid lubricating effect. In addition, for the nano-Al_2O_3 particles right on the rubbing surface of Al_2O_3-c-PAAM/epoxy and Al_2O_3-c-PS/epoxy, the surrounding grafting polymers and homopolymers can also lubricate the wear processes.

The lubricating effect of the nanoparticles can be partly evidenced by the microhardness of the materials' surfaces before and after the sliding wear tests (Fig.29). For unfilled epoxy, the microhardness of the worn pin surface is remarkably lowered as compared to the value of the unworn one. It reflects the deteriorated microstructure of epoxy led by the repeated frictional force and high frictional temperature. When nano-Al_2O_3 is added, the microhardness of the worn pin surface of the composites is either the same as or slightly lower than that of the unworn pin surface. Clearly, the severe wear in the case of unfilled epoxy has been changed to mild one due the nanoparticles.

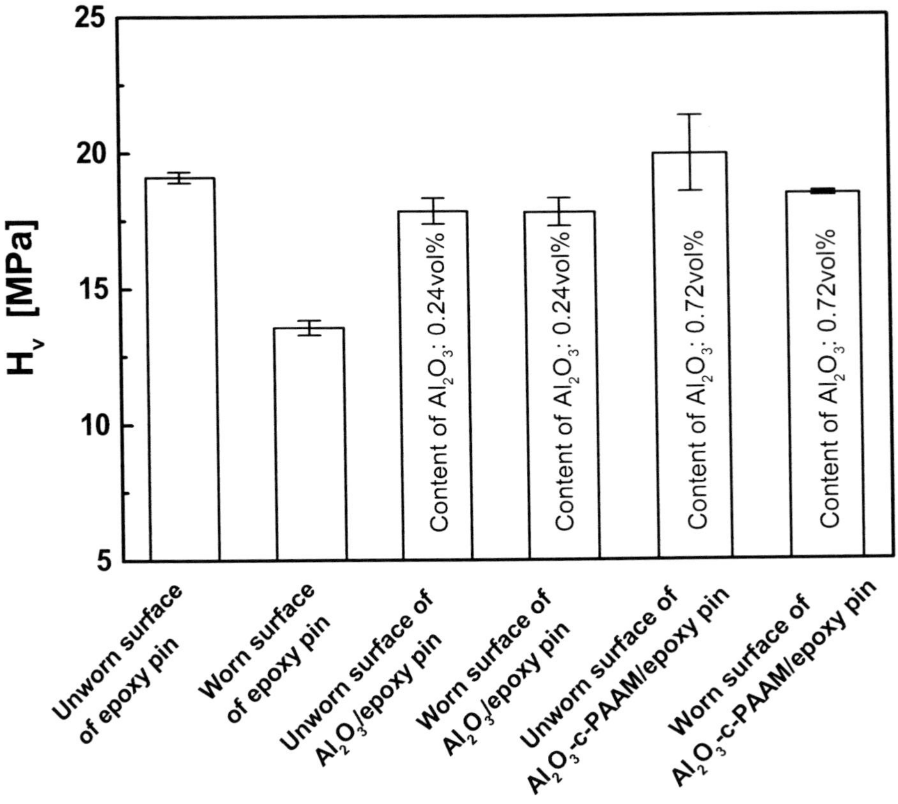

Figure 29. Vickers microhardness, H_v, of the materials' surfaces before and after sliding wear tests.

To have more information about the variation in wear behavior due to the addition of the nanoparticles, morphologies of the worn pins' surfaces are examined by SEM at an identical magnification (Fig.30). Severe damages characterized by the disintegration of top layer are observed in unfilled epoxy (Fig.30(a)). The material removal takes the form of larger blocks, which might be captured between the steel counterface and the test pin, and abrade the specimen surface leading to even more substantial material loss. In the case of filled composites, the appearances are completely different and become rather smooth. Although the ploughing grooves are still visible on the composites with untreated nano-Al_2O_3 (Fig.30(b)), the groove depths are quite shallow on the composites with treated nano-Al_2O_3 (Figs.30(c~f)) or simply invisible (Fig.30(g)). It suggests that polishing predominates the wear processes of the latter composites.

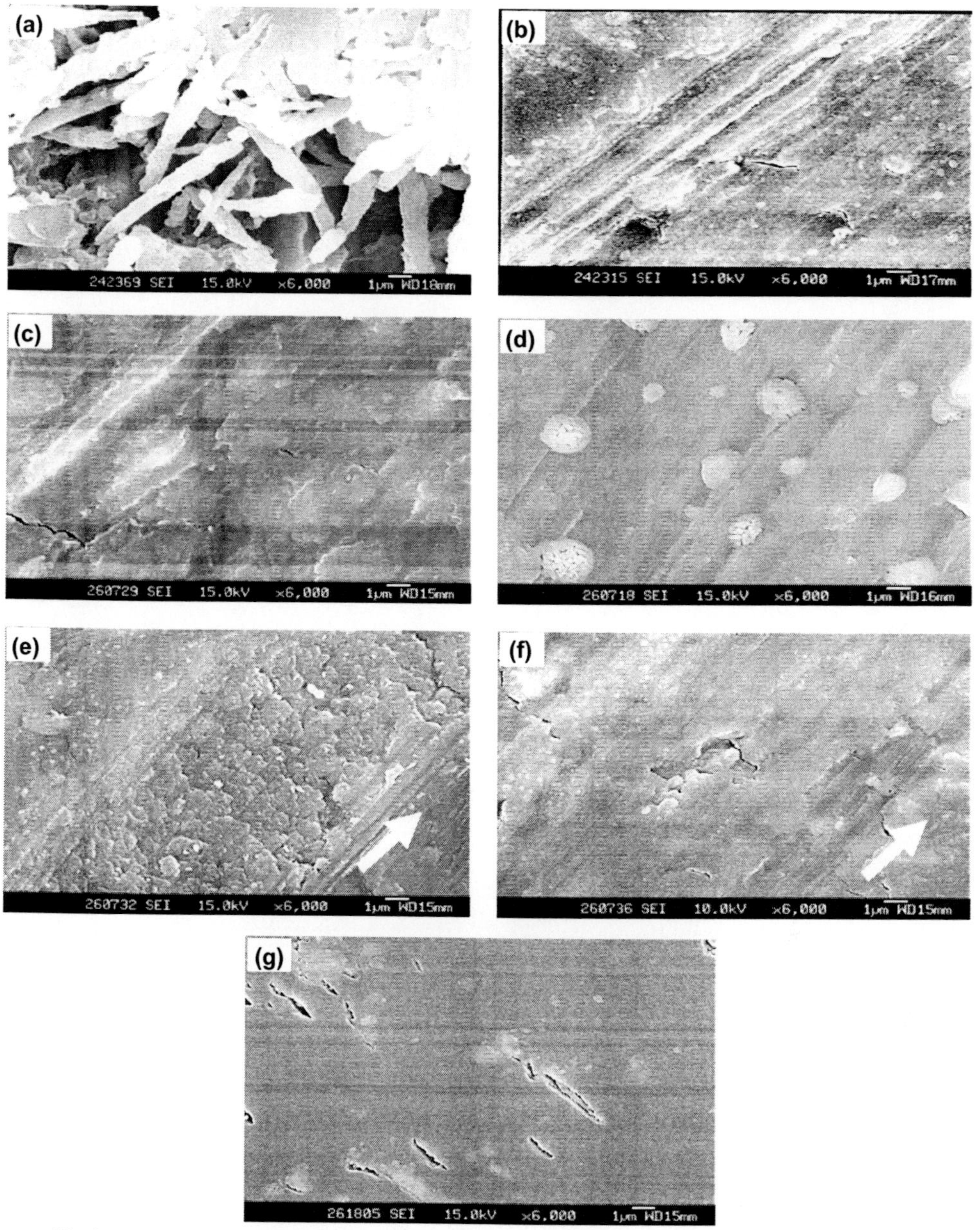

Figure 30. SEM photos of the worn surfaces of (a) unfilled epoxy and its composites filled with (b) untreated nano-Al_2O_3, (c) Al_2O_3-KH550, (d) Al_2O_3-c-PAAM, (e) Al_2O_3-g-PAAM, (f) Al_2O_3-g-PS, and (g) Al_2O_3-g-PEA at a volume fraction of nano-Al_2O_3 of 0.24vol%. The arrows indicate the sliding direction. Test conditions for the sliding wear: p=3MPa, v=0.4m/s.

It is noted that some cracks across the wear tracks are perceivable on the composites' worn surfaces (Figs.30(b), (c), (f) and (g)). They might be nucleated at sub-surface layer as a result of shear deformation induced by the traction of the harder asperities. The scale-like damage patterns (Figs.30(e) and (f)) resulting from the coalescence of the cracks imply that the effect of fatigue-delamination [64] is the main wear mechanism. It can thus be concluded that the abrasive wear of unfilled epoxy is replaced by fatigue wear when the treated nano-Al_2O_3 particles are compounded, while the wear mode of untreated nano-Al_2O_3/epoxy is a mixture of abrasive wear and fatigue wear.

Table 10 lists the elements on the steel counterpart surface before and after the wear tests, which are determined by X-ray energy distribution spectra (EDS). Having rubbed with epoxy, sulfur appears on the surface of the steel ring, implying the transfer from epoxy to the counterface. When the specimen is changed into untreated nano-Al_2O_3/epoxy composite, both sulfur and aluminum can be detected. It further proves substances transfer across the frictional surfaces. It is worth noting that the contents of sulfur and aluminum on the steel ring surface are increased as the ring has rubbed against Al_2O_3-g-PAAM/epoxy composite. This suggests that tribochemically induced transfer film [65] can be more effectively built up on the steel counterface thereby decreasing wear, as compared to the case of untreated nano-Al_2O_3/epoxy composite. According to the X-ray photoelectron spectra (XPS) analysis of the worn surfaces of the composites (Fig.31), it is known that under the joint action of high frictional temperature and pressure the aluminum no longer presents itself only in the form of Al_2O_3 but additionally reacts with Fe and S, respectively. Therefore, the above-stated formation of the transfer film is thermodynamically favorable.

Table 10. Surface elemental analysis of the steel counterpart

	Elements and content (%)			
	Fe	S	Al	Si
Steel ring before wear test	98.65	0	0	0.22
Steel ring rubbed against epoxy pin	98.55	0.42	0	0.21
Steel ring rubbed against untreated nano-Al_2O_3/epoxy composite pin at a volume fraction of nano-Al_2O_3 of 0.24vol%	98.41	0.31	0.2	0.1
Steel ring rubbed against Al_2O_3-g-PAAM/epoxy composite pin at a volume fraction of nano-Al_2O_3 of 0.24vol%	97.5	0.58	0.4	0.19

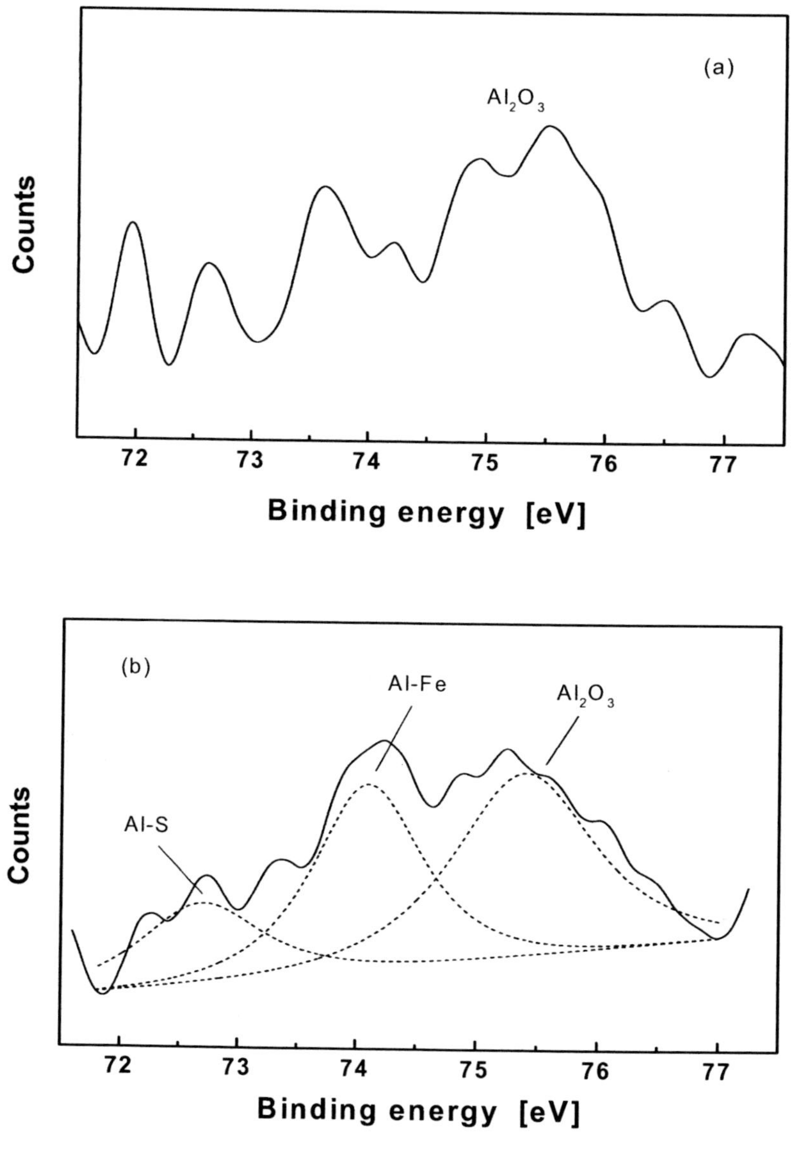

Figure 31. Al 2p spectra of the pin surface of (a) unworn nano-Al_2O_3/epoxy composites and (b) worn nano-Al_2O_3/epoxy composites at a volume fraction of nano-Al_2O_3 of 0.24vol%.

3.2. Friction and Wear Properties of Nano-SiC/Epoxy Composites

The tribological performance of epoxy and its composites filled with SiC nanoparticles are given in Fig.32. Both treated and untreated SiC nanoparticles are able to reduce the frictional coefficient of epoxy (Fig.32(a)). Especially when the content of the particles is 0.2vol%, the composites' frictional coefficients exhibit the lowest values among the results. Comparatively, the grafted SiC nanoparticles provide more significant solid lubricating effect. With a rise in the filler loading, however, the frictional coefficients of the materials increase, suggesting that the particles cannot be dispersed homogeneously in the case of increased amount of the particles and agglomeration of the fillers is disadvantageous to the lubrication between the composites and the steel counterpart. The profiles of the worn pins' surfaces (Fig.33) indicate that the resistance of the composites to surface shear failure is improved as a result of the incorporation of the nanoparticles. The roughness of the frictional surfaces decreases remarkably, and the wear process is actually characterized by polishing.

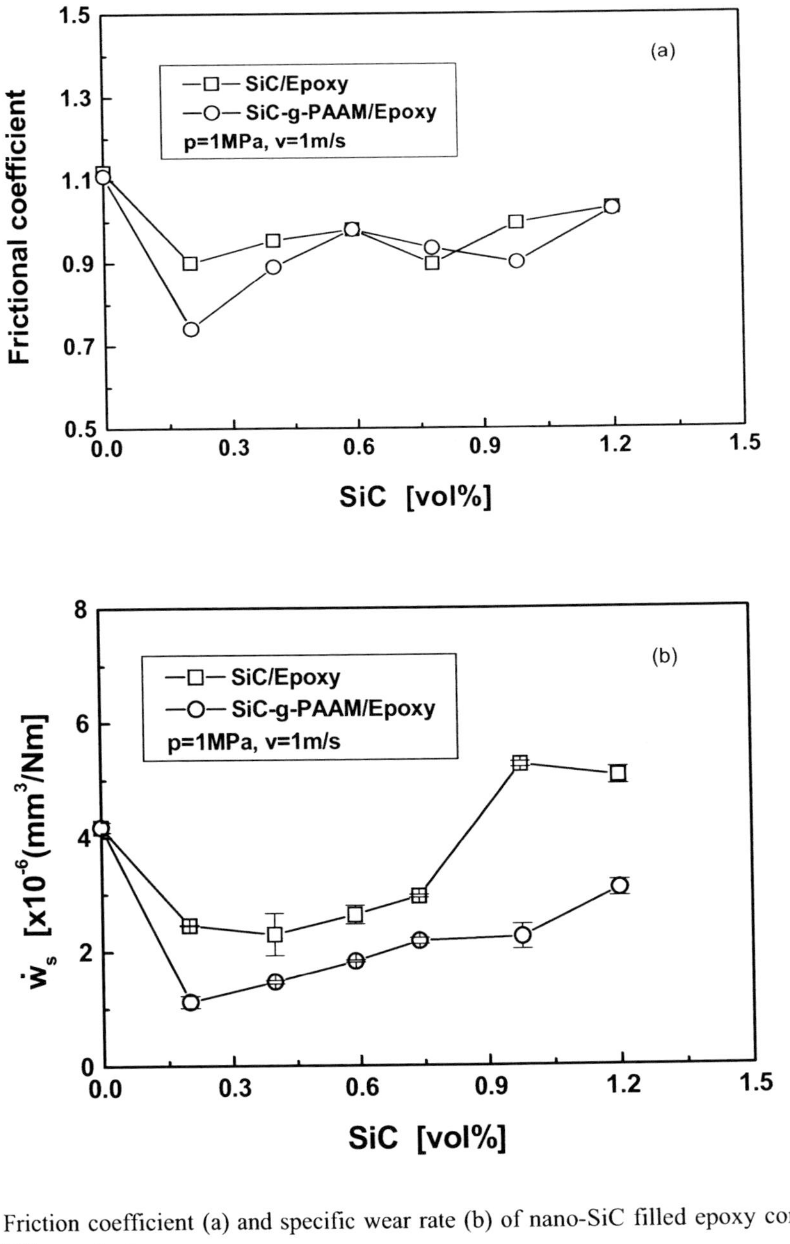

Figure 32. Friction coefficient (a) and specific wear rate (b) of nano-SiC filled epoxy composites as a function of filler content.

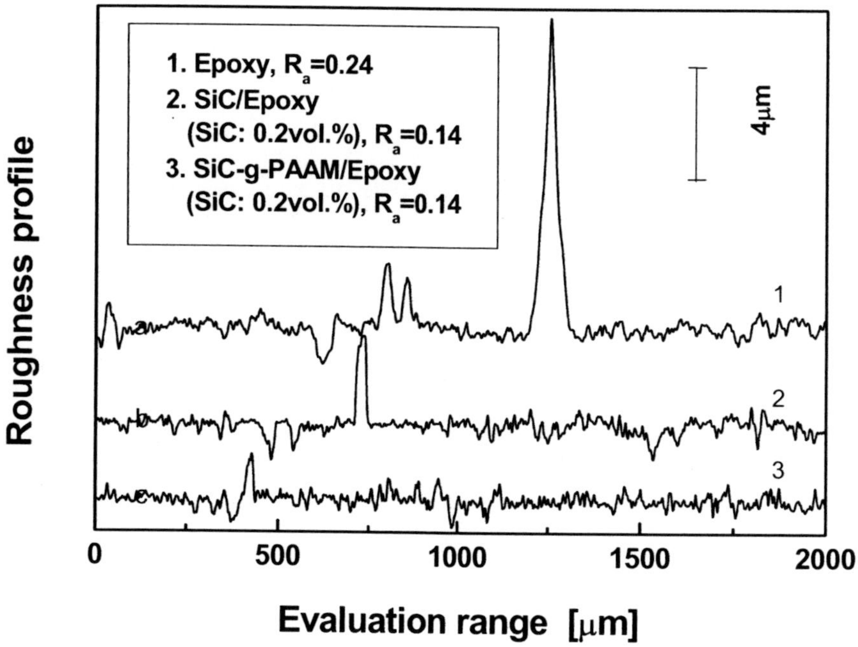

Figure 33. Profile scans of the worn surfaces of (a) epoxy, (b) SiC/epoxy and (c) SiC-g-PAAM/epoxy composites (Content of SiC: 0.2vol.%, Wear test conditions: block-on-ring, p=1MPa, v=1m/s).

Similar to the results of frictional coefficient measurements, the addition of SiC nanoparticles can also lead to decreased wear rate (Fig.32(b)). It is worth noting that the wear rates of the composites with grafted SiC nanoparticles are lower than those of the composites with untreated SiC within the entire range of filler content of interests. Although the wear rates of the composites increase with a rise in the particles content, the variation is more significant in the system of SiC/epoxy. For the content of SiC of 1~1.2vol%, for example, SiC/epoxy exhibits wear rate even higher than that of unfilled epoxy. These manifest that smaller amount of well-distributed nanoparticles can reinforce the matrix effectively [45], and prevent the composites from wear failure. Owing to the introduction of the grafting polymer chains, the interfacial adhesion between the nanoparticles and the matrix is further enhanced and thus the wear resistance can also be raised accordingly. When the concentration of the nanoparticles increases, the particles are hard to be dispersed and many weak interfaces form inside the agglomerated nanoparticles. As a result, the particles would be removed from the matrix easily under the action of frictional force and the composites' wear rate has to be increased. Surface grafting treatment overcomes the aforesaid defects to a certain extent, so that SiC-g-PAAM/epoxy composites still have higher wear resistance than SiC/epoxy in the case of higher filler fraction.

As in-situ polymerization was employed during surface grafting onto the nanoparticles, homopolymers of the monomers were inevitably produced. For simplifying the influencing factors, however, the grafted nanoparticles used in the composites cited in Figs.32 and 33 were extracted prior to the composites preparation to remove the homopolymerized PAAM.

In consideration of the fact that large quantity of solvent and longer time are required for separating homopolymers from the grafted products in practical applications, it is necessary to study the influence of the homopolymers accompanying the grafted nanoparticles on the tribological performance of the composites. As shown in Fig.34, in the case of relatively low filler content (0.2vol%), the appearance of the homopolymers in the grafted nanoparticles leads to higher wear rate of the composites (SiC-c-PAAM/epoxy) than that of the composites with grafted SiC particles excluding the homopolymerized PAAM (SiC-g-PAAM/epoxy). At the particle content of 0.98vol%, on the contrary, the wear rate of SiC-c-PAAM/epoxy becomes slightly lower than that of SiC-g-PAAM/epoxy. It is interesting that SiC-c-PAAM/epoxy (0.98vol%) and SiC-c-PAAM/epoxy (0.2vol%) have similar wear rates regardless of their particles content, implying the shielding effect of the homopolymers.

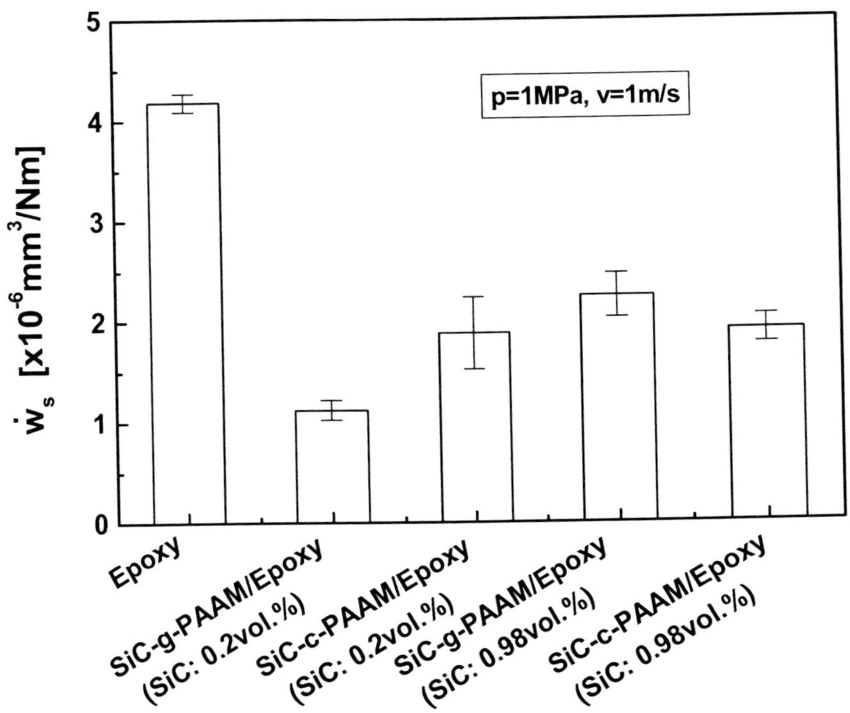

Figure 34. Effect of homopolymers generated during grafting onto nano-SiC particles on the wear rate of epoxy based composites.

For obtaining more information about the roles of the nanoparticles and their grafted versions, the pressure dependence of the wear rate of the composites is illustrated in Fig.35. Clearly, the wear rate of unfilled epoxy is increased by two orders of magnitude when the contact pressure increases from 1 to 3MPa. As the pressure is 5MPa, rupture of the epoxy specimen occurs and the value of wear rate can no longer be determined. In contrast, although the wear rates of SiC/epoxy and SiC-g-PAAM/epoxy composites increase with a rise in pressure, under the pressure of 3MPa they are only 1/5 and 1/40 of that of unfilled epoxy, respectively. Even in the case of 5MPa, steady wear is perceived in the two composites, and SiC-g-PAAM/epoxy composites exhibit much higher wear resistance than SiC/epoxy. According to the effect of reinforcement on the friction and wear of polymers [66], it is known that well dispersed nanoparticles are able to effectively bear the load transferred from the matrix and reduce the probability of fatigue wear of the composites. Since the grafting polymers (i.e. PAAM) of SiC-g-PAAM has taken part in the curing reaction of epoxy [67], the strong interfacial bonding would inhibit the fatigue induced crack propagation. Therefore, the wear rate of SiC-g-PAAM/epoxy composites is still lower than that of SiC/epoxy composites under higher pressure (i.e. 5MPa).

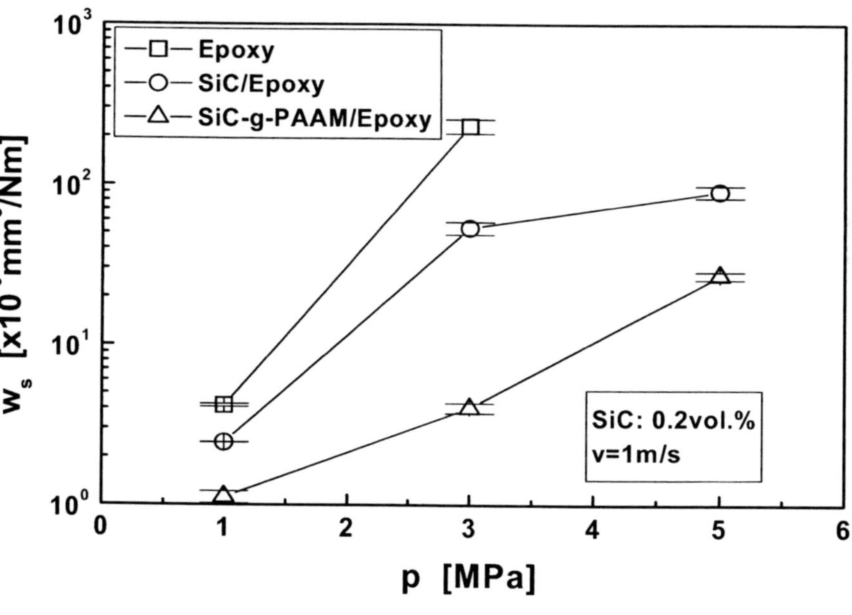

Figure 35. Effect of contact pressure on the wear rate of nano-SiC filled epoxy composites.

Surface morphological observation is a useful tool to estimate wear mechanism of materials. From the worn surfaces in Fig.36 it is seen that the cracks originate beneath the surface layer of unfilled epoxy block (Fig.36(a) and (b)). Due to the repeated friction, severe fatigue wear is presented on the neat epoxy and large fragments are detached from the surface as characterized by rather high wear rate (Fig.32(b)). Comparatively, the worn surfaces of SiC/epoxy composites are much less rough and the cracks are initiated right on the surfaces of the specimens (Fig.36(c) and (d)). When the grafted SiC nanoparticles are added, the worn surfaces become very smooth and remain high integrity (Fig.36(e) and (f)). Only trifling deformation that produces tiny wear debris appears (Fig.36(f)).

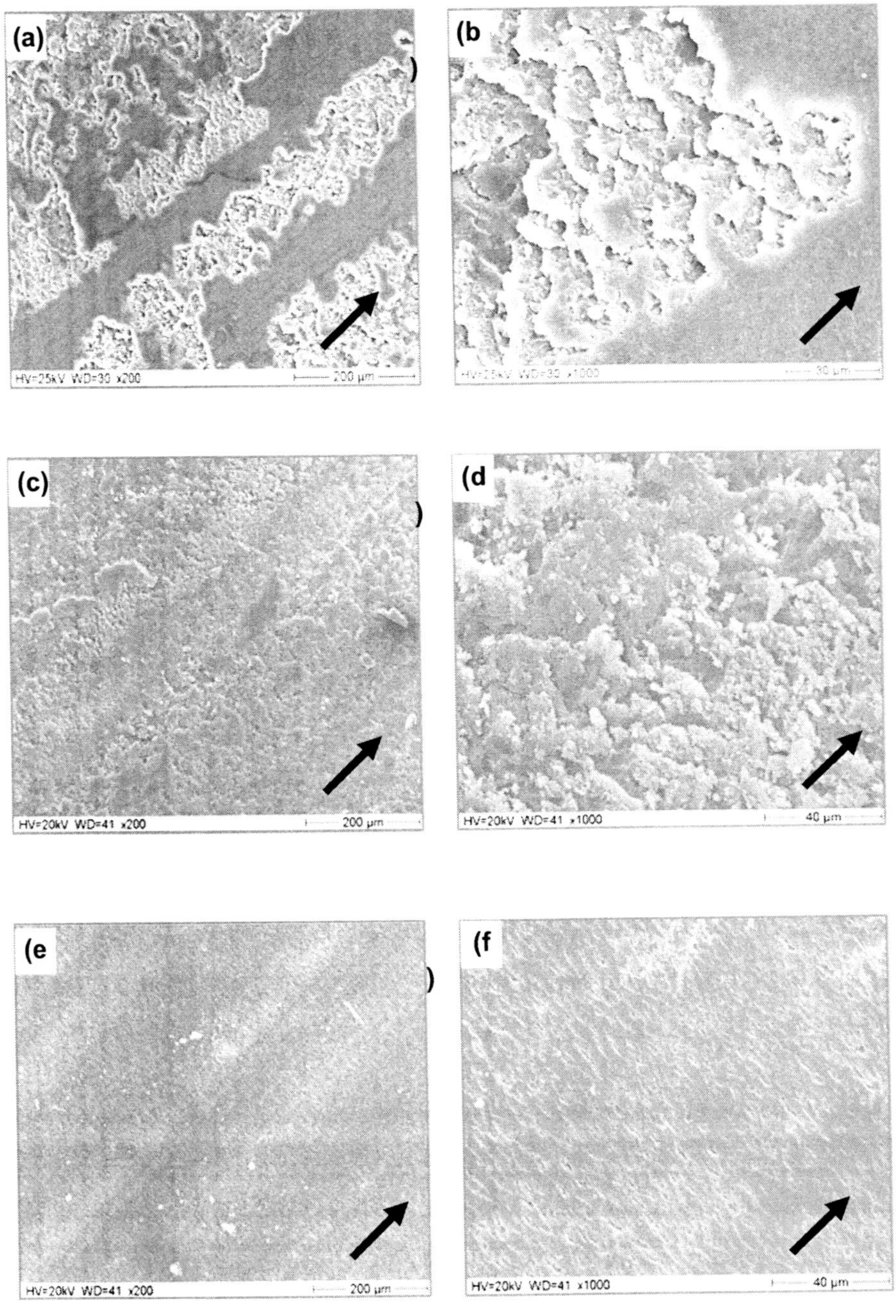

Figure 36. SEM photos of worn surfaces of (a, b) epoxy, (c, d) SiC/epoxy and (e, f) SiC-g-PAAM/epoxy composites (The arrows show the sliding directions. Content of SiC: 0.2vol.%, Wear test conditions: p=3MPa, v=1m/s).

Surface microhardness of the composites is plotted in Fig.37. The SiC nanoparticles either before or after the grafting treatment can raise the hardness of epoxy resin. Even though the content of the particles is quite low, composites' microhardness is higher than that of the unfilled epoxy. It means the load bearing ability of the nanoparticles has been brought into play at low filler loading. This coincides with the above results of frictional coefficient and wear rate of the composites. With a rise in the particulates content, agglomeration of the fillers becomes severe so that the composites' surface microhardness tends to decrease.

Unlubricated sliding wear is closely related to the frictional heat. It is thus important to examine the thermal deformation behavior of the composites, which would help to understand the tribological properties of the composites. As shown in Fig.38, the addition of grafted SiC nanoparticles improves the resistance to thermal deformation of epoxy. Both the deformation at the same temperature and the maximum deformation of SiC-g-PAAM/epoxy composites are evidently lower than those of unfilled epoxy and SiC/epoxy composites. Therefore, it is expected that material removal of SiC-g-PAAM/epoxy composites due to wearing is more difficult as compared to the case of unfilled epoxy and SiC/epoxy composites.

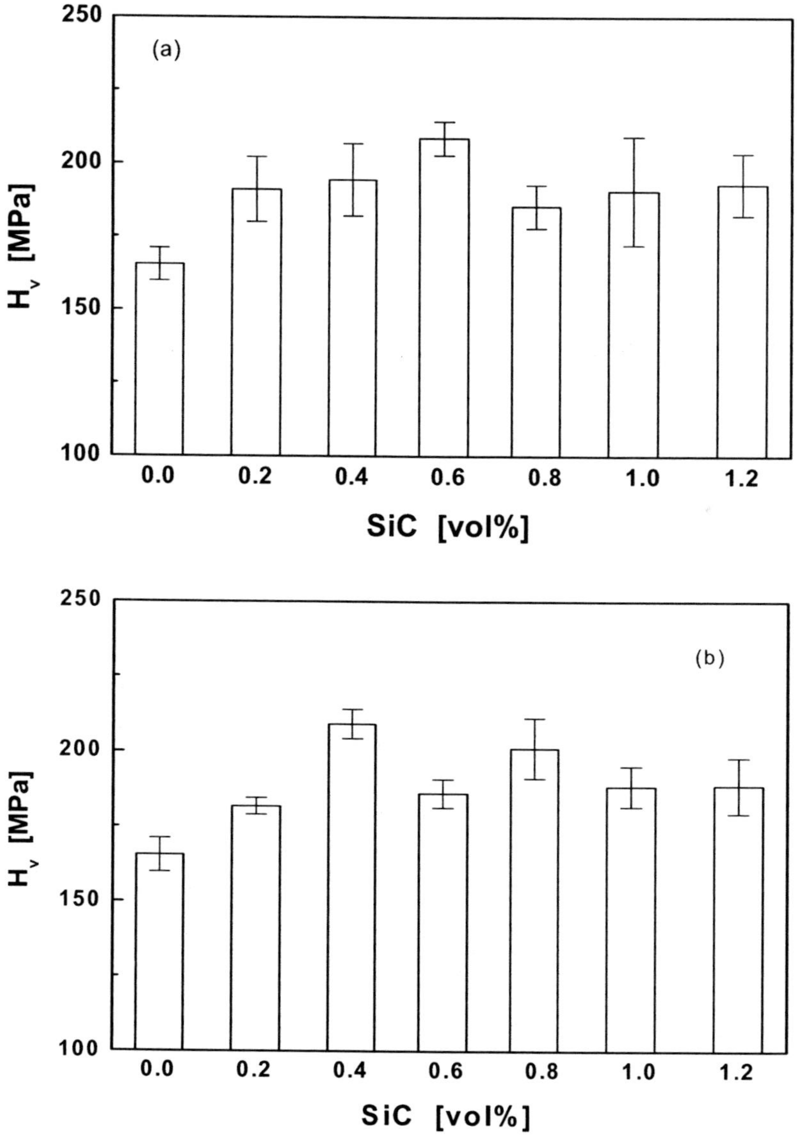

Figure 37. Microhardness of (a) SiC/epoxy and (b) SiC-g-PAAM/epoxy composites.

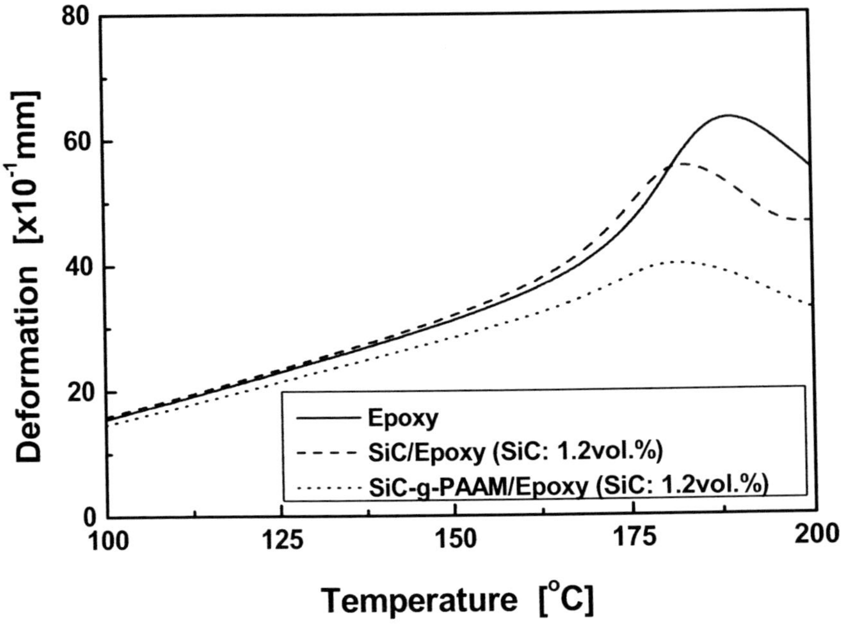

Figure 38. Heat distortion behavior of epoxy and its composites.

3.3. Friction and Wear Properties of Nano-SiO_2/Epoxy Composites

Fig.39 and Fig.40 show the sliding wear properties of the composites as a function of silica content. Frictional coefficient, μ, of the composites with unmodified silica nanoparticles keeps almost the same as that of neat matrix up to a filler fraction of about 4vol% (Fig.39). In contrast, the grafted particles can obviously reduce the value of μ even at low filler loadings. Similarly, a substantial decrease in specific wear rate, $\dot{w}_s$, can be observed in SiO_2-g-PAAM filled composites with a rise in filler content and all of the $\dot{w}_s$ values are lower than those of untreated nano-SiO_2 filled versions, although the untreated nanoparticles can also result in decreased $\dot{w}_s$ with respect to the unfilled epoxy. In the filler content varying from 2 to 6vol%, the wear resistance of epoxy is increased by a factor of about 20 by the addition of SiO_2-g-PAAM. Compared with the fact that 40wt% micron-sized SiO_2 (180μm) particles were needed to acquire a significant decrease in wear rate of epoxy [17], the present systems are clearly characterized by broader applicability.

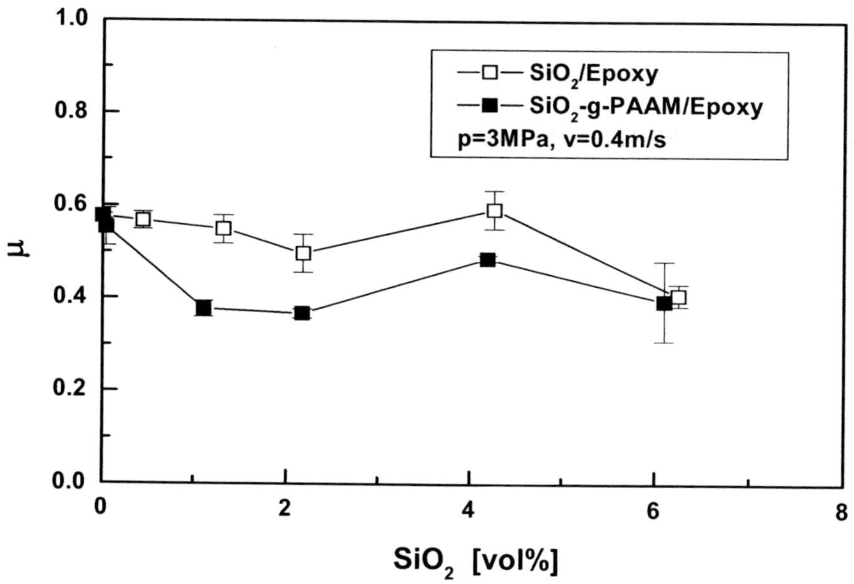

Figure 39. Filler content dependence of frictional coefficient, μ, of epoxy and its composites.

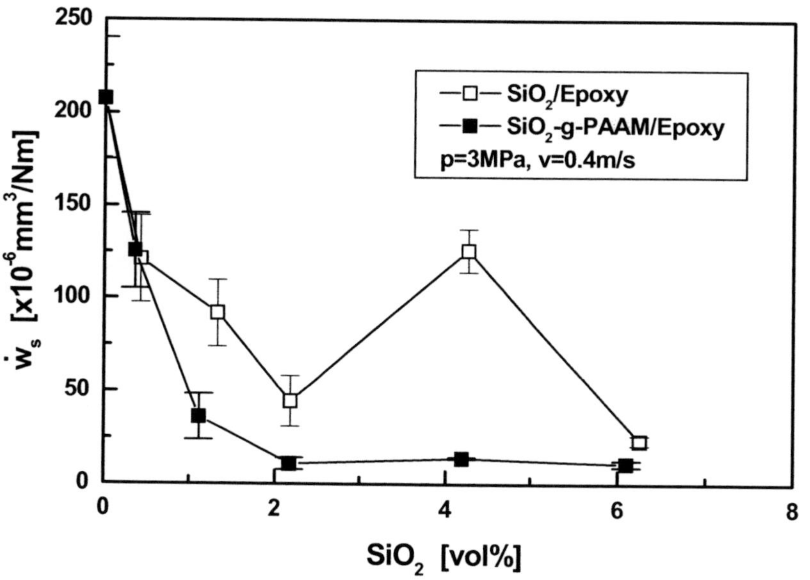

Figure 40. Filler content dependence of specific wear rate, $\dot{w}_s$, of epoxy and its composites.

As manifested by ref.[68], nanoparticles are able to significantly reduce the wear rate of epoxy because the wear mechanism changes from severe abrasive wear to mild sliding wear. A further improvement of the tribological performance of SiO_2-g-PAAM/epoxy composites may be caused by the excellent interfacial coupling between SiO_2 nanoparticles and epoxy resulting from reactions of amide groups of PAAM grafted on the particulates with epoxy groups of the matrix. In addition, the remarkably reduced material removal due to wearing (Fig.40) and the lubricating effect provided by the nanoparticles tightly embedded in the matrix [69] should account for the low frictional coefficient characteristics of SiO_2-g-PAAM/epoxy composites over the filler range examined (Fig.39). Comparatively, lack of the above-mentioned interfacial chemical bonding between untreated SiO_2 nanoparticle agglomerates and matrix resin results in higher wear rates and higher μ values of SiO_2/epoxy composites. The epoxy splinters due to severer materials loss entrapped at the interface between the steel counterpart and the composite pin might form a three-body abrasive wear situation, and thus counteract the lubricating effect of the nanoparticles, leading to μ values of SiO_2/epoxy composites similar to that of unfilled resin when SiO_2 content $\leq$ 4vol%.

In addition to the examination of the filler content dependence of the tribological performance at constant pressure and sliding velocity, effect of pressure should also be investigated. Fig.41 gives the coefficient of friction of epoxy and its composites determined at the pressures 3MPa and 5MPa under a constant sliding velocity v=0.4m/s. It is seen that the frictional coefficient of epoxy keeps almost unchanged when the pressure increases from 3 to 5MPa. This coincides with the results reported in ref.[70]. The frictional coefficients of nanosilica filled composites are lower than that of unfilled epoxy and decrease with increasing pressure. The lowest value of μ is recorded at a load of 5MPa for SiO_2-g-PAAM/epoxy composites. These phenomena imply that nanosilica can improve the friction-reducing ability of the composites especially under higher load [24]. The introduction of grafting PAAM further enhances the role of the particles.

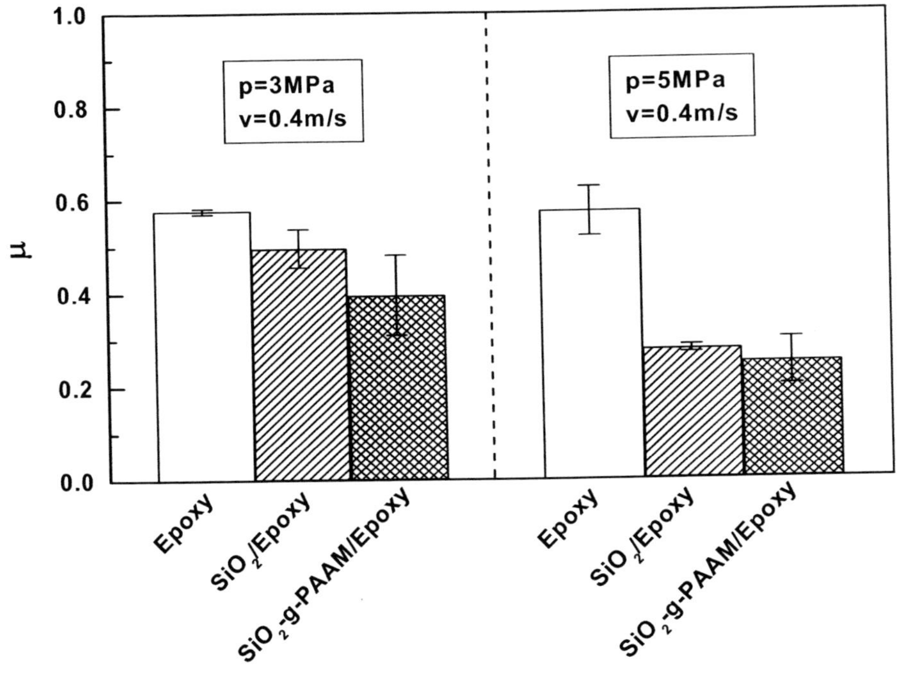

Figure 41. Frictional coefficient, μ, of epoxy and its composites at 2.17vol% nanosilica content.

The specific wear rates of the materials are exhibited in Fig.42. By comparing Fig.42 with Fig.41, it is seen that the decrement of wear rate is greater than that of frictional coefficient when other conditions being equal. Silica nanoparticles seem to be more effective for improving the anti-wear property of the composites. Moreover, in the same way as it was observed for the materials' frictional coefficient μ, the additional surface modification of the nanoparticles helps to further decrease the wear rare of the composites. On the other hand, Fig.42 shows different pressure dependencies of the wear rate. With a rise in testing pressure, the wear loss of epoxy is increased but that of the composites is decreased. This phenomenon reflects that different wear mechanisms must be involved.

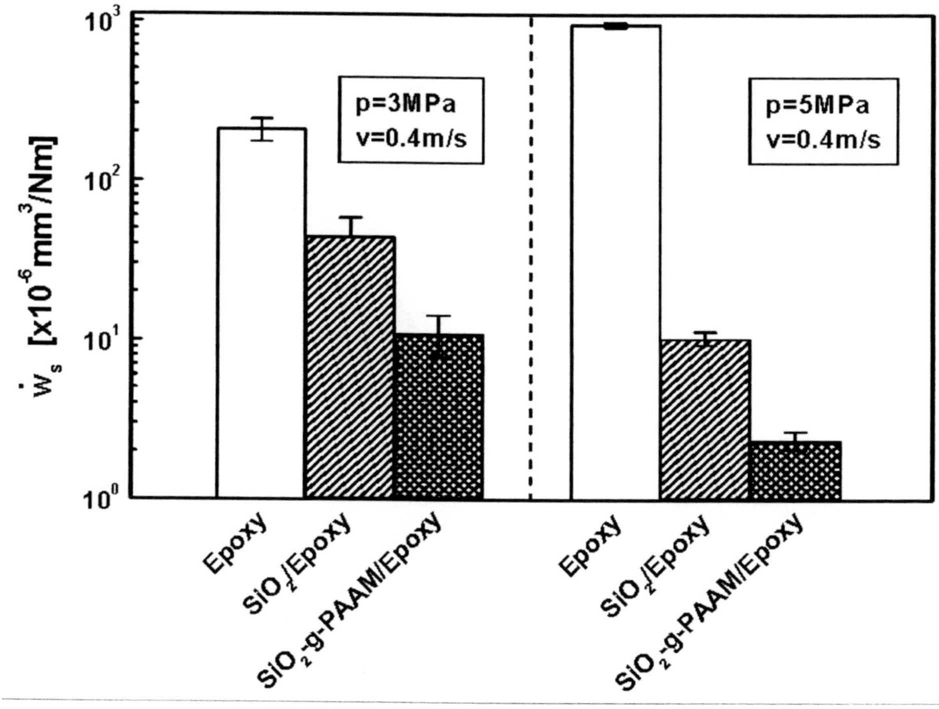

Figure 42. Specific wear rate, $\dot{w}_s$, of epoxy and its composites at 2.17vol% filler content.

Fatigue wear has been regarded as a main mechanism responsible for the sliding of epoxy against a hard counterpart [24, 71]. The model is based on the sub-surface crack nucleation and coalescence due to shear deformation of the softer surface induced by the traction of the harder asperities [64]. As shown in Fig.43(a), scale-like removal of materials has left traces on the worn surface of unfilled epoxy. Clearly it is indicative for fatigue-delamination generated under repeated loading during sliding. When a higher load was applied, large cracks appear on the surfaces (Fig.43(b)). The reason is that the fatigue mechanism of wear, which strongly depends on the load, plays a more and more important role. It gives rise to a substantial increase in the specific wear rate of epoxy (Fig.42). For SiO_2 reinforced composites, the basic wear patterns (Fig.43(c~f)) are characterized by mild fatigue wear, resembling that of the matrix tested at 3MPa (Fig.43(a)). A careful examination of the wear grooves manifested that the flaws' distribution produced on the worn surface change from a discontinuous mode (Fig.43(a)) to a continuous mode (Fig.43(c~f)). In particular, the uneven stress concentration built up inside epoxy might have been homogenized to some extent in the composites due to the effect of dispersion strengthening of the nanoparticles [68, 69]. This is certainly beneficial for reducing the amount of material loss.

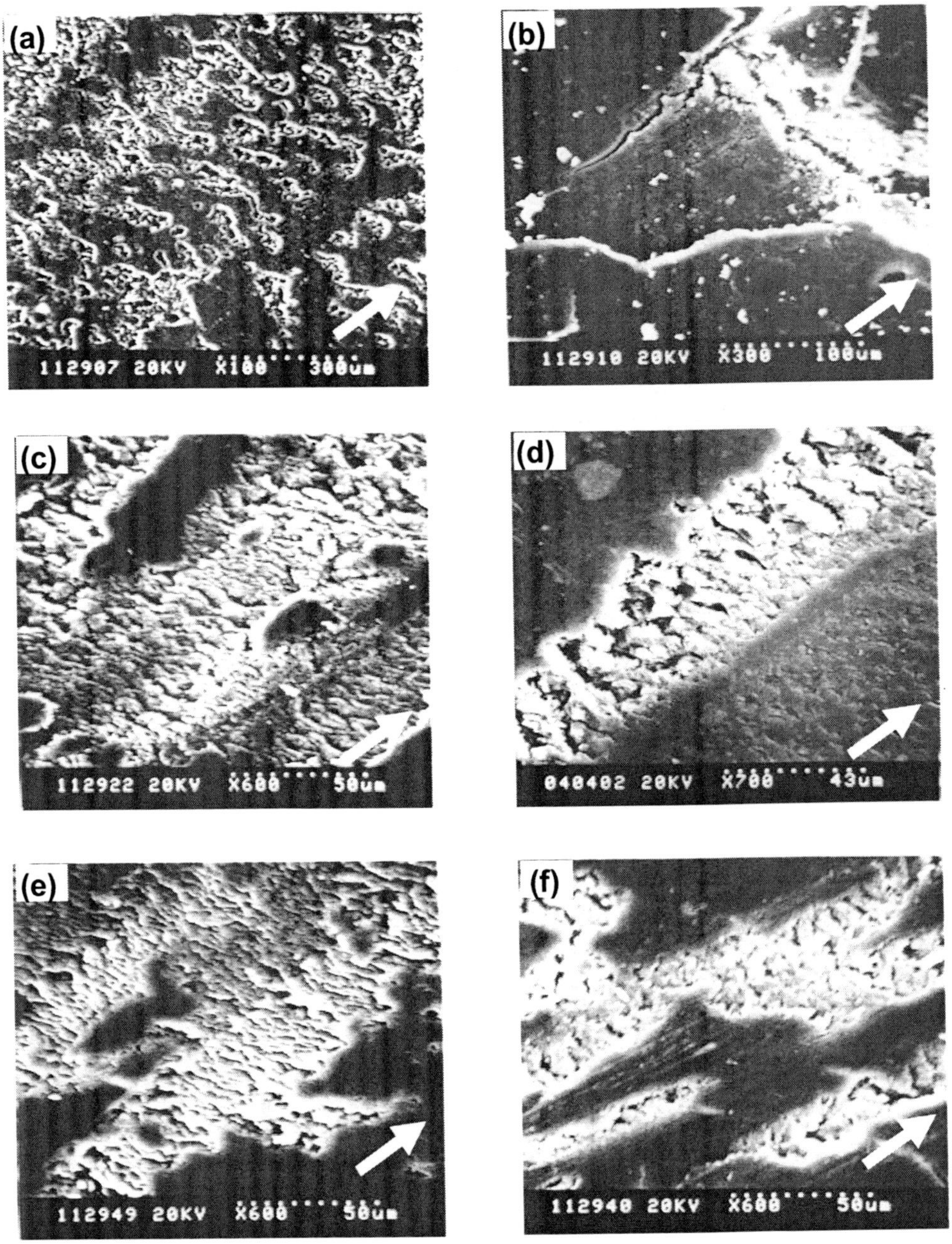

Figure 43. SEM micrographs of the worn surface of (a, b) epoxy, (c, d) SiO_2/epoxy composites and (e, f) SiO_2-g-PAAM/epoxy composites. Nanosilica content: 2.17vol%. Conditions of the sliding wear tests: (a, c, e) p=3MPa, v=0.4m/s; (b, d, f) p=5MPa, v=0.4m/s. The arrows indicate the sliding direction.

Studying the tribological behavior of epoxy sliding against inox steel, Bassani and co-workers [70] suggested that the nominal pressure controls the interfacial stress between the counterparts involved in the contacts and hence the stability of transfer films. Considering that the addition of inorganic nanoparticles into polymers may increase the adhesion strength of a transfer film on the counterface [23, 72], it can be deduced that nanometer SiO_2 not only acts as a load carrier in the composites but also helps to improve the bonding between the transfer film and the steel counterface. Moreover, the stability of the transfer film might be increased with the applied pressure. As a result, the wear rates of the composites are remarkably lower than that of the unfilled resin, and decrease with increasing load, as observed in this work. Further studies on the nature of the transfer film are required to have a better understanding of the above analysis.

It should be noted that it occurred very difficult to detect large differences in the characteristics of the wear traces between the composites filled with treated and untreated particles (e.g. Fig.43(c) and (d), Fig.43(e) and (f)). According to the experimental results plotted in Fig.42, however, it is believed that an increased interfacial interaction between SiO_2 nanoparticles and epoxy favors the aforesaid positive effects. These interactions result from reactions of the amide groups in PAAM grafted on the particles with the epoxy groups of the matrix. The SiO_2-g-PAAM/epoxy composites have therefore the highest wear resistance. Besides, the remarkably reduced material removal (Fig.42) and the lubricating effect provided by the nanoparticles tightly embedded in the matrix [69] should account for the low frictional coefficient characteristics of SiO_2-g-PAAM/epoxy composites.

3.4. Friction and Wear Properties of Nano-Si_3N_4/Epoxy Composites

In general, epoxy is not an ideal material used in sliding wear applications due to its three-dimensional network structure as compared with thermoplastics. As shown in Fig.44, both frictional coefficient and specific wear rate of unfilled epoxy is quite high. The situation is changed greatly when nano-Si_3N_4 is incorporated. It is seen that there is a significant reduction in the values of μ and $\dot{w}_s$ at filler content as low as 0.27vol%. With a rise in the concentration of the nanoparticles, the declining trend becomes gentle and is replaced by a slight increase from 1.38vol% on. It means the nanometer Si_3N_4 particles are very effective in improving the tribological performance of epoxy.

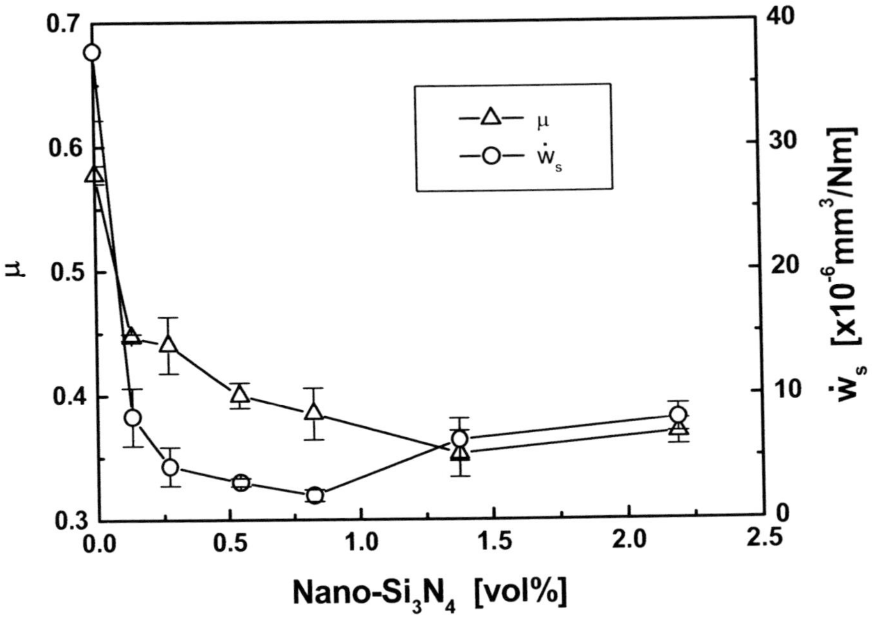

Figure 44. Frictional coefficient, μ, and specific wear rate, $\dot{w}_s$, of nano-Si_3N_4/epoxy composites as a function of filler content.

Fig.45 exhibits the SEM micrographs of the worn surfaces of epoxy and the composites. The wear scars on the epoxy pin are characterized by obvious scale-like traces (Fig.45(a)). A close view (Fig.45(b)) shows that micrometer size blocks of epoxy resin have left the materials surface. This is indicative for fatigue-delamination generated under repeated loading during sliding. Fatigue wear has been regarded as a main mechanism responsible for the sliding of epoxy against a hard counterpart [70, 71]. The model is based on the sub-surface crack nucleation and coalescence due to shear deformation of the softer surface induced by the traction of the harder asperities [64]. For filled composites, the worn surfaces are full of smoothly polished grooves (Fig.45(c), (e), (g) and (i)). This is particularly evident in the case of V_f=0.83vol% (Fig.45(e)), which corresponds to the lowest $\dot{w}_s$ as shown in Fig.44. When the surfaces are observed at high magnification (Fig.45(d), (f), (h) and (j)), they still look quite smooth besides the thin resin sheets to be removed (Fig.45(d), (j)), tiny cracks several nanometers wide and hundreds nanometers long (Fig.45(f), (h)), and the exposed nanoparticle agglomerates dozens of nanometer in diameter (Fig.45(f)). Naturally, the transition from severe wear mode of unfilled epoxy to mild one of the composites results from the addition of nano-Si_3N_4 particles.

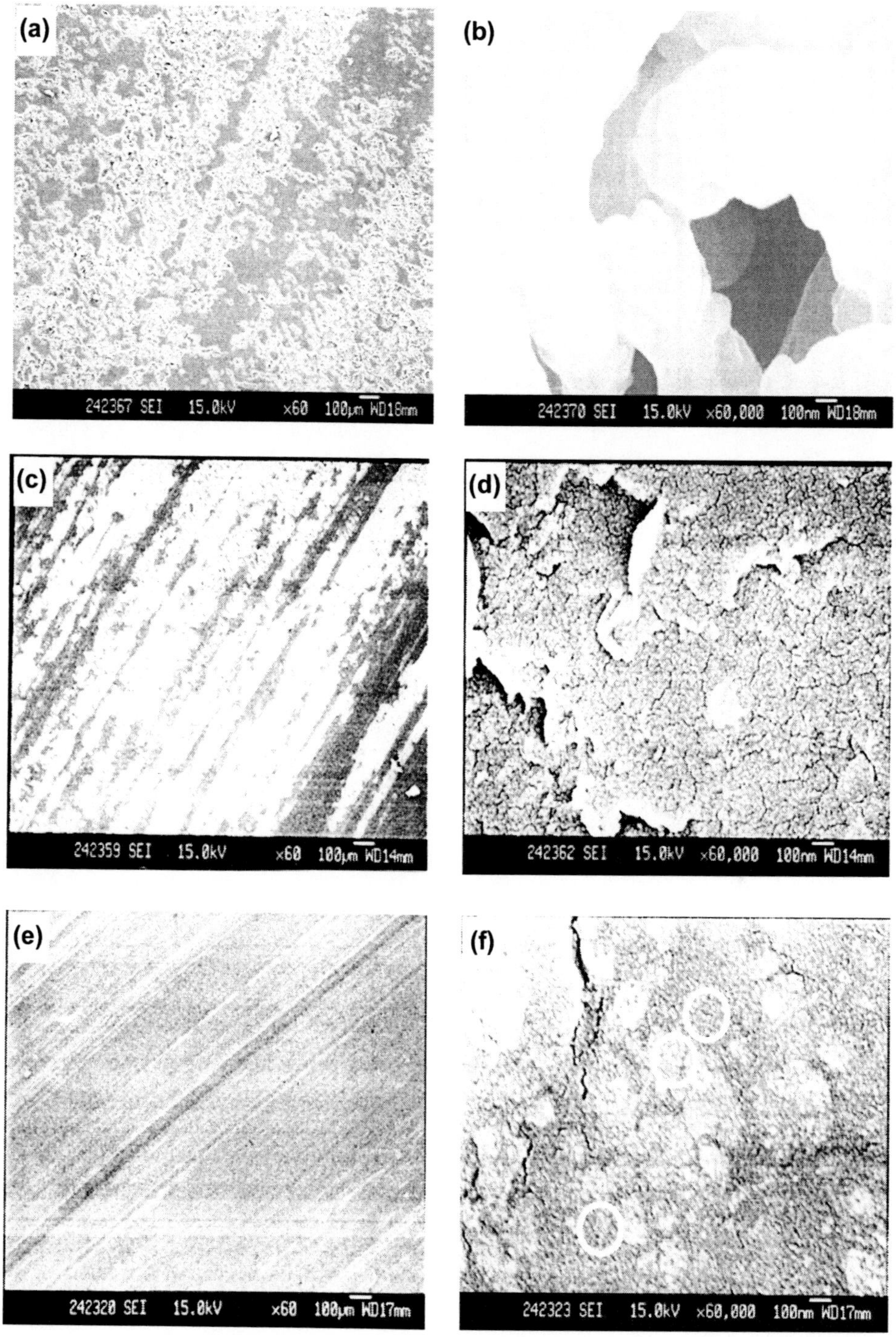

Figure 45. SEM images of the worn surfaces of (a, b), epoxy, (c, d) nano-Si_3N_4/epoxy composites (V_f=0.27vol%), (e, f) nano-Si_3N_4/epoxy composites (V_f=0.83vol%), (g, h) nano-Si_3N_4/epoxy composites (V_f=1.38vol%), and (i, j) nano-Si_3N_4/epoxy composites (V_f=2.19vol%). To ensure equal observation conditions, all the surfaces are examined at two magnifications. The white circles on Fig.45(f) indicate the agglomerated nanoparticles.

As surface hardness is generally taken as one of the most important factors that govern the wear resistance of materials, Vickers microhardness, H_v, of the composites is measured (Fig.46). Evidently, the surface hardness of the composites keeps almost unchanged until the filler content reaches 2.19vol%. In fact, the size of the micro-indenter is much larger than that of the nanoparticles. For the composites with lower nanoparticles concentration and better dispersion, the measured H_v values cannot reflect the true hardening effect around the particles but the performance of the matrix resin itself. In the case of higher particulate content (2.19vol%, for instance), agglomeration of the particles is rather severe, resulting in higher microhardness with considerable testing error, which also characterizes the uneven distribution of the nanoparticles [69].

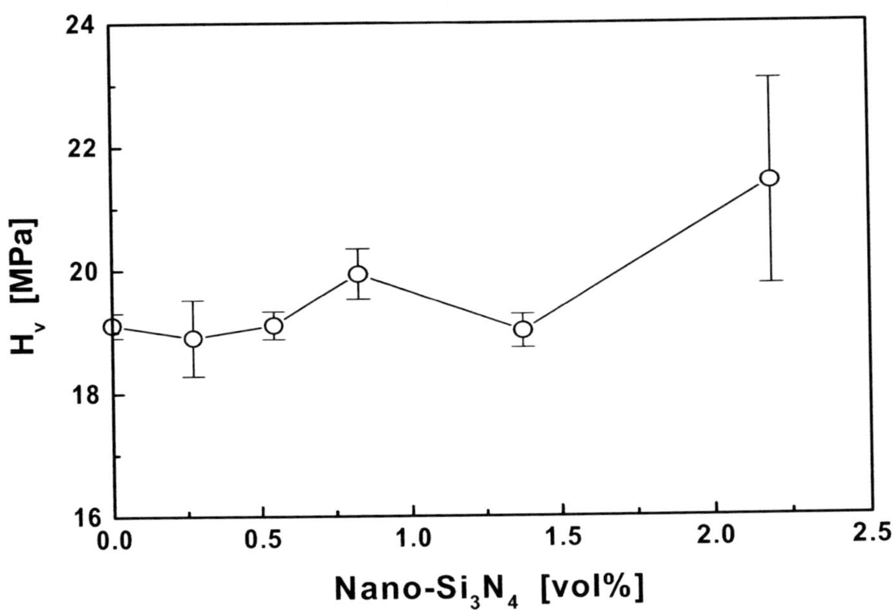

Figure 46. Vickers microhardness, H_v, of nano-Si_3N_4/epoxy composites as a function of filler content.

Since the measured microhardness is not qualified for analyzing the causes for the reduction of frictional coefficient and wear rate of the composites, the dynamic mechanical responses of the materials (Fig.47) are studied in correlation with the frictional property as follows. This is done also because of the viscoelastic nature of polymer composites that might influence the tribological behavior of the composites through hysteretic motion of the macromolecular chains. Considering that the transient surface temperature at rubbing surface is rather high, frictional coefficient of the composites is plotted as a function of the area under the α-transition peak in Tanδ~temperature (Fig.48). It is obvious that the relationship follows exponential growth, which is analogous to Arrhenius equation implying the frictional process is closely related to thermally activated motion of the molecular segments of epoxy. Since frictional coefficient increases with a rise in damping of the composites, the ability of the materials to transform mechanical energy into heat contributes to the frictional behavior. In other words, the stiffer the composites, the lower the frictional coefficient, so that the stick-and-slip phenomenon can be prevented [73]. Fig.49 shows the results of thermomechanical analysis (TMA) of the materials. The comparative measurements manifest that the thermally induced deformation of epoxy is decreased after the addition of the nanoparticles, especially when the filler content is high. It means dimensional stability of the composites is superior to that of unfilled epoxy when the specimens are heated up due to the repeated friction, which favors the reduction of frictional coefficient as concluded from Fig.48.

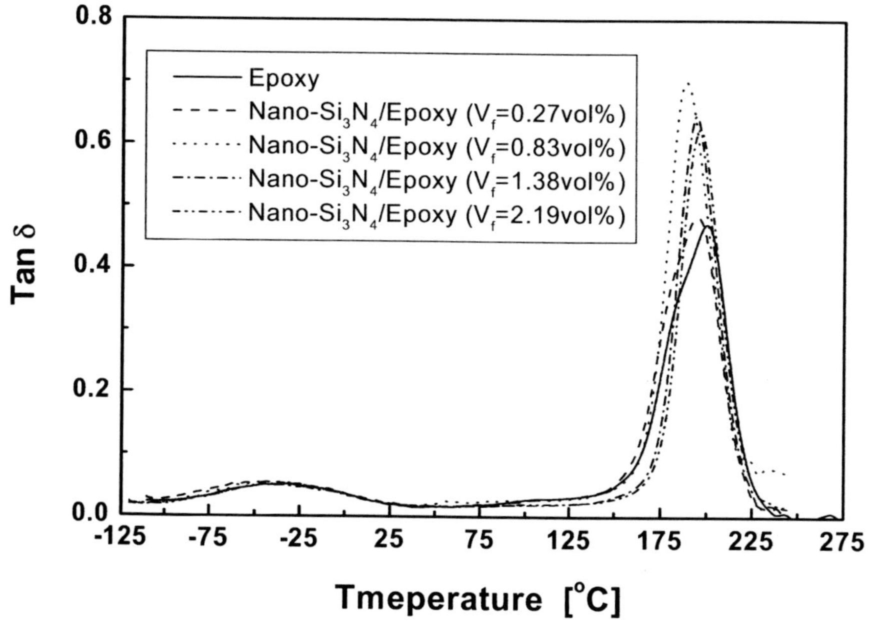

Figure 47. Temperature dependence of internal friction, Tanδ, of nano-Si_3N_4/epoxy composites measured at 1Hz.

It is worth noting that when the curve in Fig.48 is extrapolated to the position at which the α-peak area=0, the corresponding μ doesn't equal 0. Therefore, mechanical damping is not the only influencing factor. Fig.50 shows the microhardness values of the surfaces of epoxy and its composites before and after wear testing. Although no obvious variation can be seen in the case of nano-Si_3N_4/epoxy composites, microhardness of the worn surface of epoxy pin decreases significantly, suggesting structural decay of the top resin layer in the scale range of micrometer. On the basis of this finding, thermogravimetric analyses (TGA) of the surface layers of the same samples are carried out to check whether surface chemistry is involved. From Fig.51 it is seen that both unworn epoxy and nano-Si_3N_4/epoxy composites have similar pyrolytic behavior so that their TGA curves almost overlap. When the specimens had undergone sliding wear tests, however, the residual weights of the materials surface layers are much greater than those from the unworn specimens. The disproportional increase in the residual weight strongly suggests transfer from the steel counterpart to the specimen pins besides variation of chemical structures of the components. It is thus necessary to further study the tribochemistry of the worn specimens in the following section.

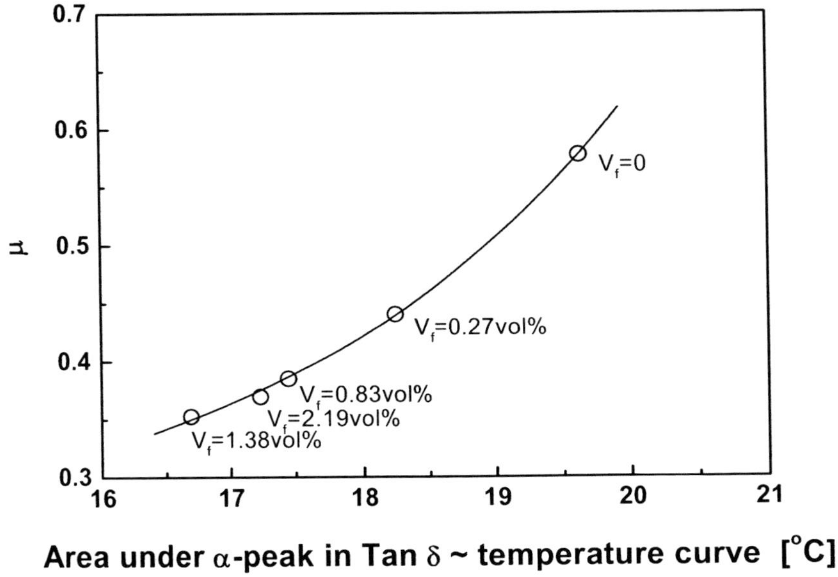

Figure 48. Frictional coefficient, μ, versus area under the α-transition peak in Tanδ~temperature curve shown in Fig.47.

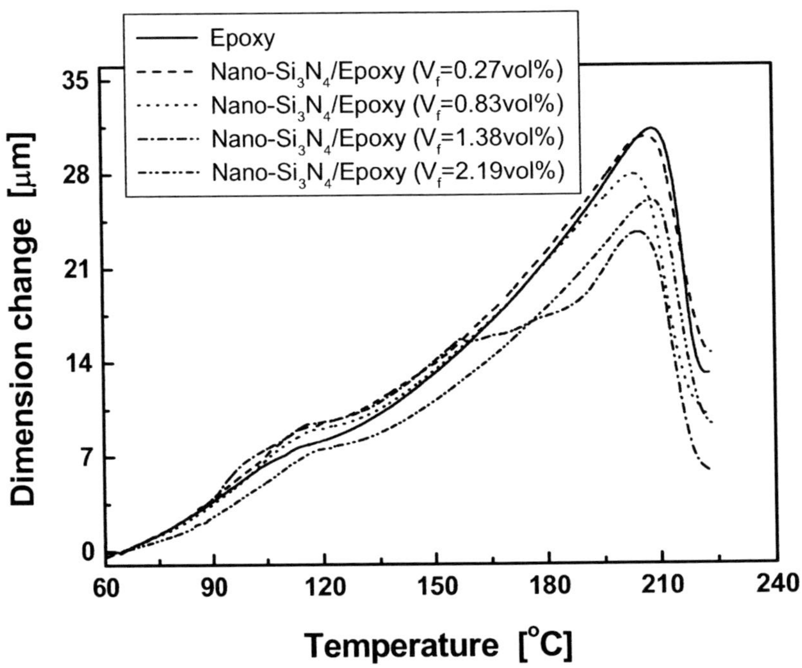

Figure 49. Thermomechanical curves of epoxy and nano-Si_3N_4/epoxy composites.

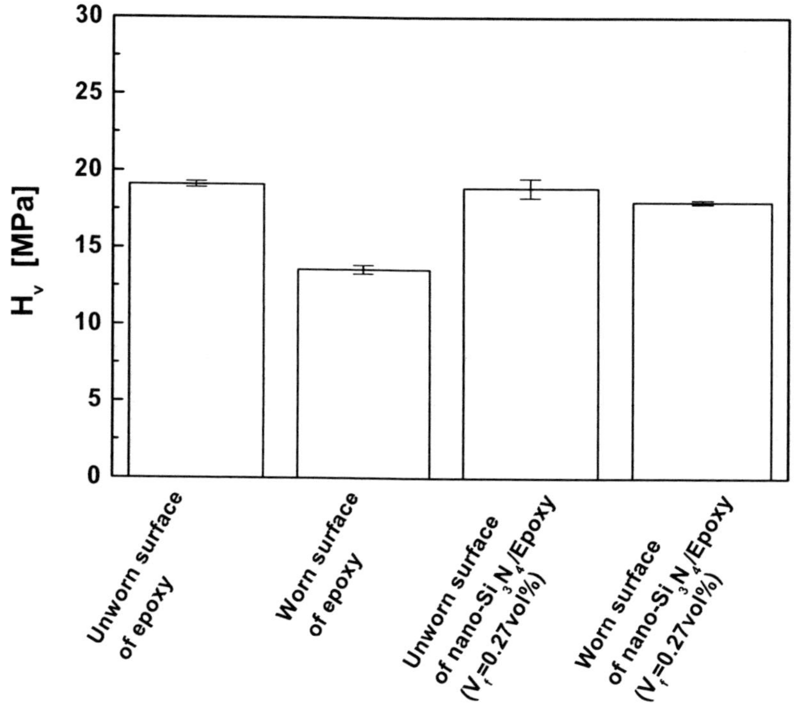

Figure 50. Vickers microhardness, H_v, of pin surfaces of epoxy and nano-Si_3N_4/epoxy composites before and after the wear tests.

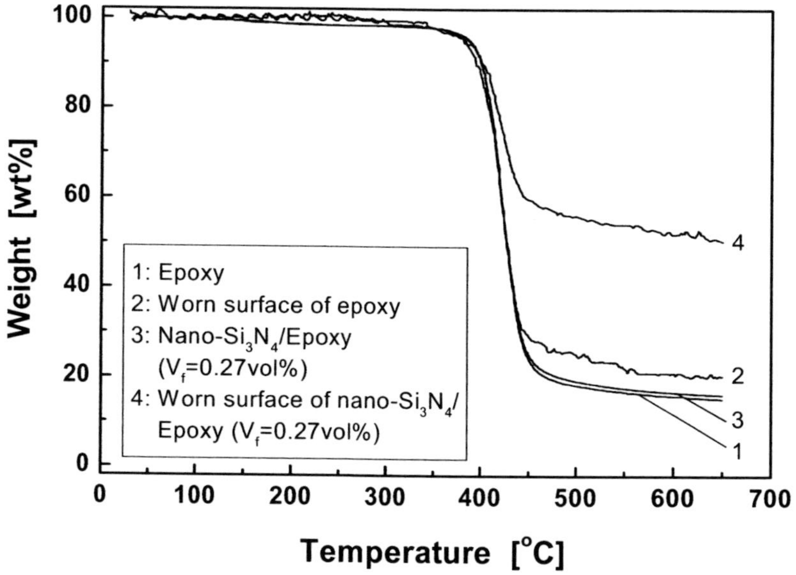

Figure 51. Thermogravimetric curves of pin surfaces of epoxy and nano-Si_3N_4/epoxy composites before and after the wear tests.

As friction and wear takes place between a pair of counterparts, examination of the surface of the steel ring would be a reasonable starting point. Table 11 records the EDS results of the steel rings before and after rubbing with epoxy and its composites. Having undergone the wear tests, the surface atomic ratios are changed. In the case of epoxy pin, for example, element S appears on the surface of the steel ring. Moreover, the addition of nano-Si_3N_4 into epoxy brings about the rise in the content of Si on the surface of the steel ring. Hence the above results (Fig.51, Table 11) evidence the mutual transfer between the specimen pins and the steel rings. To have a clearer image of the tribochemical reaction involved, XPS spectra from the surfaces of epoxy and the nanocomposites should be carefully analyzed.

Table 11. EDS analytical results of the surface of the steel counterpart

	Elements and content (%)		
	S	Si	Fe
Steel ring before wear test	0	0.22	98.65
Steel ring rubbed against epoxy pin	0.42	0.21	98.55
Steel ring rubbed against nano-Si_3N_4/epoxy composite pin (V_f=0.83%)	0.46	1.08	97.82

The low resolution XPS spectra of the pin surfaces of epoxy and nano-Si_3N_4/epoxy composites before and after the wear tests demonstrate that the atomic ratios of C/O have changed (Fig.52). The increased C/O ratios is indicative of carbonization, as evidenced by the decreased surface microhardness (Fig.50), manifesting partial chain scission and reorganization of epoxy macromolecules at the surface of the specimen pins during wearing. In consideration of the fact that the frictional surface temperature could be as high as several hundred degrees centigrade in the case of polymer/steel sliding pair [74, 75], tribochemically induced structure variation on top layers of the specimens has to take place inevitably [76].

Fig.53 illustrates the C1s spectra collected from the unworn and worn surfaces of virgin epoxy and its composites with 0.83vol% nano-Si_3N_4. It can be seen that the C1s peaks from the two worn surfaces (Figs.53(b), (d)) are somewhat broadened and shift slightly towards high binding energy regime as compared to those of the unworn surfaces of the materials (Figs.53(a), (c)). These phenomena suggest that the carbon atoms become electron-poor. Similar to the C1s spectra, the O1s spectra of the samples (Fig.54) also become broader and shift to high binding energy after sliding wear tests. As a result, it can be estimated that oxidation and carbonization are the main mechanochemical processes that had occurred on the specimen surfaces during wearing driven by the high frictional temperature and contact pressure.

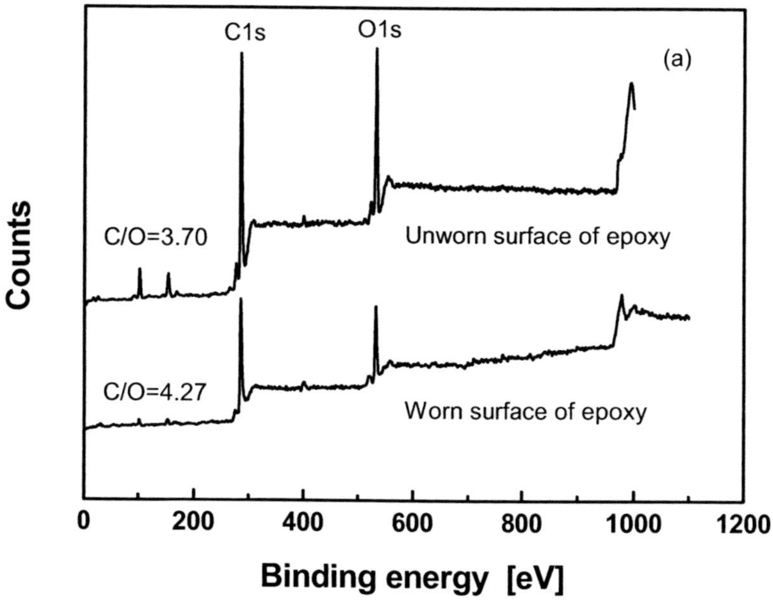

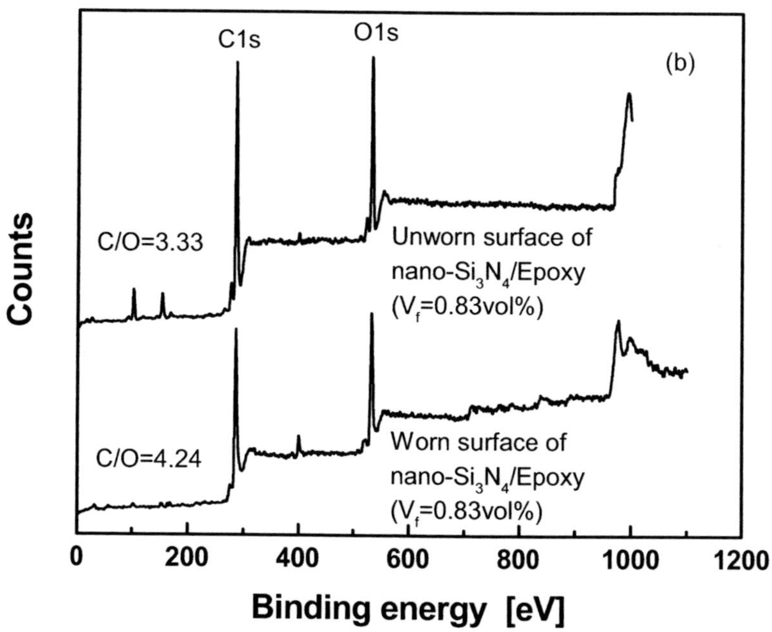

Figure 52. Low resolution XPS spectra of pin surfaces of (a) epoxy and (b) nano-Si_3N_4/epoxy composites before and after the wear tests.

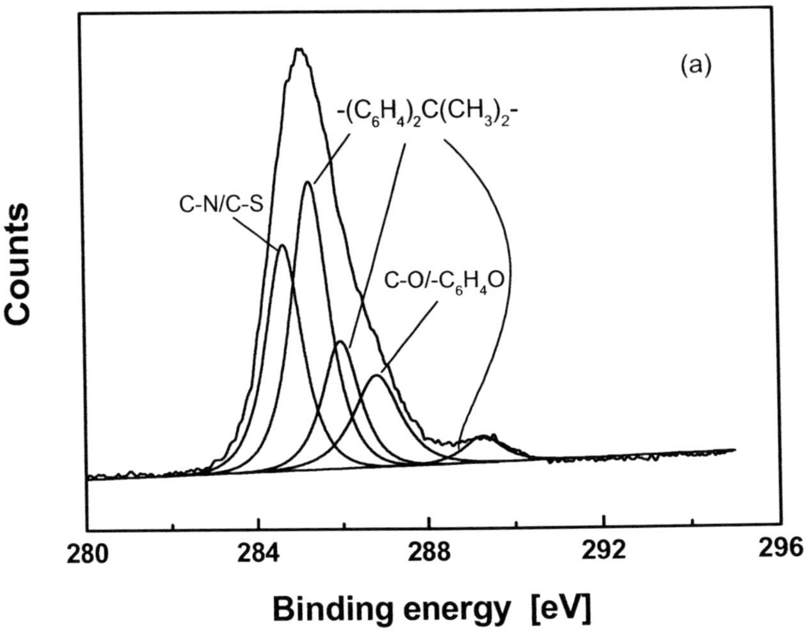
(a)
-(C6H4)2C(CH3)2-
C-N/C-S
C-O/-C6H4O
Counts
280
284
288
292
296
Binding energy [eV]

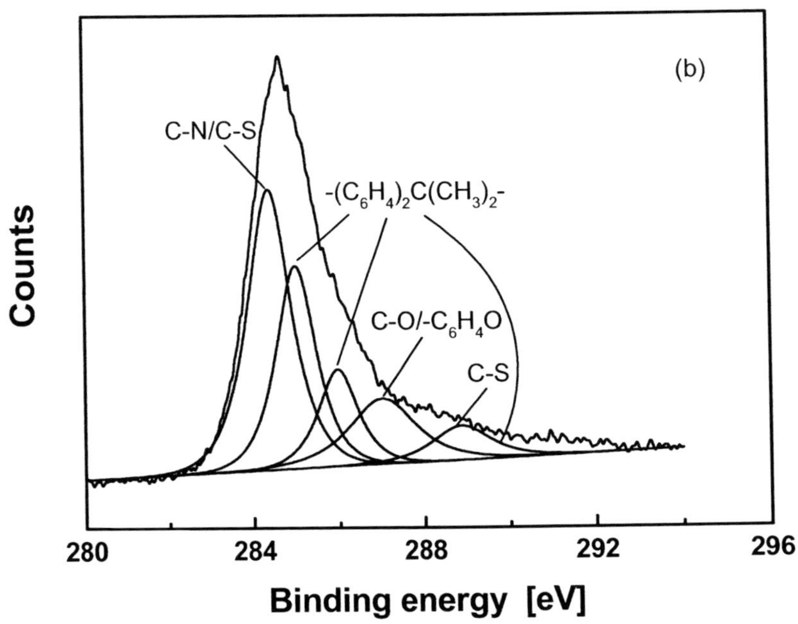
(b)
C-N/C-S
-(C6H4)2C(CH3)2-
C-O/-C6H4O
C-S
Counts
280
284
288
292
296
Binding energy [eV]

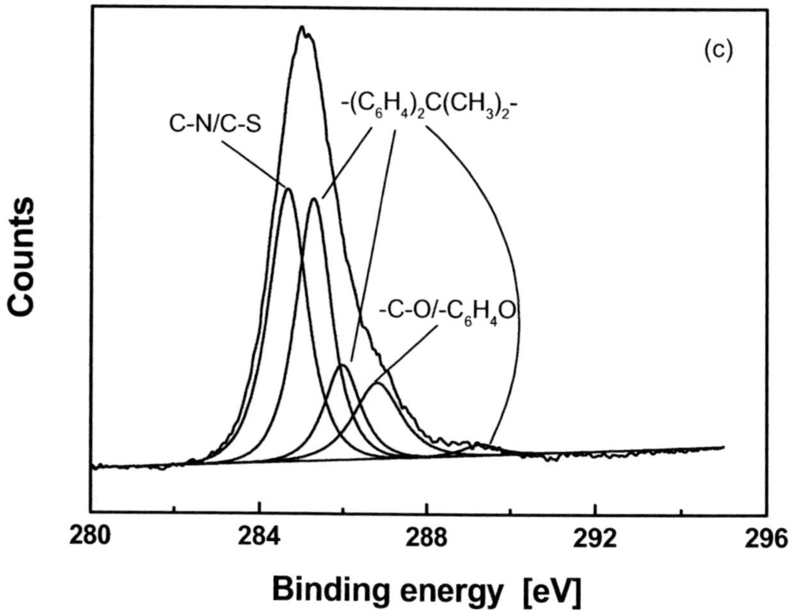

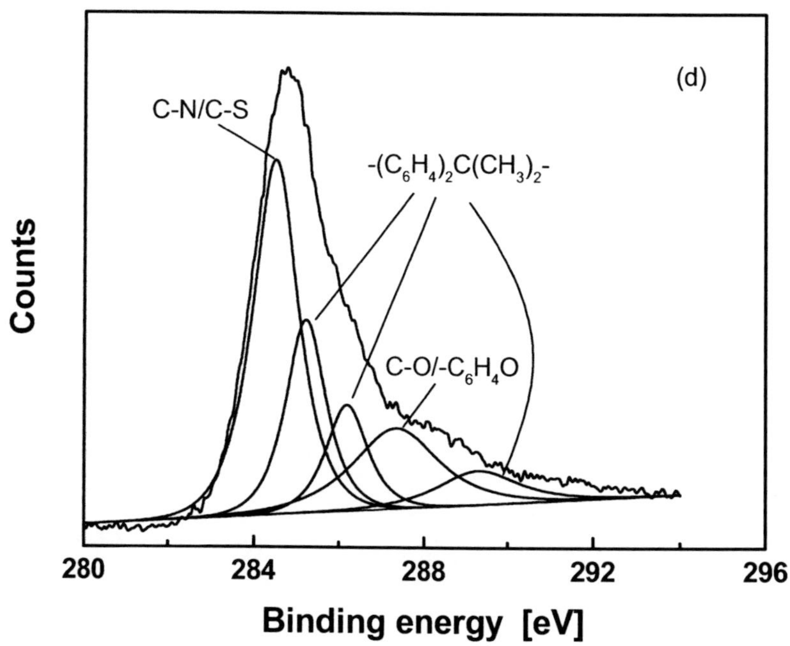

Figure 53. C1s spectra of pin surfaces of (a) unworn epoxy, (b) worn epoxy, (c) unworn nano-Si_3N_4/epoxy composites (V_f=0.83vol%), (d) worn nano-Si_3N_4/epoxy composites (V_f=0.83vol%).

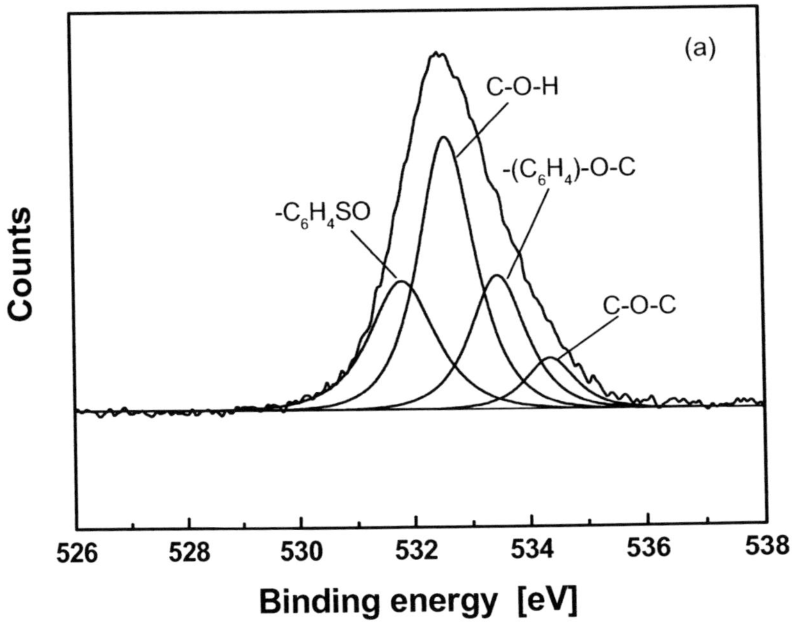
(a)
C-O-H
-(C6H4)-O-C
-C6H4SO
C-O-C
Counts
526 528 530 532 534 536 538
Binding energy [eV]

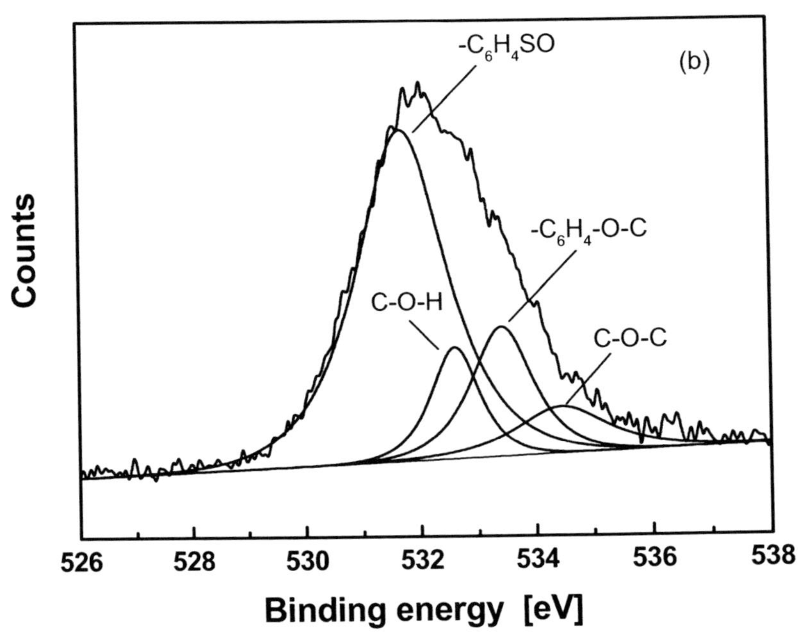
-C6H4SO
(b)
-C6H4-O-C
C-O-H
C-O-C
Counts
526 528 530 532 534 536 538
Binding energy [eV]

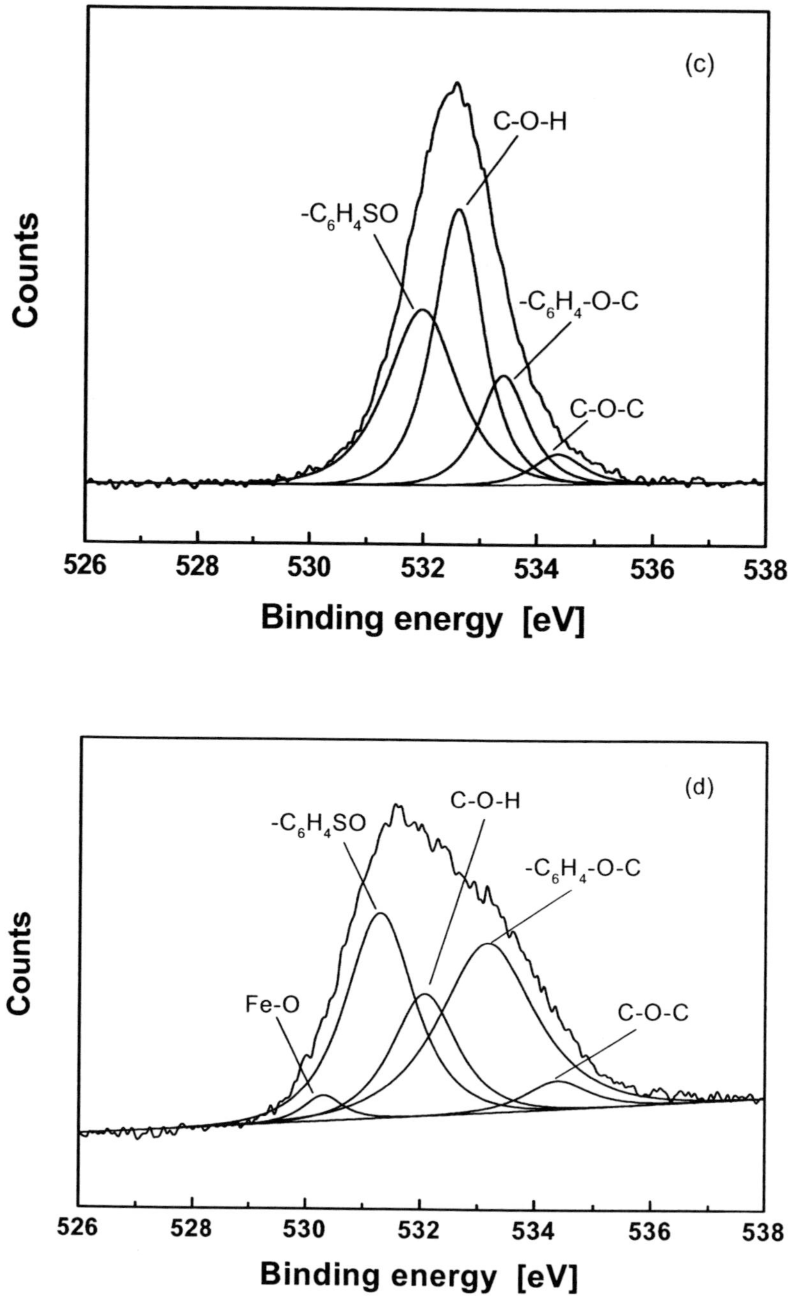

Figure 54. O1s spectra of pin surfaces of (a) unworn epoxy, (b) worn epoxy, (c) unworn nano-Si_3N_4/epoxy composites (V_f=0.83vol%), (d) worn nano-Si_3N_4/epoxy composites (V_f=0.83vol%).

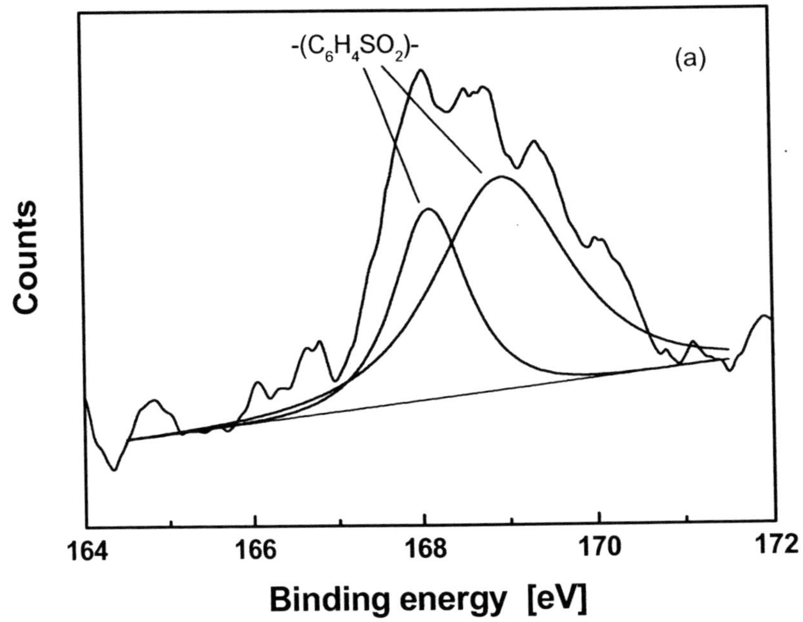
-(C6H4SO2)-
(a)
Counts
164
166
168
170
172
Binding energy [eV]

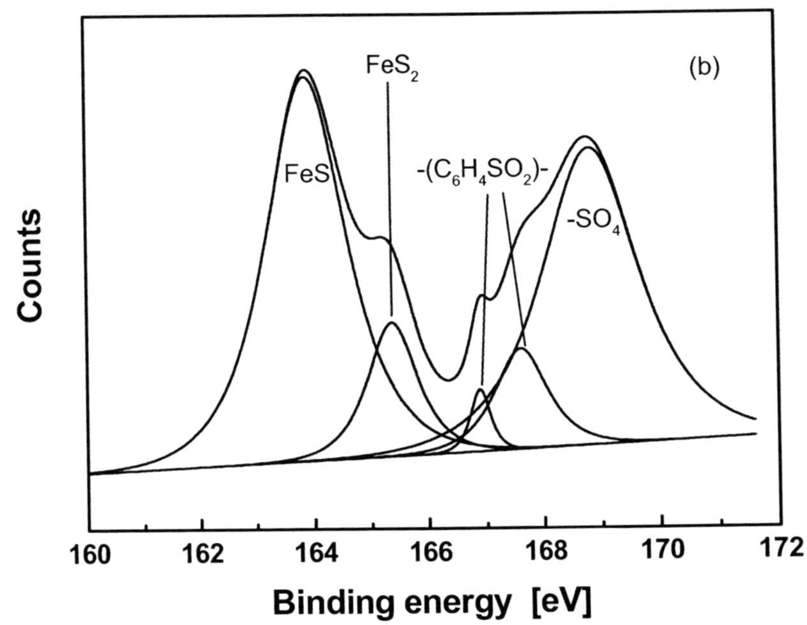
FeS2
(b)
FeS
-(C6H4SO2)-
-SO4
Counts
160
162
164
166
168
170
172
Binding energy [eV]

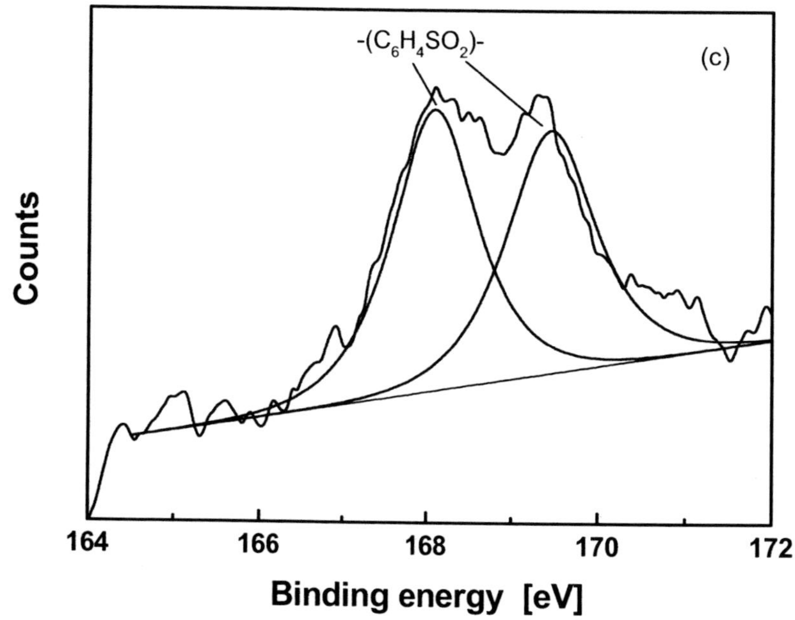

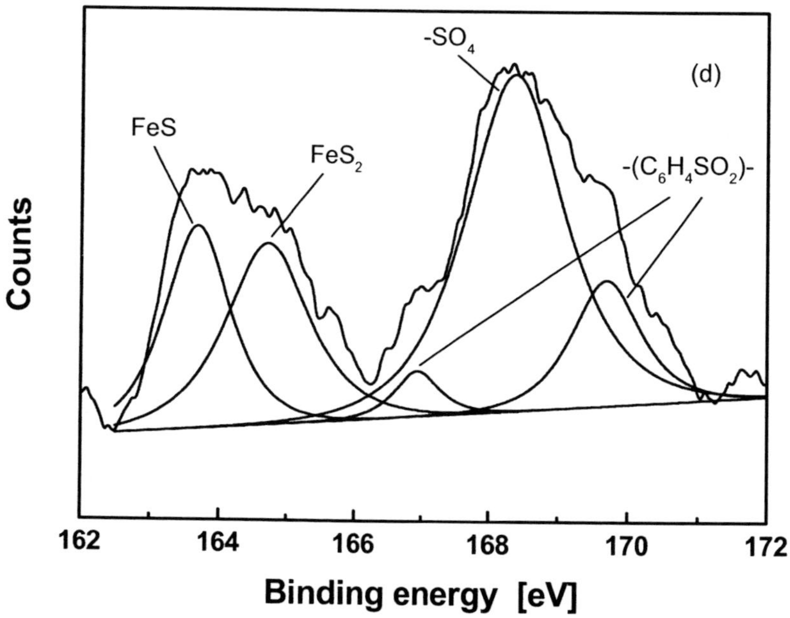

Figure 55. S2p spectra of pin surfaces of (a) unworn epoxy, (b) worn epoxy, (c) unworn nano-Si_3N_4/epoxy composites (V_f=0.83vol%), (d) worn nano-Si_3N_4/epoxy composites (V_f=0.83vol%).

S2p spectra are given in Fig.55. The S atom comes from the curing agent in epoxy. Deconvolution of the spectra indicates that a few new peaks appear on the spectra of the worn surfaces, meaning the generation of some S-containing compounds. According to the investigation in ref.[77], the new compounds are assigned to be FeS, FeS_2 and $FeSO_4$. That is, in the course of sliding wear the S atoms in epoxy react with Fe atoms at the metallic counterface and environmental water vapor under high contact temperature and pressure conditions. Then, the new products are attached to both counterfaces, as the trace of S atoms has been found on the steel ring surface (Table 11).

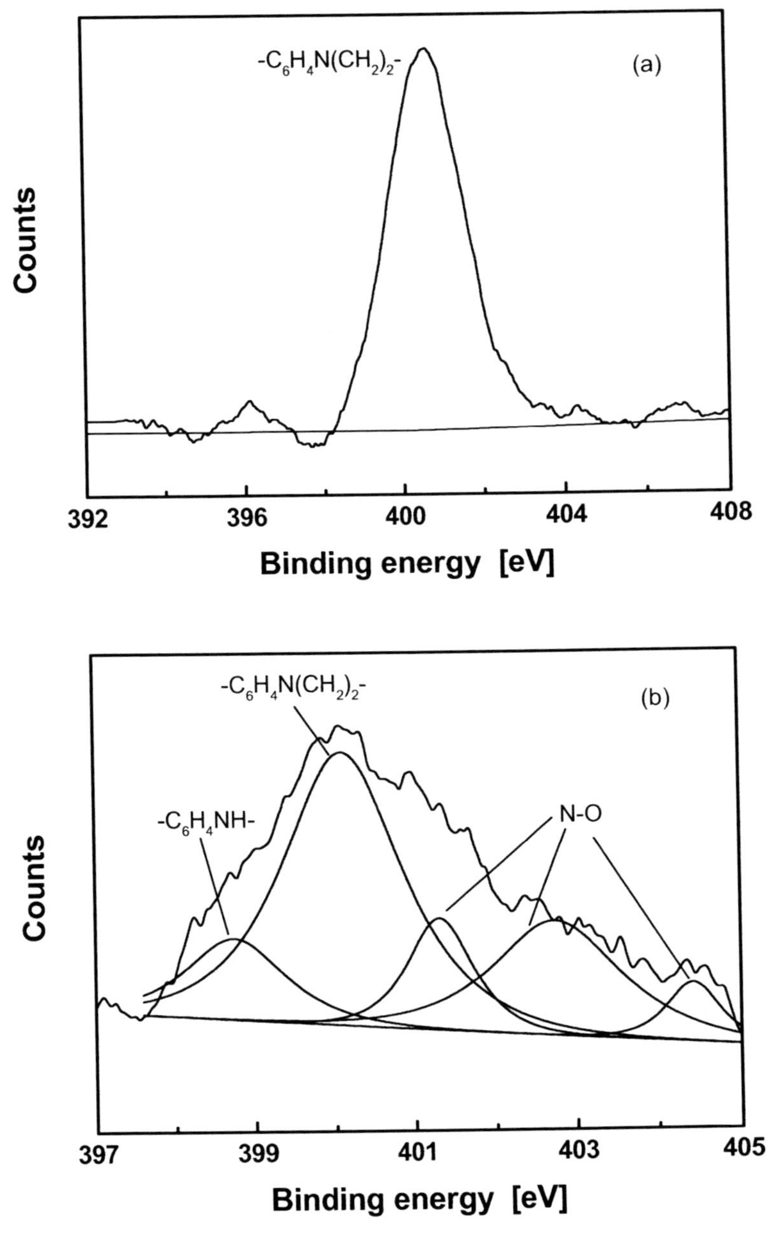

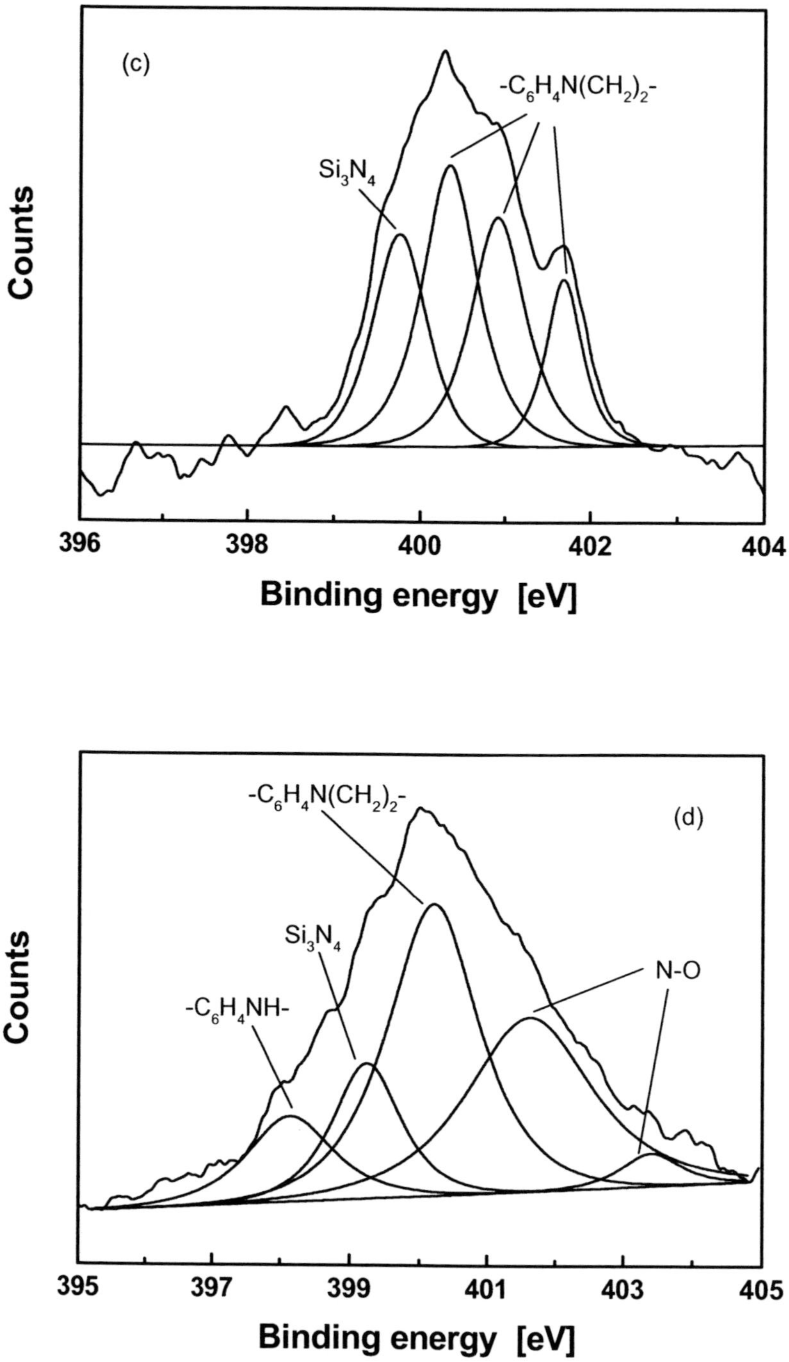

Figure 56. N1s spectra of pin surfaces of (a) unworn epoxy, (b) worn epoxy, (c) unworn nano-Si_3N_4/epoxy composites (V_f=0.83vol%), (d) worn nano-Si_3N_4/epoxy composites (V_f=0.83vol%).

Fig.56 exhibits the N1s spectra collected from the sample surfaces. The N atom comes from the curing agent in epoxy and nanometer Si_3N_4 particles in the composites. The spectra collected on the worn surfaces have different profiles from their virgin materials. Besides, the peaks from the worn specimens slightly shift to high binding energy regime, and some new sub-peaks appear. All these imply that the chemical environment of N atoms also becomes more oxidative. The N atoms might react with atmospheric O_2 under sliding wear condition.

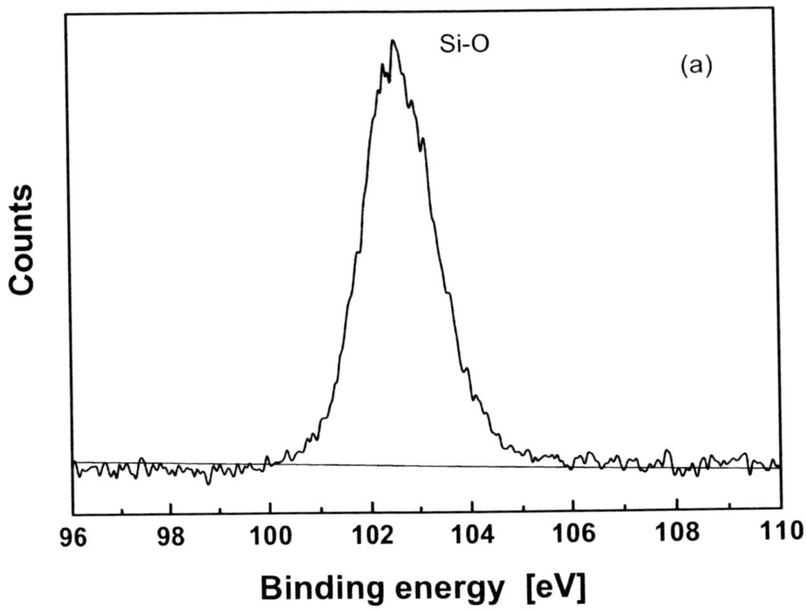

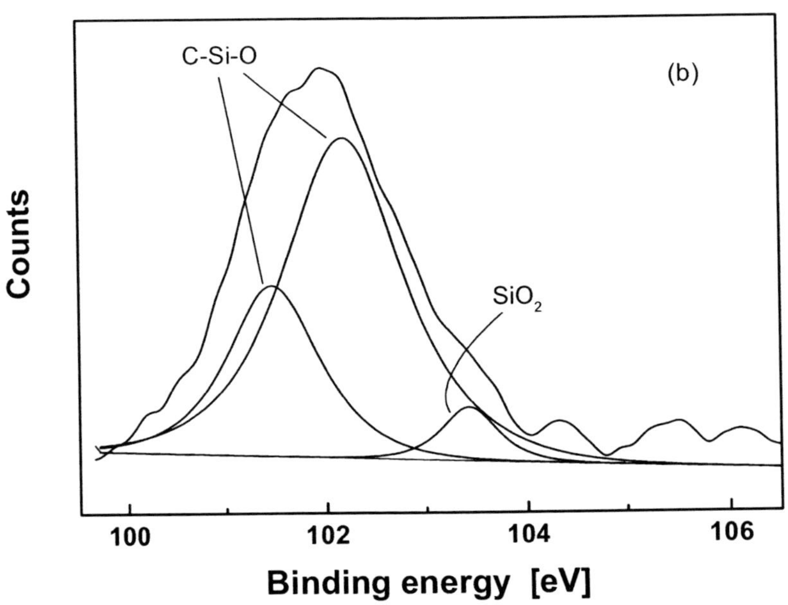

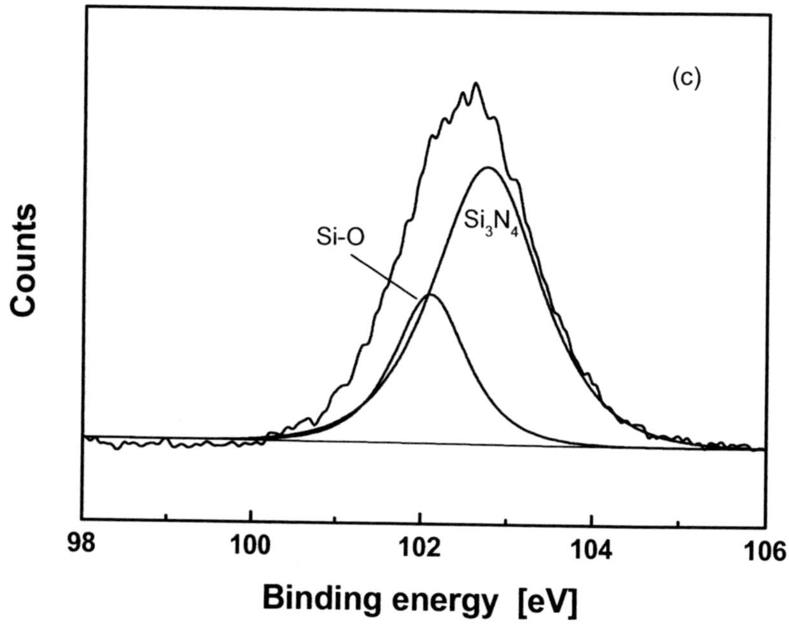

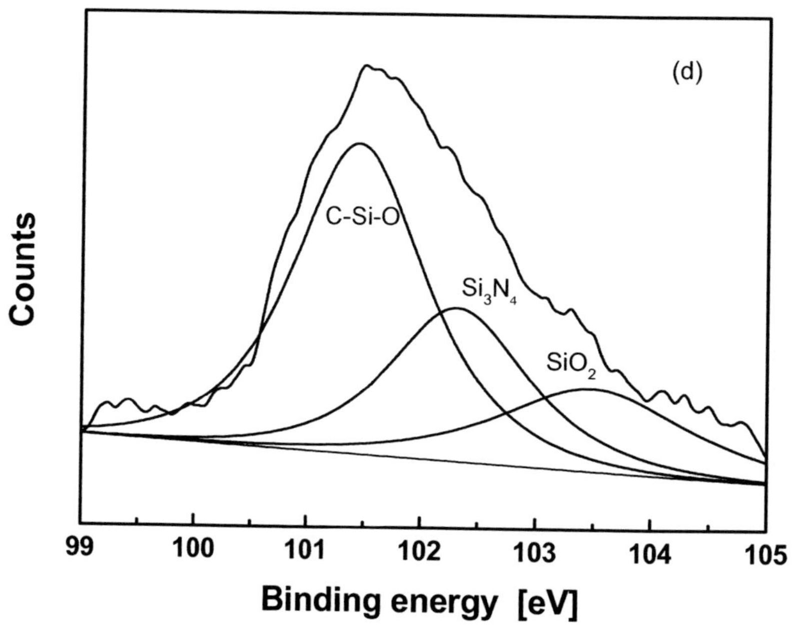

Figure 57. Si2p spectra of pin surfaces of (a) unworn epoxy, (b) worn epoxy, (c) unworn nano-Si_3N_4/epoxy composites (V_f=0.83vol%), (d) worn nano-Si_3N_4/epoxy composites (V_f=0.83vol%).

Fig.57 gives the Si2p spectra of the specimen surfaces. The Si atoms mainly come from the nanometer Si_3N_4 filler in the composites, but those transferring from the polishing paper to the materials' surfaces during samples preparation and from the steel counterpart during wear testing can also contribute to the spectra. The most distinct information yielded from the spectra before and after wear tests lies in the formation of SiO_2. It represents a tribochemical way of wear in which material is removed molecule to molecule, instead of the classic removal of fragments by fracture [78, 79]. In addition, the tribofilm of SiO_2 protects the specimens and the steel counterpart, providing friction reducing ability [80].

Since no Fe peak can be found on the spectra from the pin surfaces of unworn epoxy, worn epoxy and unworn Si_3N_4/epoxy composites, Fig.58 only shows the Fe2p spectrum collected from the worn surface of the composites. Besides the reactions between the Fe atoms from the metal counterface, the S atoms from epoxy and Si_3N_4, the Fe atoms can also be oxidized, forming FeO and Fe_3O_4. Kong et al. reported on the effect of surface oxide layers on wear behavior [81]. FeO or Fe_3O_4 layers show a significant reduction in friction and wear, while Fe_2O_3 layer promotes the wear. Therefore, the decreasing of μ and $\dot{w}_s$ of epoxy with the addition of Si_3N_4 nanoparticles can be partly attributed to the appearance of FeO and Fe_3O_4 on the counterfaces [82].

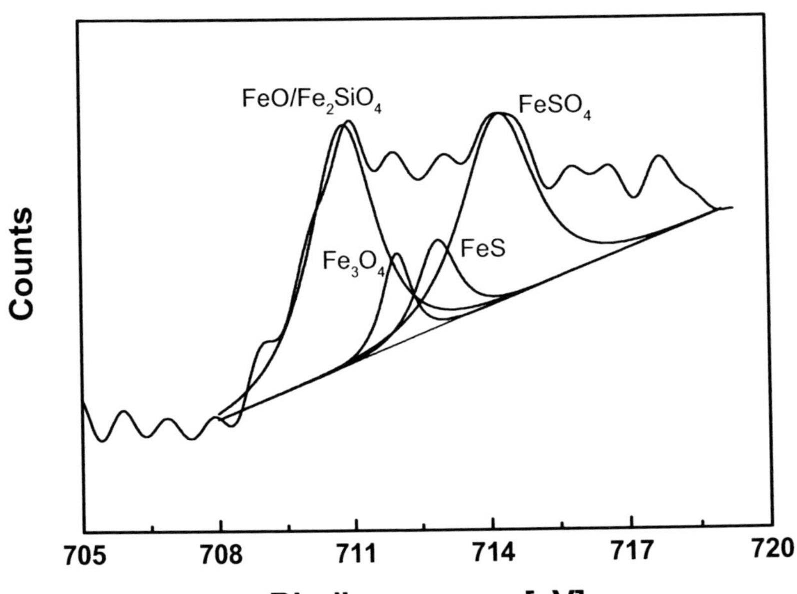

Figure 58. Fe2p spectrum of pin surface of worn nano-Si_3N_4/epoxy composites (V_f=0.83vol%).

To conclude the tribochemical reactions of epoxy and its composites, and those between the materials and the counterface metal Fe, the following Scheme I is given according to the above discussion, which might help to have an overview of the role of the nanocomposites operating under sliding wear conditions.

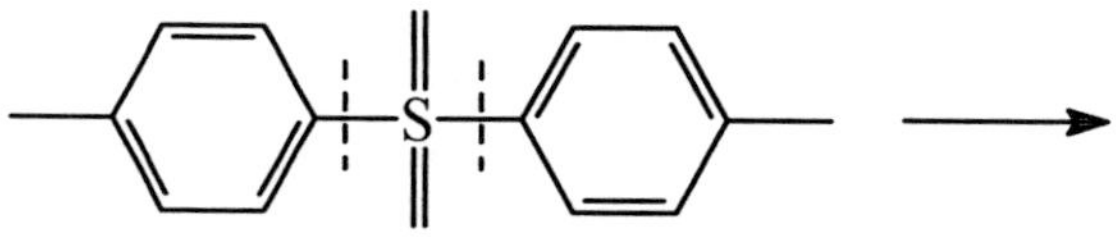

SO_2

$O_2 + \cdot NH—CH_2— \rightarrow ON—CH_2—$

$SO_2 + Fe + O_2 \rightarrow FeSO_4$

$Fe + H_2O + O_2 \rightarrow Fe_3O_4$

$Fe + O_2 + H_2O \rightarrow FeO$

$Fe + S \rightarrow FeS$

$Si_3N_4 + O_2 + H_2O \rightarrow SiO_2$

$Si_3N_4 + Fe + H_2O + O_2 \rightarrow Fe_2SiO_4$

Scheme I

4. Conclusions

1. Modification of inorganic nanoparticle agglomerates through grafting polymerization represents an attractive route to give full play to the nanoparticles in improving performance of polymer composites by enhancing the interfacial interaction between the particles and the matrix through chemical bonding. The addition of inorganic nanoparticles into epoxy can reduce wear rate and frictional coefficient of the matrix at low filler loading, but a further improvement of the tribological properties is obtained by incorporating the grafted nanoparticles. The mechanism for this improvement is ascribed to the matrix enhancement rather than the nanoparticles themselves. The key effects of the grafting polymers lie in the strengthening of the loose nanoparticle agglomerates besides the increase of the filler/matrix interfacial adhesion.
2. Grafting of PAAM onto the nanoparticles can establish covalent bonding between the particles and epoxy during the subsequent curing process, while the presence of PS as grafting polymer improves the interfacial compatibility between the hydrophilic nanoparticles and the hydrophobic matrix. Comparatively, the composites filled with PAAM grafted nanoparticles receive higher enhancement of sliding wear performance than those with PS grafted particles.
3. Unlike micrometer particles, nanoparticles can simultaneously provide epoxy with friction and wear reducing functions at rather low filler content. This provides the basis of utilizing the nanocomposites as coating materials for wear resisting and friction reducing applications in industries.
4. The untreated nanoparticles have either accelerating effect on the curing kinetics of epoxy because of their surface hydroxyl groups, or decelerating effect due to the increased viscosity of the composite system (before curing) and/or the strong interaction between the nanoparticles and the matrix polymer that hinders the

molecular motion of epoxy. The ultimate result is a competition of the two opposite factors. For PAAM grafted nanoparticles, the curing behavior of epoxy is promoted as a result of the catalytic effect via hydrogen bonding of the hydroxyl group in amide of PAAM to the oxygen of the glycidyl ether in the transition state. On the whole, the incorporation of either untreated or treated nanoparticles don't change the curing mechanism of epoxy.

5. Basically, the surface micro-hardness data reflect the particles dispersion status and coincide with the wear performance improvement of the composites, but the relationship between the micro-hardness and the wear data is not straightforward enough. Furthermore, it is hard to estimate the wear performance of the nanocomposites from their mechanical properties.

ACKNOWLEDGEMENTS

The financial support by the Volkswagen-Stiftung, Federal Republic of Germany (Grant No.I/76645), for the cooperation between the German and Chinese institutes on this subject is gratefully acknowledged. Further thanks are due to the Natural Science Foundation of China (Grants: 50273047 and 50133020), the Team Project of the Natural Science Foundation of Guangdong, China (Grant: 20003038), the Key Project of the Natural Science Foundation of Guangdong, China (Grants: 2003C50107 and 2004A10702001) and the project of Guangdong Economic & Trade Commission, China (Grant: 20040112) for supporting some parts of the chemical works involved in this project.

REFERENCES

[1] Bahadur, S. & Gong, D. (1992). The action of fillers in the modification of the tribological behaviour of polymers. *Wear*, 158, 41-59.

[2] Duand, J. M., Vardavoulias, M. & Jeandin, M. (1995). Role of reinforcing ceramic particles in the wear behaviour of polymer-based model composites. *Wear*, 181-183, 826-832.

[3] Lancaster, J. K. (1972). Polymer-based bearing materials: The role of fillers and fiber reinforcement. *Tribol. Int.*, 5, 249-255.

[4] Evans, D. C. & Lancaster, J. K. The Wear of polymers. In: Scott, D. editor. *Treatise on Materials Science and Technology*, vol.13. New York: Academic Press; 1979; 85-139.

[5] Tanaka, K. Effects of various fillers on the friction and wear of PTFE-based composites. In: Friedrich, K. editor. *Friction and Wear of Polymer Composites*. Amsterdam: Elsevier; 1986; 152-173.

[6] Briscoe, B. J. (1981). Wear of polymers: An essay on fundamental aspects. *Tribol. Int.*, 14, 231-243

[7] Cadman, P. & Gossedge, G. M. (1979). The chemical nature of metal-polytetrafluoroethylene tribological interactions as studied by X-ray photoelectron spectroscopy. *Wear*, 54, 211-215.

[8] Bahadur, S. & Gong, D. (1992). The role of copper compounds as fillers in the transfer and wear behaviour of polyetheretherketone. *Wear*, 154, 151-165.

[9] Voort, J. V. & Bahadur, S. (1995). The growth and bonding of transfer film and the role of CuS and PTFE in the tribological behavior of PEEK. *Wear*, 181-183, 212-221

[10] Bahadur, S., Gong, D. & Anderegy, J. W. (1993). The investigation of the action of fillers by XPS studies of the transfer films of PEEK and its composites containing CuS and CuF_2. *Wear*, 160, 131-138.

[11] Bahadur, S. & Gong, D. (1994). The effect of reinforcement and the synergism between CuS and carbon fiber on the wear of nylon. *Wear*, 178, 123-130.

[12] Zhao, Q. & Bahadur, S. (1999). The mechanism of filler action and the criterion of filler selection for reducing wear. *Wear*, 225-229, 660-668.

[13] Vishvanath, B., Verma, A. P. & Kameswara Rao, C. V. S. (1993). Effect of reinforcement on friction and wear of fibric reinforced polymer composites. *Wear*, 167, 93-99.

[14] Ei-Tayeb, N. S. & Gadebrab, B. M. (1996). Friction and wear properties of E-glass fiber reinforced epoxy composites under different sliding contact conditions. *Wear*, 192, 112-117.

[15] Symonds, N. & Mellor, B. G. (1999). Polymeric coatings for impact and wear resistance I: *Wear*, 225-229, 111-118

[16] Bely, V. A., Sviridenok, A. I., Petrokovets, M. I. & Savkin, V. G. *Friction and Wear in Polymer-Based Materials*. Oxford: Pergamon Press Ltd.; 1982.

[17] Yamaguchi, Y. Improvement of lubricity. In: Yamaguchi, Y. editor. *Tribology of Plastic Materials*, Tribology Series, vol.16. Amsterdam: Elsevier; 1990; 143-202.

[18] Sekiguchi, I., Kubota, K., Oyanagi, Y., Kasaka, K. & Sone, Y. (1992). Tribological properties of COPNA resin. *Wear*, 158, 171-183.

[19] Friedrich, K. Wear of reinforced polymers by different abrasive counterparts. In: Friedrich, K. editor. *Friction and Wear of Polymer Composites*. Amsterdam: Elsevier; 1986; 233-287.

[20] Song, J., Maertin, Cl. G. & Ehrenstein, G. W. The effect of self-reinforcement on the tribological behavior of thermoplastics. *Proc. ANTEC* 88, SPE, Atlanta (Society of Plastics Engineers, Brookfield, 1988)

[21] Song, J. & Ehrenstein, G. W. Friction and wear of self-reinforced thermoplastics. In: Friedrich, K. editor. *Advances in Composite Tribology*. Amsterdam: Elsevier; 1993; 19-63.

[22] Giannelis, E. P. Polymer layered silicate nanocomposites. (1996). *Adv. Mater.*, 8, 29-35.

[23] Wang, Q., Xu, J., Shen, W. & Liu, W. (1996). An investigation of the friction and wear properties of nanometer Si_3N_4 filled PEEK. *Wear*, 196, 82-86.

[24] Wang, Q., Xu, J. & Shen, W. (1997). The friction and wear properties of nanometer SiO_2 filled polyetheretherketone. *Tribol. Int.*, 30, 193-197.

[25] Wang, Q., Xu, J., Shen, W. & Zhang, J. (1998). The friction and wear properties of nanometer ZrO_2 filled polyetheretherketone. *J. Appl. Polym. Sci.*, 69, 135-141.

[26] He, J. L., Wang, L. D., Li, W. Z. & Li, H. D. (1998). Experimental observations on the mechanical properties of nanoscale ceramic/Teflon multilayers. *Mater. Chem. Phys.*, 54, 334-337

[27] Schadler, L. S., Laul, K. O., Smith, R. W., & Petrovicova, E. (1997). Microstructure and mechanical properties of thermally sprayed silica/nylon nanocomposites. *J. Therm. Spray Technol.*, 6, 475-485.

[28] Novak, B. M. (1993). Hybrid nanocomposite materials-between inorganic glasses and organic polymers. *Adv. Mater.*, 5, 422-433.

[29] Kojima, Y., Usuki, A., Kawasumi, M., Okada, A., Fukushima, Y., Kurauchi, T. & Kamigaito, O. (1993). One-pot synthesis of nylon 6-clay hybrid. *J. Polym. Sci., Part A, Polym. Chem.*, 31, 1755-1758.

[30] Yano, K., Usuki, A., Okada, A., Kurauchi, T. & Kamigato, O. (1993). Synthesis and properties of polyimide-clay hybrid. *J. Polym. Sci., Part A: Polym. Chem.*, 31, 2493-2498.

[31] Zilg, C., Thomann, R., Mülhaupt, R. & Finter, J. (1999). Polyurethane nanocomposites containing laminated anisotropic nanoparticles derived from organophilic layered silicates. *Adv. Mater.*, 11, 49-51.

[32] Zilg, C., Mülhaupt, R. & Finter, J. (1999). Morphology and toughness/stiffness balance of nanocomposites based upon anhydride-cured epoxy resins and layered silicates. *Macromol. Chem. Phys.*, 200, 661-670.

[33] Carrotenuto, G., Nicolais, L., Kuang, X. & Zhu, Z. (1995). A method for the preparation of PMMA-SiO_2 nanocomposites with high homogeneity. *Appl. Comp. Mater.*, 2, 385-393.

[34] Gonsalves, K. E., Carlson, G., Chen, X., Gayen., S. K., Perez, R. & Jose-Yacaman, M. (1995). Surface functionalized nanostructured gold/polymer composites. *Polym. Mater. Sci. Eng.*, 73, 298-299.

[35] Xu, W., Huang, R., Cai, B. & Fan, W. (1998). Nano-$CaCO_3$ filled HDPE composite. *Chin.Plast.*, 12(6), 30-34 (in Chinese).

[36] Sumita, M., Tsukuma, Y., Miyasaka, K. & Ishikawa, K. (1983). Tensile yield stress of polypropylene composites filled with ultrafine particles. *J. Mater. Sci.*, 18, 1758-1764.

[37] Rong, M. Z., Zhang, M. Q., Zheng, Y. X. & Zeng, H. M. *Surface treatment of inorganic nanoparticles by irradiation grafting of polymers.* Chinese Patent (Application No.: CN99116017), 1999.

[38] Rong, M. Z., Zhang, M. Q., Zheng, Y. X., Zeng, H. M., Walter, R. & Friedrich, K. (2001) Structure-property relationships of irradiation grafted nano-inorganic particle filled polypropylene composites. *Polymer*, 42, 167-183.

[39] Hayashi, S., Takeuchi, Y., Eguchi, M., Iida, T. & Tsubokawa, N. (1999). Graft polymerization of vinyl monomers initiated by peroxycarbonate groups introduced onto surface by Michael addition. *J. Appl. Polym. Sci.*, 71, 1491-1497

[40] Oosterling, M. L. C. M., Sein, A. & Schouten, A. J. (1992). Anionic grafting of polystyrene and poly(styrene-block-isoprene) onto microparticulate silica and glass slides. *Polymer*, 33, 4394-4400.

[41] Espiard, P. & Guyot, A. (1995). Poly(ethyl acrylate) latexes encapsulating nanoparticles of silica: 2. Grafting process onto silica. *Polymer*, 23, 4391-4395.

[42] Baraton, M. I., Chancel, F. & Merhari, L. (1997). In-situ determination of the grafting on nanosized ceramic powders by FT-IR spectrometry. *Nanostruct. Mater.*, 9, 319-322.

[43] Liu, Q., Wijn, J. R. D., Groot, K. D. & Blitterswijk, C. A. V. (1998). Surface modification of nano-apatite by grafting organic polymer. *Biomaterials*, 19, 1067-1072.

[44] Tsubokawa, N. & Yoshikawa, S. (1995). Grafting of polymer with controlled molecular weight onto silica surface. J. Polym. Sci., Part *A Polym. Chem.*, 33, 551-586.
[45] Rong, M. Z., Zhang, M. Q., Zheng, Y. X., Zeng, H. M., Walter, R. & Friedrich, K. (2000). Irradiation graft polymerization on nano-inorganic particles: An effective means to design polymer based nanocomposites. *J. Mater. Sci. Lett.*, 19, 1159-1161.
[46] Rong, M. Z., Zhang, M. Q., Zheng, Y. X., Zeng, H. M., & Friedrich, K. (2001). Improvement of tensile properties of nano-SiO_2/PP composites in relation to percolation mechanism. *Polymer*, 42, 3301-3304.
[47] Yu, T. Y. *Experimental Techniques of Polymers*. Shanghai: Fudan University Press; 1983 (in Chinese).
[48] Odian, G. *Principle of Polymerization*. New York: John Wiley; 1981.
[49] Lin, B. P., Gu, X. Y., Wang, G. L. & Yang, L. (1996). Study on polymerization of acrylamide aqueous solution. *Mod. Chem. Eng.*, (1), 29-31 (in Chinese).
[50] Shim, M.-J. & Kim, S.-W. (1998). Effect of zeolite filler on the cure and thermal characteristics of diglycidyl ether of bisphenol A/4,4"-methylene dianiline system. *Polym. J.*, 30, 73-77.
[51] Kissinger, H. E. (1957) Reaction kinetics in differential thermal analysis. *Anal. Chem.*, 29, 1702-1706.
[52] Crane, L. W., Dynes, P. J. & Kaelble, D. H. (1973). Analysis of curing kinetics in polymer composites. *J. Polym. Sci. Polym. Lett. Ed*, 11, 533-540.
[53] Rong, M. Z., Ji, Q. L., Zhang, M. Q. & Friedrich, K. (2002). Graft polymerization of vinyl monomers onto nanosized alumina particles. *Eur. Polym. J.*, 38, 1573-1582.
[54] Ji, Q. L., Rong, M. Z., Zhang, M. Q. & Friedrich, K. (2002). Graft polymerization of vinyl monomers onto nanosized silicon carbide particles. *Polym. Polym. Compos.*, 10, 531-539.
[55] Shechter, L., Wynstra, J. & Kurlziy, R. P. (1956). Glycidyl ether reactions with amines. *Ind. Eng. Chem.*, 48, 94-97.
[56] Chua, P. S. (1987). Dynamic mechanical analysis studies of the interphase. *Polym. Compos.*, 8, 308-313.
[57] Wu, H. F., Gu, W., Lu, G.-Q. & Kampe, S. L. (1997). Non-destructive characterization of fibre-matrix adhesion in composites by vibration damping. *J. Mater. Sci. Lett.*, 32, 1797-1798.
[58] Rong, M. Z., Zhang, M. Q., Liu, Y., Yan, H. M., Yang, G. C. & Zeng, H. M. (2002). Interfacial interaction in sisal/epoxy composites and its influence on impact performance, *Polym. Compos.*, 23, 182-192.
[59] Kubat, J., Rigdahl, M. & Welander, M. (1990). Characterization of interfacial interactions in high density polyethylene filled with glass spheres using dynamic-mechanical analysis, *J. Appl. Polym. Sci.*, 39, 1527-1539.
[60] Heux, L., Halary, J. L., Lauprêtre, F. & Monnerie, L. (1997). Dynamic mechanical and 13C n.m.r. investigations of molecular motions involved in the β relaxation of epoxy networks based on DGEBA and aliphatic amines. *Polymer*, 38, 1767-1778.
[61] Pogany, G. A. (1970). Gamma relaxation in epoxy resins and related polymers. *Polymer*, 11, 66-78.
[62] Rong, M. Z., Zhang, M. Q., Shi, G., Ji, Q. L., Wetzel, B. & Friedrich, K. (2003). Graft polymerization onto inorganic nanoparticles and its effect on tribological performance improvement of polymer composites. *Tribol. Int.*, 36, 697-707.

[63] Yan, H.-X., Shi, L.-P., Shen, H.-P. (2000). Friction and wear properties of nanocrystalline Al_2O_3 filled-PTFE composites. *Tribol.*, 20(2), 153-155 (in Chinese).
[64] Suh, N. P. (1973). The delamination theory of wear. *Wear*, 25, 111–124.
[65] Eliezer, Z., Schulz, C. J. & Barlow, J. W. (1978). Friction and wear properties of an epoxy-steel system. *Wear*, 46, 397-403.
[66] Lancaster, J. K. (1968). The effect of carbon fibre reinforcement on the friction and wear of polymers. *Brit. J. Appl. Phys.*, 1, 549-559.
[67] Zhang, M. Q., Rong, M. Z., Yu, S. L., Wetzel, B. & Friedrich, K. (2002). Improvement of tribological performance of epoxy by the addition of irradiation grafted nano-inorganic particles. *Macromol. Mater. Eng.*, 287, 111-115.
[68] Wetzel, B., Haupert, F., Friedrich, K., Zhang, M. Q. & Rong, M. Z. Mechanical and tribological properties of microparticulate and manoparticulate reinforced polymer composites. *Proc. ICCM-13*, Zhang, Y. editor. Beijing: Wan Fang Digital Electr. Publish.; 2001; ID1021.
[69] Rong, M. Z., Zhang, M. Q., Liu, H., Zeng, H. M., Wetzel, B. & Friedrich, K. (2001). Microstructure and tribological behavior of polymeric nanocomposites. *Ind. Lubr. Tribology*, 53(2), 72-77.
[70] Bassani, R., Levita, G., Meozzi, M. & Palla, G. (2001). Friction and wear of epoxy resin on inox steel: Remarks on the influence of velocity, load and induced thermal state. *Wear*, 247, 125-132.
[71] Bonfield, W., Edwards, B. C., Markham, A. J. & White, J. R. (1976). Wear transfer films formed by carbon fibre reinforced epoxy resin sliding on stainless steel. *Wear*, 37, 113-121.
[72] Schwartz, C. J. & Bahadur, S. (2000). Studies on the tribological behavior and transfer film-counterface bond strength for polyphenylene sulfide filled with nanoscale alumina particles. *Wear*, 237, 261-273
[73] Shimbo, M., Ochi, M. & Ohoyama, N. (1983). Frictional behavior of cured epoxide resins. *Wear*, 91, 89-101.
[74] Zhang, M. Q., Song, L., Zeng, H. M., Friedrich, K. & Karger-Kocsis, J. (1997). Frictional surface temperature determination of high temperature resistant semicrystalline polymers by using their double melting features. J. *Appl. Polym. Sci.*, 63, 589-593
[75] Zhang, M. Q., Lu, Z. P. & Friedrich, K. (1997). Thermal analysis of the wear debris of polyetheretherketone. *Tribol. Interni.*, 30, 103-111.
[76] Li, T. Q., Zhang, M. Q., Song, L. & Zeng, H. M. (1999). Friction induced mechanochemical and mechanophysical changes in high performance semicrystalline polymer. *Polymer*, 40, 4451-4458.
[77] Yu, L., Bahadur, S. & Xue, Q. (1998). An investigation of the friction and wear behaviors of ceramic particle filled polyphenylene sulfide composites. *Wear*, 214, 54-63.
[78] Tomizawa, H. & Fischer, T. E. (1987). Friction and wear of silicon nitride and silicon carbide in water: Hydrodynamic lubrication at low sliding speed obtained by tribochemical wear. *ASLE Trans.*, 30 (1), 41-46.
[79] Fischer, T. E. & Tomizawa, H. (1985). Interaction of tribochemistry and microfracture in the friction and wear of silicon nitride. *Wear*, 105, 29-45.

[80] Gao, Y.-M., Fang, L., Su, J.-Y., Xu, X.-W. (1997). An investigation on component and formation of tribochemical film in Si_3N_4-white iron sliding pair lubricated with distilled water. *Tribol. Int.*, 30, 693-700.

[81] Kong, H., Yoon, E.-S. & Kwon, O. K. (1995). Self-formation of protective oxide films at dry sliding mild steel surfaces under a medium vacuum. *Wear*, 181-183, 325-333.

[82] Nakamura, M., Hirao, K., Yamauchi, Y. & Kanzaki, S. (2002). Tribological behaviour of uni-directionally aligned silicon nitride against steel. *Wear*, 252, 484–490.

In: Nanomaterials: New Research
Editor: B.M. Caruta, pp. 81-113

ISBN: 1-59454-369-0

Chapter 2

USE OF ION BEAMS TO PRODUCE OR MODIFY NANOSTRUCTURES IN MATERIALS

J.C. Pivin
CSNSM, CNRS-IN2P3, Bâtiment 108, 91405 Orsay Campus, France

ABSTRACT

The mechanisms of structural transformations occuring in ion irradiated solids are summarized and an overview of the different types of nanostructures which can be obtained is presented. They are sorted on basis of the slowing down regime of ions and bonds nature in the material. Typical examples are given, instead of an exhaustive list.

1. INTRODUCTION

Nanostructured materials are presently the topics of many conferences and publications because their extremely small size and large surface-to-volume ratio lead to differences in their chemical and physical properties compared to bulk materials of the same chemical composition or to molecular clusters. The critical size range of the nano-domains with particular properties are quite well defined on basis of relevant dimensions in each field of physics, such as the Bohr radius of excitons in semiconductors or the correlation length of spins in magnets.

Ions penetrating in a solid lose their energy in collisions with nuclei and in electronic excitations. The latter induce no significant deflection of the ion path and, in the absence of collision cascades, the perturbed tracks are cylinders of radii ranging from 1 to 20 nm, depending on the target structure (organic, metal, semiconductor....) and on the ion nature. The spatial extension of cascades is significantly broader because of their subdivision by secondary projectiles. The mean size of nano-domains created by ions is correlated to those of tracks and secondary cascades. These parameters can be varied via a proper choice of the ion mass and energy, which determine the densities $S_e(r,t)$ ans $S_n(r,t)$ of energy transferred by the ion to electrons and nuclei. The system perturbation lasts a very short time, typically of 10^{-13} s for the cascade and of 10^{-12} 10^{-10} s for the relaxation of the lattice and electron gas. Transient melting or vaporization of the target material may occur beyond a threshold of energy transfer to the electronic system and, for this reason, such events are more characteristic of swift heavy ion irradiation (S.H.I.). On the contrary, the displacements number density decreasing with the ion velocity, low energy ion beams are generally used for producing topography changes resulting from the sputtering of surface atoms and for disordering superficial layers (disorder leading in some cases to the target amorphization). Changes of local composition are also induced by the migration of displaced atoms and by electronic spikes. A radiation-induced diffusion of atomic defects over distances limited to the cascade extent occurs during the ballistic perturbation, then a radiation-enhanced diffusion occurs when the defects are mobile at the temperature of the experiment. These two types of diffusion have for effect a variety of chemical and structural changes, which are often similar to those obtained by thermal treatments, such as the mixing of overimposed layers, the segregation and precipitation of some species in metastable systems. However, the synergic effects of displacements and lattice excitations induce also some modifications which are specific to ion beam processing.

These considerations of general nature give good reasons for believing that ion irradiation is a suitable means to synthesize nanostructures with well controlled sizes and metastable phases. Ion beam induced modifications of materials are localized either in a controlled range of depth, correlated to the ion implantation depth, or in a defined number of cylindrical tracks. In addition, the nano-patterning of thin films can be achieved by scanning a focused and pulsed beam. On the other hand, the major drawback of ion beam treatments is their cost. Therefore, most of the examples given in this overview of nanostructures produced by ion beams are the results of researches performed for fundamental purpose or for fabricating sophisticated devices and biomaterials. After a short summary of the ion-solid interaction physics, structures will be sorted on basis of the slowing down regime and of the bonds nature in the material. Ballistic disorder can for instance lead to the amorphization of metals, semiconductor or covalent compounds while ionic crystals are more sensitive to high densities of electronic excitations. Effects of electronic excitations in dielectrics will be emphasized because these materials absorb little the energy of visible laser beams and consequently an ion beam treatment constitutes an alternative route.

2. Physical Bases

The purpose of this paragraph is to provide general concepts of ions interaction with solids useful to the understanding of phenomena described hereafter. Fine reviews already exist on the subject of energy loss and fundamental expressions can be found in handbooks [1-3]. They are briefly summarized in the appendix.

2.1. The Slowing Down Process

First let me start with tutorial definitions and description of the stopping process. Ions lose their energy in a series of elastic collisions with nuclei, screened by their electron shells, and inelastic collisions with electrons in various localized orbitals and in the conduction band. The nuclear and electronic stopping powers of the target are average values of energy transfers, T, occuring for different impact conditions, weighted by the probability dσ of these events. This probability has the dimension of a section because it is determined by the distance p of the atom or electron at rest projected upon the ion path, called impact parameter. For simplifying the problem of summing the energy lost to various atoms in compound targets, the travelled thickness (range R) is generally defined under the form of a number of target atoms per unit area and the unit of energy loss is a number of $eV/atoms/cm^2$. The advantage of this unit is that the Bragg rule can be applied to calculated or measured stopping powers of elements (under different physical states), without having to assume a density value for compound targets.

An important simplification made for solving the transport equations consists in considering nuclear and electronic stopping as independent processes. This hypothesis is justified by the fact that the slowing down of the projectile due to electronic excitations is similar to the friction of an electron gas (with local fluctuations of gas density, which can be modelized by a Hartree Fock Slater distribution). The interest of this simplification can be easily understood when remembering that, although the electronic stopping is always substantial, the projectile loses little energy in each electronic collision and does not deviate significantly from its original path. On the contrary, its trajectory and residual energy vary stochastically during each nuclear collision, depending on the impact parameter p. The energy transfer $T(E_0, p)$, for a given impact parameter and projectile energy E_0 before the collision, is determined by the screened repulsion potential $V(r, E_0, Z_1, Z_2)$ of colliding atoms, which has the simple form of a Coulomb potential for short distances of cloasest approach r. A universal expression of this potential for any r value has been established for solving transport equations or performing Monte Carlo simulations of binary collisions in solids (basis of the Stopping and Range of Ion in Matter program [1]).

The expressions of T, scattering angle in a nuclear collision and stopping powers S_n, S_e, as a function of the ion energy E_0 before it penetrates in the target, atomic numbers and masses of ion (1) and target atom (2) are given in the appendix. Typical variations of S_n and S_e as a function of E_0 are shown in figure 1. Schematically, the electronic stopping power S_e increases as the product of the ion velocity by the cube root of the electron gas density up to the Bohr velocity v_B ($e^2/\hbar$, corresponding to an energy of 25 keV/amu) [2,3], then more steeply between v_B and $2Z_1v_B$, then it decreases as $1/E_0$ when the ion becomes stripped from its electrons (referred as Bethe in Fig. 1). When using the reduced energy unit ε (see appendix), $S_n(\varepsilon)$ goes through a maximum at a same ε value of 0.3 keV for all combinations of ions and targets. This optimal energy for the atomic damaging corresponds to E_0 values of 1 to 400 keV for ion masses M_1 in the range 1 to 200 penetrating in a silica target, chosen as example. Whatever the ion and target, this energy of maximum nuclear stopping is 2 to 3 orders of magnitude smaller than the energy of maximum electronic stopping.

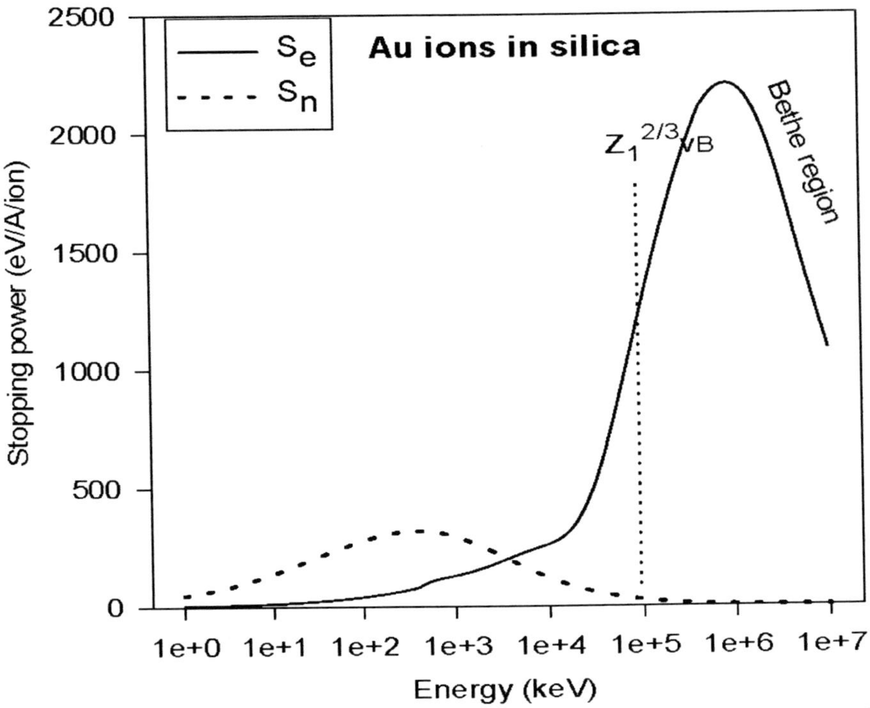

Figure 1. variations of electronic (S_e) and nuclear (S_n) stopping power of Au ions in silica as a function of their energy

2.2. Spatial Distribution of Damages in Collisional Regime

In most cases the atom set in motion during a primary collision with the incident ion (primary recoil) produces secondary collisions, which don't interfere with those resulting from other primary collisions. This regime of linear cascade, i.e. of independent sub-cascades (which is the basic assumption of SRIM calculations), takes place when the density of moving atoms is much lower than the atomic density. In such a case, the depth distribution of secondary recoils is roughly the same as the distribution of primary recoils because of the short mean free path of the formers. When the collisions density exceeds a threshold, either because of the low incident energy or high ion mass, a collision spike occurs instead of a linear cascade [4]. Atoms which do not collide with the ion or a recoil acquire nevertheless a momentum under the effect of electronic interactions with moving neighbors. These ballistic spikes have some common features with the thermal spikes produced by high densities of electronic excitations under the impact of swift ions (with a velocity $v_0 > Z_1^{2/3} v_B$, above which the charge state of the ion increases when it penetrates in the target) or by illumination with a laser, in this respect that they are modelled by using the same transport equations of heat (see paragraph 2.4). However, the expressions of the concentration of atoms set in motion and of the temperature at the end of the energy impulse are different and the heat is dissipated for a part by a transfer from phonons to the electronic system in the case of ballistic spikes, instead of the reverse in electronic spikes [4, 5].

The basic quantity defining the concentration of displaced atoms $N_d(R)$ and the threshold value for the occurence of a collision spike is the ratio of the density of nuclear energy transfer to the displacement energy E_d. The latter is the minimal energy which a recoil must receive in order that the formed Frenckel pair is not annihilated by direct recombination with the associated vacancy, located at a few interatomic distances, or by relaxation of the lattice. E_d depends on the crystallographic orientation of the displacement, because replacement collisions are favored along dense atomic rows and the binding energy is anisotropic (on the average it is correlated to the cohesion energy of the crystal). This anisotropy contributes to various phenomena, such as the preferential sputtering and disordering of some crystals in a polycrystalline target. Since nuclear collisions don't necessarily lead to effective displacements, the part of the primary energy, E_0, which is converted in defects energy, $F_d(E_0)$, amounts to only 20 to 50% (according to the used model) of the energy transferred to nuclei over the whole ion path, $\nu(E_0)$. According to the earliest estimate by Kinchin-Pease [6], the number of stable Frenkel pairs created by each ion is:

$$N_d = \nu\,(E_0)/2E_d \qquad (1)$$

The most probable ranges of ions, $<R_I>$ and of defects, $<R_d>$, can be derived directly from mean values of energy losses given in tables by writing:

$$<R_I> = \int_0^{E_0} \frac{1}{N_{at}} \frac{dE}{S_n + S_e} \qquad (2)$$

and $$<R_d> = \int_{E_d}^{E_0} \frac{1}{N_{at}} \frac{dE}{S_n} \qquad (3)$$

where N_{at} is the atomic density of the target.

Due to the stochastic nature of the nuclear stopping process, the depth distributions of implanted atoms and of energy transferred to nuclei, $f_I(E_I, R)$ by ions having a residual energy E_I at depth R (which is the derivative of ν (E_0) also labelled $F_I(E_0)$), can be approximated by Gaussian functions in the case of amorphous or polycrystalline targets. These distributions are however estimated more accurately by using transport equations defined by Lindhart [1] and computing Monte Carlo simulations of binary collision cascades with the SRIM code. Molecular dynamics simulations attract more and more interest with the increasing speed of computers for their ability to simulate spikes and crystallographic effects which are randomized in Monte Carlo simulations.

2.3. Cooperative Effects of Cascades

The overlap of cascades produces a random walk of target atoms called radiation induced-diffusion (RID also called ballistic diffusion, cascade mixing). Note that the anisotropic relocation of primary recoils must be distinguished from this RID in the analysis of transport processes such as the mixing of overimposed layers, especially when these layers are composed of atoms with very different masses [7]. In addition to RID, a migration of point defects occurs after the cascade when the temperature is sufficiently high (radiation-enhanced diffusion, RED in abbreviated form). RID and RED lead in some cases to the segregation of an atomic species (one of the target components or the implanted ions), either due to its lower mass or its lower binding energy or its tendency to form complexes with defects [8-10]. Another factor to take into account in the analysis of diffusion fluxes is that a vacancy-rich zone is formed in the core of cascades and interstitials are more numerous at their periphery. As a result, a given atomic species diffuses towards R_d or interfaces, depending on its stability and mobility on interstitial and substitutional sites, and point defects segregate into dislocation loops.

Another effect of the cascade overlap is the progressive change of surface geometry and composition related to sputtering. Let's just give here Sigmund analytical expression of the sputtering yield Y [11], obtained by applying Boltzman transport equation to describe the flux of particles. Sigmund equation is less accurate but more useful than simulations to outline the effects of the mass and binding energy of target atoms and of the beam orientation with respect to the surface normal on the yield Y and on surface modifications. An overview of these effects was given in [12] and a compilation of experimental data in [13]. The sputtering yield is proportional to the fraction F_d of the ion energy used to displace atoms in outermost layers (which includes displacements by all projectiles) and to the probability Λ that these displaced atoms escape to the surface. F_d differs from the energy deposited by the ion in the escape depth range R_e (close to zero, so that $F_1(R_e) \approx S_n$) by a factor α. This factor represents the influences of the mass ratio M_2/M_1 and of the incidence angle θ on the anisotropy of ion scattering in outer layers of an amorphous or polycrystalline target. Its value α_N for a normal incidence is a slowly varying function of M_2/M_1, increasing from 0.2 to 1, and the exponent f of the angular factor cos θ^{-f} is equal to 5/3 for not too heavy target atoms. The escape probability is inversely proportional to the Born-Mayer screening factor of the interaction potential C_0 ($3/4\pi^2 C_0 = 0.0420$) for slow recoil atoms and to the surface energy barrier U_s (half the binding energy of target atoms).

$$Y = \Lambda\, F_d(R_e) = \frac{3}{4\pi^2}\frac{1}{C_0 U_s}\alpha_N \cos\theta^{-f}\, S_n(E_0) \tag{4}$$

Y presents the same periodic variation with Z_2 in elemental targets as does the surface binding energy, with the result that volatile elements (H_2, O_2, N_2..) are preferentially sputtered from compound targets. When the binding energies of target components are comparable, a superficial impoverishment in the lighter element is usually observed. The escape depth R_e of sputtered atoms is of the order of 2 atomic distances [6], but the target composition is modified from the surface to the mean range of defects <Rd>. The surface topography changes progressively, due to statistical fluctuations in the number of atoms ejected in each point and to the differential sputtering of dislocation loops, or of precipitates in composite targets. Cones topped with precipitates are formed when their sputtering yield is lower than that of the matrix and the precipitates number density changes in all cases.

The depth profile of implanted atoms also changes with the implanted fluence, under the combined effects of lattice swelling and sputtering (disregarding the casualty of a segregation). Schematically, the surface moves outward at a rate proportional to the ion fluence ϕ for keeping approximately constant the target atomic density when ions come at rest on substitutional sites, while sputtering induces an inward motion of the surface. The concentration profile becomes an error function with a plateau value equal to $\tilde{\phi}N_{at}(1+Y)$ close to the surface.

At this point, mention must be made of the channeling phenomenon, which consists in a slighly oscillating path of ions and considerably increased penetration depth when their incident direction is parallel to dense packing planes and rows of a crystal. The lessening of scattering cross section is related to a large and constant impact parameter on the average. Channeling affects not only the depth profiles of implanted ions and defects in single crystals, but also their sputtering yield. In polycrystalline targets, the different sputtering yields of grains according to their orientation induces a surface relief.

In some cases, residual defects segregate under the form of amorphous clusters instead of dislocation loops, because the configuration energy over short distance is lower in the amorphous state. This process is particularly efficient in all semiconductors and covalent compounds (such as quartz). The amorphization occurs locally when the amount of disorder exceeds a threshold value, either in the core of subcascades, when their density is sufficiently high, or by a statistical process of cascades overlap. On the contrary, ionic crystals are amorphized with difficulty because displacements produce two types of charged Frenckel pairs, which exhibit a stronger tendency to recombine than in covalent systems for minimizing the space charge.

2.4. Electronic Damaging in Isolated Tracks Produced by Swift Heavy Ions

Beside the linear density of energy transferred to the electronic system (product of S_e by the atomic density), another parameter to take into account in the damaging process is the radial distribution of this energy in tracks, as long as they don't overlap. One generally distinguishes two regions: a high density of electronic excitations is produced in the track core extending over 1-3 nm and the energy is transported by fast secondary electrons (δ-electrons) in a track halo with a radius of some hundreds nm. For a same S_e value, the energy deposition is smeared out into a larger radius for high velocity projectiles [14]. The reason for this velocity effect is that the the maximum energy transferred to δ electrons is $T_{max} = 2\ m_e\ v_{ion}^2$. The swifter the ion is, the higher is the fraction of the ion energy swept away from the core by these electrons for a given S_e value. Polymers are sensitive essentially to ionizations produced in the core, while damaging in metals results from lattice vibrations induced by elastic collisions of δ electrons outside the core. The damaging mechanisms of semiconductors and inorganic insulators are more intricate, since they involve various processes of electron-hole recombination and charge transfer.

For most inorganic materials, there exist a threshold value of S_e above which the damaging of crystalline targets increases dramatically (Figure 2) or on the contrary crystalline order is reconstructed in some amorphous targets [15-17]. The threshold effect is particularly clear for metals, in which electronic excitations cause a partial annihilation of the defects created by atomic collisions at low energies. Two different mechanisms have been proposed for the steep increase of damaging: ion explosion spikes and thermal spikes.

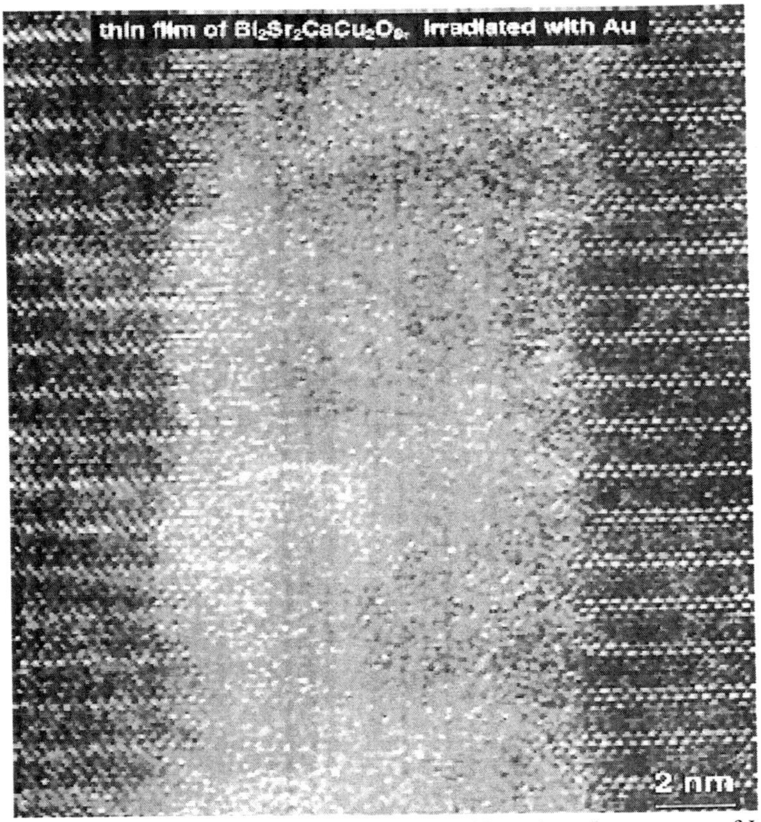

Figure 2. amorphous track in $Bi_2Sr_2CaCu_2O_8$ irradiated with swift Au ions (by courtesy of J. Wiesner et al [17]

In the ion explosion spike theory one considers that the ion creates in its wake a cylinder of highly ionized matter which is very unstable due to Coulomb repulsion between electrostatic charges. Several models were derived from this theory, being the core-plasma model, the shock-wave model, and the modified lattice potential model [18)]. In fact, damage creation via electronic excitations in metals was considered during some time as unrealistic due to the high mobility of conduction electrons, which rapidly smear out the deposited energy and very efficiently screen the atoms that were ionized in the ion wake. However, a shock-wave mechanism is pertinent in the case of metals with a low phonon frequency. Moreover, even if the charge neutrality is re-established in the track core, the interatomic potentials remain during some time different from the equilibrium potentials, setting atoms into motion and producing an athermal melting of the track. On the other hand, mainly insulators are sensitive to Coulomb explosion spikes in the strict sense of the term [19]. Their effect may be annealed by thermal spikes occuring thereafter in the same material, because the returning time of electrons expelled from the track core in a Coulomb explosion is of 10^{-14} to 10^{-13} s and the spreading of the energy in a thermal spike is much slower (10^{-13} to 10^{-12} s depending on the electron mobility).

In the thermal spike model the transfer of energy from the bombarding ion to the lattice is a two-step process [20, 21] : thermalisation of the energy deposited in the electronic system via electron-electron interaction and transfer of this energy to the lattice via electron-phonon interaction. Since the electronic system and the lattice are not in thermal equilibrium with each other, their temperatures, Te and Ta , respectively, are governed by a set of coupled nonlinear differential equations:

$$C_e(T_e)\frac{\partial T_e}{\partial t}=\frac{1}{r}\frac{\partial}{\partial r}\left[rK_e(T_e)\frac{\partial T_e}{\partial r}\right]-g(T_e-T_a)+E(r,t) \quad (5)$$

$$C_a(T_a)\frac{\partial T_a}{\partial t}=\frac{1}{r}\frac{\partial}{\partial r}\left[rK_a(T_a)\frac{\partial T_a}{\partial r}\right]+g(T_e-T_a) \quad (6)$$

where $T_{(e,a)}$, $C_{(e,a)}$, and $K_{(e,a)}$ are the temperature, the specific heat, and the thermal conductivity for the electronic ($_e$) and lattice ($_a$) subsystem, respectively. E(r,t) is the radial density of energy transferred to electrons. The electron-phonon coupling constant g is directly linked to the electron mean free path λ: $\lambda=K_e/g$. The difference between metals and insulators is that in metals energy can be transferred from the hot lattice back to the electrons when $T_a>T_e$,while this transfer is inhibited in insulators.

The damaging of materials by electronic excitations may lead to their amorphization (Fig. 1), but those which are easily amorphized by collision cascades (such as Si) are little sensitive to electronic damaging. The reason of this difference of sensitivity is that the transient disordered phase formed within swift ion tracks tends to reconstruct in epitaxy with the surrounding matrix in the case of semiconductors or covalent compounds. The recovery of structural order is less easy in ionic compounds containing charged defects. Moreover, defects on one of the ionic systems may combine to form a gaseous species, as for instance in alkali halides and consequently metal atoms in excess segregate [22]. Note that pure metals (apart Ga, Bi) are disordered but not amorphized [23] and the topological order just changes on short range in metallic glasses.

3.Ballistic Effects

3.1. Implantation

Applications of ion implantation to the doping of semiconductors or of other materials (for chemical applications in catalysis, detection of gases,...) are out of the scope of this paper. Beside this undeniable interest of the ion implantation technique, it is also one of the most versatile means to create a supersaturated solid solution in the near-surface region of a solid. With regard to nanostructures, a precipitation may occur under the effect of radiation-induced diffusion during implantation, when the local concentration of implanted atoms is much larger than the solubility limit at equilibrium. It is for instance the case of noble metals in oxides for concentrations over 1 at.% [24, 25] (Figure 3). The radiation-enhanced diffusion of interstitials is also effective in many matrices at room temperature (RT). However that may be, implantations are often followed by annealing treatments at high temperatures (or implantations performed in temperature), in order to induce a maximum yield of precipitation and to eliminate defects in the host lattice. This combination of treatments has been called Ion Beam Synthesis.

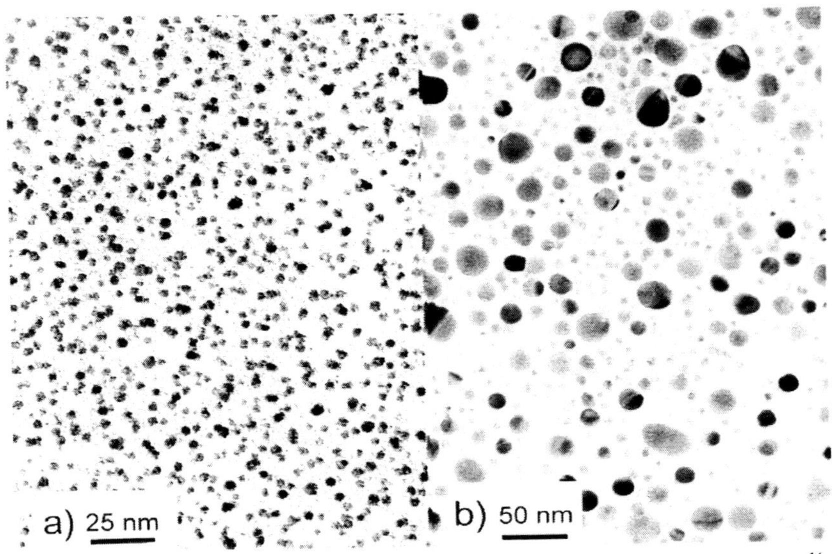

Figure 3. TEM images of silica implanted with 150 keV Ag^+ ions at fluences of (a) 10^{16} and (b) $10^{17}/cm^2$ (3 and 28 at.% at the mean range) [24]

3.1.1. Concentration Gradients in Implantation Layers

In addition to the lattice damaging, the inhomogeneous depth gradient of concentration in implantation layers complicates the interpretation of their properties and may limit their performances. Multi-implantation at several energies permits to overcome this problem, with more or less success because diffusion processes are not taken into account in SRIM simulations. Other programs, such as TRIDYN [26], neglect also the casualty of RED but permit to estimate dynamic changes in the target composition induced by sputtering, ballistic mixing and lattice swelling. Variations in the displacement and binding energies of target atoms with the composition are also considered in the inputs of these simulations.

The narrow depth distribution of ions implanted at a single energy is nevertheless interesting for some applications, as for instance the fabrication of non volatiles memories based on nanocrystals (NCs) embedded in the gate oxide of MOS transistors [27, 28]. By low energy Si^+ implantation, NCs of Si can be formed a few nm above the SiO_2 /Si interface. This allows charging of the NCs by direct electron tunnelling, which is a prerequisite for low operation voltages. Kinetic Monte Carlo Simulations (KMCS) [27] were developped for studying the process of phase separation in these systems. This process involves sequentially the nucleation and growth of particles at the expense of the Si supersaturated solution, then the Ostwald ripening of some of the Si NCs and a spinodal decomposition at higher Si concentrations. The simulations permit to predict the Si concentration threshold of percolation (which process hampers the charging of the NCs) and the optimal temperature range of implantation or post-annealing treatment, in which the trapping of Si solute atoms at the substrate interface together with a controlled growth of the NCs lead to a self alignment suitable for the fabrication of non volatile memories.

An argument put forward by many authors to praise the usefulness of the IBS technique is the obtention of high filling factors of particles close to the surface [29-31]. In fact this characteristics is generally detrimental to the performances of nanocomposite systems, because of the well known effect of dipolar interactions in optics and magnetism. The plasmon resonance in the visible of Ag particles shown in figure 3 becomes broader with the increasing Ag fluence, under the combined effects of the increase in their size scattering and in their interaction [24]. In current magnetic recording media, the written bits are comprised of an ensemble of weakly interacting magnetic grains, contrarily to what is obtained in insulators implanted with high concentrations of 3d metals (chosen high in fact in order to compensate the shallow range of doping) [30,31]. The confinement of excitons in semiconductors deteriorates also with the gathering of particles.

Beside their usefullness for the charge injection in MOS structures, Si NCs are also interesting for their luminescence or for activating rare earth elements with an excited level at an energy close that of excitons in the NCs [32-35]. Once again, the criterion of quality is a narrow size distribution of the NCs, in the range of 2-3 nm, so that their gap fits the excitation energy of Er^{3+} ions from the $^4I_{15/2}$ to the $^4I_{9/2}$ state for instance. The sensitization of Er ions implanted sequentially with Si ions has been extensively studied and the results constitute a school case of the difficulty to obtain simultaneously: (i) Si clusters with suitable size, (ii) Er atoms in solid solution in the oxide instead of in silicide particles [34], (iii) but at same depth [36]. However, some useful devices seem to have been fabricated [37-39]

3.1.2. Variety of Obtained Structures and IBS Conditions

IBS has been used to create a wide variety of nanocrystals and quantum dots made of a single element or of a compound, by sequential implantation [32, 40-42]. The nature of the precipitation may depend on the implantation order [40, 43]. Implantation of 2 metals, with the aim of obtaining alloyed particles with a controled plasmon resonance energy, results for instance in the formation of core-shell particles after annealing when the 2 elements exhibit a solubility gap [43]. NCs of almost all semiconductors have been synthesized in silica, alumina and silicon [32]. The ionicity of the host affects the crystalline nature of formed phases. As an example, it is possible to produce CdS and CdSe crystals with the hexagonal wurtzite or the cubic zincblende structure in α–Al_2O_3 by modifying the implantation conditions, because this matrix is little sensitice to ballistic damaging. When implantation is carried out at moderate temperature (~600°C), dynamic annealing keeps alumina crystalline and epitaxial relationships favor the formation of NCs with the hexagonal structure. On the contrary, when implantation is carried out at low temperature (LN_2), the near surface region of alumina is amorphized. Upon annealing, the amorphous layer first crystallises with the metastable γ-Al_2O_3 cubic structure embedding NCs with same symmetry (zincblende). Particles with latter structure are formed whatever the implantation temperature in silica. Another example of structure modification correlated to the more or less efficiency of dynamic annealing is that observed during the synthesis of β-$FeSi_2$ in Si single crystals. When implanting Fe atoms in silicon at sufficiently high temperature (about 400°C), precipitates of β-$FeSi_2$ with their [100] axis aligned parallel to the [110] axis of Si are obtained [44]. Randomly oriented particles are formed when Fe is implanted at lower temperature. After further annealing at 800°C or more, the structure of the Si single crystal is restored perfectly in latter case while a large number of dislocation loops remains in the crystal containing particles in epitaxy. Taking that β-$FeSi_2$ is often mentioned as a potential candidate for the solar energy convertion, it may be worth to note that these dislocations are more luminescent than the semiconducting compound and at a close wavelength.

Implantation in channeling conditions permits to increase significantly the ion range and to limit the damaging of the host material. Connectively to the increase in the range, the implanted species undergoes less self-sputtering and is more protected against oxidation. Buried layers of $FeSi_2$ or $ErSi_2$ were grown in such conditions [45].

Rare gas atoms usually form bubbles at high fluences in all materials, which effect is at the origin of the blistering of the walls of ion guns or reactors. These cavities can be used as preferential nucleation sites of particles, formed for instance from layers evaporated thereafter on the surface and mixed by means of a further heat or irradiation treatment. Let's mention for its exotic nature the formation of cubic porosities in MgO crystals, which were used as templates for fabricating cubic Ag and Au particles in this material [46, 47].

3.2. Sputtering

3.2.1. Cleaning, Roughening of Surface for Improving Coatings

The growth of "good quality" films (adherence, homogeneity and eventually epitaxy) owes it success to an appropriate surface cleaning step prior to deposition. Among the few techniques available, sputtering is attractive for its simplicity and insensitivity to the nature of contaminants. However, the damages caused by ions can affect the epitaxy of susbsequently grown films on crystalline substrates and must be repaired by in situ thermal annealing. Technological studies show that the optimal energy of Ar ions, commonly used in sputtering experiments, for removing the native oxide and adsorbed molecules on Si substrates without extensive damaging is of 150-200 eV (while S_n is maximum at 14 keV).

3.2.2. Surface Relief Induced by the Combined Effects of Erosion and Diffusion

The stochastic nature of sputtering makes that the surface roughness would increase monotonously if this statistical effect was not balanced by the local change of ion incidence and by radiation-enhanced diffusion. Experimental studies on amorphous materials and on semiconductors (amorphized by the bombardment) show that off-normal sputtering generates a more significant relief and an anisotropic modulation of the surface. Depending on the ion incidence angle θ, the ripples can be either parallel (θ close to grazing) or perpendicular (θ close to normal) to the projection of the ion beam direction on the surface plane, while for normal incidence (θ=0) a periodic modulation of the topography is generally not observed. These results have been explained, on basis of Sigmund theory, in terms of a linear instability caused by the surface curvature dependence of the sputtering yield (formula 4), which dominates the smoothing due to the thermal surface diffusion [48]. Schematically, the top of crests is eroded faster than the bottom of trenches dug by ions at oblique incidence and the change in the ripple orientation is related to the ratio of interlayer/ superficial diffusion induced by collision cascades. On the contrary, at temperatures where thermal diffusion is noticeable, ion sputtering of single crystal metals produces features that reflect the substrate symmetry, without any relationship with the ion beam direction [49, 50]: square pits have been observed on Cu(001) and Ag(001) or hexagonal ones on Pt(111), Au(111) and Cu(111). This relief is ascribed to the coalescence of vacancies under the surface. In a critical range of temperature and ion flux, interlayer diffusion occurs along preferential directions (<110> in fcc crystals) and ripples are formed parallel to a direction of same family in the surface plane, independently of the beam orientation with respect to the normal to the surface and to <110> directions in the plane, at least for $\theta<30°$. At lower temperatures, the relief formation is controlled by erosion and depends on θ: ripples of smaller amplitude are formed as on semiconductors. The ripples with a crystalline orientation formed at intermediate temperatures find for example applications in the nano-patterning of epitaxial layers. The magnetic anisotropy of thin Co layers can be forced to be parallel to the <100> axis by modulation of the film thickness perpendicular to this direction [51].

Arrays of asperities with a conical or sinusoidal shape were observed recently at the surface of InP, GaSb, InAs and InSb sputtered at normal incidence, or at oblique incidence with simultaneous sample rotation [52]. A theory for their formation has not yet been developped. They are characterized by a uniform size distribution (around 100 nm) and a large degree of spatial ordering. They self-organize in hexagonal or square close-packed patterns, depending on the incidence angle and temperature (in the range of 280 to 330 K).

3.3. Ion Beam Assisted Deposition (Ibad)

Similar effects of diffusion occur during the vapor deposition of thin films. Adatoms diffuse faster along dense directions at moderate temperatures and interlayer diffusion takes place at high substrate temperatures. Shadowing of hollows for the atom flux plays the same role as for ions in sputtering experiments. As a result, different regimes of deposition can be distinguished as a function of the temperature, T: (i) at low T where the grains growth is controlled by the transport geometry, the coating exhibits a columnar structure and porosities; (ii) at intermediate T, the structure densifies and the columnar grains become coarser, with their axis oriented preferentially parallel to the dense packing direction; (iii) a fully dense and equiaxed structure is formed at high T [53, 54].

Now, ion beams can be used to modify this texture through the effect of ion channeling. Molecular dynamics simulations predict the preferential growth of crystals with channeling directions parallel to the beam, due to the reduced sputtering and damaging [55]. The energy stored under the form of lattice defects leads to a migration of grain boundaries, towards the most damaged grains. This effect can be used to favor the epitaxial growth of some coatings or to alter their natural growth anisotropy. For instance, an ion bombardment at normal incidence of a fcc metal film will cause a shift from a <111> texture favored by surface energy considerations to a <110> texture, because the sputtering decreases by 2 to 5 times when the beam is parallel to <110> directions of easiest channeling in fcc crystals. MgO films, which naturally grow under the form of islands with a <001> axis perpendicular to the surface, can be forced to grow with, in addition to the <001> texture, a preferential orientation of one of their <110> axes parallel to the ion beam if $\theta=45°$ [56].

The ion bombardment tends also to improve the film density and adhesion [57-59]. The adhesion improvement may be due for a part to the mixing of interfacial layers or in other cases to the formation of precipitates anchoring the coating. Indeed, huge increases of resistance to indentation cracking and wear of diamond-like carbon coatings are obtained for instance by pre-implantation of C in the substrate, having for result the formation of carbide nanoparticles, or by irradiation throughout the coating thickness (taking care to not destroy the diamond-like pilling of atoms by cascades) [60, 61].

When implantation is performed at very low energy (some 100 eV to a few keV), the concentration of implanted atoms tends progressively towards 100%, if their coefficient of self-sputtering is lower than 1. Their segregation by RED at the surface is facilitated by the shallow implantation depth when their solubility in the host material is limited. This ion beam deposition technique (IBD), shows common features with IBAD, in this respect that in both cases the structure of deposited layers is affected by erosion and diffusion effects. However, the ratio of ion/deposited atom fluxes in IBD experiments is of 1, so that outermost layers are strongly shaken and eventually frozen in an out of equilibrium state with ultimate properties. Films of pure amorphous diamond, with a proportion of sp_3 bonds larger than 80% and a hardness close to 100 GPa, were grown by this method [62,63]. There is no upper limit to their thickness (apart a reasonable implantation time) and they are found indestructible in friction tests [60].

3.4. Cluster Beams

Beside other interests which are out of the scope of this paper, the use of a cluster beam allows an easier control of the kinetic energy of atoms impinging a target than that of monoatomic ions. Indeed, the energy of cluster ions is shared betwen the atoms when they break during the collision with the target atoms. If the energy per atom is below the cohesion energy, the clusters can be deposited on the surface without destroying their structure. Nanostructured silicon films with controlled particle size obtained by cluster beam deposition (CBD) show a higher photoluminescence yield than porous silicon [64]. The proportion of sp^2 rings in C clusters is intrinsically connected to their size, so that the size selection of cluster beams permits to grow coatings with various degrees of diamond-like hybridization [65]. The formation of composite materials characterised by a monodisperse size and an homogeneous spatial distribution of particles, which constitute quality criteria for applications in opto-electronics and magnetism, were also obtained by combining CBD with an evaporation of matrix atoms [66, 67]. $B_{10}H_{14}$ clusters were used to fabricate shallow junctions (of 7 nm) in p-type Si, which cannot be obtained by atom beam implantation due to boron enhanced diffusion. [68]

3.5. Mixing

The ion beam mixing of superimposed layers of different materials under the effects of RID and RED deserves a place in the synthesis of nanostructures by the fact that the thickness of formed alloys or compounds is often nanometric (when the target is not made of multiple layers). One can put forward several advantages of using mixing instead of ion implantation for synthesizing compound layers:

- Alloying to high concentration by ion implantation is time consuming and uneconomical.
- The maximum concentration that can be reached in the surface region is generally limited by sputtering.

- Ion implantation is not well suited to obtain flat concentration profiles, even when using multi-energy implantation, and to form alloys over thicknesses larger than a few hundreds of nanometers
- Implantation also requires to make use of a different ion source in each case.

These limitations are in principle overcome by using the alternative route of ion beam mixing. A good illustration is the mixing of metal/silicon systems, which was extensively studied in the 80th because of the technological interest for the fabrication of electronic components. Making simply use of noble gas ions selected for their mass, Xe, with an energy of the order of 100 keV, about 10^{17} atoms/cm^2 can be mixed with Xe fluences as low as 10^{15}/cm^2. The indicated value of mixing yield corresponds to a silicide thickness of 20nm and in many cases the composition of the formed silicide is homogeneous, because the enhanced-diffusion of Si atoms in metals is efficient at room temperature [69-72]. In the case of a metal implantation in Si at same energy, the sputtering yield is of same order of magnitude as the implanted dose.

An advantage of mixing over fast anneal by laser or electron beams may come from the fact that ions transfer kinetic energy to target atoms without necessarily involving melting. Thus, one may expect to form metastable alloys with zero solubility in the liquid state. In fact, numerous experiments have shown that the concentrations of crystalline solid solutions formed from overimposed layers of two metals are generally extended to the detriment of intermetallic phases and the result of mixing is the formation of a metallic glass when the metals are not miscible at high T [73]. Several authors argued that in many metal-metal or metal-silicon systems mixing occurs during the thermalizing stage of the ion-solid interaction after the cascade (for a comprehensive review of models see [74]). Indeed, they estimated the mean kinetic energy of atoms during the time wherein mixing occurs to kT_{eff} = 1-2 eV, from a fit a experimental diffusion rates [75]. If this was true, there should not be much advantage over laser or electron beam heating (apart that transparent materials cannot be heated with a laser beam) since ion mixing would involve melting. However, other experiments give evidence of a dependency of the mixing rate on the temperature of the experiment or of a diffusion anisotropy which may be explained by the occurence of RED or of recoil implantation, but certainly not by thermal spikes.

Whatever the collisional regime, linear cascades, localized or global spikes all along the ion path [74], the mixing extent is correlated to the heat of alloying in most systems. This phenomenological law was verified as well for silicides [76] as for metals in covalent compounds and insulators [77]. The metal silicide formed by mixing of a single metal layer on silicon is generally the stable phase that lies near an eutectic composition and its composition is forced by the ratio of layers thicknesses in multilayers. In a regime of low displacements density (linear cascades), the mixing rate may be controlled by recoil implantation, diffusion or an interfacial reaction, according to the system. A diffusion controlled kinetics is characterized by a variation of the number of mixed atoms N and a widening of interfaces $W=\sqrt{2Dt}$ as $\phi^{1/2}$ (D being the effective diffusion coefficient and t the equivalent time, ratio of the fluence ϕ to the flux), while in the two other cases N and W vary as ϕ (examples are given in [72]).

The above mentioned enthalpy rule is of little use to predict the mixing efficiency in the most insulating materials, such as alumina, because the charged defects which are formed in the oxide are unstable, so that displaced atoms tend to move back to the interface [77, 78]. On the other hand, when insoluble metal atoms are pushed in an insulator with a sufficient velocity (by primary collisions with ions of comparable mass), they migrate over short range before precipitating under the form of nanoparticles. Taking that, when the interface energy of metal layers embedded in oxides or on their surface is high, they spheroidize under irradiation as they do during heat treatments, complex structures are obtained, made of large particles surrounded by a halo of smaller particles created by the mixing-reprecipitation process (Figure 4). Particles of noble metals with this bimodal distribution of sizes in silica exhibit a plasmon-related resonance peak in the visible which is abnormally narrow, compared to a same ensemble of particles that are apart from each other. The effect is ascribed to a screening by nanoparticles arranged in a halo around each large particle of the polarization induced by other large particles (nanoparticles contributing directly to the absorption for less than 10%). The strong dipolar interaction between particles in implantation systems of same nature has an opposite effect because of their random distribution of size and spatial arrangement [24, 79].

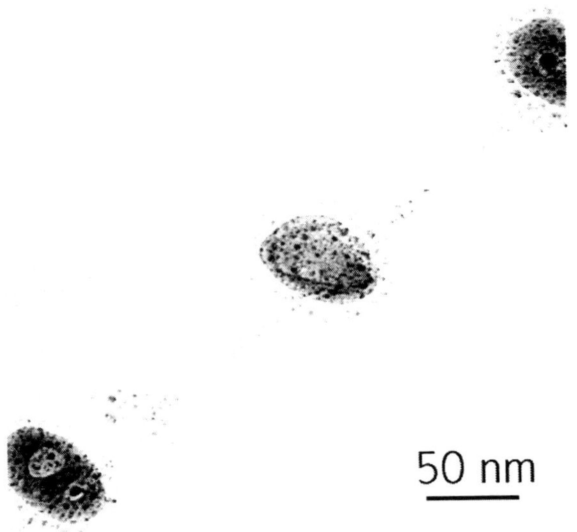

Figure 4. TEM image the cross section of a 50 nm SiO_2/ 8 nm Ag / bulk SiO_2 sample irradiated with 10^{16} Au ions/cm^2 of 4.5 MeV

3.6. Amorphization and Recrystallization

A discussion of amorphization and recrystallization mechanisms under ion irradiation may appear irrelevant in a review concerning nanostructures. It finds its justification by the fact that amorphization is the most probable change of structure in semiconductors and insulators and it proceeds from the coalescence of amorphous nuclei. This particular type of precipitation was studied first and most others obey same kinetic laws. On the other hand, the recrystallization of semiconductors after implantation treatments is a topics of major importance for applications in electronics and an understanding of the recrystallization mechanism of bulk semiconductors under irradiation (IBIEC) is needed for applying the same principles to the formation of heterostructures.

Experiments on semiconductors and metallic compounds presenting an amorphous counterpart (like Ni_3B, NiAl, NiTi) showed that amorphization can occur by two different mechanisms, depending on the energy density deposited in nuclear collisions. In the case of a displacements spike regime, amorphous clusters are formed under the impact of each ion, while the number of displacements per atom (dpa) must be accumulated until it reaches locally a critical value in a linear cascade regime. Consequently, the amorphization kinetics is a linear function of the fluence in the former case and presents a sigmoidal shape in the latter, described by the following law [80, 81]:

$$\alpha = \sum_{nc}^{\infty} P_n = \sum_{nc}^{\infty} \frac{(\sigma\phi)^n}{n!} \exp(-\sigma\phi) \qquad (7)$$

The probabililty P_n of cluster formation is proportional to that for an area of the target σ to be perturbed by n impacts and n_c is the critical number of impacts to obtain a stable nucleus. In fact σ is the cross section of damaging, product of the stopping power by its efficiency. The same law applies to many precipitation processes in regimes of nuclear or electronic stopping.

Ion implantation of high ion fluences in pure metals has also been used for synthesizing amorphous alloys, generally of same nature as those obtained by quenching from the melt but interesting for their high purity [82] . The study of amorphization kinetics has shown that the decisive parameter is the chemical ordering in the amorphous phase, which lessens the configuration energy on short range [80, 83]. At low T, where the implanted atoms are not mobile, clusters are formed where the local concentration of implanted atoms exceeds a theshold value and the amorphization kinetics obeys the Poisson law given above (equation 7). At higher T, the short range diffusion of implanted atoms favors the formation of clusters for very low concentrations of implanted atoms, so that the kinetics is a linear function of the fluence.

Epitaxial recrystallization of amorphous implantation layers may be promoted by ion irradiation at lower T than purely thermal recrystallization (called solid phase epitaxial regrowth). The ion-beam-induced epitaxial crystallization (IBIEC) is not an effect of beam heating and numerous experiments have demonstrated that only the defects which are created at the a-c interface contribute to the process [84]. Each ion produces in the vicinity of the interface the amorphization of some atoms and in the meanwhile king-like defects (along [110] ledges connecting two (111) terraces in Si). IBIEC and ion-beam-induced interfacial amorphization (IBIIA) are competing processes and the direction and rate of the a-c interface motion depend on the temperature and ion flux: (i) at low T and/or at high flux, a planar layer-by-layer amorphization occurs; (ii) IBIIA and IBIEC are in balance at a critical temperature T_r and (iii) the IBIEC rate increases above T_r. A residual amorphous layer often remains close to the surface and planar growth is blocked at too high temperatures by the formation of crystallites inside the amorphous layer [85]. Dopants such as B, P and As enhance the IBIEC rate while C, O, F produce a retardation by pinning interfacial defects. The recrystallization of implanted layers can be obtained by subsequent irradiation with an energetic ion beam having an implantation range well beyond the a-c interface or by a proper choice of implantation flux and T (self-annealing process). Beside the technological interest of IBIEC for lowering the crystallization temperature of implanted layers in Si, it found applications in the fabrication of epitaxial heterostructures [84]. The maximum thickness of strained layers free of dislocations networks is increased and the interface is more planar than by crystallization in a furnace. Higher temperatures must also be used for growing films of same composition by molecular beam epitaxy.

3.7. Patterning

A number of patterning methods have been used, for instance to obtain single magnetic domains with as small sizes as possible but exhibiting no spontaneous reversal of magnetization. The principle, when using irradiation through a mask for patterning a magnetic film, consists to create arrays of soft regions with a longitudinal magnetization in a film of higher coercivity, with a perpendicular anisotropy. However a coupling remains between strongly magnetized bits and noise in disordered regions. The ideal material is one where magnetism is either created or destroyed upon exposure to a low ions fluence. A technique consists in creating discrete islands of a magnetic phase by digging trenches with a focused ion beam (FIB) in a continuous thin film and, in addition, to poison the magnetic order in the trenches by incorporation of implanted ions or by mixing of an overcoating [86]. Collimators of diameter smaller than 100 nm are commonly available for this purpose.

Focused ion beams provide also a means to fabricate channel waveguides and laser gratings by localized mixing of semiconductors multilayers [87].

4. Electronic Effects

4.1. Radiolysis and Conversion of Polymers

Polymers are the most sensitive of all materials to radiation damaging, so that photons, electrons or ions may be used as well for promoting the crosslinking or decomposition of thin polymeric films. One of the interests of using ion beams for this purpose lies in the much higher radiolytic efficiency of ions [88-90]. The short range order in amorphous ceramic films obtained by ion irradiation is also very different from that in polymers converted into ceramics by means of other processes. Moreover, irradiation with low ion fluences permits to pattern the surface with isolated cylindrical tracks, which may thereafter be etched and filled with other materials. This use of tracks as templates is discussed in a next paragraph. Unetched tracks constitute also interesting nanostructures with particular chemical properties which will first be summarized.

4.1.1.Organic Polymers

The final product of the crosslinking process is a three-dimensional amorphous network composed principally of C, O and N atoms. The bond scission under the effect of nuclear collisions is supposed to favor the formation of a network where C atoms exhibit a high degree of sp^2 hybridization [88-91]. However, collision cascades do not affect significantly the physical properties of this network, as long as ions lose as much energy in electronic excitations than in collisions (because useful fluences are so low that few atoms are displaced). This has been shown by performing experiments with ions of energy in the range of 20 to 100 keV/nucleon on polymers with alliphatic or cyclic structures [92, 93]. The measured values of optical gap E_g (larger than 0.5 eV) and of hardness H (5 times that of turbostratic graphite) of polymer films irradiated in such conditions indicate that they exhibit a noticeable degree of diamond-like hybridization, contrarily to heat treated films. In addition, variations of E_g, H [92] and of other properties [88-90] show that the efficiency of ionizations in crosslinking the structure increases with S_e, most probably because the ability of formed radicals to combine increases.

Let's get down to tracks formed in the purely electronic stopping regime by saying that fullerenes clusters seem to be formed in the core of tracks when the electronic LET exceeds a threshold value. This fact suggests the occurence of thermal spikes since this allotrope of C is stable at high T [94-97]. In milder conditions of irradiation, phenyl rings (even in alliphatic polymers) and other types of unsaturated bonds are formed before C clusters at low fluences [98, 99]. The nature of observed moieties differs in many cases from those formed in polymers submitted to other types of ionizing radiations. They constitute grafting sites for other macromolecules or inorganic ions, which attract the interest of chemists [100]. It is also worth to note that the linearity of swift ions tracks facilitates the diffusion of dopants and tracks decorated with alcaline or halogen elements can be used as nanometric electric contacts.

4.1.2. Semi-Organic Polymers and Gels

Taking that ion irradiation of organic polymers produces carbon-rich amorphous phases (at high fluences) with more interesting physical properties than those of pyrolyzed polymers, as also with less change in the content of other elements than hydrogen, experiments were carried out on semi-organic polymers and gels . These materials made of an inorganic backbone and organic side groups are particularly useful as precursors of ceramic coatings, foams and fibers. Experiments on silicon-based polymers and gels with various ions show that, like in organic polymers, hydrogen is released selectively [101], with same kinetic laws [102], and the molecular structure is crosslinked then transformed into a glassy ceramics. Physical properties such as the density and hardness increase with same slope as a function of the transferred energy $Se\times\phi$ as do the amount of H release. Nuclear collisions appear once again to play no significant role in the conversion process and don't affect the chemical order in the fluence range useful for the conversion into ceramics.

The C content in the ceramics generally exceeds the maximum value in homogeneous glasses $SiO_{2-x}C_{x/2}$ ($x\leq 2$) and the C excess segregates in polysiloxanes with a Si-O- backbone as well as in polycarbosilanes with a Si-CH_2- backbone. Energy filtered TEM images of the C distribution in cross sections of the irradiated films put into evidence that C atoms or CH_x radicals migrate in the structure to form clusters with a diameter of 3 to 7 nm, depending on the C content and S_e value (Figure 5) [103]. In the case of phenyl-substituted precursors, clusters are also supposed to form on the spot of the radiolytic reaction [104]. C clusters are aligned along tracks or exhibit a more random distribution when ions undergo also nuclear scattering. Assuming that continuous wires may be obtained above a threshold of S_e or C concentration, they would find applications as field emission tips or electric contacts with a well defined and nanometric section. Raman analyses show that, whatever their arrangement, isolated C particles formed at low ion fluences exhibit a noticeable degree of tetragonal hybridization, while C clusters which are also formed in films of same nature by annealing in vacuum are made of turbostratic graphite. The semiconducting particles formed under irradiation emit a yellow-green luminescence, contrarily to those formed in annealed films. The PL emission wavelength and yield is the same for spherical, randomly distributed, clusters and for discontinuous cylinders obtained at high energy, for a given value of energy transfer $S_e\times\phi$. The PL peak shows a red shift and broadening with the increasing $S_e\times\phi$, ascribed to the growth of part of the clusters (in matrices where a percolation is unlikely, due to the low C excess). Rings of C atoms with a sp^2 hybridization state are known to form at the periphery of C clusters when their size increases and this graphitic state is the one stable at equilibrium (which factor explains the nature of clusters in annealed samples). Beside interesting optical properties, the tetragonal hybridization of C clusters afford irradiated films hardness 2-3 times higher than that of heat-treated films, as shown by nanoindentation tests: the hardness of irradiated polycarbosilanes reaches that of bulk SiC [101].

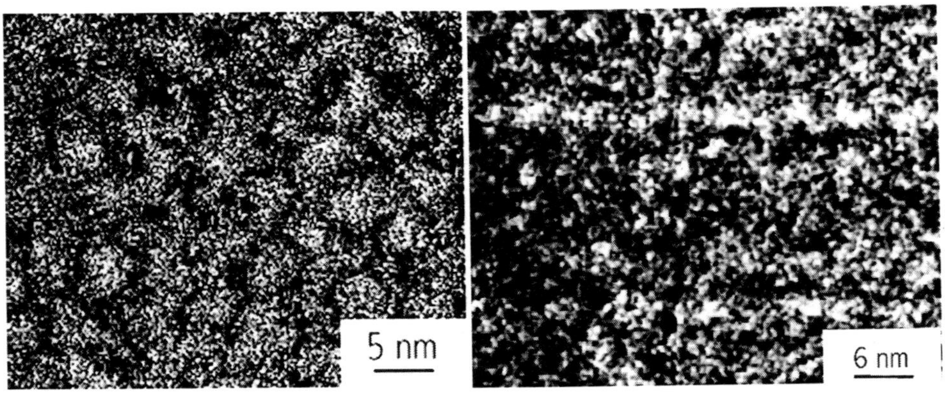

Figure 5. Energy filtered images of cross sections of methyltriethoxysilane gel films ($[Si(OH)(CH_3)-O]_n$) irradiated with 3 MeV and 100 MeV Au ions at fluences of 10^{15} and 10^{13} /cm^2 respectively [103]

Similarly to C in gels and polymers containing C in excess, Si precipitates under irradiation in the suboxide with stoichiometry $SiO_{1.5}$ derived from the triethoxysilane gel (the ethoxide precursor has for formula $SiH(OC_2H_5)_3$) and the semiconducting clusters show a red luminescence, at a wavelength which is correlated to the particles size (~1 nm) [105]. When the same gel is mixed with metal salts, SiH hydrido group react with the metal ions for forming metal nanoparticles [106]. Their distribution is relatively narrow (of Gaussian type with a standard deviation/mean size ratio of 25%) contrarily to that of particles formed in films heat-treated in vacuum. Another drawback of heat treatments is that the evolution of gases leads to the formation of ovoid porosities and the particles are segregated on the pore walls. An investigation of the precipitation kinetics, by means of electron spin resonance in the case of magnetic metals or of optical absorption for noble metals, shows that the driving force is the formation of $Si^\bullet$ free radicals under the effect of ionizations and clusters are formed when the number of neutralized metal atoms exceeds locally a threshold value for the building of a stable nucleus. The volume of metal phase therefore increases as the cumulative of a Poisson distribution function (formula 7), like that of amorphous clusters which are formed in semiconductors or metals in the ballistic regime of slowing down.

4.2. Formation of Composites and Phase Changes in other Materials

4.2.1. Demixion of out of Equilibrium Solid Solutions

Irradiation of metastable solid solutions, such as silicate glasses containing noble metals, at energies below the threshold of matrix damaging by electronic excitations, may lead to a precipitation. By varying the ratio of electronic to nuclear energy transfer, for instance via the mass of ions, it has been demonstrated that displacements contribute to the precipitation only when the dissipated power is high enough to induce a substantial target heating [107]. Otherwise the nucleation yield varies in proportion to the energy transferred to electrons $S_e \times \phi$ [108, 109]. The kinetic law of precipitation may be the cumulative of a Poisson distribution when tracks must overlap to form nuclei with a stable size [109] or a linear function of $S_e \times \phi$ when stable nuclei are very small [108]. Their size remains constant as long as the source of metal ions in solid solution is not exhausted and the clusters can be as small as 0.5 nm. Particles with such a size undergo a very high compressive stress due to their interface energy. Contractions of the order of 10% of the lattice parameter a were calculated for Ag particles in silica on basis of the observed blue shift of their plasmon resonance.

4.2.2. Growth of Particles

When pursuing the irradiation of same targets, or irradiating composites containing very few atoms of noble metal in solid solution obtained by means of another technique, a growth of the particles is observed when the energy density S_e is not too high [110]. The linear increase of the particle size with the fluence indicates that the rate controlling process is the desorption of the noble metal atoms from the surface of pre-existing particles. These desorbed atoms diffuse over a short distance and are adsorbed at another particle surface. Thus, some particles grow at the expense of others as long as the density of excitations remains low.

Above a given S_e value, in the range of 5 to 10 keV/nm, the size of same particles decreases. A detailed investigation of the density effect is still needed for defining if the critical parameter is the ratio of the desorption/adsorption rates or the threshold of matrix damaging. On the contrary, a growth of Co particles formed by ion implantation in silica has been observed when they were submitted subsequently to electronic excitations with an as high density (of about 20 keV/nm) [111]. Taking that the particles became elongated parallel to the beam direction and the density of energy transfer was 10 times larger than the threshold of silica damaging, the authors ascribed the structural transformation to a thermal spike effect. However the increasing elongation of the particles which was observed with the track overlap seems to indicate that the relaxation of energy in the transient disordered phase was so fast that a thermal equilibrium could not be reached. The occurence of Coulomb explosions or an increase in the readsorption /desorption rates ratio in the case of a particle ensemble with a very high filling factor (compared to ion exchanged glasses and other colloids studied in [110]) cannot be excluded. On a practical point of view, the Co particles elongation had for interesting effect to tilt their easy magnetization axis perpendicular to the film surface.

4.3. Latent Tracks

Since tracks in some materials can be chemically revealed, the initial damage is also called latent track. Fission fragments from nuclear accelerators are sometimes used instead of ion beam accelerators for producing tracks. Latent tracks are formed in most materials above a S_e threshold. This threshold is one order of magnitude larger in crystalline metals than in quartz and tracks have been observed only in pure metals with a low phonons frequency and exhibiting a displacive transformation (of martensitic type) such as Fe, Ti, Zr [18]. The formation threshold is also much higher in Si or Ge than in compound semiconductors and the ions must have a low velocity (together with a high stopping power, which combination is possible for cluster beams), probably because the crystalline order is more easily restored after melting of the track core when atoms are of same nature and the core diameter small. In other terms, monoatomic semiconductors of type IV are probably not amorphized as long as the rate of power dissipation dE_e/dt in the track core does not exceeds that of epitaxial reconstruction [15]. The quantity dE_e/dt may be more significant than the linear density S_e (dE_e/dR) in the modeling of transformations since these transformation depend on the lifetime of the transient disorder and on structural parameters above mentioned. The track morphology is however correlated to the magnitude of S_e. Close to the S_e threshold, the track consists of extended spherical defects. Increasing S_e leads to the percolation of these defects under the form of a discontinuous cylinder of the same radius, then to the homogenization of the damaged radius.

4.3.1. Changes in Magnetic Ordering

Latent tracks have a wide range of applications linked to their anisotropy. The radial stress in magnetic oxides leads to an anisotropic orientation of the magnetic internal field. This orientation can be parallel or perpendicular to the track axis, depending on the sign and strength of the magnetostriction effect [112-114]. The same effect is observed for magnetic colloids in an amagnetic matrix, as shown by the change in the magnetic anisotropy of iron particles embedded in a silica film after irradiation with 100 MeV Au ions in figure6. Before irradiation (spectrum labelled n.i.) the anisotropy of magnetization is determined by the shape factor (demagnetizing field) and the easy axis is parallel to the surface. After irradiation with 10^{13} Au ions/cm^2, the minimum resonance field is measured for a tilt angle φ of 90°, indicating that the easy axis is perpendicular to the surface [115].

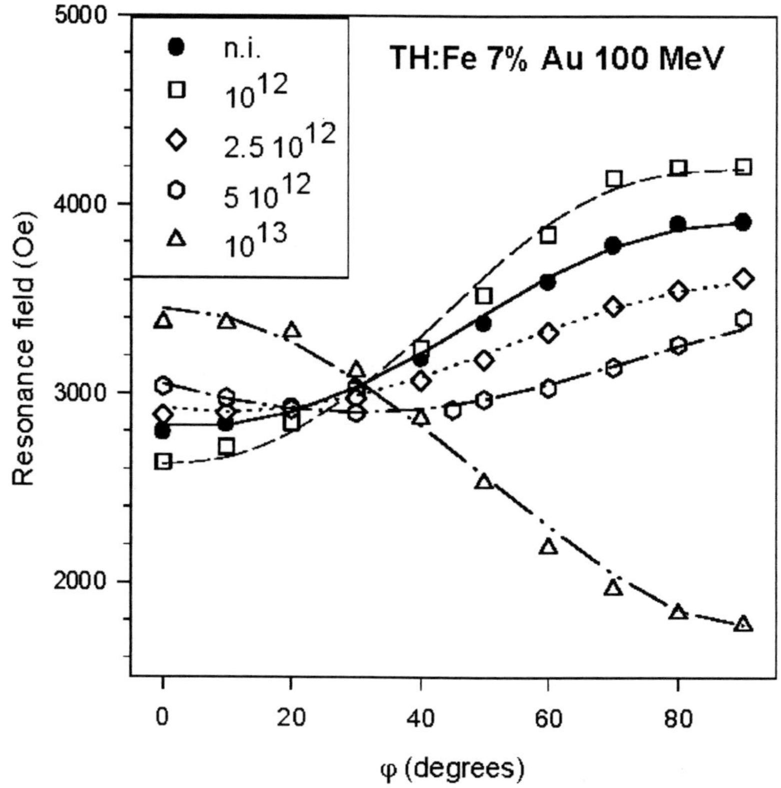

Figure 6. variation of the resonance field, in electron spin resonance experiments, as a function of the angle φ between the applied static field and the surface, for films of SiO_2:7% Fe 400 nm thick, before (n.i.) and after irradiation with 100 MeV Au ions at fluences indicated in the frame. The lines are fits

with equation: $\frac{\omega_0^2}{\gamma^2}=H_0^2=(H_{res}+H_i\cos 2\varphi)\times(H_{res}-H_i\sin^2\varphi)$,

where H_0 is the precession effective field, ω_0 the angular frequency of the cavity, γ the gyromagnetic factor and H_i the internal field, sum of the demagnetizing field and of the magnetostriction field

Paramagnetic phases may exhibit a permanent magnetization after irradiation, due to their disordering and related either to site exchanges between cations ($ZnFe_2O_4$, $NiFe_2O_4$) [116,117] or to the localization of d electrons in the amorphized structure such as in the case of YCo_2 [118]. Amorphous tracks are insulating in high T_c superconductors and, since their size is comparable to the coherence length of spins, they pin lines of magnetic flux [119], leading to an increase of the critical current by more than one order of magnitude. The pinning of walls by amorphous tracks also tends to increase the coercitivity of the matrix in other magnetic materials [120]. As well as carbon cylinders formed in polymers, conducting cylinders formed by damaging diamond like carbon film [121] may be useful as nanometric field emitters.

4.3.2. Filters and Templates

Chemical etching becomes very efficient whatever is the material when track radii are larger than 2-3 nm. To date commercial ion track membranes made of polymers, crystalline insulators (micas) and glasses with calibrated pore diameters between 15 nm and several μm are available [122, 123]. Research activities aim at even smaller pore opening (around 2 nm). They find many applications as biosensors, filters for controlling drug delivery on wounds [123] or filters with pores sizes changing as a function of the external conditions, T and P (intelligent materials) .

Using electrochemical or electroless deposition, pores can be filled with metals or semiconductors in order to fabricate micro or nanometric needles, wires or tubes [122, 124-133] (Figure 7). This replication technique is very simple and the wires or tubes can be removed from the membranes (by chemical etching or using a scotch tape) or used as an ensemble protuding from the membrane surface as the bristles of a brush. The template synthesis requires very low ion fluences (of the order of 10^6 to $10^8/cm^2$). Nanostructures with extraordinary low and monodisperse diameters are obtained, which are difficult to manufacture using lithographic techniques. In the case of galvanic deposition, one has control over the filled length of the pores and can fabricate axially structured wires, consisting for instance of Co/Cu multilayers with a giant magnetoresistance perpendicular to the membrane plane [133] or of Cu/Se resonant tunneling diodes [129]. Radially structured tubes and wires can also be fabricated by electrochemical or electroless deposition with a catalyst on the pores walls. CdSe/CdTe nanodiode arrays obtained by this technique act as retinal photocells, resembling those in the human eye [127]. Metal tubes may be used as microchannel plates or anodes in batteries.

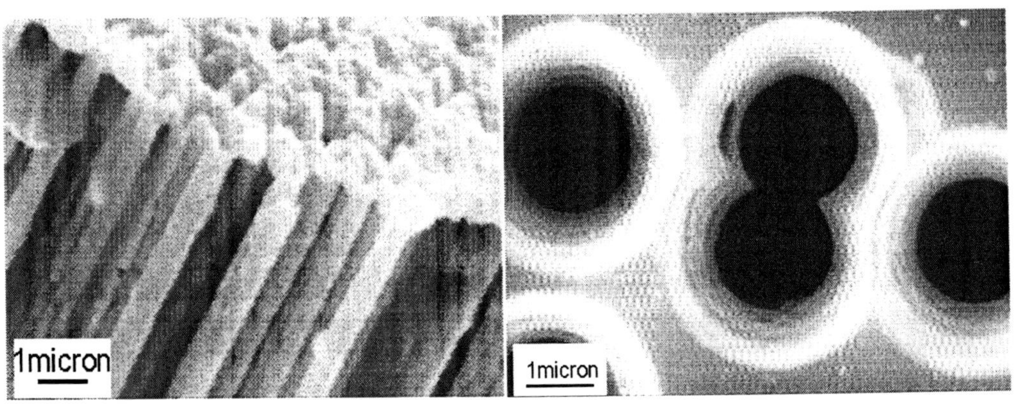

Figure 7. example of structure obtained by filling tracks with a metal: left Ag nanowires and right Cu-Ni concentric tubes , by courtesy D. Fink [127, 128]

5. CONCLUSION

During their very short passing through the target, ions induce stochastic atoms displacements and/or electronic excitations within tubular tracks of nanometric radius, depending on their velocity. The two processes of energy transfer may lead to a redistribution of atomic species and structural transformations by mechanisms involving either solid state diffusion or relaxation of kinetic energy in a liquid-like, of short life, phase.

Ballistic effects are localized within a given depth range and the displacements density can be varied by means of the ion mass and velocity. In addition, other parameters such as the damaging resistance of the matrix, epitaxy relationships, ion channeling, ion flux and irradiation temperature may be used to modify the dynamic annealing of damage. Provided that these irradiation conditions are judiciously chosen, on basis of empirical studies and Monte Carlo dynamic simulations, the nature and the nucleation and growth rate of nanoparticles synthesized by ion implantation can be predicted and controlled. Ion beam mixing of heterostructures constitutes an interesting alternative for getting rid of implantation physical limitations (sputtering, depth gradients) and for decreasing the ion fluences needed to obtain compound layers and colloids. One can also take advantage of the crystallographic anisotropy of atomic displacements and sputtering for modifying the surface topography and the texture of PVD films.

Electronic excitations in swift ion tracks permit to localize the energy deposition along the transverse direction (with respect to ballistic interactions) and the electron-lattice coupling to create cylindrical structures. Some are obtained directly through the migration of radicals and secondary ions in materials particularly sensitive to electronic excitations, such as polymers and out of equilibrium solid solutions in insulators. Atomic rearrangements during the lattice relaxation produce also changes of density or crystalline structure with interesting effects on the magnetization anisotropy of thin films. Finally, latent tracks can be easily etched in many materials to obtain pore filters and templates for the fabrication of nanowires and tubes of various natures by a chemical deposition process. This use of tracks is particularly attracting for the extraordinarily low and monodisperse diameter of the pores and for their controlled density.

A large variety of planar or cylindrical structures have been synthesized by using ion beams, with applications as waveguides, nanodiode arrays, magnetic memories, electric contacts, field emitters, transparent metallic structures, gas sensors and separators, mimics of biological systems.

6. References

[1] J. F. Ziegler, J. P.Biersack, , and U. Littmark, *The stopping and Range of Ions in Solids*, ed. J.F. Ziegler, (Pergamon Press, New York, 1985)

[2] J.W. Mayer, E. Rimini, *Ion Beam Handbook for Material Analysis*, , (Academic Press, New York, 1977).

[3] W.K. Chu, in *Materials Chacracterization Using Ion Beams* , eds. J.P. Thomas and A. Cachard , (1976) , p 3

[4] P. Sigmund and C. J. Claussen, *Appl. Phys*. 52(1981) 990

[5] Z.G. Wang, C. Dufour, E. Paumier, and M J. Toulemonde, *Phys. Condens. Matter*. 6(1994) 6733

[6] P. Sigmund, *Rad Effects* 1 (1969) 15

[7] P. Sigmund, and A. Gras-Marti, *Nucl. Instr. and Methods* 182-183(1981) 25.

[8] J.C. Pivin, and J.P. Riviere, in *Compte Rendus Congres National Société Française de Physique*, (les Editions de Physique1985), p 199.

[9] R.C. Piller and A.D. Marwick, *J. Nucl. Mat.* 83 (1979) 42

[10] R.C. Piller and A.D. Marwick, *Rad. Effects* 47 (1980) 195

[11] P. Sigmund, *Phys. Rev.* 184 (1969) 383

[12] J.C. Pivin, *J. Mat. Sci.*, 18 (1983) 1267 .

[13] R. Behrisch, *Sputtering by Particle Bombardment*, (Springer Verlag, Heidelberg,1981).

[14] Meftah, F. Brusard, J.M. Constantini, M. Hage-Ali, J.P. Stoquert, F. Studert and M. Toulemonde, *Phys. Rev. B48* (1993) 920.

[15] L.T. Chadderton, *Rad Measurements* 36 (2003) 13

[16] M. Levalois, and P. Marie, *Nucl; Instr. and Meth.* B156 (1999) 64

[17] J. Wiesner, C. Traeholt, J.G. Wen, H.W. Zandbergen, G. Wirth and H. Fuess, *Physica C* 268 (1996) 161.

[18] D. Lesueur, and A. Dunlop, *Rad Effects* 126 (1993) 163

[19] R.L. Fleischer,.P.B. Brice, and R.M. Walker, *J. Appl. Phys.* 36 (1965) 3645

[20] Z.G. Wang, C. Dufour, E. Paumier, and M. Toulemonde, *J. Phys. Condens. Matter.* 6 (1995) 2525

[21] M. Toulemonde, C. Trautmann, E. Balanzat, K. Hjort, and A. Weidinger, *Nucl; Instr. and Meth. in Phys. Res.* B216 (2004) 1.

[22] F. Beneu, *Nucl. Instr. and Meth. in Phys. Res.* B141 (1998) 241

[23] Audouard, R. Mamy, M. Toulemonde, G. Szenes, and L. Thomé, *Europhys Lett.* 40 (1997) 557

[24] J.C. Pivin, M.A. Garcia, J. Llopis, and H. Hofmeister, *Nucl. Instr. and Meth. in Phys. Res.* B 191 (2002) 794

[25] P. Mazzoldi , L. Tramontin , A. Boscolo-Boscoletto, G., Battaglin, , and G.W. Arnold, *Nucl. Instr. and Meth. in Phys. Research* B80/81 (1993) 1192

[26] W. Möller and W. Eckstein, *Nucl. Instr. and Meth.* B 2 (1984) 814

[27] T. Müller, K.H. Heinig and W. Möller,. *Appl. Phys. Lett.* 81 (2002) 3049

[28] P. Normand , E. Kapetanakis and P. Dimitrakis, *Nucl. Instr. and Meth. in Phys. Res.* B216 (2004) 355.

[29] N. Kishimoto, Y. Takeda, M. Umeda , V.T. Gritsyna, C.G. Lee, and T. Saito, *Nucl. Instr. and Meth. in Phys. Res.* B 166-167 (2000) 840

[30] T. Isobe, S.Y. Park, R.A. Weeks, and R.A. Zuhr, *J. Non-Crystal. Solids* 189 (1995) 173

[31] R.I. Khaibullin, V.N. Popok, V.V. Bazarov, E.P. Zheglov, B.Z. Rameev, C. Okay, L.R. Tagirov, and B. Aktas, *Nucl.Instr. and Meth. in Phys. Res.* B 191 (2002) 810

[32] C.W. White , J.D. Budai, S.P. Withrow, J.G. Zhu, E. Sonder, R.A. Zuhr, A. Meldrum, D.M. Hembree, D.O. Henderson, and S.Prawer, *Nucl. Instr. and Meth. in Phys. Res.* B 141 (1998) 228

[33] P.G. Kik, and A. Polman, *J. Appl. Phys.* 88 (2000) 1992

[34] J.C. Pivin, M. Jimenez de Castro, H. Hofmeister and M. Sendova-Vassileva, *Mat. Sci. Engineer.* B97 (2003) 13

[35] D.I. Tetelbaum, O.N. Gorshkov A.P. Kasatkin, V.A. Burdov, S.A. Trushin, A.N. Mikhaylov, and D.M. Gaponova, *Surf. Coat. Technol.* 158-159 (2002) 1

[36] M.L. Brongersma, A. Polman, K.S. Min, , and H.A. Atwater, *J. Appl. Phys.* 86 (1999) 759

[37] P.G. Kik and A. Polman, *J Appl Phys.* 91 (2002) 534

[38] G. Franzo, F. Iacona, V.Vincigueiro and F. Priolo, *Mat.Sci. Engineer.* B69 (2000) 335

[39] Garrido, M. Lopez, A. Perez-Rodiguez, C. Garcia, P. Pellegrino, R. Ferre, J.A.Z.Moreno, J.R. Morante, C. Bonafos, M. Carrada, A. Claverie, J. de la Torre and A. Souifi, *Nucl. Instr. and Meth. in Phys. Res.* B216 (2004) 213.

[40] Ila, *Nucl. Instr. and Meth.* B 141 (1998) 289

[41] S. Nakao, *Nucl. Instr. and Meth. in Phys. Res.* B 141 (1998) 246

[42] G. Battaglin, *Nucl. Instr. and Meth. in Phys. Research* B141 (1998) 252 and 274

[43] G. Battaglin, E. Cattaruzza, C. de Julian Fernandez, G. De Marchi, F. Gonella, G. Mattei, P. Maurizio, A. Miotello, C. Sada, and F. D'Acapito, *Nucl. Instr. and Meth. in Phys. Res.* B175-177 (2001) 410

[44] Y. Gao, S.P. Wong, W.Y. Cheung, G. Shao, and K. P. Homewood, *Nucl. Instr. and Meth. in Phys. Res.* B 206 (2003) 317

[45] Vantomme, *Nucl. Instr. and Meth. in Phys. Res.* B120 (1996) 190

[46] M.A. Van Huis, A.V. Fedorov, A. van Veen , P.J.M. Smulders, B.J. Kooi and De J.T.M. Hosson, *Nucl. Instr. and Meth. in Phys. Res.* B 166-167 (2000) 225

[47] M.A. Van Huis, A.V. Fedorov , A. van Veen , C.V. Falub , S.W.H. Eijt , B.J. Kooi , J.T.M. De Hosson , T. Hibma , and R.L. Zimmerman, *Nucl. Instr. and Meth. in Phys. Res.* B 191 (2002) 442

[48] R. Cuerno, H. A. Makse, S. Tomassone, S. T.Harrington and H. E. Stanley, *Phys. Rev. Lett.* 75 (1995) 4464

[49] S. Rusponi, C. Boragno and U. Valbusa, *Phys. Rev. Lett.* 78 (1997) 2795.

[50] S. Rusponi, G. Costantini, C. Boragno, and U. Valbusa, *Phys Rev. Lett.* 81 (1998) 2735

[51] Sekiba, R. Moroni, G. Gonella, F. Buatier de Mongeot, C. Boragno, L. Mattera and U. Valbusa, *Appl. Phys. Lett.* 84 (2004) 762

[52] Frost, B. Ziberi, T. Höche, and B. Rauschenbach, *Nucl. Instr. and Meth. in Phys. Res.* B216 (2004) 9

[53] J.A. Thornton, J. *Vac. Sci. Technol.* 11 (1974) 866.

[54] K.H. Müller, *J. Appl. Phys.* 58 (1985) 2573.

[55] L. Dong, D.J. Srolovitz, *J. Appl. Phys.* 84 (1998) 5261

[56] L. Dong, L.A. Zepeda-Ruiz, and D.J.Srolovitz, *J. Appl. Phys.* 89 (2001) 4105

[57] M. Ektessabi, *Nucl. Instr. Meth. in Phys. Res.* B 127/128 (1997) 1008

[58] A. Schmidt, *Int. Mater. Rev.* 35 (1990) 61

[59] J.E. Greene, S.A. Barnett, J.E. Sundgreen, A. Rockett, in *Ion Beam Assited Film Growth* ed. T. Itoh, , (Elsevier, 1989), pp 101

[60] J.C. Pivin, *J. Mat. Sci.* 27 (1992) 6735.

[61] J.C. Pivin, and T.J. Lee, *Nuc. Instr. and Meth. in Phys. Res.* B80-81 (1998) 1499

[62] J.C. Pivin, M. Allouard and G. Rotureau, *Surf. and Coat. Technol.*47 (1991) 433

[63] S.N. Shamin, J.C. Pivin, and E.Z. Kurmaev, *J. Appl. Phys.* 73 (1993) 4605

[64] Perez , P.Melinon, , and V. Dupuis, *J. Phys. D: Appl. Phys.* 30(1997) 709

[65] P. Milani, A. Podesta, and P. Piseri, *Diamond and Rel. Mat.* 10 .(2001) 240

[66] J.M. Meldrim, Y. Qiang, Y. Liu, H. Haberland, D.J. Sellmyer, *J. Appl. Phys.* . 87.(2000)7013

[67] Dupuis, V. Tuaillon, B. Prevel, A. Perez, and P Z. Melinon, *Phys.* D 40 (1997) 155

[68] Yamada Matsuo, *J. Mat. Sci. Semicond. Proc.* 1 (1998) 27

[69] S.S. Lau, B.X. Liu, and M.A. Nicolet, *Nucl. Instr. and Meth.* 209-210 (1983) 97

[70] J.W. Mayer, B.Y. Tsaur, S.S. Liau, and L.S. Hung, *Nucl. Instr. and Meth.* 182-183 (1981) 1

[71] D.L. Santos, J.P. de Souza, L. Amaral, and H. Boudinov, *Nucl. Instr. and Meth. in Phys. Res.* B103 (1995) 56

[72] J.C. Pivin, D. Dimova-Malinovska, M. Sendova-Vassileva, and M. Nikolaeva, *Nucl. Instr. and Meth. in Phys. Res.* B174 (2001) 453

[73] R.J. Gaboriaux, and M.A. Nicolet, *Ann. Phys. Fr.* 8 (1983) 563

[74] D. Averbach, *Nucl. Instr. and Meth. in Phys. Res.* B 15 (1996) 675

[75] Y.T. Cheng, *Matter. Sci. Rep.* 5 (1990) 45

[76] S.S. Lau, B.X. Liu and M.A. Nicolet, *Nucl. Instr. and Meth. in Phys. Res.* 209-210 (1982) 125

[77] C.J. McHargue, D.L. Joslin, and C.W. White, *Nucl. Instr. and Meth. in Phys. Res* B91 (1994) 549

[78] J.C. Pivin, *Mater. Sci. Engineer.* A293 (2000) 30

[79] J.C. Pivin, M.A. Garcia, H. Hofmeister, A. Martucci, , M. Sendova-Vassileva, M. Nikolaeva, O. Kaitasov, , and J. Llopis, *European Physical Journal* D 20 (2002) 251.

[80] Cohen, A. Benyagoub, H. Bernas, J. Chaumont, L. Thomé, M. Berti and A.V. Drigo, *Phys. Rev.* B31 (1986) 5

[81] J.F. Gibbons, Proc. *IEEE* 60 (1972) 1062

[82] J.C. Pivin, *Ann. Chim. Fr.* 11 (1985) 45

[83] L. Thomé, F. Pons, J.C. Pivin, and C. Cohen, *Nucl. Instr. Meth. in Phys. Res.* B 15 (1986) 269

[84] Priolo and E. Rimini, *Mat. Sci. Reports* 5 (1990) 319

[85] E. Glaser, T. Bachmann, R. Sculz, S. Schippel, and U. Richter, *Nucl. Instr. and Meth. in Phys. Res.* B 106 (1995) 281

[86] J. Lohau, A. Moser, C.T. Retner, M.E. Best, and B.D. Terris, *Appl. Phys. Lett.* 78 (2001) 990

[87] P. Chen, A.J. Steckl, *J. Appl. Phys.* 77 (1995) 5616

[88] J. Davenas, *Solid State Commun.* 30-31 (1993) 317

[89] T. Venkatesan, L. Calcagno, B.S. Elman and G. Foti, in *Ion Beam Modification of Insulators* eds. P. Mazzoldi and G.W. Arnold, (Elsevier, Amsterdam, 1987), pp 301

[90] T. Venkatesan, *Nucl. Instr. and Meth.* B7-8 (1985) 461.

[91] E.H. Lee, G.R. Rao, M.B. Lewis, and L.K. Mansur, *J. Mat. Res.* 9 (1994) 1043

[92] J.C. Pivin, P. Viel, G. Zalczer, and G. Marletta, *Nucl. Instr. and Meth. in Phys. Res.* B105 (1995) 185

[93] J.C. Pivin, *Thin Solid Films* 263 (1995) 185

[94] L.T. Chadderton, D. Fink, H.J. Möcker, K.K. Dwivedi, and A. Hammoudi, *Rad. Eff. and Def. in Solids* 127 (1993) 163

[95] Fink, M. Mueller, L.T. Chadderton, P.H. Canning D.C. Ellinman, and D.C. McDonald, *Nucl. Instr. and Meth. in Phys. Res.* B32 (1988) 125

[96] J. Davenas, G. Boiteaux, X.L. Xu , and E. Aden, *Nucl. Instr. and Meth. in Phys. Res.* B32 (1988) 136

[97] Y.Q. Wang, R.E. Giedd, and L.B. Bridwell, *Nucl. Instr. and Meth. in Phys. Res.* B79 (1993) 659

[98] Balanzat, M. Betz, and S. Bouffard, *Nucl. Instr. and Meth. in Phys. Res.* 105 (1995) 46

[99] Marletta, F. Iacona and A. Toth, *Macromolecules* 25 (1992) 319

[100] N. Betz, *Nucl. Instr. and Meth. in Phys. Res.* 105 (1995) 55

[101] J.C. Pivin, and P. Colombo *J. Mat. Sci.* 32 (1997) 6163 and 6175

[102] S.K. Srivastava, D.K. Avasthi and J.C. Pivin, *Nucl. Instr. and Meth.* B 191 (2002) 7185

[103] J.C. Pivin, E. Pippel , J. Woltersdorf, D.K. Avasthi, S.K. Srivastava, Z. *Metallkd.* 92 (2001) 7

[104] J.C. Pivin, P. Colombo and G.D. Soraru, *J. Am. Ceram. Soc.* 83 (2000) 713

[105] J.C. Pivin, P. Colombo, A. Martucci, G.D. Soraru, E. Pippel, and M. Sendova-Vassileva, *J. Sol-Gel Sci. and Technol.* 26 (2003) 251

[106] J.C. Pivin, *Nucl. Instr. and Meth. in Phys. Res.* B216 (2004) 239

[107] G. De Marchi, F. Gonella, P. Mazzoldi, G. Battaglin, E.J. Knytautas, and C. Meneghini, *J. Non-Cryst. Solids* 196 (1996) 79

[108] J.C. Pivin, G. Roger, M.A. Garcia, F. Singh and D.K. Avasthi, *Nucl. Instr. and Meth. in Phys. Res.* B 215 (2004) 373.

[109] Valentin, H. Bernas, C. Ricolleau, and F. Creuset, *Phys. Rev. Lett.* 86 (2001) 99

[110] J.C. Pivin, *Nucl. Instr. and Meth. in Phys. Res.* B195 (2002) 302

[111] D'Orleans, J.P. Stoquert, C. Estournès, C. Cerutti, J.J. Grob, J. L. Guille, F. Haas, D. Muller and M. Richard-Plouet, *Phys. Rev.* B67 (2003) 220101

[112] M. Toulemonde, G. Fuchs, N. Nguyen, F. Studer, D. Groult Phys. Rev. B 35 (1987) 6560

[113] Fnidiki and H. Pascard, *Eur. Phys. J.* B 24 (2001) 291

[114] S. Meillon, F. Studer, M. Hervieu, and H. Pascard, *Nucl. Instr. and Meth. in Phys. Res.* B107 (1996) 363

[115] J.C. Pivin, S. Esnouf, D.K. Avasthi, *Nucl Instr. and Meth.*, submitted for publication

[116] Dogra, M. Singh , N. Kumar, P. Sen and R. Kumar, *Nucl. Instr. and Methods in Phys. Res.* 212 (2003) 190

[117] Studer, C. Houpert, D. Groult, J.Y. Fan, A. Meftah and M. Toulemonde, *Nucl. Instr. and Meth. in Phys. Res.* B82 (1993) 91

[118] M. Ghidini, J. P. Nozières, D. Givord , and B. J. Gervais, *Magn. and Magn. Mat.* 140-144 (1995) 483

[119] Wiesner, C. Traeholt, J. G. Wen, H. W. Zandbergen, G. Wirth , and H. Fuess, *Physica* C268 (1996) 161

[120] N.M. Dempsey, *Phys Rev Lett* 81-25 (1998) 5652

[121] Krauser, J.H. Zollondz, A. Weidinger, and C.Trautmann, *J. Appl. Phys.* 94 (2003) 1959

[122] R. Spohr, in *Ion Tracks and Microtechnology. Basic Principles and Applicatio*ns ed. K. Bethge, (Vieweg ,1990)

[123] D.K. Avasthi, *Current Science* 78 (2000) 1299

[124] E. Ferain, and R. Legras, *Nucl. Instr. Meth. in Phys. Res.* B174 (2001) 116

[125] M. E. Toimil Molares, E. M. Hohberger, C. Schaeflein, R. H. Blick, R. Neumann, and C. Trautmann, *Appl. Phys. Lett.* 82 (2003) 2139

[126] S.K. Chakarvati, and J. Vetter, *J. Rad. Measur.* 29 (1998) 149.

[127] Fink, *J. Phys.* 25 (1995) 54

[128] Fink, *Rad. Eff. and Def. in Solids* 140 (1997) 263

[129] Biswas, D.K. Avasthi, B. K. Singh, . S. Lotha, J.P. Singh, D. Fink, B.K. Yadav, B. Bhattacharya, and S.K. Bose, *Nucl. Instr. and Meth. in Phys. Res.* B 151 (1999) 84.

[130] Vetter, and D. Dobrev, *Nucl. Instr and Meth. in Phys. Res.* B62 (1999) 109

[131] M.S. Gudiksen, J. Wang, and C.M. Lieber, *J. Phys. Chem.* B106 (2002) 4036

[132] J.D. Klein, R.D. Herrick, D. Palmer, M.J. Sailor, C.J. Brumlik, and C.R. Martin, *Chem. of Mat.* 5 (1993) 902

[133] Piraux, J. M. George, J. F. Despres, C. Leroy, E. Ferain, R. Legras, K. Ounadjela and A. Fert , *Appl. Phys. Lett.* 65 (1994) 2484.

APPENDIX : BASIC FORMULA OF ION STOPPING

1- The energies of recoil E_2 and scattered particle E_1 after an elastic collision in laboratory frame are given by following formula:

$$E_2 = \frac{4M_1M_2}{(M_1+M_2)^2} E_0 \cos^2\zeta = \gamma E_0 \cos^2\zeta \tag{8}$$

$$E_1 = \frac{M_1^2}{(M_1+M_2)^2}\left[\cos\psi + \left(\frac{M_2}{M_1}\right)^2 - \sin^2\psi\right]^2 E_0 \tag{9}$$

$$\sin\zeta = \left(\frac{M_1E_1}{M_2E_2}\right)^{1/2} \sin\psi \tag{10}$$

where ζ is the recoil angle and ψ the scattering of the projectile The scattering factor k, useful for instance in Rutherford backscattering formula, is defined as the ratio of E_1/E_0 and E_2=(1-k)E_0

2-Calculation of the nuclear scattering cross section:

Assuming that the force between the 2 particles act only along the line joining them, the use of center of mass (CM) coordinates reduces the problem to a one-body problem, namely the interaction of a particle with mass M_{CM} (or μ) and velocity v_{CM} with a static potential field V(r) centered at the origin of the CM coordinates. This is because the total linear momentum of the particles is always zero in this frame.

$$\frac{1}{\mu} = \frac{1}{M_1} + \frac{1}{M_2} \tag{11}$$

$$E_{CM} = \frac{1}{2}\mu v_0^2 = E_0 \frac{M_2}{M_1+M_2} \tag{12}$$

The scattering angle of the projectile in this frame is a function of the impact parameter p (projected offset of the original path of the projectile (1) from the atom at rest (2)):

$$\theta = \pi - 2\int_{r_{min}}^{\infty} \frac{p\,dr}{r^2\left[1 - \frac{V(r)}{E_{CM}} - \frac{p^2}{r^2}\right]^{1/2}} \tag{13}$$

The transferred energy E_2, also noted T, is equal to :

$$T = \gamma E_0 \sin^2 \frac{\theta}{2} \tag{14}$$

The choice of a proper interaction potential V(r) during the collision is needed for calculating values of θ(p) and T(p) used in transport equations or Monte Carlo simulations of ion impacts and the value of energy transferred per unit length of the ion path, S_n, averaged over all impact parameters p. This potential is of the form:

$$V(r) = \frac{Z_1 Z_2 e}{r} \Phi(\frac{r}{a}) \tag{15}$$

where Φ(r) is a screening function and a is a characteristic screening lenght . The unscreened potential of Rutherford collisions is valid for short r (energetic collisions). The earliest screening functions proposed by Bohr and Thomas-Fermi are:

$$\Phi_B = \exp(-x) \qquad \text{and } \Phi_{TF} = [1+(\frac{x^3}{144})^{1/3}]^{-2.4} \tag{16}$$

x being a reduced approach radius =r/a , with

$$a_B = \frac{a_0}{Z} = \frac{\hbar^2}{me^2}\frac{1}{Z} \text{ and } a_{TF} = \frac{1}{2}(\frac{3\pi}{4})^{2/3} a_0 \frac{1}{Z} \tag{17}$$

In these expressions Z is the charge of the quasi-molecule formed during the overlap of electron shells and a_0 (0.0528 nm) is the Bohr radius. Different averaging were proposed by Bohr and Thomas-Fermi:

$$Z_B = (Z_1^{2/3} + Z_2^{2/3})^{1/2} \text{ and } Z_{TF} = (Z_1^{1/2} + Z_2^{1/2})^{2/3} \tag{18}$$

Lindhard used the a_{TF} expression with the Bohr equation for Z. On basis of Hartree-Fock-Slater calculations for a large number of quasi molecules, a universal potential is now used in most calculations:

$$\Phi_u = 0.1818\, e^{-3.2x} + 05099\, e^{-0.9423x} + 0.2802\, e^{-0.4028x} + 0.0282\, e^{-0.202x} \tag{19}$$

$$\text{with } a_u = \frac{0.8854\, a_0}{(Z_1^{0.23} + Z_2^{0.23})} \tag{20}$$

For being able to give universal expressions of the scattering angle θ as a function of the impact parameter p, it is useful to normalize p to a, as also the center of mass energy E_{CM} and the range R of the projectile:

b=p/a, (21a)

$$\varepsilon = E_{CM}\frac{a}{(Z_1 Z_2 e^2)} \quad (21b)$$

$$\rho = \quad N\,\pi\, a_U^2\, \gamma\, R_{..} \quad (21c)$$

N being the atomic density. Finally, the nuclear stopping power (energy lossed by the projectile per unit depth in nuclear collisions), $S_n(\varepsilon)$, is the integrated product of the transferred energy $T(E_0, p)$ in each collision by the probability $d\sigma(p)$ for a collision with an impact parameter p. σ is the impact cross section πp^2:

$$S_n(E_0) = \int_0^{\infty} T d\sigma = \int_0^{\infty} T(E_0, p)\, 2\pi p\, dp = 2\pi\, T_{max}\, E_0 \int_0^{p\,max} \sin^2\frac{\theta}{2}\, p\, dp \quad (22a)$$

or in reduced units:

$$S_n(\varepsilon) = \varepsilon \int_0^{\infty} \sin^2\frac{\theta}{2}\, d(b^2) \quad (22b)$$

Calculations with the universal potential were fitted by an analytic expression with the form:

$$S_n(\varepsilon) = \frac{Ln(a + b\varepsilon}{2(\varepsilon + c\varepsilon^{d} + e\varepsilon^{0.5})} \quad (23)$$

in which a=1, b=1.14, c=0.01, d=0.21, e=0.20 for ε<30, a=0, b=1.0, c=d=e=0 for ε>30 (i.e. case of unscreened stopping)

3- Calculation of the electronic stopping power S_e(ε or E):

The earliest expression proposed in the 1930's for the energy loss per unit lenght of slow particles in an electron plasma is the product of the ion velocity, v, by the cube root of the electronic density of the medium, N_e. Lindhard introduced a stopping interaction function I (v,N_e) taking into account local density fluctuation of ρ_e and the perturbation of this density by the ion (individual and collective excitations):

$$S_e = \int I(v, \rho_e)\, Z_1^2\, N_e \quad dV \quad (24)$$

V being the volume of each element of the target. S is a flat function when the ion is going much faster than the mean electron density and it decreases almost linearly with N_e when $v<v_F$, $v_F$being the Fermy velocity:

$$v_F = \left(\frac{\hbar}{m_e}\right)(3\pi^2 N_e)^{1/3} \quad (25)$$

Low velocity ions are neutralized when penetrating in the target and their stopping power is:

$$S_e = 8\pi N e^2 a_0 Z_1^{1/6} \frac{Z_1 Z_2}{(Z_1^{2/3} + Z_2^{2/3})^{3/2}} \frac{v_0}{v_B} \quad (26)$$

which is proportional to $N_e^{1/3}$ as v_0. High velocity ions ares stripped of all electrons whose classical orbital velocities are less than the ion velocity. Their effective charge is γZ_1 with:

$$\gamma = 1 - \exp - \frac{v_0}{v_B Z_1^{2/3}} \quad (27)$$

where v_B is the Bohr velocity of H electrons. For $v_0 >> v_B Z_1^{2/3}$, S_e is proportional to $1/E_0$ and Z_2. The Bethe expression for S_e corrected for the partial stripping of electrons at intermediate energies and for the change of density and mass at relativistic energies is:

$$S_e = \frac{4\pi Z_2 Z_1^2 e^4}{m_e v_0^2} \left[\mathrm{Ln}\left(\frac{2 m_e v_0^2}{I}\right) - \mathrm{Ln}\left(1 - \frac{v_0^2}{c^2}\right) - \frac{v_0^2}{c^2} - \frac{c}{Z_2} - \frac{\delta}{2} \right] \quad (28)$$

with a mean ionization and excitation energy I of target atoms: $I \approx 10 eV \times Z_2$

In: Nanomaterials: New Research
Editor: B.M. Caruta, pp. 115-128
ISBN: 1-59454-369-0

Chapter 3

NANOSTRUCTURED SnO_2: TiO_2 COMPOSITE AND BILAYERED THIN FILMS: HUMIDITY SENSOR

Weon-Pil Tai
Institute of Advanced Materials, Inha University,
Yonghyun-dong, Nam-ku, Inchon 402-751, South Korea

ABSTRACT

The nanostructured SnO_2:TiO_2 composite and bilayered thin films are prepared using a sol-gel process by spin coating onto the alumina substrate and the humidity sensitive properties of the films are investigated. The nanostructured films possess the grain size of nanometer order and have porous structures with capillary nanopores. The nanostructured films facilitate the adsorption of water vapors due to the large surface area and capillary nanopores. The TiO_2-20 wt.% SnO_2 composite film shows high sensitivity over three orders change in the resistance during the relative humidity variation from 30 to 90%. The SnO_2/TiO_2 bilayered film exhibits a better linearity with narrower hysteresis loop in the resistance variation for relative humidity than the SnO_2 and TiO_2 monolayered films. The humidity sensing properties in the nanostructured SnO_2:TiO_2 composite and bilayered films are discussed.

1. INTRODUCTION

Humidity sensors have found increasing application with the advancement of automation systems. Materials as humidity sensors include ceramic, polymer and composite. The ceramic humidity sensors based on porous and sintered oxides compared with other materials have received much attention due to their chemical and physical stability [1-4]. Furthermore, the humidity sensors of thin film types having the nano-sized grains and nanoporous structure have attracted considerable interest because the miniaturization of the sensing devices is possible [5, 6]. Nanostructured films are optimal candidates for humidity sensing because of the high surface area of sensing element that facilitates the adsorption of water molecules.

SnO_2 and TiO_2 thin films have been fabricated using a variety of techniques, such as, sputtering [7], chemical vapor deposition [8, 9], pulsed laser deposition [10, 11], laser molecular-beam epitaxy method [12], spray pyrolysis technique [13], ion implantation [14], and sol-gel process [15-18], etc. The sol-gel process has distinct advantages over the other techniques due to excellent compositional control, homogeneity on the molecular level due to the mixing of liquid precursors, and lower crystallization temperature. Moreover, the microstructural properties, i.e., the pore size, pore volume and surface area of the thin film can be tailored by the control of sol-gel processing variables [19]. In this regard, the TiO_2 thin films prepared by sol-gel process have been found to be extremely wide and important applications in many fields, such as humidity sensors, gas sensors, photocatalysis and dye-sensitized solar cells [20-24]. The addition of alkali ions to TiO_2 improved the performance of humidity sensors, in which charge carriers were alkali ions instead of surface protons [25, 26]. SnO_2 is a well-known material exhibiting exceptional gas sensing property as well as the humidity sensing behavior [4, 17, 18, 27]. Thus, nanocrystalline and nanoporous SnO_2:TiO_2 composite and bilayered thin films are prepared by sol-gel process and the composite and bilayered thin films have been tried to be applied as a new humidity sensor.

In this paper, nanostructured SnO_2:TiO_2 composite and bilayered thin films were prepared using a sol-gel process by spin-coating onto the alumina substrate. Nanostructured SnO_2 and TiO_2 monolayered thin films were also prepared in identical manner for direct comparison. The humidity sensitive properties of the nanostructured SnO_2:TiO_2 composite and bilayered thin films were investigated. The variation of resistance was studied as a function of relative humidity (RH).

2. Experimental Details

2.1. Synthesis

SnO_2 coating solution was prepared by the following procedure. Tin chloride pentahydrate ($SnCl_4 \cdot 5H_2O$, Wako pure chemical) was dissolved in ethanol (0.4 M). The solution was stirred and then refluxed for 3h. The solution was finally aged at room temperature for 10 days. In order to synthesize SnO_2 colloidal solution for the composite films, an 5.5 M aqueous ammonia solution (Wako pure chemical, 25~27.9%) was added dropwise to a refluxed solution and the resulting precipitate was washed thoroughly with deionized water. Finally, SnO_2 colloidal solution was prepared by adding deionized water.

TiO_2 colloidal solution was prepared as follows. 150 ml of titanium tetraisopropoxide ($Ti(C_3H_7O)_4$, Wako pure chemical, 95%) was rapidly added to 270 ml of deionized water. The resulting precipitate was washed with deionized water. The precipitate cake was transferred into a well-sealed autoclave vessel containing 0.5 M tetramethylammonium hydroxide solution ($(CH_3)_4NOH$), Aldrich). Peptization occurred after heating at 110°C for 6h. The suspension which resulted from peptization was treated hydrothermally in the autoclave at 190°C for 6h. TiO_2 coating solution was prepared as follows. TiO_2 colloidal solution of 6g (18.1 wt% TiO_2) and commercial TiO_2 (Nippon Aerosil, P25) of 0.08g was ground in a mortar. A detergent (Triton X-100) of 20 μ L was added to facilitate the spreading of the colloid on an alumina substrate. Polyethylene glycol(PEG 20000) of 0.35g was added to make porous film, which facilitate the adsorption of water molecules. Finally, the colloid was diluted by the addition of ethanol (3mL). TiO_2-SnO_2 composite coating solutions were prepared by adding SnO_2 colloidal solution to TiO_2 colloidal solution for each ratio.

2.2. Preparation of Thin Films

The inter-digital Ag electrodes are screen printed on polycrystalline alumina (Al_2O_3) substrate of 10 mm x 10 mm x 0.5mm. TiO_2-SnO_2 composite thin films were deposited by spin coating onto the inter-digital Ag electrodes for humidity sensing measurement, and the schematic diagram is shown in Fig. 1. The spin coating was performed at room temperature, with a rate of 3000rpm. TiO_2/SnO_2 (T/S, SnO_2 on TiO_2) and SnO_2/TiO_2 (S/T) bilayered thin films were deposited in identical manner. After deposition, the films were annealed in air at 500°C for 30min, at a heating rate of 5°C /min. SnO_2 (S) and TiO_2 (T) monolayered thin films were also prepared in identical manner for direct comparison with the composite and bilayered films.

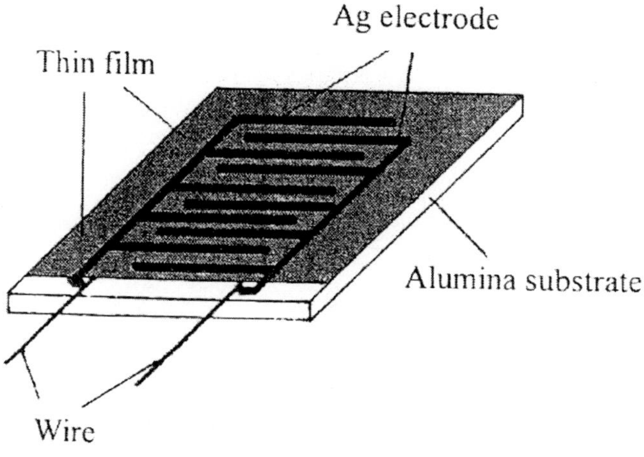

Figure 1. Schematic diagram of humidity sensor.

2.3. Measurements and Analyses

The surface and cross section of thin films were observed by scanning electron microscope (SEM, Hitachi S-4200). The thickness of the films was evaluated from SEM images of the cross section of the films. X-ray diffraction (XRD, Philips X-PERT-MPP, DY 616) analyses of the films were conducted using CuK$_\alpha$ radiation to determine the phases and the crystallite size. The crystallite size was calculated from the full width at half maximum (FWHM) of the first peak using the Scherrer formula [28].

To measure the relative humidity characteristics, the sensor element was placed into a 2 neck glass flask, partially filled with water. The relative humidity inside the glass flask was varied using an ice-salt mixture placed outside the glass flask, which was placed in a chamber and the basic measurement was performed using the two temperature method [29]. The relative humidity value was calculated from the saturated vapor pressure, i.e., the sample and water noted during experimental process. The values of saturated vapor pressure were obtained from CRC handbook [30]. The electrical resistance of the films was measured using a programmable Keithley 617 electrometer at room temperature.

3. RESULTS AND DISCUSSION

3.1. TiO_2-SnO_2 Composite Thin Films

3.1.1. Characteristics of Composite Films

Nanostructured TiO_2-SnO_2 composite thin films were prepared using sol-gel process by spin coating on polycrystalline alumina substrate. All the films were annealed at 500°C for 30min. The films were transparent and semiconducting in nature. Fig. 2 shows the SEM images of TiO_2 and TiO_2-SnO_2 thin films. The SEM image reveals that the surfaces of TiO_2-SnO_2 composite films are more rough than that of TiO_2 monolayered film, which may be due to a slight agglomeration by mixtures of both SnO_2 and TiO_2 colloids. The films possess nano-sized grains and nanoporous structure. It means that such nanostructured films are likely to facilitate the adsorption process of water vapors because of the capillary nanopores and large surface area.

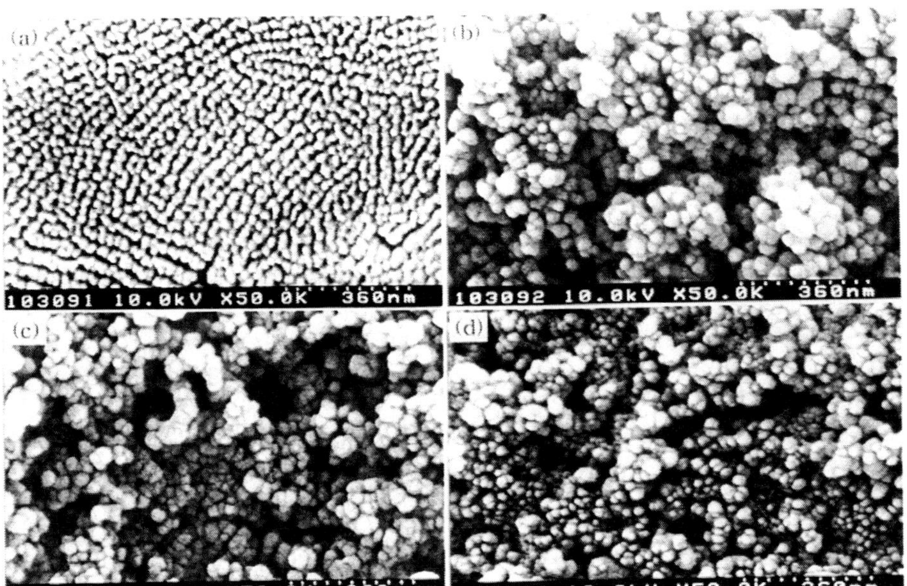

Figure 2. SEM micrographs for TiO_2-SnO_2 films: (a) TiO_2, (b) TiO_2-5 wt.% SnO_2, (c) TiO_2-20 wt.% SnO_2 and (d) TiO_2-40 wt.% SnO_2.

XRD studies were carried out on the TiO_2-SnO_2 thin films to characterize the film crystal structure. Subsequently, the crystallite size was calculated from the Scherrer formula [28]:

$$D = k\lambda /(B \cos\theta)$$

where D is the crystallite size, k, a fixed number of 0.9, λ, the X-ray wavelength, θ, the Bragg's angle in degrees, and B, the full width at half maximum of the first peak.

The average size of crystallites for the TiO_2-SnO_2 composite films with 5, 20 and 40 wt.% SnO_2 content is 13.1, 12.5, and 11.6 nm, respectively. While, it is 10.8 nm for the pure TiO_2 film. The crystallite size for the TiO_2-SnO_2 composite films is nearly same, which have no large change by adding SnO_2 and exhibits a similar tendency as obtained from SEM micrographs shown in Fig. 2. The TiO_2 phase in the TiO_2-SnO_2 composite films measured by XRD technique is anatase, containing a small amount of rutile. Further, no second phases formed in the TiO_2-SnO_2 composite films except TiO_2 and SnO_2.

The thickness of the TiO_2 and TiO_2-SnO_2 films on alumina substrate was measured by identifying the cross section in the SEM images. The films were deposited well on the alumina substrate without any microcracks. The thickness of the TiO_2-SnO_2 films with 0, 5, 20 and 40 wt.% SnO_2 content was 480, 460, 540 and 560 nm, respectively.

3.1.2. Humidity Sensing Properties of Composite Films

Fig. 3 shows the variation of resistance as a function of the relative humidity for the TiO_2-SnO_2 composite thin films. The resistance of the films slightly decreases with increasing SnO_2 content over almost all relative humidity range. The resistance variation on the relative humidity shows almost similar behavior, i.e., the resistance of the films decreases linearly with increasing relative humidity with about three orders change in the resistance during the relative humidity variation of 30 to 90%, exhibiting a good exponential relationship. In particular, the resistance of TiO_2-20 wt.% SnO_2 composite film decreases largely with increasing 30 to 90% in the relative humidity, showing very high sensitivity.

In the electrical properties for the relative humidity, the nanostructured TiO_2-SnO_2 thin films responded quickly to exposure of the water vapor atmosphere. The response time for the TiO_2-SnO_2 films with 0, 5, 20 and 40 wt.% SnO_2 content was 5, 6, 15 and 20 seconds, respectively, at 70% relative humidity. The shorter response time in the films with decreased SnO_2 content, i.e., increased TiO_2 content seems due to hydrophilic property of TiO_2 [31-33]. The ceramic humidity sensors consisting of nano-sized grains and nanopores were found to be quite stable for about 3h at 60% relative humidity atmosphere.

A large decrease in resistance with increasing relative humidity in the nanostructured ceramic films is related to the adsorption of water vapors on the film surfaces with large surface area and capillary nanopores. All the films have nano-sized grains and nanopores. The addition of SnO_2 to TiO_2 produces more rough surfaces with the capillary nanopores of wide distribution. The nano-sized grains having more rough surfaces result in a larger surface area. The nanoscaled grain size leads to many more grain boundaries and nanopores, leading to more active sites available for condensed water to react [34]. The higher surface area provides

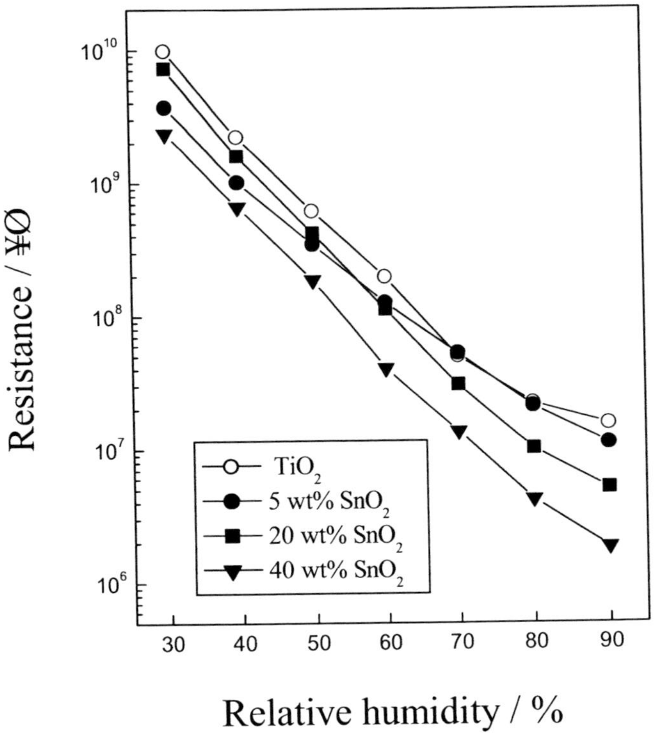

Figure 3. Humidity sensing properties for TiO_2-SnO_2 composite thin films.

more sites for water adsorption [35]. Fig. 4 shows the adsorption-desorption behaviors for the TiO_2 and TiO_2-40 wt.% SnO_2 films. The TiO_2-40 wt.% SnO_2 composite film exhibited narrower hysteresis loop than TiO_2 film. The narrower hysteresis loop indicates the facility of adsorption and desorption process of water vapor.

The TiO_2-SnO_2 composite films show a linearly large decrease in resistance with relative humidity. It is very likely that the increased conduction phenomenon with increasing relative humidity is due to an increase in the number of adsorbed water vapors in the nanostructured films with the capillary nanopores of wide distribution. Gusmano et al. [20] observed in compact and low-porosity TiO_2 film prepared by sol-gel process that the resistance variation was small during the relative humidity variation of 5% to 50%, whereas it exhibited a good exponential relationship for the higher relative humidity range of 50 - 85%. Porous materials with a wide pore-size distribution exhibit a better sensitivity even at low relative humidity [36]. The water vapors can be occupied more easily on nano-sized grain than large-sized grain. The water vapors adsorbed on the nanostructured film surface enhance electrolytic conduction as well as protonic conduction by permitting capillary condensation of water within the pores [37, 38]. The high humidity sensitivity of TiO_2-SnO_2 composite films at low and high relative humidity seems due to the protonic and electrolytic conduction between hydroxyl ions and water molecules adsorbed on the film surfaces with nano-sized grain and capillary nanopores.

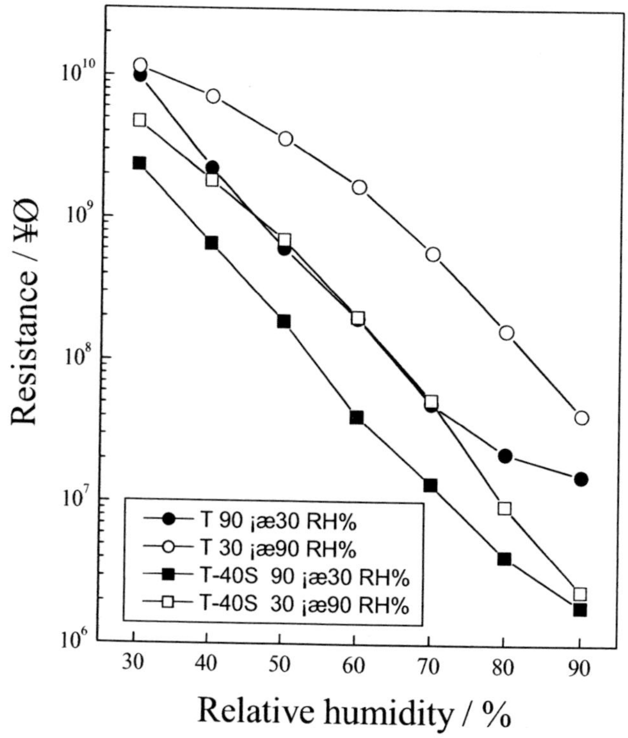

Figure 4. Adsorption and desorption behaviors for TiO_2 and TiO_2-40 wt.% SnO_2 Films.

3.2. SnO_2:TiO_2 Bilayered Thin Films

3.2.1. Characteristics of Bilayered Films

Nanostructured SnO_2:TiO_2 bilayered thin films were prepared using sol-gel process by spin coating on polycrystalline alumina substrate. Fig. 5 shows the SEM micrographs for TiO_2/SnO_2 and SnO_2/TiO_2 bilayered thin films. Here, the SnO_2/TiO_2 bilayered film indicates a upper TiO_2 layer on a lower SnO_2 layer. The films possess the grain size of nanometer order and have nanoporous structure. The films also have capillary nanopores connected by nanopores. Such structure of films facilitates the adsorption of water vapors due to the large surface area and capillary nanopores.

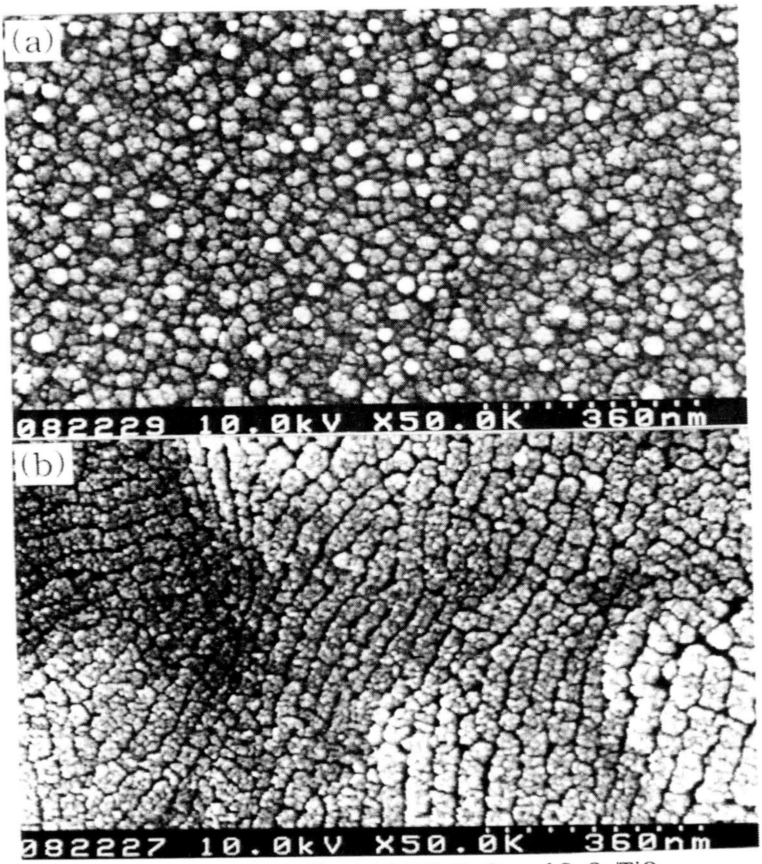

Figure 5. SEM micrographs for bilayered thin films: (a) TiO_2/SnO_2 and SnO_2/TiO_2.

The crystallite size for the TiO_2/SnO_2 and SnO_2/TiO_2 bilayered films calculated from the Scherrer formula [28] was 7.6 and 11.5 nm, respectively. While, it was 7.9 and 10.8 nm for the SnO_2 and TiO_2 monolayered films. The crystallite size of same surface phases in the monolayered and bilayered films was nearly same and exhibits a similar tendency as obtained from SEM micrographs shown in Fig. 5. The phases in the SnO_2 and TiO_2 monolayered films measured by XRD technique were polycrystalline SnO_2 and anatase TiO_2 having tetragonal structure. The phases in the TiO_2/SnO_2 bilayered films were SnO_2, containing a small amount of anatase TiO_2. The phases in the SnO_2/TiO_2 bilayered films were anatase TiO_2, containing a small amount of SnO_2.

The thickness of the SnO_2:TiO_2 monolayered and bilayered films on alumina substrate was measured by identifying the cross section in the SEM images, as shown in Fig. 6. The films were deposited well on the alumina substrate. The thickness of the SnO_2 and TiO_2 monolayered films was 500 and 480 nm, respectively. While, the thickness of the TiO_2/SnO_2 and SnO_2/TiO_2 bilayered films was 620 and 635 nm, respectively. The thickness for each monolayered and bilayered films is nearly same, respectively.

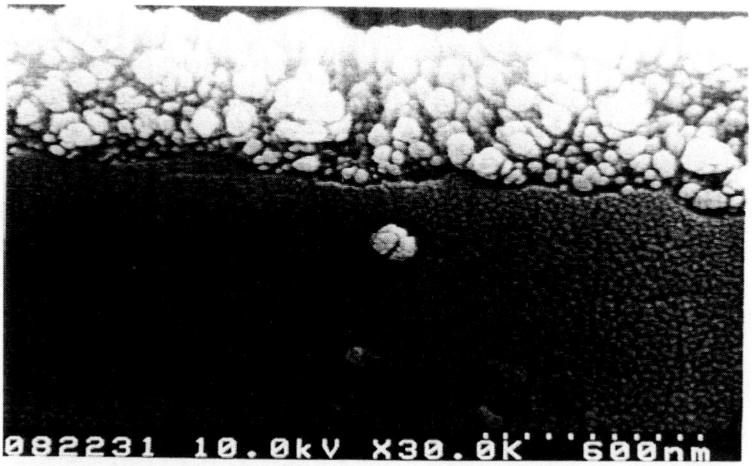

Figure 6. Cross sectional view for SnO_2 film.

3.2.2. Humidity Sensing Properties of Bilayered Films

Fig. 7 shows the variation of resistance as a function of the relative humidity for the SnO_2(S), TiO_2(T), TiO_2/SnO_2(T/S) and SnO_2/TiO_2(S/T) thin films. The resistance of TiO_2 film was higher than that of SnO_2 film in the relative humidity range from 30 to 60% and a reversed behavior was observed for the higher relative humidity. The resistance of the bilayered films decreased almost linearly with increasing relative humidity as compared to the monolayered films, exhibiting a good exponential relationship. In particular, the SnO_2/TiO_2 bilayered film showed high sensitivity with nearly three orders change. Further, the TiO_2/SnO_2 bilayered film exhibited a better linearity in the resistance variation for relative humidity than monolayered SnO_2 film. In the SnO_2 monolayered film, the resistance-relative humidity variation showed low sensitivity with a nonlinearity in the relative humidity range from 60 to 90%.

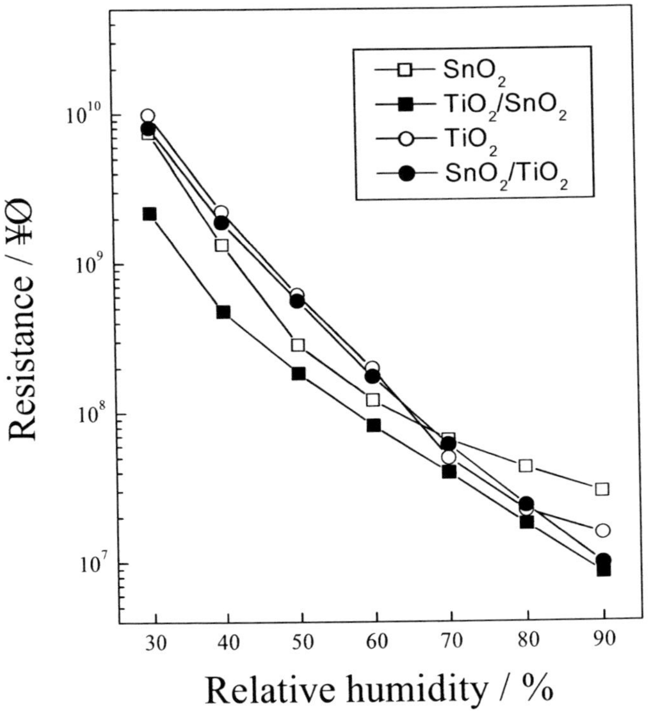

Figure 7. Humidity sensing properties for SnO_2:TiO_2 mono- and bi-layered films.

Fig. 8 shows the adsorption-desorption behaviors for SnO_2 and TiO_2/SnO_2 films. The TiO_2/SnO_2 bilayered film exhibited narrower hysteresis loop than SnO_2 monolayered film. The improved linearity with narrower hysteresis loop means the facility of adsorption and desorption process of water vapors and hence the sensitivity is increased. The hysteresis loop of SnO_2/TiO_2 bilayered film also was narrower than that of TiO_2 film. The SnO_2:TiO_2 humidity sensors consisting of nano-sized grains and nanopores were stable for minimum 3 h at 60% relative humidity.

The SnO_2/TiO_2 and TiO_2/SnO_2 bilayered films showed improved linearity and larger decrease in resistance with increasing relative humidity than the SnO_2 and TiO_2 monolayered films. The large decrease in resistance with increased relative humidity is related to the adsorption of water vapors on the nanostructured film surfaces having the nano-sized grains and capillary nanopores. The water vapors are adsorbed on the grain surface and in the nanopores. The water vapors also can be occupied more easily on nano-sized grains than large-sized grains. The nanoscaled grains lead to many more grain boundaries and nanopores, thus leading to more active sites available for condensed water to react [34]. The higher surface area provides more sites for the adsorption of water vapors and produces more charge

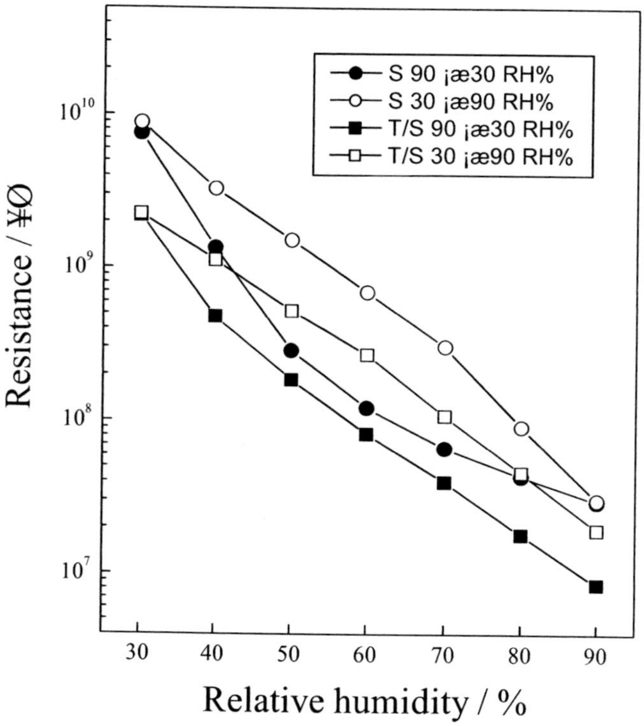

Figure 8. Adsorption and desorption behaviors for SnO_2 (S) monolayered and TiO_2/SnO_2 (T/S) bilayered films.

carriers for electrical conduction [35]. Further, TiO_2 have hydrophilic property [31, 32]. Thus, the resistance of TiO_2 film with relative humidity is lower than that of SnO_2 film at higher relative humidity, even though the resistivity of TiO_2 is higher than that of SnO_2. Moreover, the SnO_2/TiO_2 bilayered film was first deposited SnO_2 on alumina substrate containing Ag electrode and then TiO_2 was deposited on a lower porous SnO_2. Thus, the bilayered SnO_2/TiO_2 film of different chemical compositions may have more porous with capillary nanopores than monolayered SnO_2 and TiO_2 films, in which the lower film layer acts as a buffer layer. It means that the adsorption-desorption process of water vapors occurs more easily in the SnO_2/TiO_2 bilayered film. Niranjan et al. [39] showed that a tandem of nanoscale thin film of ZrO_2 on SnO_2 film minimises the hysteresis loop. The nanostructured SnO_2/TiO_2 and TiO_2/SnO_2 bilayered films exhibited improved linearity with narrower hysteresis loops compared to the SnO_2 and TiO_2 monolayered films, due to the large surface area and capillary nanopores. At higher relative humidity, the water vapors adsorbed on the nanostructured-bilayered film having nano-sized grains and capillary nanopores enhance the electrolytic conduction as well as the protonic conduction by permitting capillary condensation of water molecules within the pores [37, 38, 40].

4. CONCLUSIONS

Nanostructured SnO_2:TiO_2 composite and bilayered thin films were prepared using a sol-gel process by spin coating onto the alumina substrate and investigated for the application as a new humidity sensor. Nanostructured SnO_2 and TiO_2 monolayered thin films were also synthesized in identical manner for direct comparison. The films possess nano-sized grains and nanoporous structure, which facilitate the adsorption process of water vapors. The TiO_2-20 wt.% SnO_2 composite film exhibits the highest sensitivity for the humidity, which shows over three orders change in the resistance during the relative humidity variation of 30 to 90%. The SnO_2:TiO_2 bilayered films exhibit better linearity with narrower hysteresis loop in the resistance variation for relative humidity than the SnO_2 and TiO_2 monolayered films. In particular, the SnO_2/TiO_2 bilayered film shows high sensitivity with nearly three orders change in the resistance during the relative humidity variation of 30 to 90%. A humidity sensor with high sensitivity and good linearity could be developed from low-cost SnO_2:TiO_2 composite and bilayered films prepared by sol-gel spin-coating method.

REFERENCES

[1] Nitta, T., Terada, Z., & Hayakawa, S. (1980). Humidity-sensitive electrical conduction of $MgCr_2O_4$-TiO_2 porous ceramics. *J.Am.Ceram.Soc.*, 63, 295-300.

[2] Shimizu, Y., Shimabukuro, M., Arai, H., & Seiyama, T. (1985) Enhancement of humidity sensitivity for perovskite types oxides having semiconductivity. *Chem.Lett.*, 7, 917-920.

[3] Yeh, Y.-C., Tseng, T.-Y., & Chang, D.-A. (1990) Electrical properties of TiO_2-$K_2Ti_6O_{13}$ porous ceramic humidity sensor. *J.Am.Ceram.Soc.,* 73, 1992-98.

[4] Fagan, J.G., & Amarakoon, V.R.W. (1993) Reliability and reproducibility of ceramic sensors: Part III, Humidity sensors. *Am.Ceram.Soc.Bull.*, 72 119-130.

[5] Wu, Q., Lee, K.M., & Liu, C.C. (1993) Development of chemical sensors using microfabrication and micromachining techniques. *Sensors and Actuators* B, 13, 1-6.

[6] Rittersma, Z.M. (2002) Recent achievements in miniaturised humidity sensors- a review of transduction techniques. *Sensors and Actuators A*, 96, 196-210.

[7] Chow, L.L.W., Yuen, M.M.F., Chan, P.C.H., & Cheung, A.T. (2001) Reactive sputtered TiO_2 thin film humidity sensor with negative substrate bias. *Sensors and Actuators B*, 76, 310-315.

[8] Tuan, A., Yoon, M., Medvedev, V., Ono, Y., Ma, Y., & Rogers Jr, J.W. (2000) Interface control in the chemical vapor deposition of titanium dioxide on silicon(100). *Thin Solid Films,* 377-378. 766-771.

[9] Kang, B.-C., Lee, S.-B., Boo, & J.-H. (2000) Growth of TiO_2 thin films on Si(100) substrates using single molecular precursors by metal organic chemical vapor deposition. *Surface and Coatings Technology*, 131, 88-92.

[10] Liu, X., Yin, J., Liu, Z.G., Yin, X.B., Chen, G.X., & Wang, M. (2001) Structural characterization of TiO_2 thin films prepared by pulsed laser deposition on GaAs(100) substrates. *Applied Surface Science* ,174, 35-39.

[11] Suda, Y., Kawasaki, H., Ueda, T., & Ohshima, T. (2004) Preparation of high quality nitrogen doped TiO_2 thin films as a photocatalyst using a pulsed laser deposition method. *Thin Solid Films*, 453-454, 162-166.
[12] Ong, C.K., & Wang, S.J. (2001) In situ RHEED monitor of the growth of epitaxial anatase TiO_2 thin films. *Applied Surface Science*, 185, 47-51.
[13] Abou-Helal, M.O., & Seeber, W.T. (2002) Preparation of TiO_2 thin films by spray pyrolysis to be used as a photocatalyst. *Applied Surface Science*, 195, 53-62.
[14] Zheng, S.K., Wang, T.M., Hao, W.C., & Shen, R. (2002) Improvement of photocatalytic activity of TiO_2 thin film by Sn ion implantation. *Vacuum*, 65, 155-159.
[15] Tang, H., Prasad, K., Sanjines, R., & Levy, F. (1995) TiO_2 anatase thin films as gas sensors, *Sensors and Actuators B*, 26-27, 71-75.
[16] Garzella, C., Comini, E., Tempesti, E., Frigeri, C., & Sberveglieri, G. (2000) TiO_2 thin films by a novel sol-gel processing for gas sensor application, *Sensors and Actuators B*, 68, 189-196.
[17] Rella, R., Serra, A., Siciliano, P., Vasanelli, L., De, G., & Licciulli, A. (1997) CO sensing properties of SnO_2 thin films prepared by the sol-gel process, *Thin Solid Films*, 304, 339-343.
[18] Racheva, T.M., & Critchlow, G.W. (1997) SnO_2 thin films prepared by the sol-gel process, *Thin Solid Films*, 292, 299-302.
[19] Brinker, C.J., & Scherer, G.W. *Sol-Gel Science: The Physics and Chemistry of Sol-Gel Processing, Academic press*, New York, 1990.
[20] Gusmano, G., Montesperelli, G., Nunziante, P., Traversa, E., Montenero, A., Braghini, M., Mattogno, G., & Bearzotti, A. (1993) Humidity-sensitive properties of titania films prepared using the sol-gel process, *J.Ceram.Soc.Jpn.*, 101, 1095-1100.
[21] Li, Y., Wlodarski, W., Galatsis, K., H.Moslih, S., Cole, J., Russo, S., & Rockelmann, N. (2002) Gas sensing properties of p-type semiconducting Cr-doped TiO_2 thin films. *Sensors and Actuators B*, 83, 160-163.
[22] Guillard, C., Beaugiraud, B., Dutriez, C., Herrmann, J.-M., Jaffrezic, H., Jaffrezic-Renault, N., & Lacroix, M. (2002) Physicochemical properties and photocatalytic activities of TiO_2-films prepared by sol-gel methods. *Applied Catalysis B: Environmental*, 39, 331-342.
[23] O'Regan, B., & Gratzel, M. (1991) A low-cost, high-efficiency solar cell based on dye-sensitized colloidal TiO_2 films. *Nature*, 353, 737-739.
[24] Tai, W.-P., Inoue, K., & Oh, J.-H. (2002) Ruthenium dye-sensitized SnO_2/TiO_2 coupled solar cells, *Solar Energy Mat. & Solar cells*, 71, 553-557.
[25] Traversa, E., Gnappi, G., Montenero, A., Gusmano, G. (1996) Ceramic thin films by sol-gel processing as novel materials for integrated humidity sensors. *Sensors and Actuators B*, 31, 59-70.
[26] Gusmano, G., Bianco, A., Montesperelli, G., & Traversa, E. (1996) An EIS study of the humidity-sensitive electrical conduction of alkali-doped TiO_2 films. *Electrochimica Acta*, 41, 1359-1368.
[27] Arndt, J., Ceramics and Oxides. In: Gopel, W., Hesse, J., Zemel, J.N. In: Grandke, T., Ko, W.H., *Sensors, Fundamentals and General Aspects*. Vol.1, VCH; 1989; p.248.
[28] Cullity, B.D., *Elements of X-ray diffraction*. Addison-Wesley Publishing Company, Inc., London, 1978.

[29] Seiyama, T., Yamazoe, N., & Arai, H. (1983) Ceramic humidity sensors. *Sensors and Actuators*, 4, 85-96.

[30] *Handbook of chemistry and physics*, 60th edition, CRC press, 1979-1980.

[31] Yu, J., Zhao, X., Zhao, Q., & Wang, G. (2001) Preparation and characterization of super-hydrophilic porous TiO_2 coating films. Mater.*Chem.Phys.*, 68, 253-259.

[32] Nakamura, M., Makino, K., Sirghi, L., Aoki, T., & Hatanaka, Y. (2003) Hydrophilic properties of hydro-oxygenated TiO_2 films prepared by plasma enhanced chemical vapor deposition. *Surface and Coating Technology*, 169-170, 699-702.

[33] Guan, K., Lu, B., & Yin, Y. (2003) Enhanced effect and mechanism of SiO_2 addition in super-hydrophilic property of TiO_2 films. *Surface and Coating Technology*, 173, 219-223.

[34] Chauhan, P., Annapoorni, S., & Trikha, S.K. (1999) Humidity-sensing properties of nanocrystalline haematite thin films prepared by sol-gel processing. *Thin Solid Films*, 346, 266-268.

[35] Chou, K.-S., Lee, T.-K., & Liu, F.-J. (1999) Sensing mechanism of a porous ceramic as humidity sensor. *Sensors and Actuators B*, 56, 106-111.

[36] Gusmano, G., Montesperelli, G., Nunziante, P., & Traversa, E. (1993) Microstructure and electrical properties of $MgAl_2O_4$ and $MgFe_2O_4$ spinel porous compacts for use in humidity sensors. *Br.Ceram.Trans.*, 92, 104-108.

[37] Kulwicki, B.M. (1984) Ceramic sensors and transducers, *J.Phys.Chem.Solids*, 45, 1015-1031.

[38] Kulwicki, B.M. (1991) Humidity sensors, *J.Am.Ceram.Soc.*, 74, 697-708.

[39] Niranjan, R.S., Sathaye, S.D., & Mulla, I.S. (2001) Bilayered tin oxide: zirconia thin films as a humidity sensor. *Sensors and Actuators B*, 81, 64-67.

[40] Tai, W.-P., & Oh, J.-H. (2002) Preparation and humidity sensing behaviors of nanocrystalline SnO_2/TiO_2 bilayered films. *Thin Solid Films*, 422, 220-224.

In: Nanomaterials: New Research
Editor: B.M. Caruta, pp. 129-167

ISBN: 1-59454-369-0

Chapter 4

SYNTHESIS OF ZNO NANOPOWDER BY SOLUTION COMBUSTION METHOD AND ITS PHOTOCATALYTIC CHARACTERISTICS

Sung Park*, Jae-Chun Lee and Ju-Hyeon Lee[1]

Department of Materials Science and Engineering, Myongji University,
382 San, Nam-dong, Yongin, Kyunggi-do 449-728, Korea
[1]Department of Electronic Materials Engineering,
SunMoon University, Asan, Choongnam 336-708, Korea

ABSTRACT

The main objectives of the present work were to synthesize zinc oxide powder, to investigate its photocatalytic activity and to compare its activity with that of the present day state-of-the-art commercial semiconductor oxide photocatalyst powders. The work was focused mainly on the synthesis of zinc oxide powder for the degradation of organic and inorganic pollutants. Commercial zinc oxide powder shows low photocatalytic activity for degradation of organic and inorganic pollutants as it contains many defect structures, which enhance the recombination rate of generated electron-hole pairs responsible for redox reactions during photocatalytic experiments.

To obtain high purity zinc oxide powder free of defects, a new self-propagating process initiated at low temperature using redox compounds and mixtures in solution was investigated. The process makes use of highly exothermic redox chemical reactions between metals and non-metals. The method is referred to as the "solution-combustion method (SCM). Different zinc oxide powders were synthesized using a number of oxidants and fuels (reductants) in various proportions using the SCM. The formed zinc oxide powders were analyzed using different powder characterization techniques such as SEM, TEM, BET, XRD, and PL spectra measurements. SEM and TEM revealed the formation of uniform particle size in the nanometer range. As-synthesized primary particles were as small as 30 nm in size and the specific surface area of the nanopowder

* Corresponding Author : spark@mju.ac.kr

was about 120 m^2/g. Single phase was confirmed by XRD and PL spectra revealed the defect-free nature and high UV light absorption capacity of the synthesized nanopowder.
The photocatalytic performance of the synthesized nanopowder was evaluated to remove organic pollutants and metal ions from aqueous solutions in a batch-type reactor. Other photocatalyst powders such as state of the art commercial ZnO (Junsei, Japan), commercial titanium dioxide powder (P-25 TiO_2, Degussa, Germany) and titanium dioxide powder prepared by homogeneous precipitation process at low temperature (HPPLT TiO_2) were also used in duplicate experiments to compare their degradation and removal rates. In all cases, the SCM ZnO nanopowder showed a much higher rate of degradation of phenol and removal rate of metal ions than that other photocatalyst powders.
Photocatalysis is a surface phenomena and the method of preparing the photocatalyst powder determines its efficiency. Here, all the characteristics of the obtained powder such as nanometer size, very high surface area, defect-free nature, and high UV absorption capacity have played a positive role in enhancing its efficiency in photocatalytic reactions.

1. INTRODUCTION

1.1. Zinc Oxide

Zinc oxide (ZnO) is a wide direct bandgap II-VI semiconductor that has a Wurtzite structure. Its significant applications include varistors, phosphors, pigment material, rubber additive, gas sensor, photocatalyst, etc. [1,2]. It is optically transparent in the visible region and electrically conductive with appropriate dopants. Therefore, this material is used as transparent conducting electrodes for displays and solar cells [3,4]. With a particle size in the nanometer range, it has proven to be an excellent UV absorbing material that can be used in sunscreen lotions [5].

The minimum value of bandgap energy stated in literatures is 3.1 to 3.3 eV [6]. This high bandgap makes ZnO highly suitable for optical applications. The recent development of thin-film fabrication techniques now allows the growth of large single crystals, which, essential for optical devices, demands high quality materials. There have been reports on the construction of blue laser diodes based on ZnO and of electrodes for solar cells and flat panel displays [7, 8]. The reactivity of the surfaces for methanol synthesis and other catalytic processes has been utilized on an industrial scale.

1.2. Crystal Structure of Zinc Oxide

ZnO crystallizes in a hexagonal wurtzite structure in which the oxygen atoms are arranged in a hexagonal close-packed (HCP) type of lattice with zinc atoms occupying half the tetrahedral sites. The Wurtzite structure in figure 1.1 can be described as two HCP lattices, which are inserted into each other. The O-lattice is displaced a fraction 0.38 of the unit cell height in the c-direction with respect to the Zn- lattice. All atoms in ZnO have tetrahedral coordination with four nearest neighbors of the opposite type. This means that close packed planes of Zn- and O- are stacked along the c-axis in the cell, forming a polar crystal with the polarization in this direction. The mean lattice constants are a = 3.250 Å and c = 5.206 Å, which depend slightly on stoichiometry deviation. The c/a ratio of 1.602 is a little less than the ideal value of 1.633. The Zn-O distance is 1.992 Å parallel to the c-axis and 1.973 Å in the other three directions of the tetrahedral arrangement of the nearest neighbors [6].

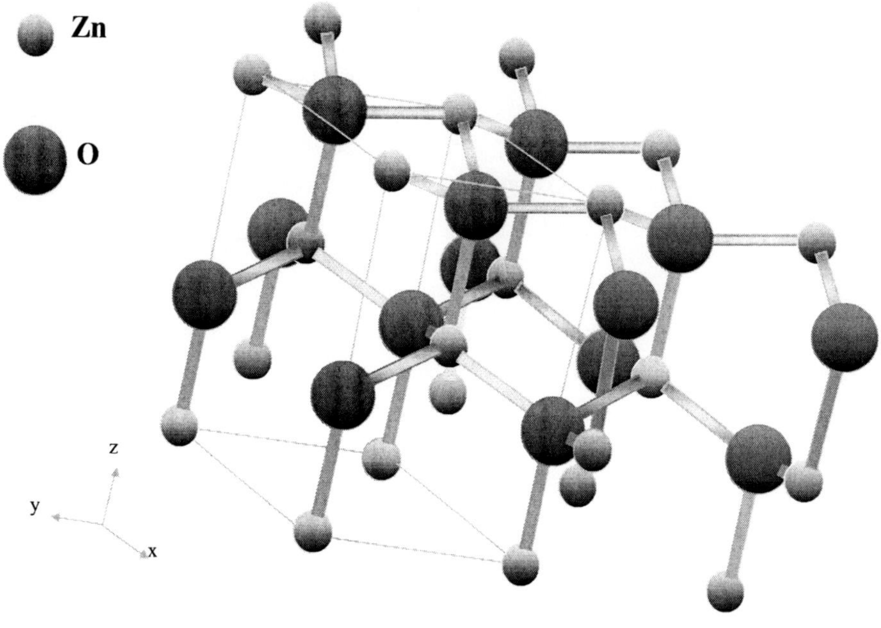

Figure 1. The unit cell of ZnO (hexagonal wurtzite).

1.3. Electronic Structure of Zinc Oxide

The Zn-atoms in ZnO to a large extent have donated its two 4s-valence electrons to their neighboring O-atoms; however, there is a significant delocalized charge between the atoms, consequently giving ZnO a mixed ionic-covalent character. According to the Phillips ionicity scale, ZnO is therefore on the borderline between an ionic and a covalent crystal. This mixed ionic-covalent character is probably one reason for the difficulties that have occurred in determining the electronic structure of ZnO. The bandstructure of the Wurtzite-phase of ZnO has been investigated [6]. ZnO has a wide direct optical band gap at near 3.3 eV.

1.4. Scope of This Work

The main scope of the present work was:

1. to investigate a new method of synthesizing oxide powders referred to as the 'solution-combustion method'
2. to synthesize zinc oxide (ZnO) powder by the solution-combustion method
3. to determine the effectiveness of the synthesized powder in the photocatalytic oxidation of organic pollutants in aqueous solution
4. to determine the effectiveness of the synthesized powder in the photocatalytic reduction of metal ions in aqueous solution, and
5. to compare the photocatalytic activity of the synthesized powder with that of other state-of-the-art photocatalyst powders like titanium dioxide powder (P-25 TiO_2; Degussa, Germany)

2. Synthesis of ZnO Nanopowder

2.1. Background

When ZnO is irradiated with UV light of appropriate energy greater than its bandgap, highly mobile electron-hole pairs can be generated. These carriers then migrate to the surface and in turn are trapped by reactants adsorbed on the surface, giving rise to powerful redox chemistry [9]. Therefore, ZnO has attracted interest as a photocatalyst, especially, in the degradation of environmental pollutants [10-12]. It has almost the same bandgap energy as titanium dioxide (TiO_2). Thus its photocatalytic activity is predicted to be similar to that of TiO_2. But the research carried out to realize its full potential as a semiconductor photocatalyst is limited [13-17].

Chemical methods have shown several distinct advantages for the synthesis of nanophase particles [18]. Several chemical methods for the synthesis of zinc oxide have been reported (e.g., preparations of fine zinc oxide by means of spray pyrolysis, sol-gel technique, vapor method and thermal decomposition [19-23]). The synthesis of zinc oxide through precipitation of organic solutions has also been reported [24]. However, the characteristics of zinc oxide synthesized by these methods revealed that it was not good enough to used as a photocatalyst compared to other materials such as TiO_2. That is the reason for the use of TiO_2 as a photocatalyst.

One innovative technique for synthesizing fine ceramic powders with good homogeneity is 'combustion synthesis'. This technique offers added advantages over alternatives, such as a simple experimental set-up, the surprisingly short time between preparing the reactants and obtaining the final product, and the savings in external energy consumption [25-31]. The combustion synthesis technique begins with combining reactants that oxidize easily, (eg., nitrates) and a suitable organic fuel (like glycine, urea, carbohydrazide) that acts as a reducing agent. The mixture is brought to boil until it ignites and a self-sustaining and rather fast combustion reaction occurs, resulting in a dry, crystalline and unagglomerated, fine oxide powder. The large amount of gases formed can result in the appearance of flames, which can reach temperatures that exceed 1500^0C.

In combustion synthesis, the energy released from the exothermic reaction between the nitrates and the fuel, which is usually ignited at a temperature much lower than the actual phase transformation temperature, can rapidly heat the system to a high temperature and sustain it long enough for the synthesis to occur, even in the absence of an external heat source.

The combustion synthesis technique is based on the thermochemical concepts used in the field of propellants and explosives. Self-propagating combustion reaction occurs when explosives are ignited.

The need for a clear indication of the effective constitution of a fuel-oxidizer mixture led Jain et al. to devise a simple method of calculating the oxidizing to reducing character of the mixture [32]. Stoichiometry of the metal nitrate and fuel mixture can be calculated based on the total oxidizing and reducing valency of the oxidizer and the fuel, which serves as a numerical coefficient for the stoichiometric balance so that the equivalence ratio (φ_e) is equal to unity and the energy released is maximum. As an example, the oxidizing valence of zinc nitrate is −10, while the reducing valence of carbohydrazide is +8 and that of glycine is +9. Hence, 1 mole of zinc nitrate requires 1.25 moles of carbohydrazide or 1.11 moles of glycine to keep the equivalence ratio (φ_e) unity.

In a typical combustion synthesis, a pyrex dish containing an aqueous redox mixture of stoichiometric amounts of zinc nitrate and glycine is heated on a hot plate inside a chamber. The solution boils and froths, followed by the appearance of flame yielding a voluminous product.

2.2. Experiment

Zinc hydroxide powder [$Zn(OH)_2$, Junsei (Japan)] or zinc nitrate powder [$Zn(NO_3)_2$ $6H_2O$, 3N, High purity chemicals lab.(Japan)] was used as the starting material. Glycine [H_2NCH_2COOH, Yakuri pure chemicals co. Ltd (Japan)] or carbohydrazide [$H_2NNHCONHNH_2$, Aldrich (USA)] was used as the fuel. Here, the zinc hydroxide powder was dissolved in nitric acid before use, forming zinc nitrate. The starting material (zinc nitrate or zinc hydroxide dissolved in nitric acid) was dissolved in distilled water in a beaker, and fuel (glycine or carbohydrazide) was added to the starting material solution. The solution mixture was then heated on a hot plate while being stirred. As the distilled water evaporated, the solution became viscous and generated small bubbles. The viscous solution was then transferred to another stainless steel beaker and heated inside a chamber for ignition (fig. 2). The nitrate group (NO_3^-) reacted with the fuel and formed highly explosive $CO(N_3)_2$ [33]. At this point, the temperature rose to 1500–1800°C instantaneously with flame and combustion. This intense heat resulted in instantaneous high pressure, which led to an explosion. The ZnO powder was formed in this high temperature and pressure environment. At this point the powder was gathered by the collector, and placed above the beaker. The powder was annealed for one hour at 400^0C.

X-ray diffractometer (XRD) was used to confirm the crystalline phase of the synthesized ZnO powder. A scanning electron microscope (SEM) was used to investigate the average particle size and shape. Specific surface area of the powder was measured by the brunauer emett teller (BET) method. Fluorospectrometer (SIM-AMINCO) was used to measure photoluminescence (PL) emission values as a function of wavelength. Different ZnO powders were synthesized, changing the amount of carbohydrazide.

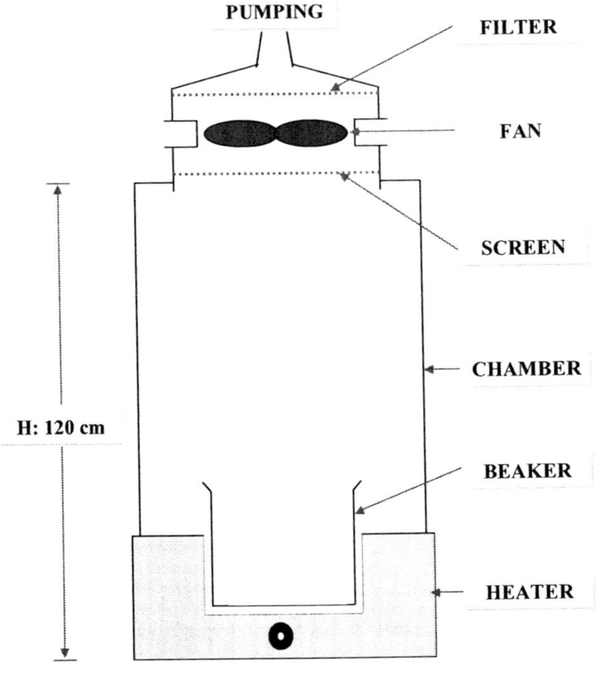

Figure 2. Schematic diagram of the SCM ZnO synthesis apparatus

2.3. Results and Discussion

The crystalline phases of the powders were confirmed by the XRD patterns shown in fig.3. When the molar ratio of fuel (carbohydrazide) to oxidant (zinc hydroxide dissolved in nitric acid) was 0.8 or 1.0, XRD patterns showed that the synthesized ZnO powders were not single phase ZnO but a mixture of materials including the remainders of an incomplete combustion. XRD patterns showed that peaks of single phase ZnO started to form only when the molar ratio of fuel to oxidant was higher than 1.2. At the molar ratio of 1.333, single

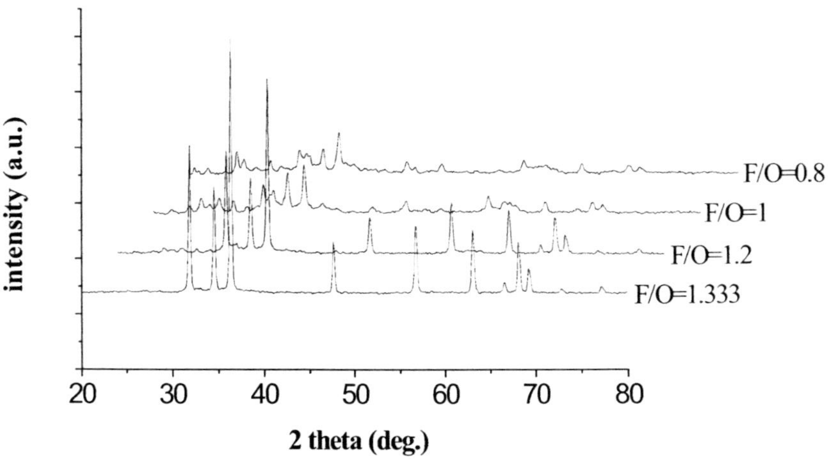

Figure 3. XRD patterns of ZnO powders synthesized using carbohydrazide and zinc hydroxide (dissolved in nitric acid) with different molar ratios (F: fuel and O: oxidizer).

phase ZnO was completely formed. The ratio of 1.333 is the ratio in which the reaction formula forms complete $CO(N_3)_2$ from the reaction between nitrate group and carbohydrazide. Similar results were obtained up to the molar ratio of 1.6, a case of fuel excess. During the combustion reaction in the reaction chamber, the degree of explosion appeared to be similar even though the ratio was increased. However, it showed a slightly higher degree of explosion when the molar ratio exceeded 1.4. When the molar ratio was lower than 1.2, carbohydrazide was completely consumed with the nitrate group partially remaining. This resulted in a mixture of materials rather than single phase ZnO. The intensity of the peaks was inconsiderable even though the peaks of single phase ZnO were detected. At the molar ratio of 1.333, the fuel (carbohydrazide) and oxidant (nitrate group) were completely consumed to form highly explosive $CO(N_3)_2$. In the case of fuel excess(molar ratio higher than 1.4), the remaining fuel decomposed and evaporated in the air.

Figure 4 shows XRD peaks of ZnO powders synthesized using glycine instead of carbohydrazide as a fuel. Generally, using glycine as a fuel, oxide powders are synthesized adding the fuel in equilibrium (oxidant: fuel = 1), fuel lean or fuel rich states considering the degree of explosion during self-combustion, based on the calculation of oxidation number for oxidant and fuel. Five different ZnO powders were synthesized with varying fuel/oxidant molar ratios (F/O=0.75~1.3). It is easy to obtain single-phase ZnO powder regardless of the fuel/oxidant ratio. Especially the ZnO powder with a fuel/oxidant molar ratio of 0.8 showed highest XRD peaks that indicate best crystalline quality.

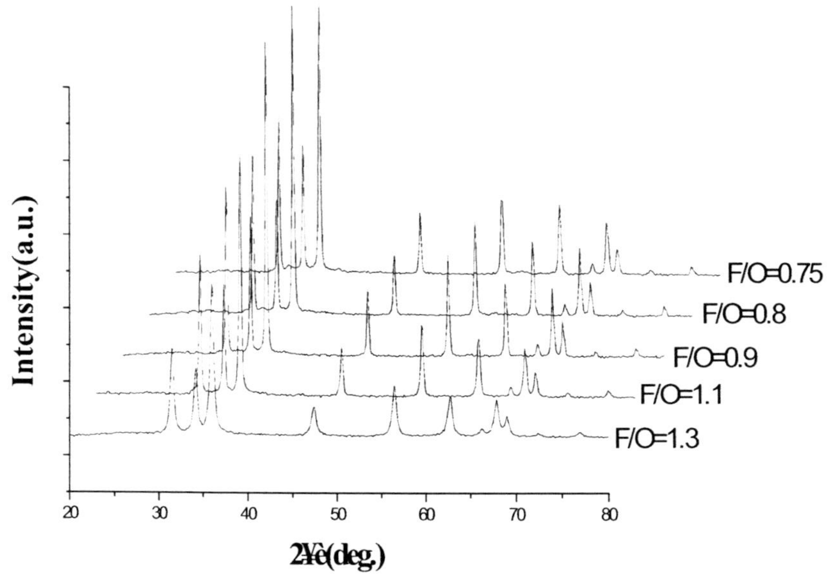

Figure 4. XRD patterns of ZnO powders synthesized using glycine and zinc hydroxide (dissolved in nitric acid) with different molar ratios (F: fuel and O: oxidizer).

Table 1 shows the average size of ZnO particles synthesized by SCM with various starting materials and fuels. The average particle size determined from SEM images is shown in fig. 5 and 6. Here, the particle size was greatly depended on the types of oxidants and fuels used during synthesis.

Table1. Average Particle Size of ZnO Powders Synthesized by SCM Using Various Starting Materials and Fuels

Starting Materials / Fuels	$Zn(NO_3)_2 \cdot 6H_2O$	$Zn(OH)_2$
Carbohydrazide	320 nm	110 nm
Glycine	125 nm	30 nm

Figure 5. SEM photographs of ZnO powders synthesized by SCM using (a) $Zn(NO_3)_2{\cdot}6H_2O$ and carbohydrazide, (b) $Zn(OH)_2$ and carbohydrazide, (c) $Zn(NO_3)_2{\cdot}6H_2O$ and glycine and (d) $Zn(OH)_2$ and glycine.

The difference in particle size was more than four fold depending on the oxidants and fuels used. Plate-like particles were obtained when carbohydrazide was used as a fuel. On the other hand, when using glycine as a fuel, the shape of the particles was spherical and their size uniform. The finest particles (30 nm), as shown in fig. 6, were obtained when $Zn(OH)_2$ and glycine (molar ratio: F/O=0.8) were used. In this case, $Zn(OH)_2$ was dissolved in nitric acid solution to form zinc nitrate. There would have been more NO_3^- groups in the solution than the case of using zinc nitrate as the starting material. The NO_3^- group acts as an igniter for the combustion. This probably means that more igniter is available for the combustion process. At this point it is not clear, but it may be considered that this is conductive to finer particle size.

Table 2 shows the specific surface areas of the synthesized ZnO powders. The specific surface area depended on the types of oxidants and fuels. The largest specific surface area of the powder (120 m^2/g) was obtained when glycine and zinc hydroxide at a molar ratio of 0.8 were used to synthesize the ZnO powder. The difference in surface area depending on oxidants and fuels was about five fold. This result is consistent with the average particle size data. This confirms that smaller particle size results in larger specific surface area.

Figure 6. High magnification SEM photograph of fig.5(d)

Table 2. Specific Surface Area of ZnO Powders synthesized by SCM Using Various Starting Materials and Fuels

Starting Material / Fuel	$Zn(NO_3)_2 \cdot 6H_2O$	$Zn(OH)_2$
Carbohydrazide	19 m^2/g	32m^2/g
Glycine	27m^2/g	120 m^2/g

Figure 7 shows photoluminescence (PL) spectra of commercial ZnO powder (Junsei, Japan) and ZnO powders synthesized by SCM with different glycine/zinc hydroxide molar ratios. As shown in the figure, commercial ZnO powder showed two peaks: one is in the vicinity of 500 nm, and the other one is near 400 nm. The peak near 500 nm was probably from the energy transition between oxygen vacancy level and Zn vacancy level. The UV peak near 400 nm might be from band to band transition. However, ZnO powder synthesized by SCM showed only one sharp peak near 390 nm that was slightly shifted to UV side. This peak is equivalent to the energy gap of ZnO (~ 3.2 eV). These results indicate that the ZnO powder synthesized by SCM did not show defect energy levels inside the energy gap. The defects were probably annealed out as a result of the high temperature during the synthesis process. Again, the powder showed higher PL intensity at UV than the commercial ZnO powder. Especially, ZnO powder with the fuel/oxidant molar ratio of 0.8 showed highest PL intensity at UV. The intensity was almost three fold higher than that of the commercial ZnO powder given the same wavelength. This suggests that SCM ZnO powder absorbs much more UV light than the commercial ZnO powder.

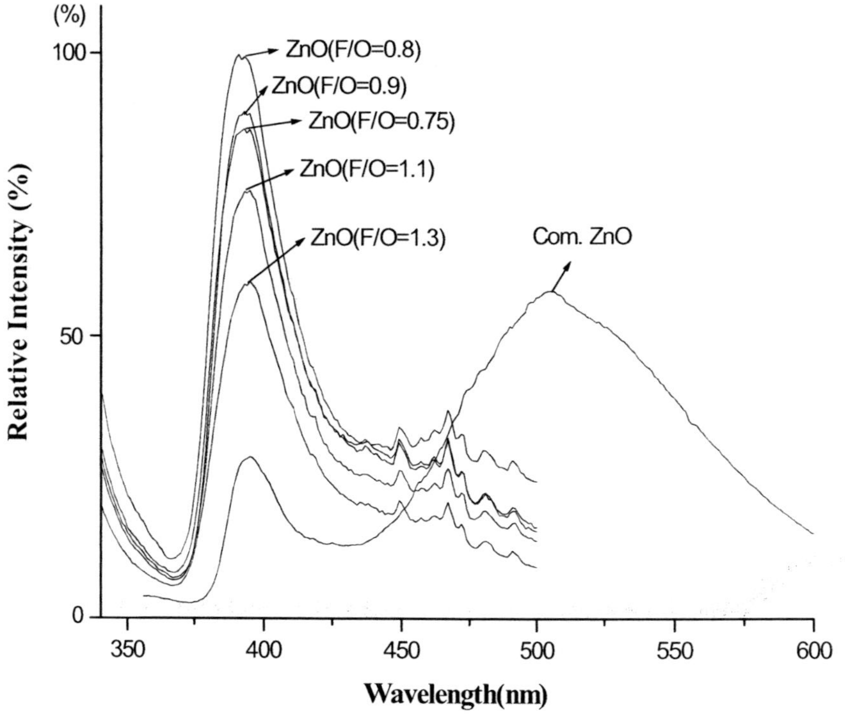

Figure 7. Photoluminescence (PL) spectra of commercial ZnO (Junsei, Japan) and ZnO nanopowders synthesized by solution combustion method with different molar ratios of glycine and zinc hydroxide (F/O)

2.4. Summary

Nano-sized single-phase ZnO powders could be easily obtained using SCM regardless of starting materials and fuels. However, the particle size of the synthesized ZnO powders greatly varied, depending on the selection of oxidants and fuels. The particle size difference was more than four fold. Especially, the use of glycine and zinc hydroxide (molar ratio: F/O=0.8), the synthesized ZnO powder showed the best powder characteristics, such as an average particle size of 30 nm and specific surface area of 120 m^2/g.

Preparation methods affect surface properties such as surface defect levels. Generally, it is known that the smaller particle size results in more surface defects. In the above case (SCM ZnO), however, the level of surface defects seemed to be minimized even though the powder was synthesized in nano-size. The surface defects might have been annealed out on short exposure at high temperature, which reaches up to 1500- 1800 ^{0}C during synthesis.

3. Removal of Metal Ions from Wastewater

3.1. Recovery of Ag ions from wastewater

3.1.1. Background

Photocatalytic processes involving aqueous suspensions of semiconductors have received considerable attention in view of solar energy conversion [34, 35]. Recent studies mainly concentrate on environmental problems such as purification of contaminated water or air [36-38]. Semiconductors for photocatalytic reactions should have conditions such as high photoactivity, high photostability, high sensitivity for UV-visible light and low fabrication cost. There is an ample interest in wide band gap oxide semiconductors and ease of handling [39-43].

ZnO is an important material in various fields of applications. For photocatalysts, ZnO is an n-type semiconductor that has a wide band gap of 3.2 eV. When ZnO is irradiated by light with greater energy than the ZnO band gap, electron-hole pairs are generated in the conduction and valence bands of the semiconductor, respectively. These charge carriers migrate to the semiconductor surface and have suitable redox potentials.

It is known that nano-particles have different physical and chemical properties compared to bulk materials. High catalytic activity is expected from their large surface area and different surface properties such as surface defects [44, 45].

In this work, synthesis of ZnO powder was investigated to obtain semiconductor particles smaller than 30 nm for photocatalytic applications. Two methods, a vapor method and a sol-gel method, are generally being used to obtain ZnO nanopowders. In the case of the vapor method, the resulting powders are agglomerated rather than separated because it is very difficult to control the reaction condition during the process. Therefore, this method is not recommended for obtaining nano-sized ZnO powders. In contrast, the sol-gel method results in uniform ZnO powders. However, strict control of the reaction condition is necessary because of its violent hydrolysis reaction in air during synthesis. In addition, the material cost for this method is high. For this reason, the sol-gel method is not commercialized but is utilized in small laboratory scale only [46, 47].

Park et al. proposed the SCM for preparing of ceramic powders [48-50]. In this process, by heating mixture solution containing the oxidant (source material) and fuel, there is an ignition, instantaneously producing high temperature and pressure by explosion. This instantaneous high temperature and pressure lead to the formation of very fine sized and high quality oxide ceramic powders. In this work, ZnO nanopowders were synthesized by this SCM process and used to recover Ag ions from wastewater.

3.1.2. Experiment

Photocatalytic activity of the synthesized ZnO powder was then confirmed by removing Ag ions from a waste development solution that contained them. Ag recovery rate was measured as photocatalytic efficiency. For this, water was used as a solvent for the waste development solution. The light source for the photocatalytic reaction was a UV lamp (6 W, maximum energy at 365 nm). The remaining Ag ion concentration was determined by atomic absorption spectrophotometer (Model 5100 PC, Perkin-Elmer).

3.1.3. Results and Discussion

Figure 8 shows photoluminescence (PL) spectra of state of the art, commercial ZnO (Junsei, Japan), HPPLT (Homogeneous Precipitation Process at Low Temperature) TiO_2, commercial state of the art TiO_2 (P-25 Degussa, Germany) and ZnO powders synthesized by SCM with different glycine/$Zn(OH)_2$ ratios. Figure 9 represents the energy band diagram of the commercial, state of the art ZnO powder. The peak near 500 nm can be attributed to the energy transition between O vacancy level and Zn vacancy level. The UV peak near 400 nm might be from band to band transition. However, the SCM ZnO nanopowder showed only one sharp peak near 390 nm that was slightly shifted to the UV side. This peak is equivalent to the energy gap of ZnO (~ 3.2 eV). These means that the SCM ZnO nanopowder did not show defect energy levels inside the energy gap. The defects were probably annealed out from the high temperature during the synthesis process. The SCM ZnO nanopowder showed a UV absorption that is threefolds than that of other ZnO and TiO_2 powders.

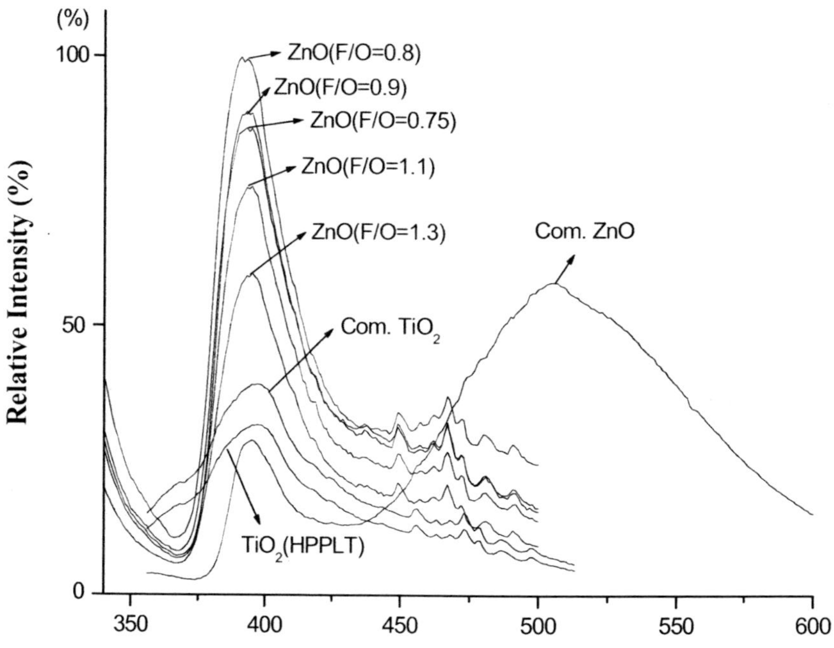

Figure 8. Photoluminescence (PL) spectra of commercial state of the art ZnO (Junsei, Japan), HPPLT TiO_2, commercial state of the art TiO_2 (P-25 Degussa, Germany) and the SCM ZnO powders synthesized with different glycine/$Zn(OH)_2$ ratios.

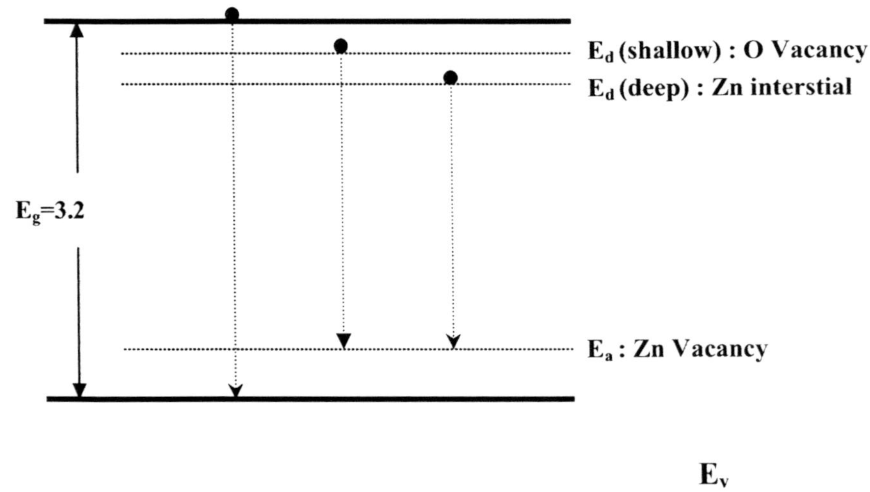

Figure 9. Schematic diagram of ZnO energy band gap and defect energy levels.

As mentioned above, results from XRD (fig. 4) and PL measurements led to select the ZnO powder with glycine/$Zn(OH)_2$ ratio of 0.8 for this Ag recovery experiment. To confirm the photocatalytic characteristics, there were attempts to remove Ag ions from waste development solution. Figure 10 shows the Ag recovery rate of commercial state of the art ZnO (Junsei, Japan), HPPLT TiO_2, commercial state of the art TiO_2 (P-25 Degussa, Germany) and ZnO powders synthesized by SCM. Here, state of the art commercial ZnO powder did not show detectable photocatalytic reaction while ZnO powders synthesized by SCM showed remarkable photocatalytic reactions. Especially, the powder synthesized using $Zn(OH)_2$ and glycine completely removed the Ag ions within 15 min. This Ag recovery rate is at least 3 folds higher than that of photocatalytic powders including HPPLT TiO_2 and commercial state of the art TiO_2 (P-25 Degussa, Germany). These results were strongly supported by the PL measurement data as mentioned above.

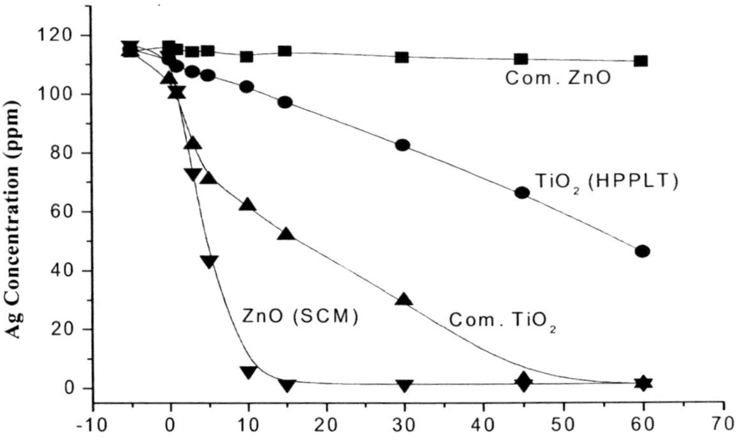

Figure 10. Ag recovery rate by photocatalytic reaction of commercial state of the art ZnO (Junsei, Japan), HPPLT TiO_2, commercial state of the art TiO_2 (P-25 Degussa, Germany) and the SCM ZnO powders synthesized with glycine/$Zn(OH)_2$ ratio of 0.8.

3.1.4. Summary

Surprisingly, the Ag ions in the waste development solution were completely removed within just 15 mins when the ZnO powder was used for photocatalytic reaction. This result confirms the outstanding photocatalytic characteristics of ZnO powder synthesized using SCM. The Ag recovery rate with the ZnO powder was at least 3 times higher than that of commercial state of the art photocatalytic powders including ZnO and TiO_2. This result strongly correlated with PL measurement data showing that the PL intensity of the ZnO powder was 3 times higher than that of the commercial state of the art TiO_2 powder. The high quality of the ZnO powder might be due to the fact that the high temperature, generated during SCM removed any defects.

To the author's knowledge, photocatalytic Ag removal from actual waste development solution (not simulated solution) has not been reported. The ZnO powder synthesized by SCM could be utilized for high efficiency photocatalytic reaction, UV-blocking cosmetics and other UV-related areas.

3.2. Removal of Cu^{++} Ions from Aqueous Cu-EDTA Solution

3.2.1. Background

Heterogeneous photocatalysis has been under extensive research not only for the removal of non-degradable organic chemicals like phenol [51-55] and its derivatives, but also for the recovery of heavy metal ions from waste water. The process has many advantages like simple system, lower operating cost and formation of more stable byproducts in the environment as compared to the conventional processes such as precipitation, carbon adsorption, ion exchange, membrane separation, air stripping, etc.used for degradation of organics, and for either disposal or recovery of metal ions in waste water [56].

Metal ions are generally non-degradable. They have infinite lifetimes, and build up their concentrations in food chains to toxic levels. In recent years, an array of industrial activities has disrupted the geological equilibrium of metal ions through release of large quantities of toxic metal ions into the environment. Again, the demand for metals increases significantly with the development of industry. Thus, waste metal recovery has the potential simultaneously to resolve two issues: metal pollution prevention and resource conservation.

The reduction of metal ions with semiconductor photocatalysis couples low-energy UV light with semiconductor particles acting as catalyst and is based on the reduction by photogenerated electrons. The metals are deposited onto the surface of semiconductor photocatalyst powder, and can be extracted from the slurry by physical and/or chemical means.

If the size of the photocatalyst powder decreases and reaches nano level, then its surface properties change as the ratio of the surface molecules with the bulk molecules increases simultaneously. This leads to the easy diffusion of the conduction band electrons and valence band holes through the surface to rapidly react with decomposing materials [57]. When the particle size is smaller than the wavelength of the incident light, light scattering is negligibly small. Thus, the nano-sized photocatalyst particles have the additional advantage of providing a transparent solution for efficient photoredox processes.

Titanium dioxide is the most used semiconductor photocatalyst powder these days and it has become nearly synonymous to the best photcatalyst powder. Our group is investigating the substitute of titanium dioxide and working on zinc oxide, another potential semiconductor photocatalyst. In this work, we report the comparative results of the reduction rates of copper ions in aqueous solution using the zinc oxide photocatalyst powder prepared in our laboratory and two different titanium dioxide photocatalyst powders.

3.2.2. Experiment

ZnO nanopowder was synthesized by the solution-combustion method as described above. For the purpose of comparing photocatalytic removal rates, P-25 titanium dioxide powder (Degussa, Germany) was purchased while the TiO_2 powder using homogeneous precipitation process at low temperature (HPPLT) was prepared following the synthesis method given in reference [58].

XRD and TEM were used to confirm the crystalline phase and particle size and shape respectively. The powder was then used as a photocatalyst for the removal of metal ions from aqueous solution. The reaction was carried out in a 100 ml batch-type quartz reactor with a diameter of 37 mm and height of 120 mm. A high-pressure mercury arc lamp was used as an external UV source. 52 ppm aqueous Cu-ethylenediaminetetraacetic acid (EDTA) solution was prepared by complexing 1:1 molar Na_2EDTA (Aldrich), the sacrificial donor agent [59-61] and reagent grade copper nitrate [$Cu(NO_3)_2$] (Aldrich) in distilled water. 3.0 g/L of the photocatalyst powder was mixed in the Cu^{++} solution and mixed ultrasonically for 5 minutes and left for half an hour in the dark for adsorption/ desorption equilibrium, stirring it magnetically. Then the UV light was turned on for the photocatalytic reaction. The concentrations of Cu^{++} ions remaining in the solution during different time intervals were detected with an AA spectrophotometer (Perkin-Elmer 5100 PC). Before the metal ions were dectected, the solution was passed through a syringe filter having pore size of 0.2μm for the removal of photocatalyst particles. TEM (JEOL JEM-4010, 200 kV) equipped with an energy-dispersive x-ray spectrometer (EDS) was used for analyzing the composition and shape of the respective photocatalyst-metal complexes containing metal that had been removed by the photoreduction reaction from the aqueous solutions.

3.2.3. Results and Discussion

Single-phase zinc oxide powder was obtained from the above experiment. Authors had selected two other semiconductor photocatalyst powders for the purpose of evaluating their efficiency in removing Cu^{++} ions from its aqueous solution in similar conditions and comparing the efficiency with the SCM prepared ZnO nanopowder. P-25 TiO_2 powder and HPPLT TiO_2 powder were selected for this purpose. P-25 powder is a commercially available photocatalyst powder and it has become one of the standard powders in photocatalytic experiments. In fact, many researchers have tried to compare other photocatalyst powders using it as a standard photocatalyst powder [62]. Lee et al. [58] has claimed that the HPPLT TiO_2 powder had 1.5 folds faster removal rate of Cu^{++} ions and Pb^{++} ions than P-25 powder.

The P-25 TiO_2 powder was a mixture of 70% anatage and 30% rutile phases having specific surface area of 55 m^2/g. The HPPLT TiO_2 powder was purely rutile phase powder with the specific surface area of 180-200 m^2/g, while the SCM ZnO powder was a single phase powder having the specific surface area of ~120 m^2/g.

Figure 11 shows the results of removal of Cu^{++} ions using different photocatalyst powders (SCM ZnO, P-25 TiO_2, and HPPLT TiO_2) from the aqueous metal-EDTA solution with an initial Cu^{++} concentration of 52 ppm. For convenience, the concentrations at 0 and 1 minutes of irradiation indicate the initial concentration and the equilibrium concentration of Cu^{++} ions after stirring the solution magnetically in the dark for half an hour, respectively. Complete removal of Cu^{++} ions from the solution was observed within the UV irradiation time of 90 minutes using SCM ZnO powder. As for the other two powders, however, complete removal of the ions could not be observed within the reaction time of 180 minutes. From this result, we could confirm that the Cu^{++} ions removal efficiency of SCM ZnO powder was at least twice the efficiency of other photocatalyst powders investigated.

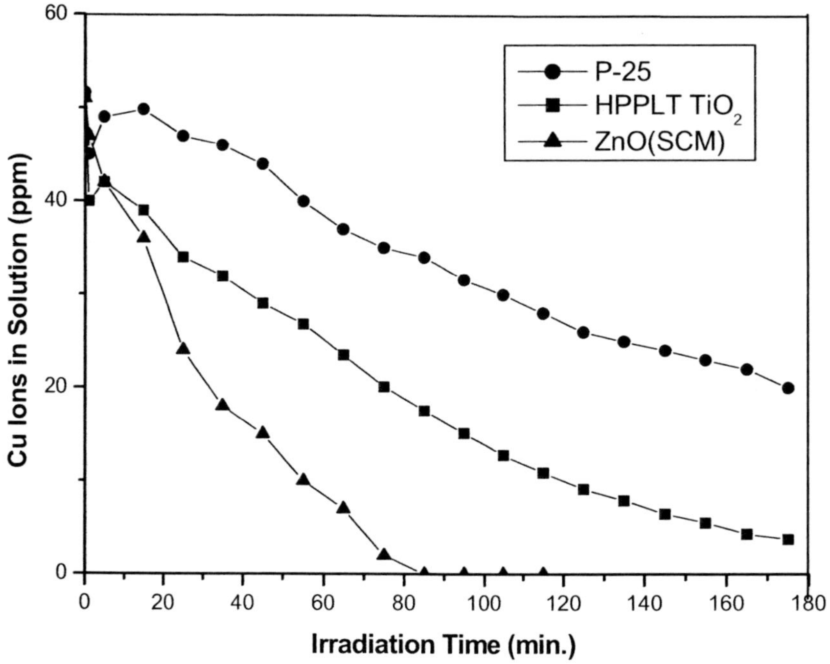

Figure 11. Comparison of Cu^{++} ions removal effeciency of differentphotocatlayst powders from the aqueous Cu-EDTA solution.

Figure 12 shows the TEM images of all the photocatalyst powders investigated after the photcatalysis experiments. In the images copper lumps can be clearly seen in SCM ZnO powder and on the surface edges, of HPPLT TiO_2 powder, but the lumps are larger in the former case. On the other hand, the copper lumps are small and sparse in the agglomerated P-25 powder. These results are also in agreement with the above results. The highest efficiency of the SCM ZnO powder among the above-investigated powders is attributed to its highest UV absorption capacity, which could be confirmed by the PL spectra.

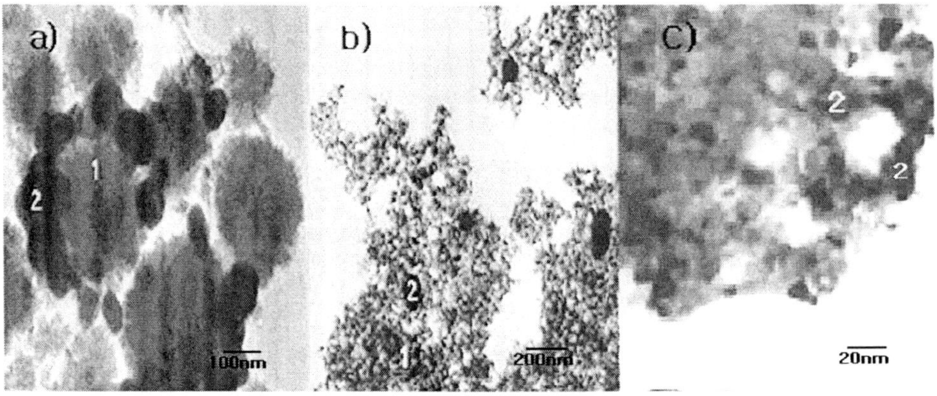

Figure 12. TEM images of different photocatalyst powders, showing lumps of copper on their surfaces, taken after the experiment. (a) HPPLT TiO_2 powder, (b) P-25 TiO_2 powder, and (c) SCM ZnO powder, in the figures: number1 represents the respective powder while number 2 represents the copper lumps.

3.2.4. Summary

To the best of our knowledge, this is the first time that such a fast removal of Cu^{++} ions from aqueous solution using photocatalyst powder has been reported. Zinc oxide nanopowder seems far more efficient than other photocatalyst powders like P-25 TiO_2 powder for removing toxic metal ions from solutions.

3.3. Removal of Pb^{++} Ions from Aqueous Wastewater

3.3.1. Background

Heterogeneously dispersed semiconductor surfaces provide an environment for influencing the chemical reactivity of a wide range of molecules and serve as a means to initiate light-induced redox reactivity in these molecules. The semiconductor surfaces basically are of the oxides of titanium, zinc, and tin. Upon photoexcitation of such surfaces, simultaneous oxidation and reduction reactions occur. The incident light that initiates this sequence is in the visible or low-energy ultraviolet regions of the spectrum. Investigations in the field began in order to develop photochemical and photocatalytic methods for utilizing the solar energy, widening the applications in chemical and environmental technologies [63]. Recent studies mainly focus on environmental problems such as purification of contaminated water and air [64, 65].

At a certain concentration, lead is a health hazard to both humans and animals and exerts its most toxic effects on the nervous system and kidneys. It is not biodegradable and cannot be decontaminated chemically in an aquatic environment. However, it can be removed by photocatalytic methods [66-68]

Titanium dioxide is the most widely used semiconductor photocatalyst powder as of now. Our research group is investigating the substitute of titanium dioxide and working on zinc oxide, another potential semiconductor photocatalyst. In this work, we report the comparative results of the reduction rates of lead ions in aqueous solution using SCM ZnO powder and two other different titanium dioxide photocatalyst powders.

3.3.2. Experiment

ZnO nanopowder was prepared by the solution-combustion method described above. Other photocatalyst powder, titanium dioxide (TiO_2, P-25), was purchased from Degussa, Germany and rutile TiO_2 powder was prepared by HPPLT.

XRD spectra of all the photocatalyst powders were taken to confirm their crystalline phases. At the same time, SEM images of the two synthesized powders were captured to observe their particle shape and size. The powders were then used as photocatalysts for removing metal ions from the aqueous solution. The reaction was carried out in a 100 ml batch-type quartz reactor with the diameter of 37 mm and height of 120 mm (fig.13.). A high-pressure mercury arc lamp was used as an external UV source. 150 ppm aqueous lead-ethylenediaminetetraacetic acid (Pb-EDTA) solution was prepared by complexing 1:1 molar Na_2EDTA (Aldrich, USA), the sacrificial donor agent [69] and reagent grade lead nitrate [$Pb(NO_3)_2$] (Aldrich, USA) in distilled water. 3.0 g/L of the above-prepared ZnO nanopowder was mixed in the Pb-EDTA solution and it was mixed ultrasonically for 5 minutes. The mixture was then stirred magnetically in the dark for half an hour for adsorption/ desorption equilibrium. UV light was then turned on for the photocatalytic reaction. The concentration of Pb^{++} ions remaining in the solution during different time intervals was detected with an AA spectrophotometer (Perkin-Elmer 5100 PC). Before the metal ions were dectected, the solution was passed through a syringe filter having a pore size of 0.2μm to remove photocatalyst particles. The same experiment was repeated for two types of photocatalyst powders (P-25 TiO_2 and HPPLT TiO_2). TEM (JEOL JEM-4010, 200 kV) equipped with an energy dispersive x-ray spectroscope (EDS) was used to analyze the composition and shape of the respective photocatalyst-metal/ metal oxide complexes after the photoreduction of lead (II) ions from the aqueous solutions.

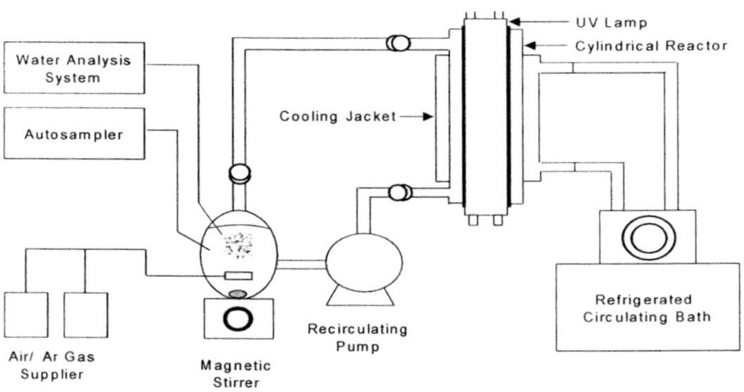

Figure 13. Schematic diagram of recirculating-cylindrical batch type reactor

3.3.3. Results and Discussion

As shown in fig. 14, the XRD patterns of P-25 TiO_2 showed anatage and rutile phases; however, the HPPLT TiO_2 powder showed only the rultile phase. Figure 15 shows the TEM image of HPPLT TiO_2 powder. It shows the chestnut burr shaped powder having a grain size of 200-400 nm. The grains are made up of needle-shaped primary particles having a diameter of 3-7 nm and length of 20-30 nm.

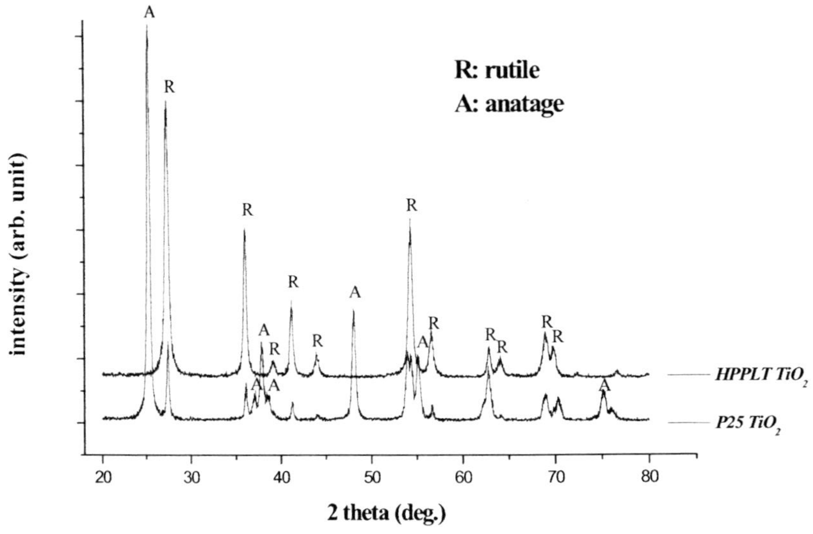

Figure 14. XRD spectra of HPPLT TiO_2 and P-25 TiO_2 powders

The ZnO powder was then subjected to a photocatalytic experiment, which aims to remove heavy metal ions. Other two powders, P-25 TiO_2 and HPPLT TiO_2 were also subjected to similar experiments for the purposes of evaluating their efficiency in removing Pb^{++} ions from its aqueous solution in similar conditions and comparing the efficiency of the SCM prepared ZnO nanopowder. P-25 TiO_2 is a commercially available photocatalyst powder and has become a standard photocatalyst powder in photocatalytic experiments. In fact, many researchers have tried to compare other photocatalyst powders by using it as a standard powder [62]. As mentioned above, the HPPLT TiO_2 powder was claimed to have 1.5 folds faster removal rate of Cu^{++} ions and Pb^{++} ions than P-25 powder.

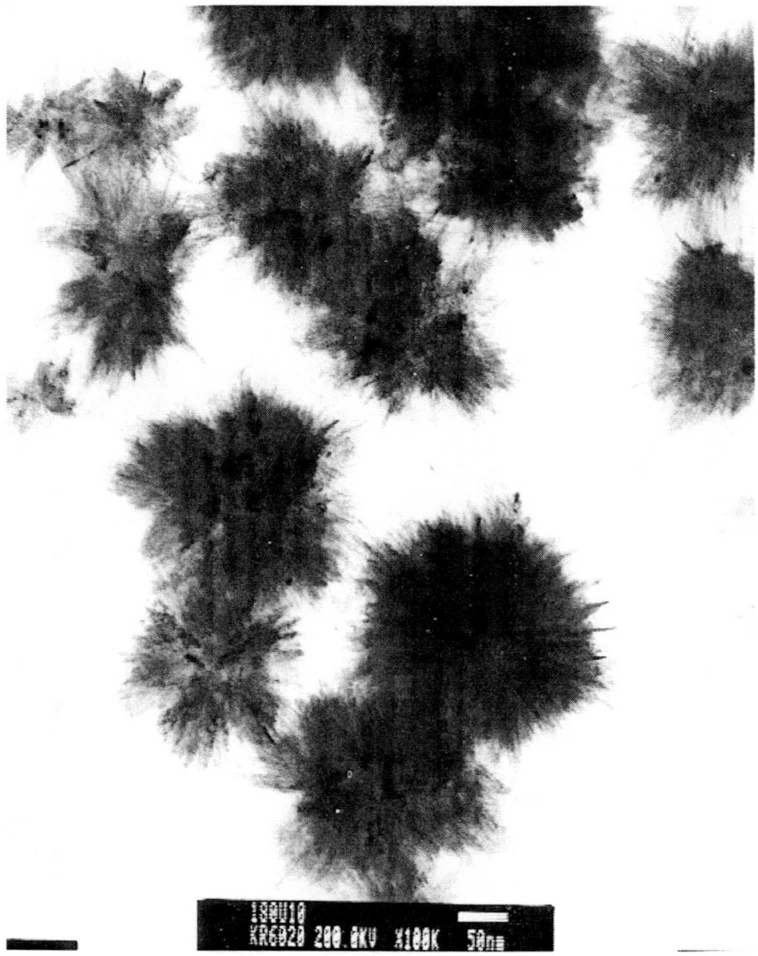

Figure 15. TEM image of HPPLT TiO_2 powder

Figure 16 shows the results of remaining Pb^{++} ions using different photocatalyst powders (SCM ZnO, P-25 TiO_2, and HPPLT TiO_2) from the aqueous Pb-EDTA solution with an initial Pb^{++} concentration of 150 ppm. For convenience, the concentrations at 0 and 1 minutes of irradiation indicate the initial concentration and the equilibrium concentration of Pb^{++} ions after stirring the solution magnetically in the dark for half an hour, respectively. Complete removal of Pb^{++} ions from the solution was observed within the UV irradiation time of 20 minutes using SCM ZnO powder. For the other two powders, however, it took almost 60 minutes in similar conditions to completely remove the lead ions with P-25 TiO_2 . The HPPLT TiO_2 took almost 40 minutes for the same. From this result, we could confirm that the Pb^{++} ions removal efficiency of SCM ZnO powder is at least twice the efficiency of other photocatalyst powders investigated.

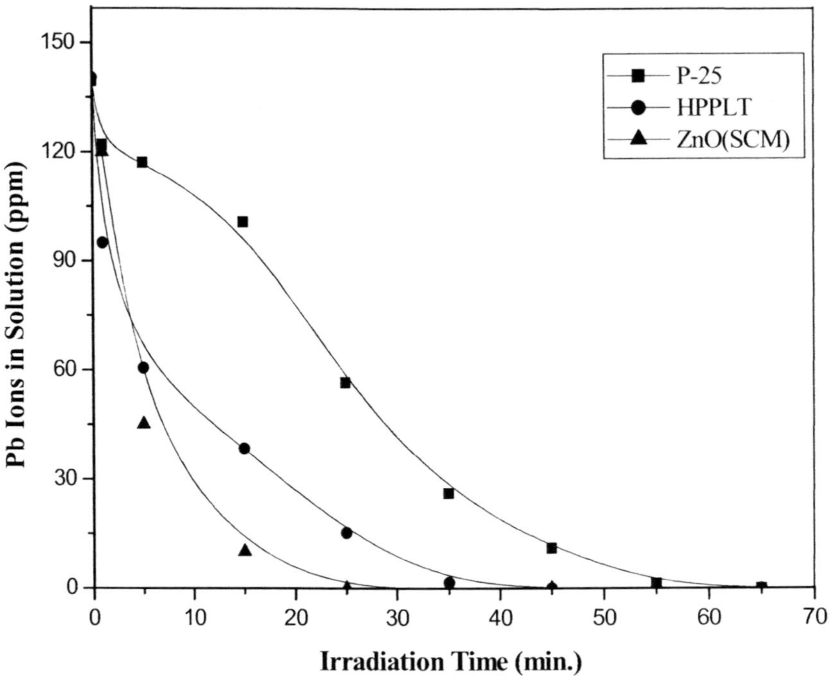

Figure 16. Comparison of Pb^{++} ions removal effeciency of different photocatlayst powders from the aqueous Pb-EDTA solution

Figure 17 shows TEM images of all the photocatalyst powders used after the photcatalysis experiments. In the images, platelet-shaped lead lumps (assigned with number 2 in the figure) can be clearly seen in SCM ZnO powder and HPPLT TiO_2 powder on the surface, with the lumps being larger in the former case. On the other hand, the lead lumps are small and sparse in the agglomerated P-25 powder. These results are also in agreement with the above results. The highest efficiency of the SCM ZnO nanopowder among the above-investigated powders is attributed to its highest UV absorption capacity, which could be confirmed by the PL spectra.

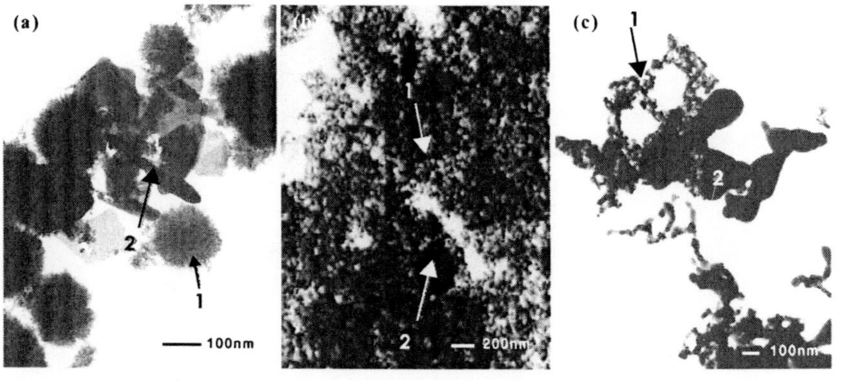

Figure 17. TEM images of different photocatalyst powders, showing lumps of lead on their surfaces, taken after the experiment. (a) HPPLT TiO_2 powder, (b) P-25 TiO_2 powder, and (c) SCM ZnO powder, in the figures: number 1 represents the respective powder while number 2 represents the lead lumps

3.3.4. Summary

ZnO nanopowder (~30 nm) was synthesized and the powder used in the photocatalytic removal of lead ions. Its removal capacity was compared with that of another commercially available photocatalyst powder, P-25 TiO_2. In our investigation, the zinc oxide nanopowder was far more active in removing lead ions from the aqueous lead-EDTA solution than the commercially available photocatalyst powder. The powder could be used in the efficient removal of heavy metal ions from aqueous waste.

3.4. Recovery of Au Ions from Wastewater

3.4.1. Background

Conventionally, precipitation has been the method most often used to remove heavy metals. Of the few precipitation methods, hydroxide precipitation is the most widely used one. However, this method is problematic, since all metal hydroxides do not completely precipitate at a single pH. This means that all of the various metals present in the wastewater cannot be accounted for. This limitation makes researchers study photocatalysts.

Photocatalysts have the unique capability of not only seperating and converting heavy metal ions from aqueous solution to their less toxic, readily recoverable metallic forms, but also destroying the toxic organic contaminants. Photocatalysis using titanium dioxide (TiO_2) has been extensively studied for oxidation and is known to be effective in the destruction of organics. Work on photocatalytic metal removal has been much less extensive. A process that can remove metals and destroy organics at the same time would represent a significant breakthrough for the treatment of heavy-metal-contaminated waters. In addition, metals deposited on the photocatalyst particle surface could be recovered. The particular aspect of being able to recover the heavy metals in metallic form minimizes the heavy metal toxicity and reduces the number of steps required for recovery. It was reported that metal ions such as lead, chromium, copper, silver and mercury could be removed/recovered from dilute aqueous solutions using TiO_2. [70-100] However, few studies have been conducted to recover metal ions using ZnO since it is well-known that TiO_2 is the best photocatalyst. [101]

In this study, ZnO nanopowder was prepared by a new "solution-combustion method (SCM)". To confirm its applicability, our attempts to recover gold metal ions took place in real plating wastewater, not simulated wastewater.

3.4.2. Experiment

ZnO nanopowder was synthesized by the solution-combustion method as reported earlier. For the purpose of comparing photocatalytic recovery rates, TiO_2 nanopowder (Degussa, Germany) was purchased. The powder was then used as a photocatalyst for removing metal ions from the aqueous solution. The reaction was carried out in a 100 ml batch-type quartz reactor with a diameter of 37 mm and height of 120 mm (fig.13). A high-pressure mercury arc lamp was used as an external UV source. Plating wastewater containing 60 ppm of gold ions was. 3.0 g/L of the photocatalyst powder was mixed in plating wastewater, and mixed ultrasonically for 5 minutes and left for 15min in the dark for adsorption/desorption equilibrium, stirring it magnetically. Then the UV light was turned on for the photocatalytic reaction. The concentrations of gold ions remaining in the plating wastewater during different time intervals were detected with an AA spectrophotometer (Perkin-Elmer 5100 PC). Before the detection of metal ions, the solution was passed through a syringe filter having pore size of 0.2 um to remove photocatalyst particles. A scanning electron microscope (SEM) was used to investigate the remaining materials after evaporation of water. An EDX (Energy Dispersive X-ray Spectrometer) was used to confirm the composition of the recovered materials. An optical microscope was also used to examine the recovered gold after removing the ZnO powder.

3.4.3. Results and Discussion

As shown in fig. 18, the photocatalytic reaction using SCM ZnO nanopowder shows that the gold ions were completely recovered after 45min of UV irradiation. However, the photocatalytic reaction using the state of the art commercial TiO_2 (P-25 Degussa, Germany) shows that only 17% of the gold ions were recovered after identical treatment. The photocatalytic gold recovery efficiency of SCM ZnO nanopowder is about 6 fold higher compared to that of the state of the art commercial TiO_2 nanopowder. Furthermore, when 10% of methanol (CH_3OH) was added to the solution, the gold ions were completely recovered after 30min of UV irradiation. Here the methanol acts as hole scavenger. This hole scavenger improved the photocatalytic efficiency by 33%. This is a surprising result. As well-known, TiO_2 is the best photocatalyst of its kind.

As shown in fig. 19, large particles were observed after the photocatalytic reaction, but no particle was observed before it. Furthermore, the color difference was also observed. It was gold and gray before photocatalytic reaction. However, it showed a pure gold color after photocatalytic reaction. Figure 20 shows the schematic representation of above photocatalytic reaction. At first, the gold ions and ZnO nanopowders were mixed together (fig. 20(a)). Then the gold ions were adsorbed on the ZnO nanopowder surfaces (fig. 20(b)). Eventually, the positive gold ions were reduced to neutral gold metal by receiving electrons that were generated on ZnO nanopowder surfaces by UV irradiation (fig. 20(c)). The SEM photograph of fig. 19(a) represents the state in which the gold ions and ZnO nanopowder were mixed together as shown in fig. 20(a). The SEM photograph of fig. 20(b) represents the state in which the gold ions were neutralized to gold metal on ZnO nanopowder surfaces as shown in fig. 20(c).

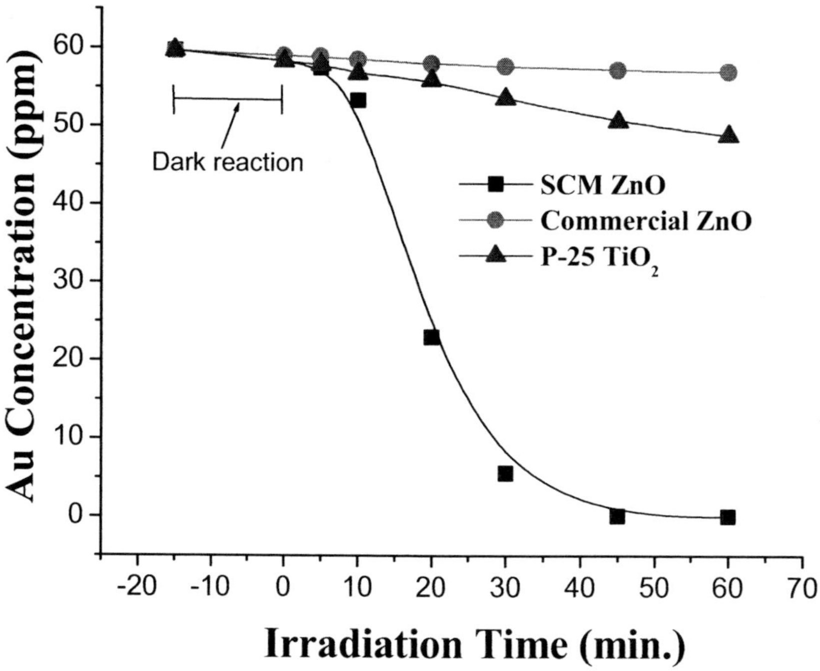

Figure 18. Au recovery rate by photocatalytic reaction of commercial ZnO (Junsei, Japan), commercial TiO_2 (P-25 Degussa, Germany) and the SCM ZnO powders synthesized in this study.

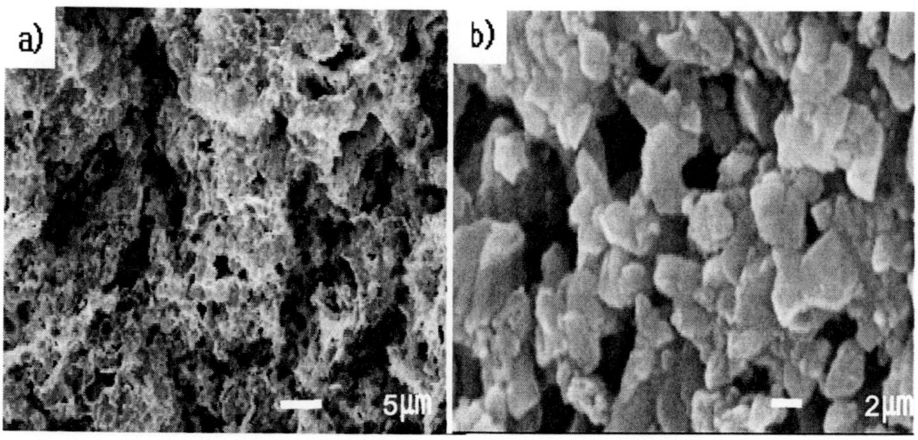

Figure 19. SEM photographs (a) before and (b) after photocatalytic reaction

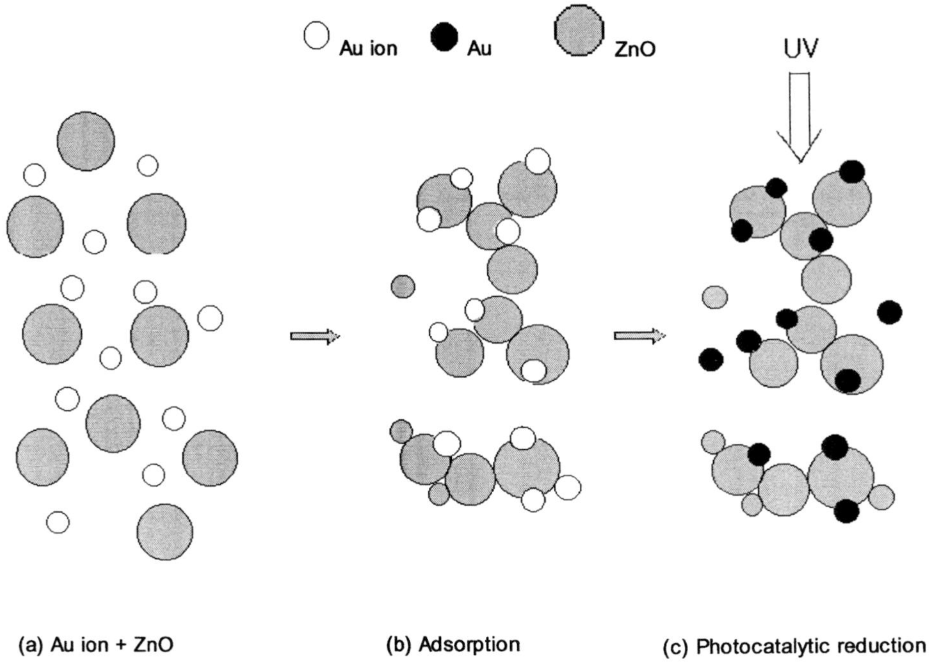

Figure 20. Schematic representation of photocatalytic reaction

EDX measurement was performed to confirm if this recovered metal was gold. Figure 21 showed weak gold peaks before photocatalytic reaction; however, it showed strong and sharp gold peaks after photocatalytic reaction. This suggests that photocatalytic reaction by SCM ZnO nanopowder produces gold particles from gold ions in solution. The calculation based on EDX measurement data showed that the purity of recovered gold was about 99.6% in weight% and 98.8% in atomic%.

Finally, the optical photograph of the recovered gold powder was obtained. Figure 22 clearly shows the recovered gold powders. The color is that of pure gold.

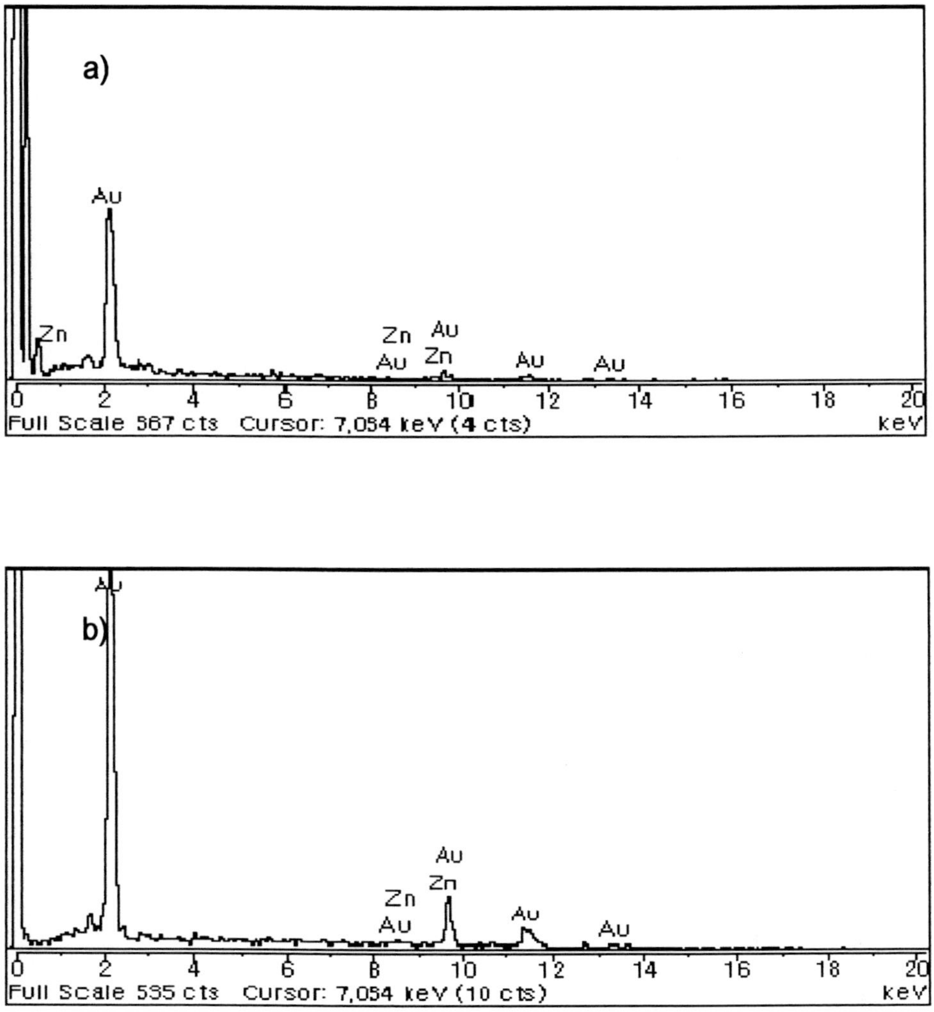

Figure 21. EDX patterns (a) before and (b) after photocatalytic reaction

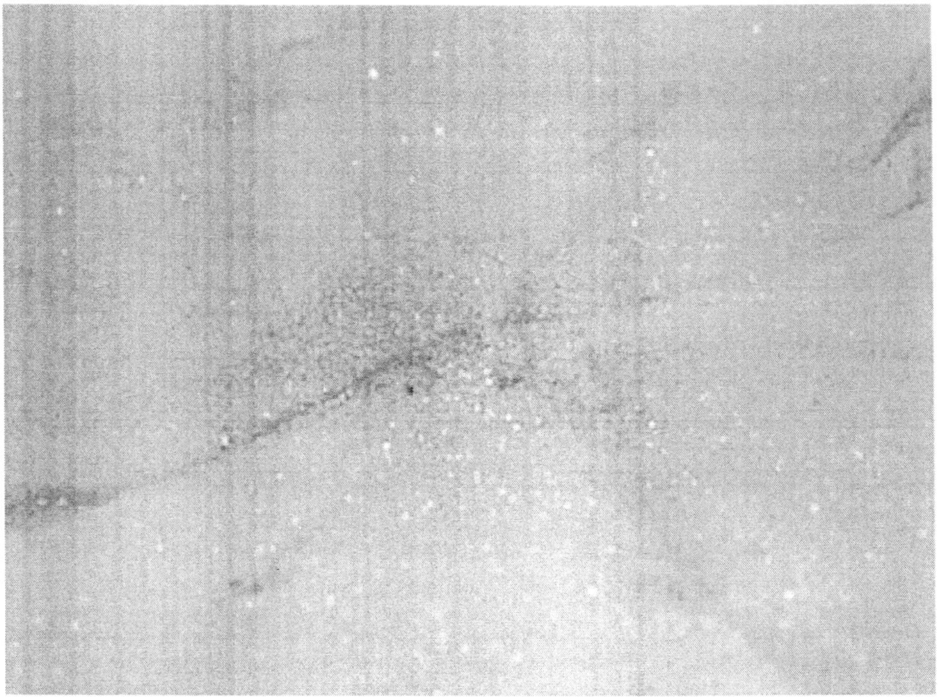

Figure 22. Optical photograph of recovered Au after photocatalytic reaction

3.4.4. Summary

In this study, ZnO nanopowders were synthesized by SCM. The photocatalytic gold recovery efficiency of this SCM ZnO nanopowder was about 6 fold higher compared to that of state of the art commercial TiO_2 nanopowder.

The purity of recovered gold was about 99.6% in weight% and 98.8% in atomic%. Furthermore, the ZnO nanopowder method of synthesis and gold recovery process are very cost-effective. This technology is very viable in obtaining high purity gold from plating wastewater.

Photocatalytic reactivity seems to depend on the preparation method of photocatalytic powders rather than the crystalline phase, specific surface area or even kinds of material. Preparation methods affect surface properties such as surface defect levels. Generally it is known that smaller particle size results in more surface defects. In the present SCM ZnO case, however, the level of surface defects seemed to be minimized even though the powder was synthesized in nano-size. This might be due to the high synthesis temperature that reaches about 1500-1800°C.

4. Destruction of Organic Pollutants in Wastewater

4.1. Background

The term 'heterogeneous photocatalysis' is associated with the process occurring in the intrinsic absorption band of semiconductor oxide catalyst, basically the oxides of titanium, zinc and tin. [103-105]. Investigations in the field began as a result of the demand for the development of photochemical and photocatalytic methods for utilizing solar energy, widening the application of photoinduced reactions in chemical and environmental technologies. Recent studies mainly concentrate on environmental problems such as purification of contaminated water and air. Semiconductors for photocatalytic reactions should have conditions such as high photoactivity, high photostability, and high sensitivity for UV-visible light and low cost for manufacture. Oxide semiconductors are getting much attention as they have a wide band gap energy and are easy to handle.

These days nanoparticles are getting considerable attention, as they possess different physical and chemical properties compared to their bulk counterparts. Improved catalytic efficiency of the semiconductor system can be expected as the surface area and modified surface sites in such particles increase.

In this work, the photocatalytic characteristics of the SCM ZnO nanopowder were investigated through the attempts at removing the total organic carbon (TOC) content from the aqueous phenol solution.

4.2. Experiment

ZnO nanopowder was synthesized by the solution-combustion method as reported earlier. The powder was then used as a photocatalyst to remove the total organic carbon (TOC) from aqueous phenol solution using a batch reactor as shown in the schematic diagram of fig.13. It consisted of a tubular cylindrical reactor with a centrally mounted UV lamp. A jacketed cooling system was used for temperature control. The aqueous phenol solution was mixed with the ZnO nanopowder using a magnetic stirrer and the solution mixture was circulated in the reactor where the reaction took place. The removal rate of TOC using the above-prepared ZnO nanopowder was compared with other photocatalytic powders to measure its catalytic efficiency.

4.3. Results and Discussion

The average particle size of the above prepared powder was calculated from TEM images shown in fig. 23. Finest particles (30 nm) were obtained when $Zn(OH)_2$ and glycine as an oxidant and fuel (F/O=0.8) were used, respectively. Here, the powder had a uniform nanometer size and was spherical in shape. At the same time, the specific surface area of the powder was $120m^2/g$. To prepare this powder, $Zn(OH)_2$ was dissolved in nitric acid solution to form zinc nitrate. Therefore, there would be excess nitrate (NO_3^-) groups in the solution. The (NO_3^-) group acts as an igniter for combustion, which presumably would be helpful for the fine particle size.

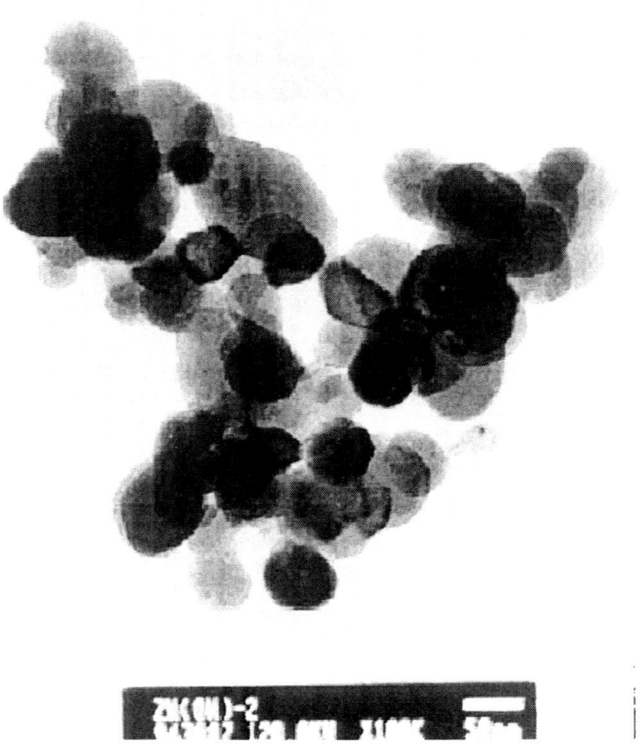

Figure 23. TEM image of the prepared ZnO nanopowder using glycine and $Zn(OH)_2$ (at the ratio of 0.8)

For the experiment, phenol was selected as a typical organic pollutant in water. Aqueous phenol solution of known concentration(~100ppm) was taken. We tried to degrade the phenol completely using the above mentioned ZnO nanopowder. Then its reaction rate was compared with other phtocatalysts to evaluate photocatalytic efficiency. The rates of reaction of different photocatalysts are shown in fig. 24. Here, ZnO nanopowder showed rapid photocatalytic reactions. When there was 300min of UV light irradiation, the nanotube type TiO_2 destroyed just 30% of phenol, P-25 TiO_2 nanopowder destroyed 50%, HPPLT TiO_2 nanopowder 60% and SCM ZnO nanopowder 80%. Therefore, SCM ZnO nanopowder shows 1.6 fold higher destruction rates of organic pollutants than P-25 TiO_2 nanopowder.

Here, small particle size might have led to greater photocatalytic efficiency. But the particle size may not be the only reason behind such a fast reaction rate. It might be strongly dependent on the UV absorption sensitivity of the prepared powder, which is supported by the PL measurement data.

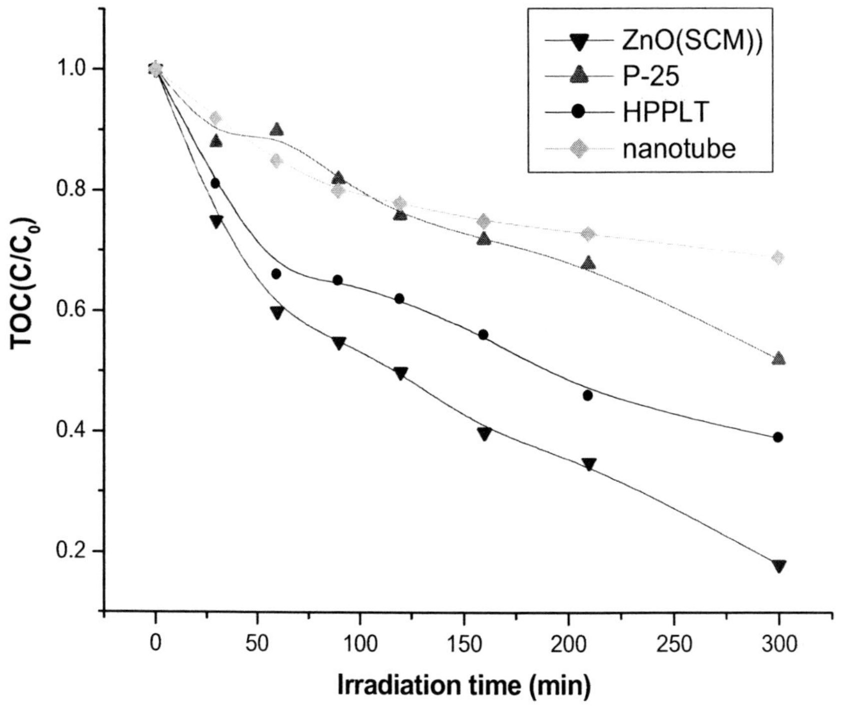

Figure 24. Comparison of TOC removal efficiency of the above prepared ZnO nanopowder with other powders and nanotube in the photocatalytic process

4.3. Summary

When SCM ZnO nanopowder was used as a photocatalyst to remove TOC from an aqueous phenol solution, the level of TOC in the solution decreased faster than other commercially available powders. This result confirms the outstanding photocatalytic characteristics of ZnO nanopowder synthesized using the solution combustion method. This result was strongly supported by the PL measurement data showing that the PL intensity of the ZnO powder was much higher than that of the commercial TiO_2 and ZnO powders. The high quality of the ZnO powder might be due to the defect removal by the high temperature generated during the synthesis process.

5. Summary and Conclusions

Zinc oxide is a large band-gap semiconductor having a bandgap energy of ~3.2 eV, which is similar to the bandgap energy of titanium dioxide, another prominent semiconductor photocatalyst used commercially in the removalof environmental pollutants. This study mainly focused on the synthesis of zinc oxide powder having high photocatalytic activity. Commercial zinc oxide powder shows low photocatalytic activity for degradation of organic and inorganic pollutants as it contains many defect structures, which enhance the rate of recombination of the generated electron-hole pairs responsible for redox reactions during photocatalytic experiments.

To obtain defect free and high purity zinc oxide powder, a novel self-propagating process initiated at low temperature using redox compounds and mixtures in solution was investigated. The process makes use of highly exothermic redox chemical reactions between metals and non-metals. The method is referred to as the "solution-combustion method (SCM). The process is simple, fast, and cost-effective and yields high purity products compared to the conventional methods used to prepare the same material.

Two different fuels (reductants), glycine and carbohydrazide were used in varying proportions with oxidant precursors (zinc nitrate hexahydrate or zinc hydroxide dissolved in nitric acid to form zinc nitrate solution) to synthesize different powders. The fuel was mixed with a precursor dissolved in water and the mixture was heated to a temperature between 100-200^{0}C whereby a highly exothermic reaction took place with the formation of pure oxide powder of very fine morphology.

The formed zinc oxide powders were characterized using different powder evaluation techniques such as SEM, TEM, BET, XRD, and PL spectra measurements. SEM and TEM revealed the formation of uniform particle size in the nanometer range. Finest particles were obtained at the fuel: oxidant molar ratio of 0.8 when glycine and zinc hydroxide dissolved in nitric acid was used as a fuel and an oxidant, respectively. The finest particles were 30 nm and the surface area of the nanopowder was measured to be 120m^2/g. XRD measurement showed single-phase zinc oxide particles. PL spectra of the above-prepared nanopowder was taken and compared with the PL spectra of the commercial zinc oxide powder. The spectra revealed the defect free nature and high UV absorption capacity of the synthesized nanopowder.

To confirm photocatalytic activities of the synthesized ZnO powder, we tried to remove Ag ions from waste development solution. The Ag ions were completely removed within 15 min. This Ag recovery rate is at least 3 fold higher than that of commercial state of the art TiO_2.

The removal of copper ions from the aqueous solution of Cu-EDTA and lead ions from Pb-EDTA was carried out and the removal efficiency of the SCM ZnO nanopowder was again compared with the removal efficiencies of the P-25 TiO_2 and HPPLT TiO_2 powders. Here the removal efficiency of the SCM ZnO was at least 1.5 fold higher than the other photocatalyst powders.

The photocatalytic gold recovery efficiency by this SCM ZnO nanopowder was about 6 fold higher compared to the state of the art commercial TiO_2 nanopowder. The purity of the recovered gold was about 99.6% in weight% and 98.8% in atomic%. Furthermore, the ZnO nanopowder synthesizing method and gold recovery process are very cost-effective. Our attempts to recover gold metal ions took place in real plating wastewater, not simulated wastewater. This technology is therefore very viable in obtaining high purity gold from plating wastewater.

The synthesized nanopowder was then used in aqueous solutions for the degradation of representative organic pollutant, phenol (photocatalytic oxidation process) in aqueous solution. A comparison of degradation rates shows SCM ZnO nanopowder has 1.6 fold higher destruction rates of organic pollutants than P-25 TiO_2 nanopowder.

Photocatalysis is a surface phenomena and the method of preparing the powder plays a vital role in obtaining efficient photocatalyst powder. Such a high photocatalytic efficiency of the SCM ZnO nanopowder was probably due to the same reason. The powder size was in the nanometer range and had a high surface area, which would have enhanced the adsorption of the substrate molecules. From the PL spectra, the powder showed no defect levels inside the bandgap region thus decreasing the recombination rate of the formed electron-hole pairs. As the PL intensity in the UV region was almost 3 fold higher than other photocatalyst powders, the SCM ZnO nanopowder would have absorbed more UV light, forming more electrons and holes in the conduction and valence band, which could either reduce or oxidize the substrate molecules having suitable redox potentials. All those favorable characteristics of the ZnO powder enhanced its photocatalytic efficiency and showed the highest efficiency for the degradation of organic contaminants and removal of heavy metal ions from aqueous solution.

Photocatalytic reaction using SCM ZnO nanopowders could be very valuable technology in view of the following two applications. Expensive noble metals such as silver and gold could be economically recovered using this technology while simultaneously removing toxic heavy metal ions and organic pollutants from wastewater for environmental purposes.

REFERENCES

[1] Levinson L. M. (Editor) (1988) *Electronic Ceramics - Properties, Devices, and Applications* (Marcel Dekker, Inc., New York).

[2] Wada K., Yoshida K., Takatani T.& Watanabe Y. "Selective photo-oxidation of light alkanes using solid metal oxide semiconductors." (1993) *Appl. Catal. A- Gen.,* 99 (1) 21.

[3] Zin Z. C., Hamberg I. & Granqvist C. G. "Optical properties of sputter-deposited ZnO:Al thin films." (1988) *J. Appl. Phys.,* 64, 5117.

[4] Li Y., Thompa G. S., Liang S., Gorla C., Lu Y.& Doyle J. " Transparent and conductive Ga-doped ZnO films grown by low pressure metal organic chemical vapor deposition." (1997) *J. Vac. Sci. Technol. A*, 15, 1063.

[5] Brown H. E. (1976) *Zinc oxide* (International Lead Zinc Research Organization, Inc., New York).

[6] Hirschwald W. H. et al. (1981) *Current Topics in Materials Science*, 7, Chapter 3, 143.

[7] Bagnall D. M., Chen Y. F., Zhu Z. Q., Yao T., Koyama S, Shen M. Y.& Goto T. "Optically pumped lasing of ZnO at room temperature." (1997) *Appl. Phys. Lett.,* 70, 2230.

[8] Bagnall D. M, Chen Y. F., Zhu Z. Q., Yao T., Shen M. Y.& Goto T. "High temperature excitonic stimulated emission from ZnO epitaxial layers." (1998) *Appl. Phys. Lett.,* 73, 1038.

[9] Mills A. & Hunte S. L. "An Overview of semiconductor photocatalysis." (1997) *J. Photochem. Photobiol.*, 108, 1.

[10] Sehili T., Boule P.& Lemaire J. "Photocatalysed transformation of chloroaromatic derivatives on zinc oxide III: Dichlorobenzenes." (1989) *J. Photochem. Photobio. A*, 50, 103.

[11] Villasenor J., Reyes P.& Pecchi G. "Photodegradation of pentachlorophenol on ZnO." (1998) *J. Chem. Technol. Biotechnol.*, 72, 105.

[12] Driessen M. D., Miller T. M. & Grassian V. H. "Photocatalytic oxidation of trichloroethylene on zinc oxide : characterization of surface-bound and gas-phase products and intermediates with FT-IR spectroscopy." (1998) *J. Mol. Catal. A: Chem.*, 131, 149.

[13] Khalil L. B., Mourad W. E. & Rophael M. W. "Photocatalytic reduction of environmental pollutant Cr(VI) over some semiconductors under UV/visible light illumination." (1998) *Appl. Catal. B: Environ.*, 17, 267.

[14] Poulios I., Kositzi M. & Kouras A. "Photocatalytic decomposition of triclopyr over aqueous semiconductor suspensions." (1998) *J. Photochem. Photobio. A:Chemistry* 115, 175.

[15] Mansilla H. D., Yeber M. C., Freer J., Rodriguez J. & Baeza J. "Homogeneous and heterogeneous advanced oxidation of a bleaching effluent from the plup and paper industry." (1997) *Wat. Sci. Tech.*, 35 (4) 273.

[16] Sakthivel S., Neppolian B., Shankar M. V., Arabindoo B., Palanichamy M. & Murugesan V. "Solar photocatalytic degradation of azo dye: comparison of photocatalytic efficency of ZnO and TiO_2." (2003) *Sol. Energy Mat. & Sol. Cells*, 77, 65.

[17] Li D. & Haneda H. "Morphologies of zinc oxide particles and their effects on photocatalysis." (2003) *Chemosphere*, 51, 129.

[18] Muhammed M. "Gas phase synthesis and mechanical properties of nanomaterials." (1996) *Analusis*, 24, M12.

[19] Liu T., Sakurai O., Mizutani N. & Kato M. "Preparation of spherical fine ZnO particles by the spray pyrolysis method using ultrasonic atomization techniques." (1986) *J. Mater. Sci.*, 21, 3698.

[20] Westin G. & Nygren M. "On the formation of M^{2+}-Sb^{3+}-alkoxide precursors and sol-gel processing of M-Sb oxides with M=Cr,Mn,Fe,Co,Ni,Cu and Zn."(1992) *J. Mater. Sci.*, 27, 1617.

[21] Westin G., Ekstrand A., Nygren M., Osterlund R. & Merkelbach E.A. "Preparation of ZnO-based varistors by the sol-gel technique." (1994) *J. Mater. Chem.*, 4, 615.

[22] Meulenkamp E.A. "Synthesis and Growth of ZnO Nanoparticles." (1998) *J. Phys. Chem. B,* 102, 5566.

[23] Chiou B., Tsai Y. J. & Duh J. "Thermal evolution in synthesized ZnO varistors by the urea process." (1988) *J. Mater. Sci. Lett.*, 7, 785.

[24] Costa M. E. V. & Baptista J. L. "Characteristics of zinc oxide powders precipitated in the presence of alcohols and amines."(1993) *J. Eur. Ceram. Soc.*, 11, 275.

[25] Sekar M. A. & Patil K. C. "Combustion synthesis and properties of fine-particle dielectric oxide materials."(1992) *J. Mater. Chem.*, 2, 739.

[26] Dhas A & Patil K. C. "Combustion synthesis and properties of Zircornia-Alumina powders." (1994) *Ceram. Int.*, 20, 57.

[27] Fumo D. A., Morelli M. R. & Segadaes A. M. "Combustion synthesis of Calcium Aluminates." (1996) *Mater. Res. Bull.*, 31 (10) 1243.

[28] Park S., Lee K. R., Jung C. H., Kim S. J. & Shin H. C. "Preparation of $La_{0.84}Sr_{0.16}CrO_3$ powders by pH-controlled glycine-nitrate process."(1996) *Jpn. J. Appl. Phys.*, 35, L996.

[29] Park S., Park I. S., Kim S. J. & Lee B. H. "Sintering and electrical properties of $(CeO_2)_{0.9}(Gd_2O_3)_{0.1}$ powders prepared by glycine-nitrate process for solid oxide fuel cell applications." (1997) *Jpn. J. Appl. Phys.*, 36, 6426.

[30] Aruna S. T., Ghosh S. & Patil K. C. "Combustion synthesis and properties of $Ce_{1-x}Pr_xO_{2-\delta}$ red ceramic pigments." (2001) *Int. J. Inorg. Mater.*, 3, 387.

[31] Anuradha T. V., Ranganathan S., Mimani T. & Patil K. C. "Combustion synthesis of nanostructured Barium Titanate." (2001) *Scripta Mater.*, 44, 2237.

[32] Jain S. R., Adiga K. C. & Verneker V. R. P. "A new approach to thermochemical calculations of condensed fuel-oxidizer mixtures." (1981) *Combust. Flame*, 40, 71.

[33] Budavari S., O'Neil M. J., Smith A., Heckelman P. E. & Kinneary J. F. (1996) *The Merck Index, 12th ed.* (Merck & Co., Inc, New Jersey, p.1849).

[34] Parmon V. N. "Photocatalysis as a phenomenon : Aspects of terminology." (1997) *Catalysis Today*, 39, 137.

[35] Krasnovsky A. A. & Nikandrov V. V. "The Photobiocatalytic system : Inorganic semiconductors coupled to bacterial cells." (1987) *FEBS Letters*, 219 [1] 93.

[36] Farrauto R. J. & Heck R. M. "Environmental catalysis into the 21st century." (2000) *Catalysis Today*, 55, 179.

[37] Fujishima A. & Rao T. N. "Interfacial photochemistry: Fundamentals and applications." (1998) *Pure & Appl. Chem.*, 70, 2177.

[38] Lee S. H. & Lim H. S. "TiO_2-The principles and applications of photocatalytic reaction." (1999) *Ceramist*, 2 [2] 79 (in Korea).

[39] Zou Z., Ye J., Sayama K. & Arakawa H. "Direct splitting of water under visible light irradiation with an oxide semiconductor photocatalyst." (2001) *Nature*, 414, 625.

[40] Bahnemann D. W., Kholuiskaya S. N., Dillert R., Kulak A. I. & Kokorin A. I. "Photodestruction of dichloroacetic acid catalyzed by nano-sized TiO_2 particles." (2002) *Appl. Catal. B: Environ.*, 36, 161.

[41] Volodin A. M. "Photoinduced phenomena on the surface of wide-band-gap oxide catalysts." (2002) *Catalysis Today*, 58, 103.

[42] Chatterjee D. & Mahata A. "Demineralization of organic pollutants on the dye modified TiO_2 semiconductor particulate system using visible light." (2001) *Appl. Catal. B: Environ.*, 33, 119.

[43] Wilcoxon J. P., Thurston T. R. & Martin J. E. "Applications of metal and semiconductor nanoclusters as thermal and photo-catalysts." (1999) *Nanostructured Materials*, 12, 993.

[44] Carnes C. L. & Klabunde K. J. "Synthesis, isolation and chemical reactivity studies of nanocrystalline zinc oxide." (2000) *Langmuir*, 16, 3764.

[45] Wang L. & Muhammed M. "Synthesis of zinc oxide nanoparticles with controlled morphology." (1999) *J. Mater. Chem.*, 9, 2871.

[46] Vanheusden K., Seager C. H., Warren W. L., Tallant D. R., Caruso J., Hampden-Smith M. J. & Kodas T. T. "Green photoluminescence efficiency and free-carrier density in ZnO phosphor powders prepared by spray pyrolysis." (1997) *J. Lumin..*, 75, 11.

[47] Chu S. Y., Yan T. M. & Chen S. L. "Characteristics of sol-gel synthesis of ZnO-based powders." (2000) *J. Mater. Sci. Lett.*, 19 [4] 349.

[48] Park S., Kim S. J., Lee B. H. & Park I. S. "Sintering and electrical properties of $(CeO_2)_{0.9}(Gd_2O_3)_{0.1}$ powders prepared by glycine-nitrate process for solid oxide fuel cell applications." (1997) *Jpn. J. Appl. Phys.*, 36, 6426.

[49] Park S., Lee H. W., Song J. S., Kim W. W. & Lee C. R. "Synthesis and Ag recovery of nanosized ZnO powder by solution combustion process for photocatalytic applications." (2001) *Journal of Materials Synthesis and Processing*, 9 [5] 281.

[50] Park S., Song J. S. & Lee K. R. "Characteristics of $La_{0.7}Ca_{0.3}MnO_3$ powders prepared by solution combustion method and solid state reaction method for CMR applications." (2002) *Journal of Materials Synthesis and Processing*, 10 [1] 47.

[51] Ilisz, Laszio Z.& Dombi A., "Investigation of the photodecomposition of phenol in near-UV-irradiated aqueous TiO_2 suspensions. I: Effect of charge-trapping species on the degradation kinetics." (1999) *Appl. Catal. A: Gen.*, 180, 25.

[52] Chen D. & Ray A.K. "Photocatalytic kinetics of phenol and its derivatives over UV irradiated TiO_2." (1999) *Appl. Catal. B: Environ.*, 23, 143.

[53] Li X., Cubbage J. W., Tetzlaff T. A.& Jenks W. S. "Photocatalytic degradation of 4-chlorophenol: 1. The hydroquinone pathway." (1999) *J. Org. Chem.*, 64 (23) 8509.

[54] Li X., Cubbage J. W., Tetzlaff T. A. & Jenks W. S. "Photocatalytic Degradation of 4-chlorocatechol: 2. The 4-Chlorocatechol Pathway." (1999) *J. Org. Chem.,* 64 (23) 8525.

[55] Mills A. & Sawunyama P. "Photocatalytic degration of 4-chlorophenol mediated by TiO_2: a comparative study of the activity of laboratory made and commercial TiO_2 samples." (1994) *J. Photochem. Photobiol. A: Chem.,* 84, 305.

[56] Serpone N., Boragarello E. & Pelizzette E. (1988) *In M. Schiavelb (Ed.), Photocatalysis and Environment, Trends and Applications*, (Dordrecht: Kluwer p. 527).

[57] Beydoun D., Amal R., Low G. & McEvoy S., "Role of nanoparticles in photocatalysis" (1999) *J. Nanoparticle Res.,* 1 (4) 439.

[58] Lee K. R., Kim S. J., Song J. S., Lee J. H., Chung Y. J. & Park S. "Photocatalytic characteristics of nanometer-sized titania powders fabricated by a homogeneous-precipitation process." (2002) *J. Am. Ceram. Soc.* 85 (2) 341.

[59] Hoffmann M. Z., Prasad D. R., Jones II G. & Malba V. "Formation of photoactive charge-transfer complexes between methyl viologen and sacrifical electron donors. EDTA and triethanolamine." (1983) *J. Am. Chem. Soc.,* 105, 6360.

[60] Ayres J. A. (1970) *Decontamination of Nuclear Reactors and Equipment* (Ronald, New York, p.6)

[61] Loy L. & Wolf E. E. "Photo induced hydrogen evolution from water in the presence of EDTA and a Pt/TiO_2 supported catalyst." (1985) *Sol. Energy* 34 (6) 455.

[62] Matthews R. W. & McEvoy S. R. "A comparison of 254 nm and 350 nm excitation of TiO_2 in simple photocatalytic reactors." (1992) *J. Photochem. Photobiol. A: Chem.,* 66, 355.

[63] Ollis D. F., Pellizetti E. & Serpone N. (1989) *Heterogeneous Photocatalysis in Water Purification* (Wiley, New York).

[64] Fujisima A.& Rao T. N. "Interfacial photochemistry: fundamental and applications" (1998) *Pure & Appl. Chem.,* 70 (11) 2177.

[65] Lee S. H.& Lim H. S. "Principles and applications of TiO_2-photocatalytic reactions" (1999) *Ceramist* 2, 79 (in Korean).

[66] Lawless D., Res A., Harris R., Serpone N., Minero C., Pelizzetti E. & Hidaka H. "Removal of toxic metal from solutions by photocatalysis using irradiated platinized titanium dioxide: removal of lead." (1990*) Chim. & Ind. (Milan)* 72, 139.

[67] Tennakone & Wijayantha K.G.U. "Heavy-metal extraction from aqueous solution with an immobilized TiO_2 photocatalyst and a solid sacrificial agent." (1998) *J. Photochem. Photobiol. A: Chem.,* 113, 89.

[68] Muhammad S. V. & Allen P. D., "TiO_2-assisted photocatalysis of lead-EDTA" (2000) *Wat. Res.,* 34 (3) 952.

[69] Loy E.E. Wolf, "Photo induced hydrogen evolution from water in the presence of EDTA and a Pt/TiO_2 supported catalyst." (1985) *Sol. Energy* 34 (6) 455.

[70] Aguado M. A., Gimenez J. & Cervera-March S. "Continuous photocatalytic treatment of chromium(VI) effluents with semiconductor powders." (1991) *Chem. Eng. Commum.,* 104, 71.

[71] Garcia Gonzalez M. L. & Salvador P. "Titanium dioxide photoetching mechanisms: efficient photocatalytic corrosion of rutile in the presence of dichromate." (1992) *J. Electroanal. Chem.,* 326, no. 1-2: 323.

[72] Prairie M. R., Evans L. R. & Martinez S. L. "Destruction of organics and removal of heavy metals in water via TiO_2 photocatalysis." (1992) *Chemical Oxidation: Technology for the Nineties, Second Int. Symp. Nashville, Tennessee,* 19 February.

[73] Prairie M. R., Evans L. R., Stange B. M., & Martinez S. L. "An investigation of TiO_2 photocatalysis for the treatment of water contaminated with metals and organic chemicals." (1993) *Environ. Sci. Technol.,* 27, no. 9: 1776.

[74] Sabate J., Anderson M. A., Aguado M. A., Gimenez J., Cervera-March S. & Hill Jr. C. G. "Comparison of TiO_2 powder suspensions and TiO_2 ceramic membranes supported on glass as photocatalytic systems in the reduction of chromium(VI)." (1992) *J. Mol. Cat.,* 71, 57.

[75] Yoneyama H., Matsumoto N., Furusawa T. & Tamura H. "Temperature dependence on the rate of heterogeneous reactions on titanium(N) oxide photocatalysts." (1984) *Nippon Kagaku Kaishi,* no. 2 253.

[76] Zhang C., Jiarg Y., Liu W., Yang H., Li T. & Xiao L. "Study of titania ultrafine powder photocatalyst in reducing dichromate(Cr2O72-)." (1991) *Taniyangneng Xuebao 12,* no. 2 176.

[77] Bideau M., Claudel B., Faure L. & Kazouan H. "The photooxidation of propionic acid by oxygen in the presence of titania and dissolved copper ions." (1992) *J. Photochem. Photobiol., A* 67 no. 3, 337.

[78] Butler E. C. & Davis A. P. "Photocatalytic oxidation in aqueous titanium dioxide suspensions: the influence of dissolved transition metals." (1993) *J. Photochem. Photobiol. A: Chem.,* 70, 273.

[79] Reiche H., Dunn W. W. & Bard A. J. "Heterogeneous photocatalytic and photosynthetic deposition of copper on titanium dioxide and tungsten(VI) oxide powders." (1979) *J. Phys. Chem.,* 83, no. 17 2248.

[80] Bideau M., Claudel B., Faure L. & Kazouan H. "The photooxidation of acetic acid by oxygen in the presence of titanium dioxide and dissolved copper ions." (1991) *J. Photochem. Photobiol., A* 61, no. 2 269.

[81] Bideau M., Claudel B., Faure L. & Rachimoellah M. "Photooxidation of formic acid by oxygen in the presence of titanium dioxide and dissolved copper ions: oxygen transfer and reaction kinetics." (1990) *Chem. Eng. Commun.,* 93, 167.

[82] Lawless D., Res A., Harris R., Serpone N., Minero C., Pelizzetti E. & Hidaka H. "Removal of toxic metal from solutions by photocatalysis using irradiated platinized titanium dioxide: removal of lead." (1990) *Chim. Ind.* 72, no. 2 139.

[83] Torres J. & Cervera-March S. "Kinetics of the photoassiated catalytic oxidation of lead(II) in titania suspensions." (1992) *Chem. Eng. Sci.,* 47, no. 15-16, 3857.

[84] Prairie M. R., Pacheco J. & Evans L. R. *"Solar detoxification of water containing chlorinated solvents and heavy metals via TiO_2 photocatalysis."* (1992) Proc. of ASME Int. Sol. Engineering conf. 2 April 1992. Solar Engineering 92, Stein, W., Kreider, J., and Watanabe, K., Eds. New York, NY, ASME 1.

[85] Serpone N., Ah-You Y. K., Tran T. P., Harris R., Pelizzetti E. & Hidaka H. "AM1 simulated sunlight photoreduction and elimination of mercury(+2) and methylmercury (CH3Hg)(+2) chloride salts from aqueous suspensions of titanium dioxide." (1987) *Sol. Energy* 39, no. 6, 491.

[86] Hutchinson B., Cockrum D., Clark C., Pamplin K., Scoggins T., Sloan D. & Reeves P. "Photocatalytic destruction of toxic organic compounds in aqueous solution."(1990) *Sol. 90 Conf.* Austin, Texas, March.

[87] Tennakone K., Thaminimulle C. T. K., Senadeera S. & Kumarasinghe A. R. "TiO_2-catalyzed oxidative photodegradation of mercurochrome: an example of an organo-mercury compound." (1993) *J. Photochem. Photobiol., A* 70, no. 2, 193.

[88] Baciocchi E., Rol C., Rosato G. C. & Sebastiani G. V. "Titanium dioxide photocatalyzed oxidation of benzyltrimethylsilane in the presence of silver sulfate." (1992) *J. Chem. Soc., Chem. Commun.,* no. 1, 59.

[89] Kobayakawa K., Nakazawa Y., Ikeda M., Sato Y. & Fujishima A. "Influence of the density of surface hydroxyl groups on TiO_2 photocatalytic activities." (1990) *Ber. Bunsenges. Phys. Chem.,* 94, 1439.

[90] Ohtani B., Kakimoto M., Miyadzu H., Nishimoto S. & Kagiya T. "Effect of surface-adsorbed 2*propanol on the photocatalytic reduction of silver and/or nitrate ions in acidic TiO_2 suspension." (1988) *J. Phys. Chem.,* 92, 5773.

[91] Ohtani B., Zhang S., Handa J., Kajiwara H., Nishimoto S. & Kagiya T. "Photocatalytic activity of titanium(N) oxide prepared from titanium(N) tetra-2-propoxide: reaction in aqueous silver salt solutions." (1992) *J. Photochem. Photobiol. A: Chem.,* 64, 223.

[92] Ohtsni B. & Nishimoto S. "Effect of surface adsorptions of aliphatic alcohols and silver ion on the photocatalytic activity of titania suspended in aqueous solutions." (1993) *J. Phys. Chem.,* 97, no. 4, 920.

[93] Pelizzetti E., Borgarello M., Minero C., Pramauro E., Borgarello E. & Serpone N. "Photocatalytic degradation of polychlorinated dioxins and polychlorinated biphenyls in aqueous suspensions of semiconductors irradiated solar light." (1988) *Chemosphere 17,* no. 3, 499.

[94] Sakata T., Kawai T. & Hashimoto K, "Heterogeneous photocatalytic reactions of organic acids and water. New reaction paths besides the photo-Kolbe reaction." (1984) *J. Phys. Chem.* 88, 2344.

[95] Sato S. & Kadowaki T. "Photoevolution of oxygen from metal oxide semiconductor suspension in aqueous silver salt solution." (1989) *Denki Kagaku oyobi Kogyo Butsuri Kagaku* 57, no. 12, 1151.

[96] Sato S., Sobczynski A., White J. M., Bard A. J., Campion A., Fox M. A., Mallouk T. E. & Webber S. E. "Photochemical properties of ultrathin titaium dioxide films prepared by chemical vapor deposition." (1989) *J. Photochem. Photobiol., A* 50, no. 2, 283.

[97] Sclafani A., Palmisano L. & Davi E. "Photocatalytic degradation of phenol by TiO_2 aqueous dispersions: Rutile and anatase activity." (1990) *New J. Chem.,* 14, 265.

[98] Sclafani A., Palmisano L. & Davi E. "Photocatalytic degradation of phenol in aqueous polychrystalline TiO_2 dispersions: The influence of Fe(+3), Fe(+2), and Ag(+) on the reaction rate." (1991) *J. Photochem. Photobiol. A: Chem.,* 56, 113.

[99] Sclafani A., Mozzanega M. N. & Pichat P. "Effect of silver deposits on the Photocatalytic activity of titanium dioxide samples for the dehydrogenation or oxidation of 2-propanol." (1991) *J. Photochem. Photobiol. A : Chem.,* 59, no. 2, 181.

[100] Wakoh H., Honda K. & Fujishima A. "Photocatalytic properties of titanium oxide powders." (1989) *Kenkyu Hokoku - Kanagawa - ken Kogyo Shikensho,* no. 60, 68.

[101] Peral J. & Domenech X. "Photocatalytic cyanide oxidation from aqueous copper cyanide solutions over titania and zinc oxide." (1992) *J. Chem. Technol. Biotechnol.* 53, no. 1, 93.

[102] Park S., Lee K. R., Lee K. W. & Lee J. H. “Rapid Ag recovery using photocatalytic ZnO nanopowders prepared by solution combustion method.” (2003) *J. Mater. Sci. Lett.,* 22, 65.

[103] Bickley R. L., (1982) *Catalysis*, (Specialist Periodical Report) Vol 5, The Royal Society of Chemistry, London, 308.

[104] Formenti M. & Teichner S. J. (1978) *Catalysis*, (Specialist Periodical Report) Vol 2, The Chemical Society, London, 87.

[105] Yesodharan E. P., Ramakrishnan V. & Kuriacose J. C. “Photoinduced heterogeneous catalysis” (1976) *J. Sci. Ind. Res.,* 35, 712.

In: Nanomaterials: New Research
Editor: B.M. Caruta, pp. 169-195

ISBN: 1-59454-369-0

Chapter 5

AL-BASED AMORPHOUS AND NANOCRYSTALLINE ALLOYS

Q. Jiang and J. C. Li*

Key Laboratory of Automobile Materials (Jilin University),
Ministry of Education, and Department of Materials Science and Engineering,
Jilin University, Changchun 130025, China

ABSTRACT

Aluminum alloys have received considerable attention especially in automobile and aerospace industries due to their high specific strengths. However, the use of these conventional strengthening mechanisms leads to an upper limit of tensile fracture strength of about 600 MPa. To obtain higher tensile strength, new strengthening mechanisms must be utilized. In this chapter, the recent progresses on manufacturing and processing of Al-based amorphous and nanocrystalline alloys with high strength, such as that of AlSi alloys, AlCeMn alloys and AlLaNi alloys, are introduced. In addition, the related microstructures, mechanical and thermal properties of these alloys are also described. Moreover, the considerations on further development for consolidation processes and other possible ways to develop new Al-based alloys with high strength and good toughness are indicated.

1. INTRODUCTION

Considerable efforts have been devoted to the development of novel lightweight engineering materials during the last decades. Al-based alloys have received great attention especially in automobile and aerospace industries due to their high specific strengths. Most works concerned with Al-based alloys are further increase of the specific strengths. It is well

* Author to whom all correspondence should be addressed. Fax: +86-431-5095876. E-mail: jiangq@jlu.edu.cn (Q. Jiang)

known that ordinary high strength Al-based alloys have been developed by the use of the following conventional strengthening mechanisms; i.e. solid solution, precipitation, grain size refinement, dispersion, work hardening and fiber reinforcement. However, the uses of these conventional solid solution strengthening and grain size refinement strengthening mechanisms lead to an upper limit of tensile fracture strength of about 600 MPa, and precipitation, work hardening and fiber reinforcement decrease largely the plasticity and toughness of alloys. If a new Al-based alloy with higher tensile strength would be fabricated, new strengthening mechanisms must be utilized.

Since the first synthesis of an amorphous phase in an Au-Si system by rapid solidification in 1960 [1], a great number of amorphous alloys have been synthesized by various preparation methods of rapid quenching from liquid or vapor and of solid-state reactions [2-5]. The formation of Al-based amorphous alloys by liquid quenching has been tried in binary alloys of Al-metalloid and Al-transition metal systems. A co-existing structure of amorphous and crystalline phases in Al-Si [6], Al-Ge [7] and Al-Cu [8], Al-Ni [9], Al-Cr [10] and Al-Pd [11] alloys can be built only near the holes in their thin foils prepared by the gun quenching technique in which the cooling rate is higher than that of the melt spinning method. However, no single amorphous phase was prepared by melt spinning as well as by the gun- and piston-anvil methods. The first formation of a single amorphous phase in Al-based alloys containing more than 50% Al was found in 1981 for Al-Fe-B and Al-Co-B ternary alloys [12]. Subsequently, Al-Fe-Si, Al-Fe-Ge and Al-Mn-Si amorphous alloys were also found by the melt-spun technique [13, 14]. During the last decade, some researchers have paid attention to non-periodic structures such as amorphous and icosahedral phases, with which the tensile strengths of the corresponding alloys exceed 1000 MPa [15-17]. Structure and mechanical properties of Al based alloys developed are summarized in Fig. 1.

For an industrial alloy, Al based alloys must retain their low specific weight, which leads to the requirement of further increase of percentage of Al element in the alloy. In 1987, Al-Ni-Si and Al-Ni-Ge alloys with about 80% Al in amorphous structure with good bending ductility were discovered [18]. The further decrease of metalloid elements in the alloys results in improvement of glass-forming ability and that of mechanical strength [19-22].

Since the limitation of the maximum thickness of amorphous ribbons has prevented a wide extension of application fields, especially for structural materials, great efforts have been devoted to prepare bulk amorphous alloys [23-24]. The bulk amorphous alloys can be made from powders (vapor condensed powders, atomized alloyed powders or mechanically alloyed powders), or melt-spun alloy ribbons, by using various techniques of warm pressing, warm extrusion, explosive compaction etc. [23-24]. These powders or ribbons have metastable structures consisting of amorphous, quasicrystalline and nanocrystalline phases. The subsequent condensation of these raw materials into a bulk form is done at elevated temperatures, leading to a structural change into various nanogranular structures. These bulk nanostructured alloys exhibit good mechanical and physical properties and can be used as structural materials. However, the obtained bulk alloys have lower mechanical, chemical and soft magnetic properties than the corresponding melt-spun amorphous ribbons [25]. Bulk nanocrystalline alloys with a mixed structure of intermetallic compounds embedded fcc-Al or α-Al matrix by the crystallization of Al-based amorphous phase have already been investigated [26]. The bulk nanostructured alloys exhibits high mechanical strength of 700-1000 MPa and have been commercialized with a commercial name of GIGAS [27]. Subsequently, the researched results have been reported that bulk nano-quasi-crystalline alloys in Al-based system exhibit a good combination of high tensile strength, large elongation, high fatigue strength and high elevated-temperature strength [28].

In this review, recent progresses on manufacturing and processing of Al-based amorphous and nanocrystalline alloys with high strength, such as that of AlSi alloys, AlCeMn alloys and AlLaNi alloys, are introduced. In addition, the related microstructures, mechanical and thermal properties of these alloys are also described. Moreover, the considerations on further development for consolidation processes and other possible ways to develop new Al-based alloys with high strength and good toughness are given.

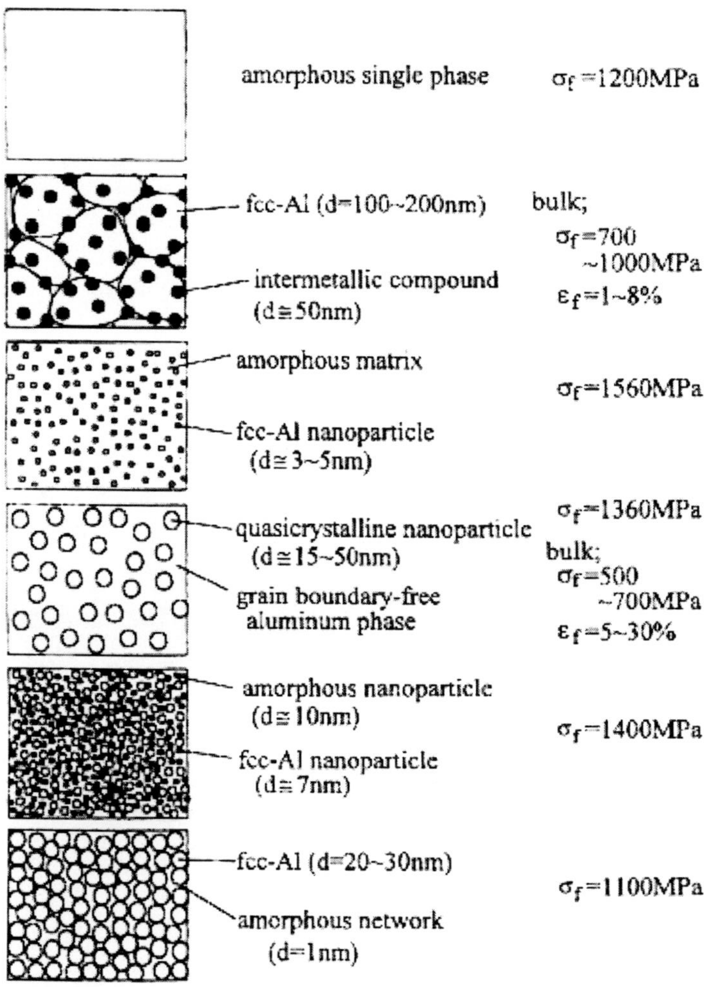

Figure 1. Microstructure and mechanical strength of aluminum base alloys developed for the last decade [18].

2. Al-Si Amorphous Alloy by Melt Spinning Method

Although an Al-Si binary alloy has a wide industrial application with lower cost, it has not been paid great attention since the eutectic Al-Si alloy has a bad glass forming ability (GFA) while a eutectic alloy should have the best GFA among the alloy system due to its lowest melting point. Although ternary Al-Fe-Si, Al-Fe-Ge and Al-Mn-Si alloys have amorphous structure by the melt-spun technique [29-30], the structures of binary Al-Si [31] and Al-Ge [7] alloys through a gun quenching technique are mixtures of amorphous and crystalline phases where the amorphous phase is unstable and crystallize even at room temperature. However, according to a polymorphous diagram of Al-Si system, which is schematically shown in Fig. 2, when the composition range of Si% (atom percentage) is located between 25% and 45%, amorphous phases may be formed from liquid with a high cooling rate where the polymorphous crystallization is absent [32-33]. The model predictions for the largest solubility of elemental crystals based on a consideration on a binary chemically random solid solution with local strain instability are also given in the figure with the following equation [34-35],

$$C^*_A \approx 2\lambda R_B^3 / \left|R_B^3 - R_A^3\right|, \tag{1}$$

$$C^*_B \approx 2\lambda R_A^3 / \left|R_B^3 - R_A^3\right|, \tag{2}$$

where C^*_A is the maximal solubility of A atom with an atom radius of R_A in a B solution with an atom radius R_B and C^*_B denotes the same meaning for that of the B atom in A solution. λ is a constant. When C_B is located within $C^*_B < C_B < 1 - C^*_A$, the solution becomes topologically unstable and thus has the possibility to form glass. Substituting $\lambda = 0.05$ [34], $R_{Al} = 0.143$ nm and $R_{Si} = 0.118$ nm [37] into Eqs. (1) and (2), $C^*_{Al} = 12.8\%$ and $C^*_{Si} = 22.9\%$ are obtained. Thus, there is a possibility to form glasses within the composition range of $22.9\% < C_{Si} < 87.2\%$. When a cooling rate used is not large enough, a structure consisting of amorphous phase and supersaturated nanocrystals should be present [38], which is the case of an $Al_{88}Si_{12}$ eutectic alloy [39]. Note that as C_{Si} increases, the liquidus line of Al-Si system increases quickly due to the large difference of melting temperatures between Al and Si, which is favorable for the primary crystallization of Si during the liquid quenching, C_{Si} should be as low as possible for glass production in the above composition range.

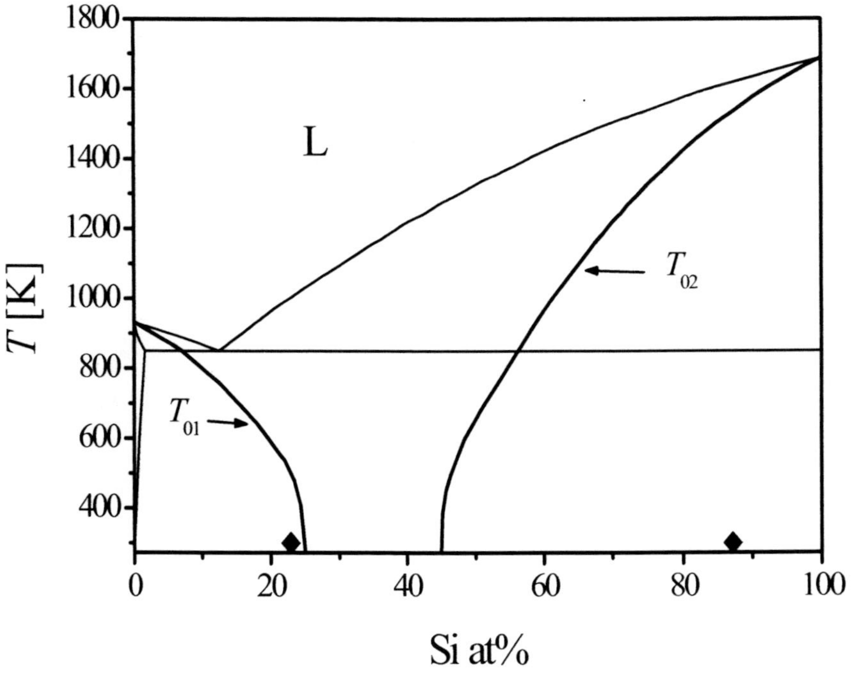

Figure 2. A schematic polymorphous phase diagram of Al-Si system. T_{01} and T_{02} are polymorphous lines for Al and Si solutions [32-33], which are simply plotted in the middle between the solidus lines and the liquidus lines of each component and extended to the solid zone along the original slopes. The symbol ◆ at Si% = 22.9% and Si% = 87.2% denotes the critical solubility determined by Egami's theory [34-35]. The equilibrium binary Al-Si phase diagram is cited from Ref. [36].

Based on the above consideration, $Al_{55}Si_{45}$, $Al_{60}Si_{40}$, $Al_{65}Si_{35}$, $Al_{70}Si_{30}$ and $Al_{75}Si_{25}$ alloys are selected to study GFA of the alloys by the melt spinning technique. It is found that although all alloys consist of embedded supersaturated α-Al nanocrystals, primary Si nanocrystals and amorphous matrix, the relative amounts of them in the alloys are composition dependent.

The alloy ingots with different compositions $Al_{75}Si_{25}$, $Al_{70}Si_{30}$, $Al_{65}Si_{35}$, $Al_{60}Si_{40}$, and $Al_{55}Si_{45}$ were prepared by arc melting of the mixture of Al (99.997%) and Si (99.9%) elements in argon atmosphere. Ribbon samples with 20-30 μm in thickness and 2.0 mm in width were obtained by the melt spinning technique.

TEM micrographs of five kinds of the quenched Al-Si alloys are shown in Fig. 3. The alloys consist of the matrix marked as "A" and the primary Si marked as "B" in micrometer size. The pattern of SAED made by TEM on the primary Si is marked as "B". The primary Si is always present by the melt spinning technique due to the high primary crystallization temperature of the alloy in about 1150 K (see Fig. 2). However, the diffraction ring on Fig. 3a indicates that the primary Si has a fine structure. When the structure of the matrix is further magnified as shown in Fig. 3b, the matrix itself consists of a matrix and uniformly distributed nanoparticles without clear interfaces between them. The pattern of SAED on the matrix shown in Fig. 3b indicates that the α-Al nanoparticles are embedded in amorphous matrix where the tropism of the α-Al particles is stochastic [40]. Indexing the rings of the diffraction patterns associated to primary Si (Fig. 3a) and Al nanocrystals embedded in amorphous matrix (Fig. 3b) can support the above conclusions on microstructures of the alloys. Note that although the ring patterns taken from diamond structure or fcc structure can look similar, an additional index of (200) of Al can be found in Fig. 3b. This result differs from the early work where no amorphous phases are found in $Al_{70}Si_{30}$ alloy possibly due to different cooling rates during the manufacture of the alloy [41]. The x-ray diffraction result of Fig. 4 shows also a widening of α-Al diffraction peak, which is in agreement with the diffraction pattern of Fig. 3b, both imply that α-Al is in nanometer size range.

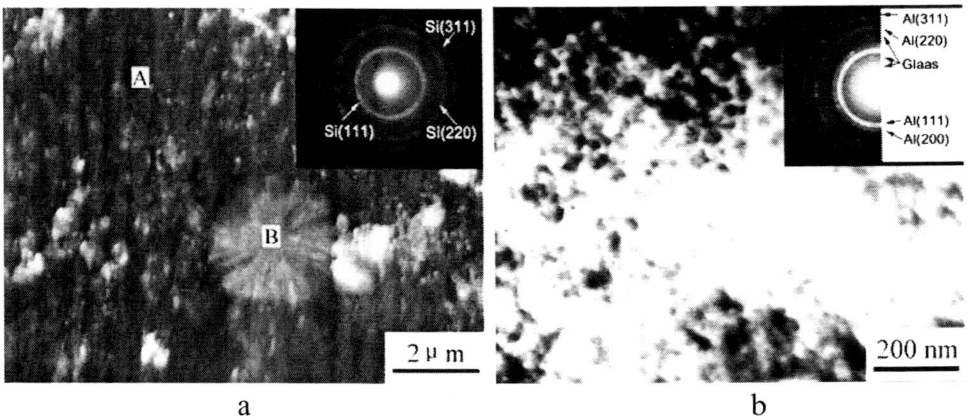

Figure 3. TEM dark field image of the $Al_{60}Si_{40}$ sample and its SAED pattern on the "B" (a), TEM bright field image of the matrix and its SAED pattern (b) where the matrix and the primary Si have marked as "A" and "B" in the (a).

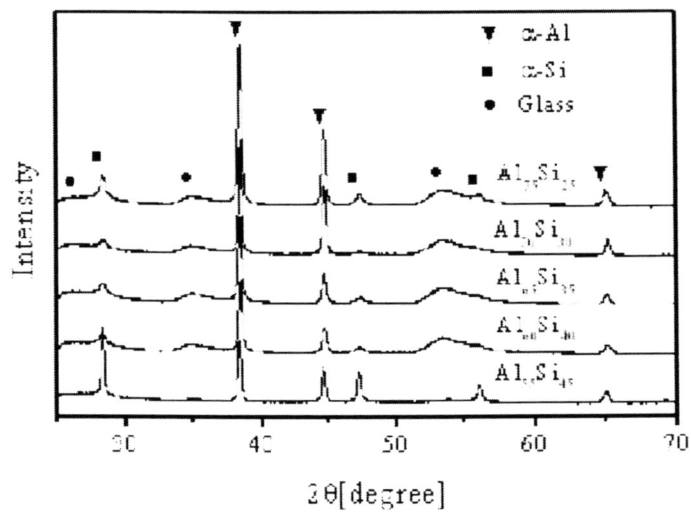

Figure 4. X-ray diffraction curves of the Al-Si alloys

X-ray diffraction curves of five kinds of Al-Si alloys is present in Fig. 4 where the intensity of the Si diffraction peak does not monotonously increase as Si% increases. Integral intensity percentage of each phase is determined based on the XRD curves in Fig. 4, which is shown in Fig. 5. When $30\% \leq C_{Si} \leq 40\%$, integral intensity percentages of the α-Si or α-Al phases are smaller than that when $C_{Si} = 25\%$ and $C_{Si} = 45\%$ while the quantities of amorphous phase have a reverse tendency. This result implies that Al-Si alloy in a composition range of $30\% < C_{Si} < 40\%$ has better GFA than that in other composition ranges. Since the solubility of the α-Si or α-Al is limited [34], as C_{Si} increases to 40%, the percentage of Si crystals in the amorphous matrix increases.

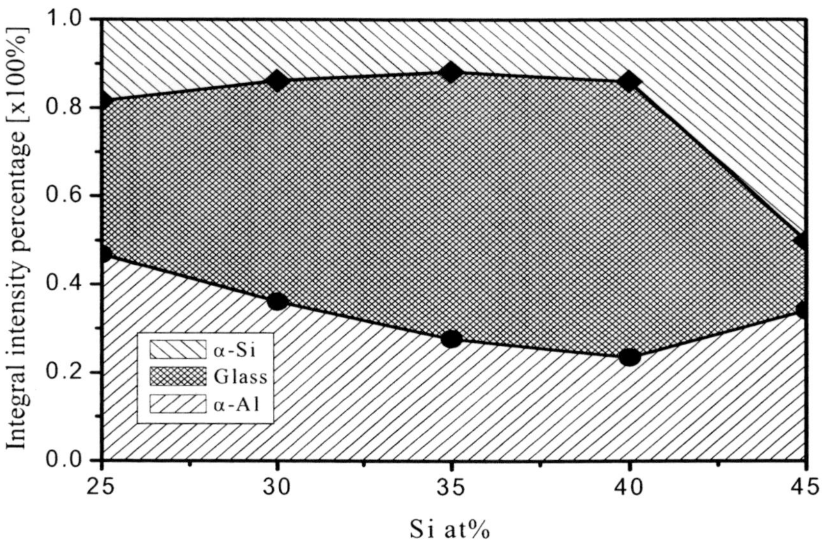

Figure 5. Integral intensity percentage of each phase in the alloys for XRD curves in Fig. 4.

Fig. 6 shows DSC traces of alloys where there are two exothermic peaks in all measured curves. T_{ons} and heat flow (H_{out}) of these peaks are shown in Fig. 7. $H_{out\ 1}$ and $H_{out\ 2}$ denoting the first and the second peaks in the curves have contrary trends as C_{Si} increases where $H_{out\ 1}$ decreases and $H_{out\ 2}$ increases. $T_{ons\ 1} \approx 0.4{\sim}0.5T_{m\ Al}$ ($T_{m\ Al} = 933$ K is the melting point of aluminum) and the $T_{ons\ 2} \approx 0.4T_{m\ Si}$ ($T_{m\ Si} = 1685$ K is the melting point of silicon). Thus, the former peaks should denote the precipitation of α-Al from the amorphous phase and its subsequent growth; the latter should do that of Si both from the amorphous phase and from supersaturated α-Al nanocrystals. In the meantime, crystallization of the amorphous phase may also occur. Since $T_{ons\ 1}$ increases with increasing C_{Si} while $T_{ons\ 2}$ has a reverse tendency, the precipitation and grain growth of α-Al are more difficult with increasing C_{Si} content while that of Si become easier.

Fig. 8 gives microhardness of $Al_{75}Si_{25}$ and $Al_{55}Si_{45}$ alloys annealed at different temperatures. The as quenched $Al_{75}Si_{25}$ and $Al_{55}Si_{45}$ alloys have the highest hardness of 1200 MPa and 2100 MPa, which imply that the content increase of Si% leads to evident enhancement of alloys. When the alloys are annealed, as the annealing temperature increases, the hardness gradually drops. This drop may be related to the internal stress relaxation and the growth of the α-Al nanocrystals. Since there are two hardening peaks in the curves, which are similar to that of the DSC results, it seems that after the nanoparticles have just precipitated from the amorphous phase, the hardness of the alloys increases since the nanocrystalline crystals have higher hardness than that of amorphous phase [42]. As the grain growth occurs, the hardness decreases again.

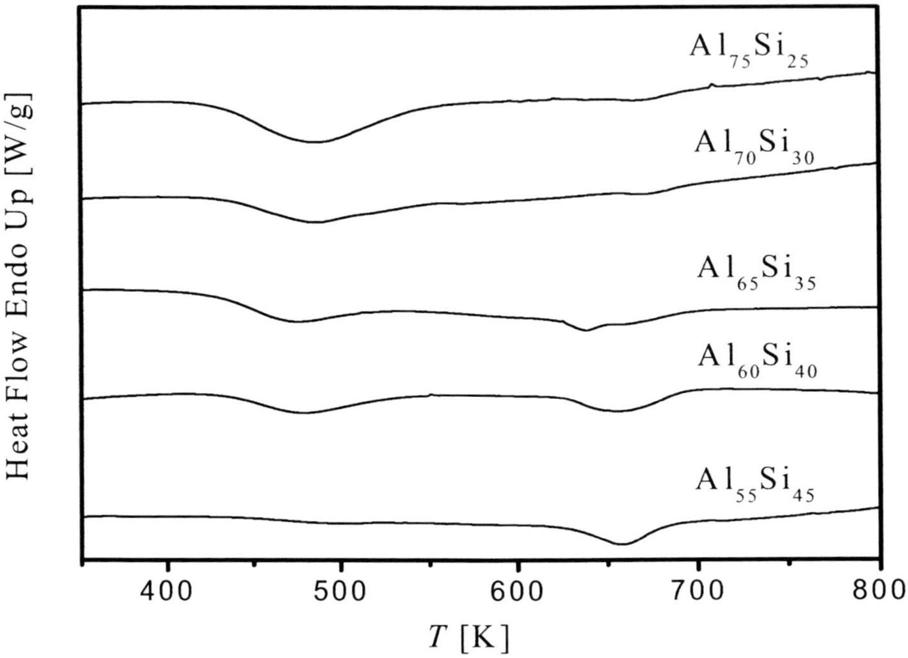

Figure 6. DSC curves of the Al-Si alloys.

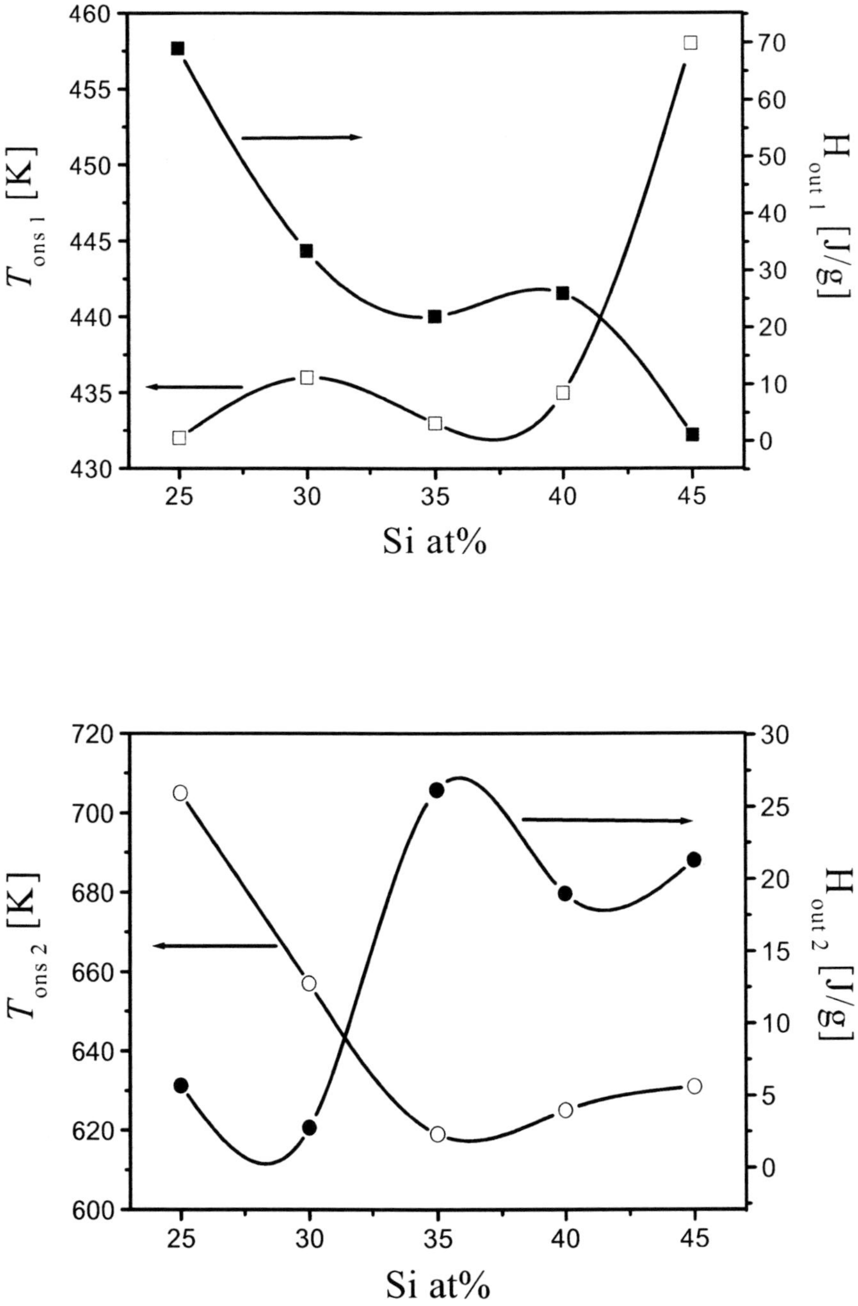

Figure 7. Dependence of T_{ons} and H_{out} on C_{Si}.

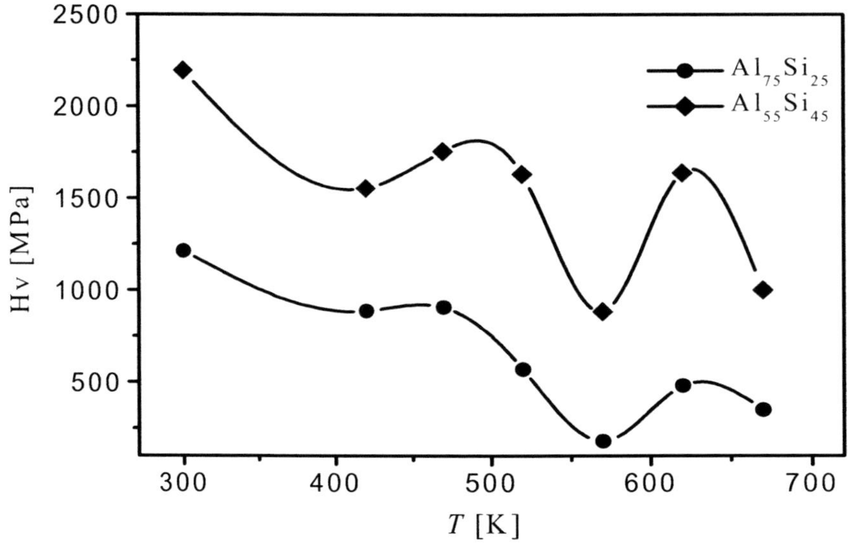

Figure 8 Vickers hardness (HV) curves of $Al_{75}Si_{25}$ and $Al_{55}Si_{45}$ alloys after the annealing at different temperatures.

In summary, five quenched Al-Si alloys with different compositions have been manufactured and whose mechanical properties and structures are determined. The results show that the alloys consist of supersaturated α-Al nanocrystals, amorphous matrix and primary Si crystals. When $30\%<C_{Si}\%<40\%$, there is more than 50% amorphous phase in the corresponding alloy. Crystallization of the amorphous phases and Si separation from the supersaturated α-Al nanocrystals occur as temperature increases.

3. Thermal Stability of Ternary Amorphous Al Based Alloys

Alloys with Al content of 80 to 90% have a combination of good ductility and high strength [19-22,43-45] due to their full amorphous structure. For these kinds of Al-based alloy, crystallization is the essential factor affecting the properties of the amorphous alloys, and the extent of crystallization is consequently crucial to the alloy's application. It has been reported that partial crystallization may enhance the alloy's strength [46] although the full crystallization leads to embattlement of the alloys [47]. The necessary conditions to avoid the full crystallization are that the alloy has a higher activation energy of crystallization E_a and a higher crystallization temperature T_x, which is obtained through alloying [48]. Moreover, it has been found that ternary alloys having 80 to 90% Al crystallizes in several stages [49-53]. X-ray results show that the precipitation in the first stage is the primary precipitation of α-Al while in the second stage intermetallic compounds of Al_3La, La_3Al_{11}, Ni_5La and Al_3Ni are present [53-54]. The multiple stages of crystallization benefit the formation of a composite structure where the amorphous phase is partly crystallized to increase strength of alloys.

However, if T_x, which is the precipitation temperature of supersaturated α-Al, is too low, the growth of Al grains and precipitation from the supersaturated α-Al must lead to a strong drop of strength. T_x is composition dependent and can be adjusted by alloying since alloying improves the glass forming ability of the Al based alloy and stabilizes the amorphous phase with larger values of E_a and T_x where E_a is the activation energy for crystallization. On the other side, in industry, the alloying amount should be as small as possible. The necessary smallest amount of alloying on the thermal stability of AlLaNi alloys can be determined by changing La and Ni amount in Al.

Fig. 9 shows the crystallization curves of $Al_{82}La_9Ni_9$ amorphous alloy at different q's with q being heating or cooling rate. The corresponding T_x values are given in table 1. Two peaks on the curves indicate clearly two stages of crystallization the same as other AlLaNi alloys [53-54] where crystallization enthalpies for the first and the second crystallization ΔH are 29.96 and 57.47 J/g, respectively with q = 40 K/min. The first crystallization curve represents the precipitation of α-Al while the second denotes that of La_3Al_{11}, Al_3Ni, Ni_5La and Al_3La intermetallic compounds. At higher q, a small decalescence peak can be observed, which is caused by glass transformation before the first crystallization. The glass transition cannot be found in the thermal analysis curve at low q since crystallization occurs at the same temperature. It is shown that precipitation of α-Al is slow and the crystallization fraction of α-Al increases with temperature increasing.

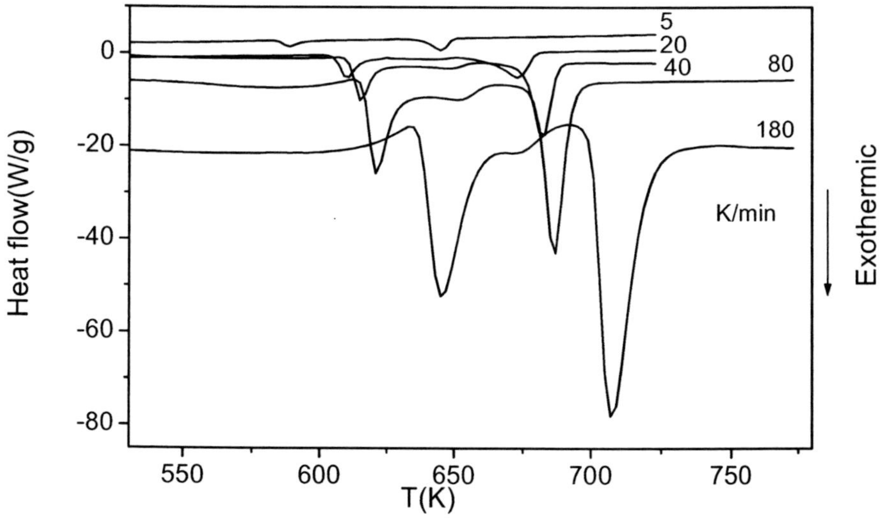

Figure 9. DSC curves of $Al_{82}La_9Ni_9$ alloy at different heat rates q.

Table 1. The crystallization temperature of an $Al_{82}La_9Ni_9$ amorphous alloy with different heating rates *q*

q, K/min		5	20	40	80	180
1[st]peak	T_x/K	585	606	611	637	637
2[nd]peak	T_x/K	639	661	675	677	698

By use of the Kissinger method [51], the corresponding E_a for the precipitation of α-Al determined from Fig. 9 is shown in table 2. The relevant AlLaNi and AlYNi alloys are also shown in table 2 and Fig. 10. It is found that E_a in measuring error range remains a constant as La(Y)+Ni content increases. This result implies that the supersaturated amount of La and Ni in α-Al is the same in the composition range of 9% < La(Y)+Ni < 18%. Since ΔH of $Al_{82}La_9Ni_9$ for the first peak is about 1/3 of the total ΔH, if the La and Ni are randomly distributed in the alloys, the saturated solution of La (Y) and Ni in Al is about 6 at.%. Thus, it is possible that any further increase of La (Y) and Ni does not change E_a as long as La(Y)+Ni > 6%.

Fig. 11 gives a comparison of T_x values of AlLaNi and AlYNi alloys for the first transition peak. It is clear that as RE+Ni increases where RE denotes rare earth elements, T_x values increase with a slope about 20 K/[(RE+Ni)at.%]. From the view of thermal stability for industrial application, T_x value of an alloy must be at least 500 K. Under this condition, if La(Y) and Ni in the alloy has the same content, the necessary alloying composition for AlLaNi alloy is $Al_{88}La_6Ni_6$ while that for AlYNi alloy is $Al_{85}La_7Ni_7$. Thus, the AlLaNi alloys have better thermal stability than AlYNi alloys with the same alloying amount. Moreover, for a ternary system, Al content of the alloys cannot be larger than 88% for any possible industrial application in the above alloying systems although full amorphous structures can be built even if Al = 91at.% [53].

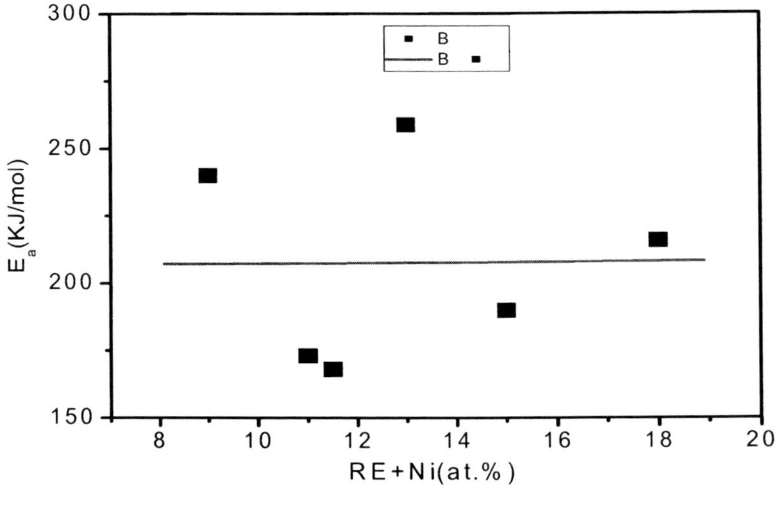

Figure 10. E_a of the precipitation of fcc Al as a function of concentration of RE+Ni where RE denotes the elements of La or Y.

Table 2. E_a of $Al_{82}La_9Ni_9$ alloy compared with that of relevant alloys

E_a, KJ/mol	1st	2nd	3rd	Ref.
$Al_{82}La_9Ni_9$	216	222		[57]
$Al_{89}La_6Ni_5$	173	207		[58]
$Al_{91}La_5Ni_4$	240±39	229±7		[54]
$Al_{85}Y_{10}Ni_5$	190			[56]
$Al_{88.5}Y_{6.5}Ni_5$	168	163	285	[59]
$Al_{87}Y_8Ni_5$	259	413	317	[60]

Table 3. T_x of $Al_{82}La_9Ni_9$ alloy compared with that of relevant alloys with q = 20 K/min

T_x, K	1st	2nd	3rd	Ref.
$Al_{82}La_9Ni_9$	606	661		[57]
$Al_{89}La_6Ni_5$	500	612		[58]
$Al_{91}La_5Ni_4$	413			[54]
$Al_{85}Y_{10}Ni_5$	531			[56]
$Al_{88.5}Y_{6.5}Ni_5$	453	469	600	[59]
$Al_{87}Y_8Ni_5$	488	582	622	[60]

4. High Strength Al-Based Alloys Prepared by Powder Metallurgy Method

Among Al alloys, Al-RE-TM (TM = V, Cr, Mn, Fe, Mo) amorphous Al alloys of melt-spun ribbons possess high strength [60-64]. The tensile strengths of the alloys σ_b are more than 1000 MPa while the highest σ_b value reaches 1250 MPa. If supersaturated α-Al or supersaturated icosahedral Al quasi-crystals embedded in amorphous matrix with coherent interfaces are in nanometer size, the strengths of the alloys can be further improved [65-68]. Although these ribbons exhibit σ_b values exceeding the performance of conventionally produced Al-alloys by a factor of two to three, they cannot be directly utilized as structural materials due to their small size. Thus, the P/M (powder metallurgy) technique was recently utilized to fabricate bulk alloys [69-72]. The mechanical properties, such as strength, plasticity and wear resistance, of AlCeMn and AlLaNi alloys prepared by P/M are reported. It is found that when different P/M treatments are utilized due to emphasis to a special mechanical property, different materials characterizations can arise, which is meaningful for multiformity of materials applications.

The alloys were prepared from Al, Ni, La, Ce, and Mn elements with purities of 99.9% by melting them together in a vacuum induction furnace under argon atmosphere. The powders of the alloy were obtained by ultrasonic atomization method with a cooling rate about 10^3 K/s, the sizes of the powders were among 5 and 40 μm. The compositions of the alloy powders were $Al_{85}La_{10}Ni_5$ and $Al_{90}Mn_8Ce_2$ (at%). The bulk alloys were obtained by hydraulic pressing at different temperatures between 453 and 853 K under a pressure of 1.2 GPa. The porosity of the alloy δ was determined as follows:

$$\delta=(\rho_t-\rho_m)/\rho_t, \tag{3}$$

where ρ_m and ρ_t are the measured density of the alloy and the theoretical density determined by the density of the constituent elements.

Fig. 12 shows how the porosity of the alloys changes as a function of the pressing temperature T. In Fig. 12, as T increases, δ decreases. $\delta < 2\%$ at $T > 753$ K. Note that the theoretically calculated δ values differ a little from the measured δ value due to differences of δ values between elements and compounds. Therefore, δ values are only approximate results.

The corresponding microstructures of the above alloys are present in Fig. 13. The microstructures in Fig. 13 support the above observation on δ values: When $T = 473$ K, the original spherical powders in diameter of 5-30 μm remain. As $T \rightarrow 753$ K, crystallization or re-crystallization arises and evident porosity is microscopically absent where $\delta < 2\%$. At $T >$ 753 K, the structure remains.

The X-ray result of the alloys in Fig. 14 shows the presences of α-Al, intermetallic compounds and alumina at $T = 753$ K. The appearance of the compounds and alumina should contribute to the strength of the alloys.

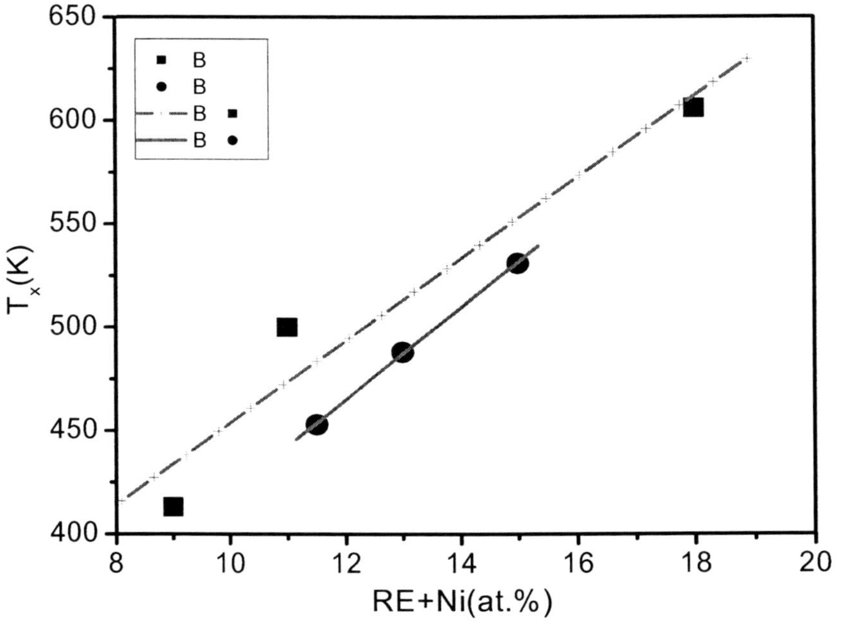

Figure 11. T_x of the precipitation of fcc Al as a function of concentration of RE+Ni where RE denotes the elements of La or Y.

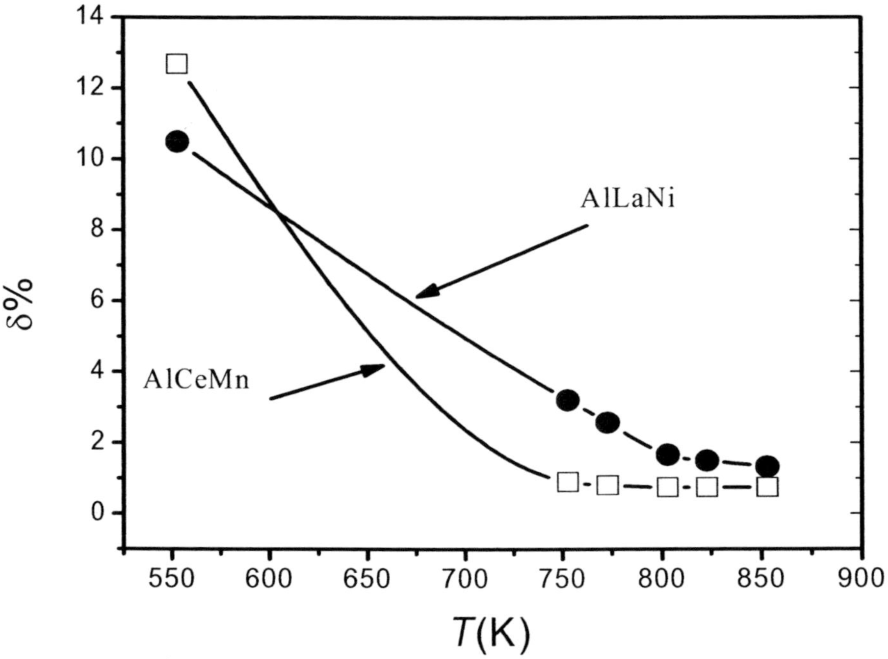

Figure 12. Porosity of the alloy as a function of pressing temperature.

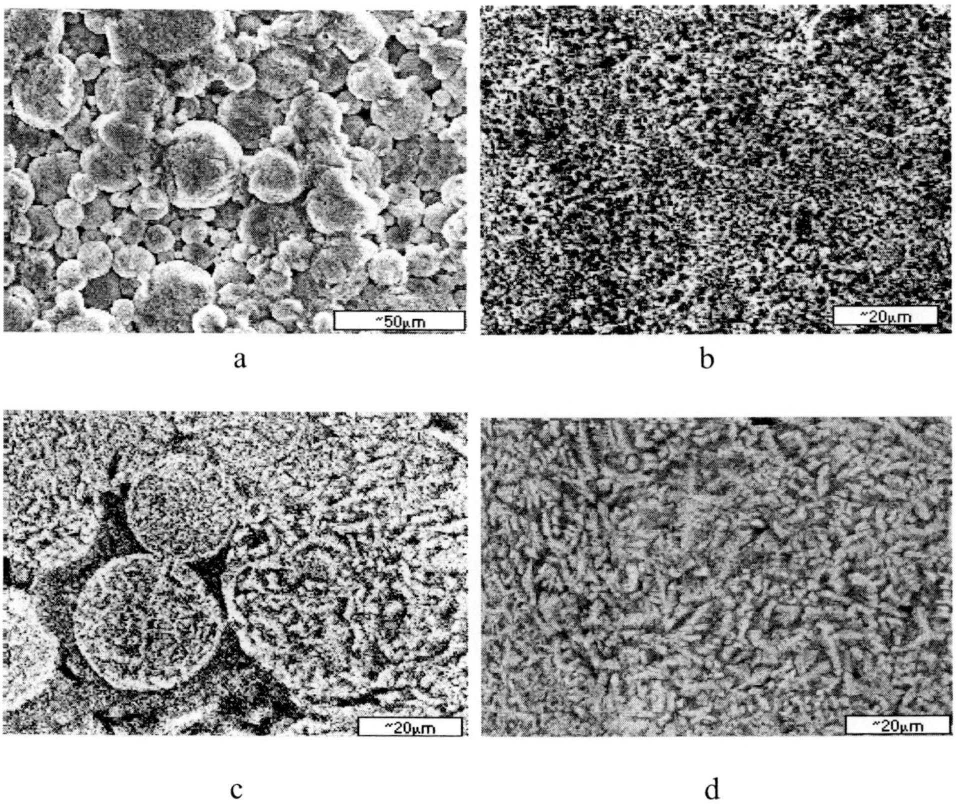

a b

c d

Figure 13. SEM micrographs of the alloy pressing at different *T*. (a) AlCeMn alloy at 473 K, (b) AlCeMn alloy at 753 K, (c) AlLaNi alloy at 473 K, (d) AlLaNi alloy at 753 K.

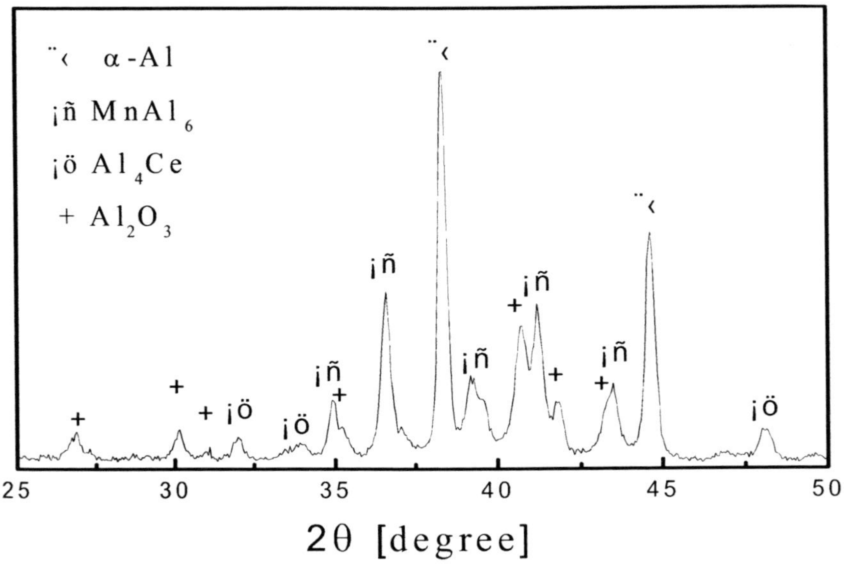

a

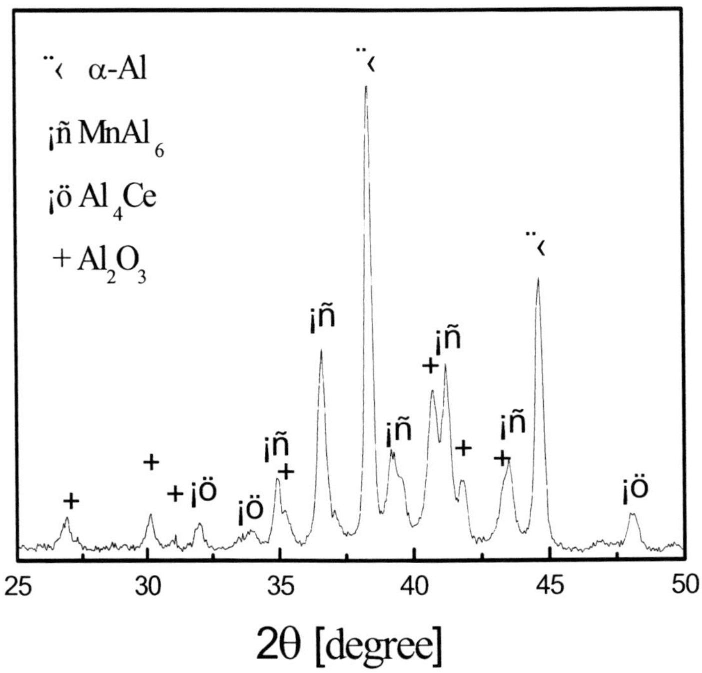

b

Figure 14. X-ray structure analysis of the sample pressing at 753 K. (a) AlCeMn alloy, (b) AlLaNi alloy.

To obtain compact P/M products, surface melting even melting must occur. The former takes place when $T > 0.8T_m$ (T_m denotes the melting temperature) [55-56, 73-74]. When the surface melting is present, full density P/M alloys are possible to obtain under larger pressure. The DSC results show that $T_m = 922$ K for AlCeMn alloy and $T_m = 894$ K for AlLaNi alloy [66-67]. Therefore, when $T > 0.8T_m = 740$ K, δ may take its minimum. On the other side, a too high pressing temperature leads to grain growth or grain coarsening, which leads to drop of the strength. Thus, to achieve the highest strength, $T < 800$ K should be selected. Note that existed alumina on powder surfaces produced during both the manufacture and storage of the powders is the essential reason to decrease packing density of the alloys. Only when surface melting of the alloys occurs, which leads to mechanical instability of alloy surface or that of interface between alloy surface and alumina surface layer. Under this condition, the alumina surface layers on the powder surface can be easily destroyed and the fresh surfaces of the powders are in contact directly. As a result, a compacted bulk alloy can be obtained. Note also that the destroying of the alumina surface layers also brings out dispersion distribution of alumina powders, which evidently improves the plasticity and ductility of the alloys.

Fig. 15 shows stress-strain curves of the alloys pressing at different *T*. According to the figure, as *T* increases, the compression strength increases due to the precipitation of the compounds. The alloy presents hardly plasticity at $T < 653$ K or $T > 803$ K. The former is produced by existence of large amounts of porosity while the latter is due to appearance of large amount of compounds accompanied with the grain growth. The highest compression strength of AlMnCe and AlLaNi alloys are 850MPa and 950 MPa at 803 K respectively. At 753 K, the compression strength is 725 MPa with a plastic strain of 5.5% for AlCeMn alloy, and 700 MPa with a plastic strain of 5% for AlLaNi alloy. Further increase of *T* leads to an increase of strength but a drop of plastic strain.

The above results for temperature dependence of strength and plasticity of the alloys are supported by the microstructure observations shown in Fig. 16. Fig. 16a and Fig. 16c give the microstructure of the fracture of the sample at $T = 753$ K, which denote a ductile dimpled fracture while the cleavage fracture of the sample in Fig. 16b and Fig. 16d are fully brittle at $T = 803$ K.

The excellent strength of the alloy may be accompanied with high wear resistance. The P/M Al alloy presents improved wear resistance over the A355 aluminum alloy as shown in Fig. 17. The AlCeMn alloy pressed at 753 K and AlLaNi alloy pressed at 773 K exhibit the best wear resistance among the alloys, which are three times as high as the A355 Al alloy.

Fig. 18 presents the SEM micrographs of wear surface of the alloys, which consists of ploughs and areas where obvious plastic flow occurs. Thus, the good wear resistance of the alloy pressed at 753 K should be related with not only good strength, but also good plasticity of the alloy.

In summary, the bulk of AlCeMn and AlLaNi alloys manufactured by P/M method have high strengths due to their complicated structures. The best mechanical properties of the alloy made by P/M technique are obtained under the following processing conditions: The pressing temperature is 753 K and pressure is 1.2 GPa where the δ reaches the minimum, the plasticity reaches the maximum with a moderate strength.

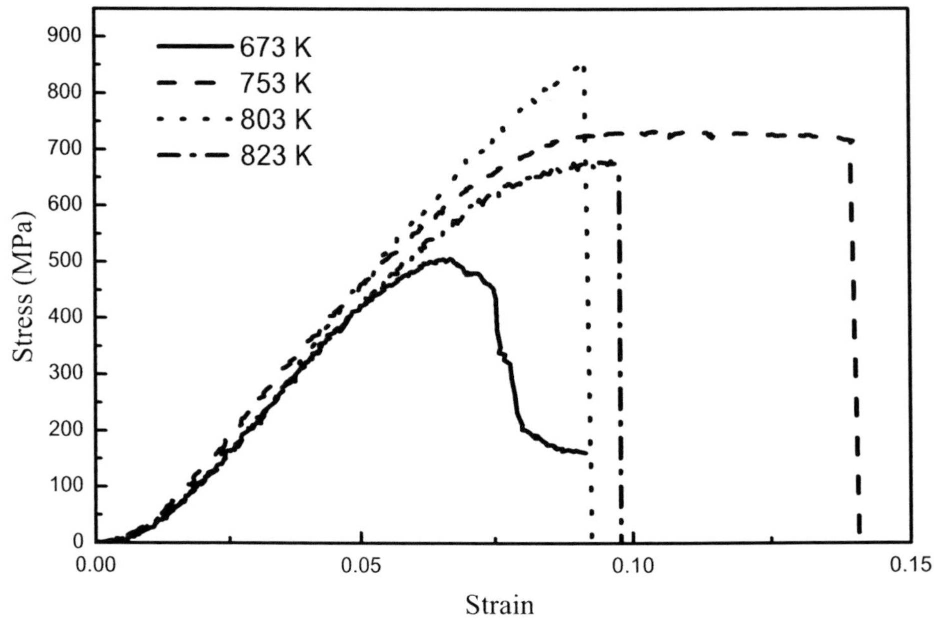

a

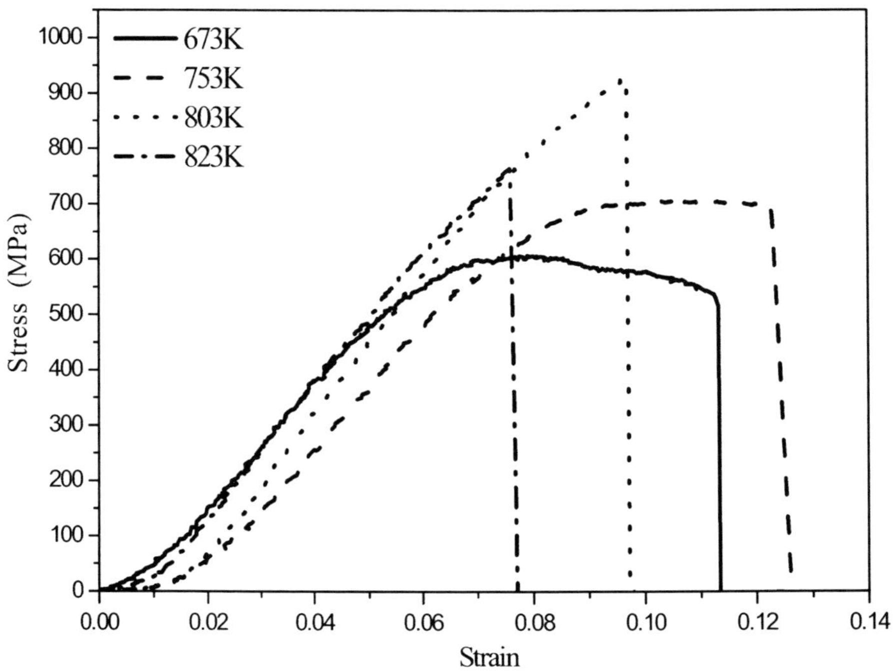

b

Figure 15. Stress-strain curve of the alloy as a function of *T*. (a) AlMnCe alloy, (b) AlLaNi alloy.

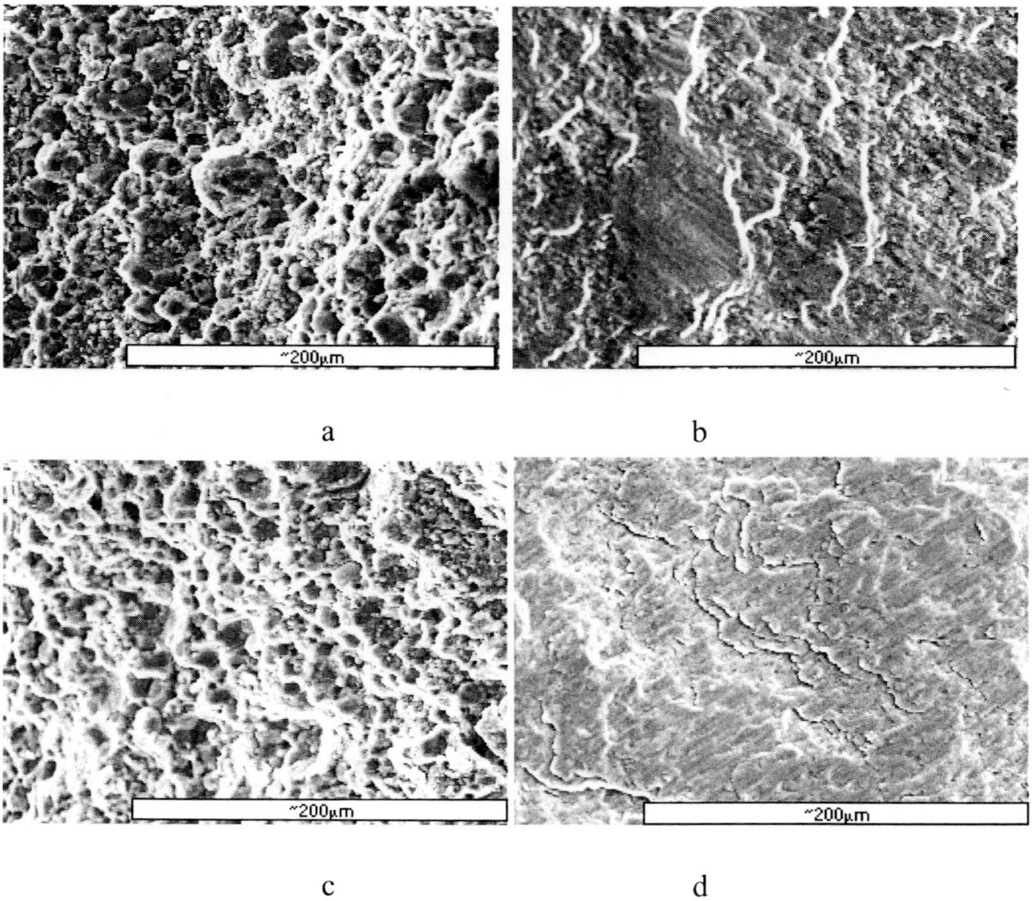

Figure 16. Fracture structure of the alloy at different *T*. (a) AlCeMn alloy at 753 K, (b) AlCeMn alloy at 803K, (c) AlLaNi alloy at 753 K, AlLaNi alloy at 803 K.

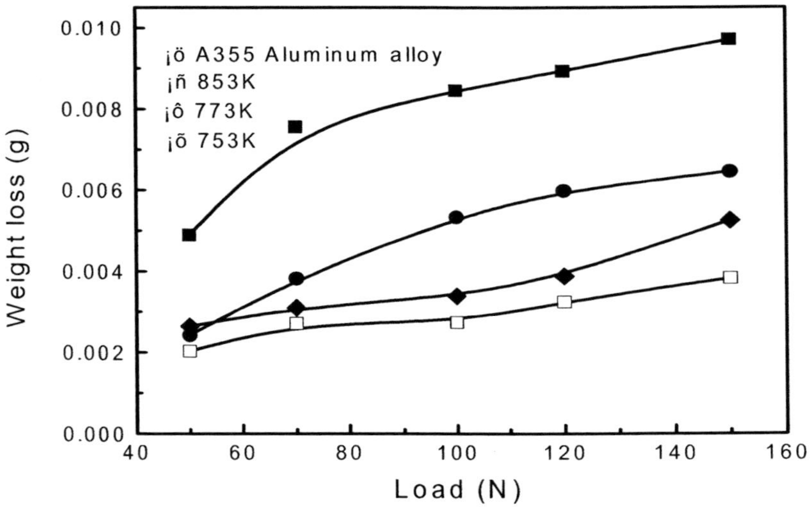

a

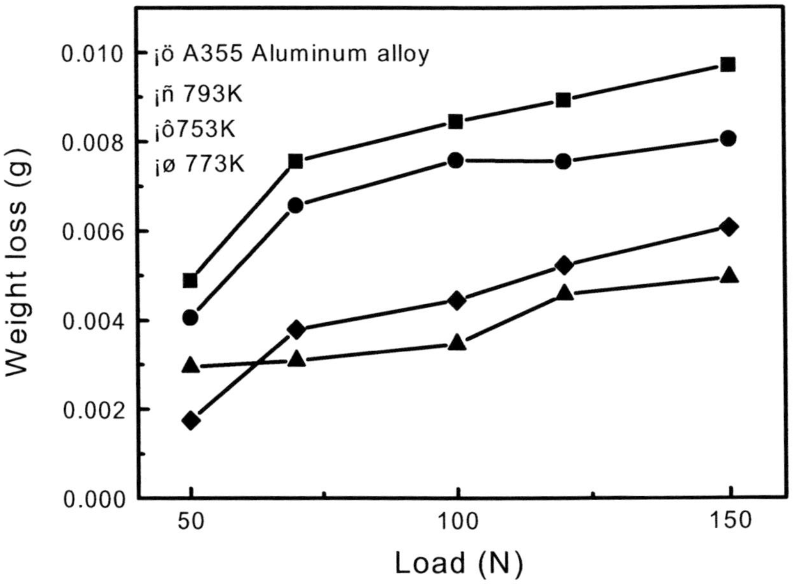

b

Figure 17. Wear curve of the alloy pressed at 753 K with different sliding times under 150 N. (a) AlCeMn alloy, (b) AlLaNi alloy.

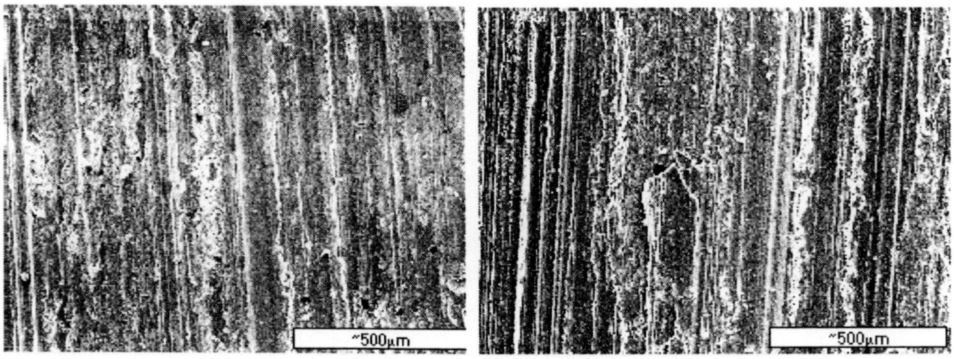

a b

Figure 18. SEM micrograph of wear surface of the alloy pressed at 753 K. (a) AlMnCe alloy, (b) AlLaNi alloy.

5. The Consideration on Further Development

5.1. Nanostructured High-Entropy Alloys with Multiple Principal Elements

The large numbers of intermetallic compounds of amorous Al alloys is expected to result in brittleness, difficulty in processing, and challenging in analysis. Thus, although alloying is a good technique to increase strength of an alloy, usual alloying elements are less than 50% except that the alloying element has full solubility in matrix element. However, a recent progress for high alloying is achieved by considering high entropy in an alloy based on thermodynamics, which focused on a new approach to alloy design with multiple principal elements in equimolar or near-equimolar ratios [75].

Based on a general understanding of physical metallurgy and facts concerning binary and ternary phase diagrams, the formation of many intermetallic compounds using multiple principal elements may be anticipated [76], which has discouraged alloy design with multiple principal elements. Nonetheless, solid solutions of many elements will tend to be more stable because of their large mixing entropies. Following Boltzmann's hypothesis on the relationship between entropy and system complexity [76], the configurational entropy change per mole, ΔS_{conf}, during the formation of a solid solution from *n* elements with equimolar fractions may be calculated from the following equation,

$$\Delta S_{conf} = -k\ln w = -R\left(\frac{1}{n}\ln\frac{1}{n} + \frac{1}{n}\ln\frac{1}{n} + \ldots\frac{1}{n}\ln\frac{1}{n}\right) = -R\ln\frac{1}{n} = R\ln n \qquad (4)$$

where *k* is Boltzmann's constant, *w* is the number of ways of mixing, and *R* is the gas constant. By Richards' rule [76], the entropy changes in fusion of the most metals are only empirically equal to *R* at their melting points, In comparison, equimolar alloys with three elements already have a ΔS_{conf} value of 1.10*R*, larger than that of metal fusion, let alone those with five or more constitute elements. In fact, considering other positive contributions from factors such as vibrational, electronic, and magnetic moment randomness, ΔS_{conf} of an equimolar alloy is even higher than that calculated [76]. Furthermore, if the formation enthalpies of two strong intermetallic compounds, such as NiAl and TiAl were divided by their respective melting points, the resulting ΔS_{conf}, $1.38R$ and $2.06R$, are in the same range as the entropy changes of mixing in a system with more than five elements. This indicates that the tendency of ordering and segregation would be lowered by the high ΔS_{conf} [77]. Consequently, alloys with a higher number of principal elements will more easily yield the formation of random solid solution during solidification, rather than intermetallic compounds, except for those with very large heats of formation. In practice, to fully utilize the merit of high mixing entropy in the liquid- or solid-solution state, which is defined by such high-entropy alloys (HE alloys) as those composed of five or more principal elements in equimolar ratios. Extensive trials have led to many alloy systems with simple crystalline structures of fcc, bcc and fcc+bcc and extraordinary properties [75,78-79]. These simple structures with high alloying lead to that the alloys could hold high strength and good plastics at the same time.

Although many trials in alloying systems have been carried out, the light alloy systems can never be considered. Thus, the above alloying method can be applied to light alloys, especially Al base alloys. The possible alloy element selections for Al base alloys are Li, Mg, Si, RE, B etc. The adding of these elements will remain the characteristic of low specific weight of the Al alloy. However, the corresponding strength will increase evidently. The corresponding works are in progress.

5.2. Spark Plasma Sintering Technique for P/M Processing

The powders of Al base alloys are usually covered with alumina film due to the rapid oxidation ability of the alloys. Thus, the alloys with a high packing density cannot be sintered by normal and hot press sintering under usual temperature since alumina films with high melting temperature on the surface of the powders remain perfect and cannot be broken and/or removed. Even if the powders are forged into a dense body under high temperature sintering conditions, the plasticity of the high strength Al alloy prepared by M/P method is lower.

To avoid the above problem, a best way during the use of M/P technique is that heating the powders in an inhomogeneous mode, namely, the temperature at the powder surface is much higher than that within the particles. This mode leads to, in the one side, the melting of the alunima on the powder surface and re-solidify in particle shapes with small size; and in the other side, the tendencies of the precipitation of compounds and grain growth in the particles are inhibited. Both guarantee the alloys having a good plasticity and a high strength. In addition, since the sintering temperature can be much lower, the cost of the P/M processing technique is lowered in many aspects. This kind of consideration can be realized by the Spark Plasma Sintering (SPS) technique [80-83].

SPS is a new sintering technology developed in recent years [80-85]. It enjoys certain inherent advantages, which are the following:

1. A high thermo-efficiency, which is determined by the way of heating as in a SPS furnace, the electricity is put directly into the samples and the electricity conducting dies bearing the samples and is transformed into thermal energy.
2. A quick heating-up, which is mainly due to the high pulse power source.
3. A better self-purification of the surface of the particle and sintering activity. A strong enough electrical field is produced in the small gaps of the particles to make the electrons, cations and anions to strike the surface of the opposite particle and purify its surface.
4. Enabling fast sintering under low temperatures. On one hand, the movement of the above-mentioned particles fulfils the material transportation and a local high temperature is created in the contacting areas of the particles resulting in the quick formation of the neck while the temperature is still comparatively low. On the other hand, the temperature at the neck is much higher than that of the inside of the particles. The neck grows quickly and fast sintering is done.

The present authors have used the above technique to manufacture new series of Al base alloys with high strength and high plasticity under a low sintering temperature. Evident advances have been achieved. The ultimate goal of the research is to find a new Al-base alloy with a σ_b value of more than 1000 MPa and a plasticity of more than 6-8%.

ACKNOWLEDGEMENTS

The financial supports from Foundation of National Key Basic Research and Development Program under Grant No. 2004CB619301 and Project 985-Automotive Engineering of Jilin University are acknowledged.

REFERENCES

[1] Klement W., Willens R. H., Duwez P. (1960). Non-crystalline structure in solidified gold-silicon alloys. *Nature*, 187, 869-870.
[2] Luborsky L. E. (1983). *Amorphous Metallic Alloys*, London, Butterworths.
[3] Masumoto T. (1982). *Materials Science of Amorphous Metals*, Tokyo, Ohmu.
[4] Inoue A. (2000). Stabilization of metallic supercooled liquid and bulk Amorphous alloys. *Acta Mater.*, *48*, 279-306.
[5] Chen H. S. (1980). *Glassy metals. Rep. Prog. Phys.*, *43*, 353-432.
[6] Kui H. W., Greer A. L., Turnbull D. (1984). Formation of bulk metallic glass by fluxing. *Appl. Phys. Lett.*, *45*, 615-616.
[7] Ramachandrarao P., Scott M. G., Chadwick G. A. (1972). Constitution and microstructure of rapidly solidified aluminium-germanium alloys. *Philosophical Magazine*, 25, 961-982.
[8] Ramachandrarao P., Laridjani M., Cahn R. W. (1972). Diamond as a splat-cooling substrate. *Z. Metallkd.*, *63*, 43-49.

[9] Davies H. A., Hull J. B. (1973). Noncrystalline phase in splat-quenched germanium. *Scrip. Metall.*, *7*, 634-641.

[10] Chattopadyay K., Ramachandrarao R., Lele S., Anantharaman T. R. In: Grant NJ, B. C. Giessen, editors. (1977). Proceedings of 2nd international conference on rapidly quenched metals, Cambridge, MA: MIT Press, p. 157.

[11] Furrer P., Warlimont H. (1977). Crystalline and amorphous structures of rapidly solidified Al-Cr alloys. *Mater. Sci. Eng.*, *28*, 127-137.

[12] Davies H. A. (1981). Diffuse scattering and chemical short range order in binary metallic glasses. *Trans Indian Inst. Met.*, *31*, 292-297.

[13] Inoue A., Kimura H. M., Masumoto T., Tsai A. P., Bizen Y. (1987). Al-Ge-(Cr or Mn) and Al-Si-(Cr or Mn) quasicrystals with high metalloid concentration prepared by rapid quenching. *J. Mater. Sci. Lett.*, *6*, 771-774.

[14] Suzuki R. O., Komatsu Y., Kobayashi K. E., Shingu P. H. (1983). Formation and crystallization of Al-Fe-Si amorphous alloys. *J. Mater. Sci.*, *18*, 1195-1201.

[15] Inoue A., Matsumoto N., Masumoto T. (1990). Al-Ni-Y-Co amorphous alloys with high mechanical strengths, wide supercooled liquid region and large glass-forming capacity. *Mater. Trans. JIM*, *31*, 493-500.

[16] Kim Y. H., Inoue A., Masumoto T. (1990). Ultrahigh tensile strengths of $Al_{88}Y_2Ni_9M_1$ (M=Mn or Fe) amorphous alloys containing finely dispersed fcc-Al particles. *Mater. Trans. JIM*, *31*, 747-749.

[17] Inoue A., Ohtera K., Tsai A. P., Masumoto T. (1988). Aluminum-based amorphous alloys with tensile strength above 980 MPa. *Jpn. Appl. Phys.*, *27*, 479-482.

[18] Inoue A., Kimura H. (2000). High-strength aluminum alloys containing nanoquasicrystalline particles. *Mater. Sci. Eng. A*, *286*, 1-10.

[19] Rizzi P., Doglione R., Battezzati L. (2004). Mechanical properties of Al-based amorphous/nanocrystalline alloys. *Mater. Sci. Eng. A*, *375-377*, 969-974.

[20] Hu L., Bian X., Wang W., Zhang J., Jia Y. (2004). Liquid fragility and characteristic of the structure corresponding to the prepeak of AlNiCe amorphous alloys. *Acta Mater.*, *52*, 4773-4781.

[21] Boucharat N., Rösner H., Perepezko J. H., Wilde G. (2004). Devitrification of Al-based glass forming alloys. *Mat. Sci. Eng. A*, *375-377,* 713-717.

[22] Zhu A. Joseph Poon S., Shiflet G. J. (2004). On glass formability of Al– Gd– Ni (Fe). *Scripta Mater.*, *50*, 1451– 1455.

[23] Shingu P. H., Ishihara K. N. (1993). *Rapidly solidified alloys*. New York, Marcel Dekker.

[24] Schwarz R. B. (1993). *Rapidly solidified alloys*. New York, Marcel Dekker.

[25] Catalog Y. K. K. (1994). *High-strength aluminium alloys.* Tokyo, GIGAS.

[26] Ohtera K., Inoue A., Terabayashi T., Nagahama H., Masumoto T. (1992). Mechanical properties of an $Al_{88.5}Ni_8Mm_{3.5}$ (Mm=misch metal) alloy produced by extrusion of atomized amorous plus fcc-Al phase powders. *Mater. Trans. JIM*, *33*, 775-787.

[27] YKK Catalog. (1995).

[28] Inoue A., Kimura H. M. (1997). High-strength Al-based alloys consisting mainly of nanoscale quasicrystalline or amorphous particles. *Mater. Sci. Forum*, *235-238*, 873-880.

[29] Suzuki R. O., Komatsu Y., Kobayashi K. E., Shingu P. H. (1983). Formation and crystallization of Al-Fe-Si amorphous Alloys. *J. Mater. Sci.*, *18*, 1195-1201.

[30] Inoue A., Bizen Y., Kimura H. M., Yamamoto M., Tsai A. P., Masumoto T. (1987). Development of compositional short-range ordering in an AlGeMn amorphous alloy upon annealing. *J. Mater. Sci. Lett.*, *6*, 811-814.

[31] Zhao Z. K., Li J. C., Jiang Q. (2004). Hypereutectic Al-Si binary alloys prepared by melt spinning method. *Adv. Eng. Mater.*, *6*, 303-306.

[32] Johnson W. L. (1986). Thermodynamic and kinetic aspects of the crystal to glass transformation in metallic materials. *Prog. Mater. Sci.*, *30*, 81-134.

[33] Jiang Q. (2000). A contribution to the kauzmann temperature. *Z. Metallkd.*, *99*, 97-100.

[34] Egami T., Waseda Y. (1984). Atomic size effect on the formability of metallic glasses. *J. Non-cryst. Solids*, *64*, 113-134.

[35] Egami T. (1997). Universal criterion for metallic glass formation. *Mater. Sci. Eng. A*, *226-228*, 261-267.

[36] Massalski T. B. (1986). *Binary alloys Phase Diagrams. Vol. 1*, Metals Park, Ohio, American Society for Metals, p.158.

[37] King H. K. (1970). *Physical Metallurgy*. Amsterdam, North-Holland Pub. Co. p.59.

[38] Bendijk A., Delhez R., Katgerman L., Keijser Th. H. De., Mittemeijer E. J., Van Der Pers N. M. (1980). Characterization of Al-Si alloys rapidly quenched from the melt. *J. Mater. Sci.*, *15*, 2803-2810.

[39] Antonione C., Battezzati L., Marino F. (1986). Structure and stability of rapidly solidified Al-Si based alloys. *J. Mat. Sci. Lett.*, *5*, 586-588.

[40] Inoue A., Horio Y., Kim Y. H., Masumoto T. (1993). New amorphous Al-Ni-Fe and Al-Ni-Co alloys. *Mater. Trans. JIM*, *34*, 85-88.

[41] Apaydin N., Smith R. W., (1988). Microstructural characterization of rapidly solidified Al-Si alloys. *Mater. Sci. Eng. A*, *98*, 149-152.

[42] Eckert J., Reger-Leonhard A., Weiß B., Heilmaier M. (2001). Nanostructured materials in multicomponent alloy systems. *Mater. Sci. Eng. A*, *301*, 1-11.

[43] Inoue A., Yamamoto M., Kimura H. M., Masumoto T. (1987). Ductile aluminium-base amorphous alloys with two separate phases. *J. Mater. Sci. Lett.*, *6*, 194-196.

[44] Inoue A., Ohetera K., Tsai A., Masumoto T. (1988). Aluminum-based amorphous alloys with tensile strength above 980 MPa (100 kg/mm^2). *Jpn J Appl Phys*, *27*, L479-L482.

[45] Kim Y. H., Inoue A., Masumoto T. (1990). Ultrahish tensile strengths of $Al_{88}Y_2Ni_9M_1$ (M=Mn or Fe) amorous alloys containing dispersed fcc-Al particles. *Mater. Trans. JIM*, *31*, 747-749.

[46] Inoue A. (1998). Amorphous, nanoquasicrystalline and nanocrystalline alloys in Al-based systems. *Prog Mater Sci*, *43*, 365-520.

[47] Manov V., Rubshtein A., Popcl P., Vereshagin, A. (1994). Effect of melt temperature on the electrical resistivity and crystallization temperature of $Al_{91}La_5Ni_4$ and Al_{91} Ce_5Ni_4 amorphous alloys. *Mater. Sci. Eng.* A, *179-180*, 91-96.

[48] Lück R., Jiang Q., Predel B. (1990). Specific heat investigation of the glass transition and crystallization of amorphous $NiZr_2$ using low heating rates. *J Non-Cryst Solids*, *117-118*, 911-914.

[49] Lu K. (1996). Nanocrystalline metals crystallized from amorphous solids: nanocrystallization, structure, and properties. *Mater Sci Eng R*, *16*, 161-221.

[50] Ye F., Lu K. (1999). Crystallization kinetics of amorphous solids under pressure. *Phys Rev B, 60*, 7018-7024.

[51] Allen D. R., Foley J. C., Perepezko J. H. (1998). Nanocrystal development during primary crystallization of amorphous alloys. *Acta Mater 46*, 431-440.

[52] Pradell T., Crespo D., Clavaguera N. (1997). Kinetics of microstructural development in nanocrystalline materials. *Nanostruc. Mater., 8*, 345-357.

[53] Tokar A., Levin L. (1998). The amorous metallic $Al_{91}La_5Ni_4$ alloy: Kineties of crystallization. *Z. Metallkd 89*, 16-22.

[54] Ye F. (1999). Pressure effect on crystallization kinetics of an Al-La-Ni amorphous alloy. Ph. D thesis, Shenyang, Institute of metal research, Chinese Academy of Science.

[55] Kissinger H. E. (1957). Reaction kinetics in differential thermal analysis. *Anal. Chem. 29*, 1702-1706.

[56] Li J. C., Zhou X. H., Jiang Q. (2001). Crystallization kinetics of $Al_{82}La_9Ni_9$ amorphous alloy. *J. Mater. Sci. Lett., 20*, 1679-1680

[57] Kwong V., Koo Y. C., Thorpe S. J., Aust K. T. (1991). Crystallization behaviour of $Al_{85}Y_{10}Ni_5$ by isochronal and isothermal annealing. *Acta Metall. Mater., 39,* 1563-1570.

[58] Cao B., Li S., Yi D. (1991). Study on the crystallization of $Al_{88.5}Y_{6.5}Ni_5$ (at.%) amorphous alloy. *J. Less-Comm. Metals, 171,* 1-8.

[59] Yewondwossen M., Dunlap R. A., Lloyd D. J. (1992). Thermal and electronic properties of amorphous $Al_{87}Y_8Ni_{5-x}TM_x$ (TM=Mn, Fe, Co, Cu). *J. Phys. Condens. Matter, 4*, 461-472.

[60] Inoue A. (2000). Stabilization of metallic supercooled liquid and bulk amorphous alloys. *Acta Mater., 48*, 279-306.

[61] Kawamura Y., Mano H. and Inoue A. (2001). Nanocrystalline aluminum bulk alloys with a high strength of 1420 MPa produced by the consolidation of amorphous powders. *Scrip. Mater., 44*, 1599-1604.

[62] Watanabe M. and Inoue A. (1993). High mechanical strength of rapidly solidified $Al_{92}Mn_6Ln_2$ (Ln = lanthanide metal) alloys with finely mixed icosahedral and Al phases. *Mater. Trans. JIM, 34*, 162-168.

[63] Takagi M., Ohta H., Imura T. and Inoue A. (2001). Wear properties of nanocrystalline aluminum alloys and their composites. *Scripta Mater., 44*, 2145-2148.

[64] Schurack F., Eckert J., Schultz L. (2000). Quasicrystalline Al-alloys with high strength and good ductility. *Mater. Sci. Eng. A, 294-296*, 164-167.

[65] Manaila R., Macovei D., Popescu R., Devenyi A., Jianu A., Vasile E., Barna P. B. and Labar J. L. (2000). Nano-icosahedral Al-Mn-Ce phases: structure and local configurations. *Mater. Sci. Eng., A, 294-296*, 82-85.

[66] Adachi H., Osamura K., Ochiai S., Kusui J. and Yokoe K. (2001). Mechanical property of nanoscale precipitate hardening aluminum alloys. *Scrip. Mater., 44*, 1489-1492.

[67] T. Mukai, K. Higashi, (2001). Ductility enhancement of ultra fine-grained aluminum under dynamic loading. *Scrip. Mater., 44*, 1493-1496.

[68] Schurack F., Eckert J. and Schultz L. (2001). Synthesis and mechanical properties of cast quasicrystal-reinforced Al-alloys. *Acta Mater., 49*, 1351-1361.

[69] Li J. C., Zhao Z. K. and Jiang Q. (2002). Bulk high strength $Al_{85}La_{10}Ni_5$ alloy prepared by hot pressing. *Mater. Res. Bull., 37*, 297-304.

[70] Li J. C., Zhao Z. K. and Jiang Q. (2003). Properties of high strength $Al_{85}La_{10}Ni_5$ alloy. *Mater. Sci. Eng. A, 339*, 205-208.

[71] Li J. C., Zhao M. and Jiang Q. (2002). Bulk high hardness $Al_{90}Ce_2Mn_8$ alloy prepared by a powder metallurgy method. *Powder Metallurgy, 45*, 80-82.

[72] Li J. C., Zhao Z. K. and Jiang Q. (2003). Mechanical properties of high strength $Al_{90}Mn_8Ce_2$ alloy. *Adv. Eng. Mater.*, 5, 119-122.

[73] Dash J. G. (1999). History of the search for continuous melting. *Rev. Mod. Phys., 71*, 1737-1743.

[74] Wen Z., Zhao M., Jiang Q. (2003). Surface melting of polycrystals Pb and In within 1 K below melting temperature. *Mater. Lett., 57*, 2515-2518.

[75] Yeh J. W., Chen S. K., Lin S. J., Gan J. Y., Chin T. S., Shun T. T., Tsau C. H., Chang S. Y. (2004). Nanostructured high-entropy alloys with multiple principal elements: novel alloy design concepts and outcomes. *Adv. Eng. Mater., 6*, 299-303.

[76] Greer L. A. (1993). Confusion by design. *Nature, 366*, 303.

[77] Swalin R. A. (1992). *Thermodynamics of solid.* NY, Wiley.

[78] Boer F. R. de, Boom R., Mattens W. C. M. (1998). *Cohesion in metals: Transition metal alloys.* NY, Elseveir.

[79] Huang P. K., Yeh J. W., Shun T. T., Chen S. K. (2004). Multi-principal-element alloys with improved oxidation and wear resistance for thermal spray coating. *Adv. Eng. Mater., 6*, 74-78.

[80] Hsu C. Y., Chen S. K., Yeh J. W., Shun T. T. (2004). Wear resistance and high-temperature compression strength of fcc CuCoNiCrAl0.5Fe alloy with boron addition. *Meatll. Mater. Trans. A, 35*, 1465-1469.

[81] Risbud S.H., Shan C.H. (1995). Fast consolidation of ceramic powders. *Mater. Sci. Eng. A, 204*, 146-151.

[82] Hong J., Gao L., Torre S. D. D. L., Miyamoto K., Miyamoto H. (2000). Spark plasma sintering and mechanical properties of $ZrO_2(Y_2O_3)$-Al_2O_3 composites. *Mater. Lett., 43*, 27- 31.

[83] Gao L., Wang H. Z., Hong J. S., Miyamoto H., Miyamoto K., Nishikawa Y., Torre S. D. de la. (1999). SiC-ZrO_2(3Y)-Al_2O_3 nanocomposites superfast densified by spark plasma sintering. *Nanostruct. Mater., 11*, 43-49.

[84] Wang Y. C., Fu Z. Y. (2002). Study of temperature field in spark plasma sintering. *Mater. Sci. Eng. B, 90*, 34-37.

[85] Xü C.Y., Jia S. S., Cao Z. Y. (2005). Synthesis of Al–Mn–Ce alloy by the spark plasma sintering. *Mater. Charact., 54*, 394-398.

In: Nanomaterials: New Research
Editor: B.M. Caruta, pp. 197-218

ISBN: 1-59454-369-0

Chapter 6

QUANTITATIVE ANALYSES OF NANOCLAY DISPERSION IN MOLDED EPOXY DISKS: EFFECTS OF MIXING TEMPERATURE

Levent Aktas, Sudha Dharmavaram, Youssef K. Hamidi and M. Cengiz Altan *

School of Aerospace and Mechanical Engineering
University of Oklahoma, Norman, OK 73019

ABSTRACT

Effects of mixing temperature on the quality of dispersion of nanoclay in an epoxy resin are investigated. Cloisite® 25A nanoclay is mixed at 5wt.% loading with EPON 815C epoxy resin at 30, 50 and 75°C by the aid of a sonicator. The resin/nanoclay compound is then mixed with Epi-cure 3282 curing agent and molded into center-gated disk shaped parts with a diameter of 152.4mm. From each molded disk, a sample along the radius is cut and dispersion of nanoclay on its through-the-thickness surface is analyzed. It is observed that nanoclay exists in the form of clusters with sizes ranging from nano-meter scale up to ~50μm. Nanoclay clusters larger than 1.5μm are characterized by performing digital image analyses on the scanning electron micrographs taken along the disk radius, whereas clusters smaller than 1.5μm are quantified by wavelength dispersive spectrometry. It is found that increasing mixing temperature leads to larger nanoclay clusters. For instance, contribution of large clusters (Area>50μm^2) to the overall nanoclay content increased from 8.9 to 10.4% when the mixing temperature increased from 30 to 75°C. Similarly, in the same temperature range, contribution of small clusters (Area<3μm^2) decreased from 43.3 to 40.8%. The size and shape evolution of nanoclay clusters in the flow direction are also analyzed. Considerable nanoclay breakdown is observed in the radial direction. Contribution of small clusters to the nanoclay content at the outer edges of the disk is observed to be as much as 30% higher compared to the

---

* Correspondent author. E-mail: altan@ou.edu

inlet. Cluster breakdown also caused the nanoclay clusters to assume more irregular shapes at the outer edges of the disk.

1. Introduction

Particulates of nano-meter scale, such as carbon nanotubes and nanoclay, are receiving considerable research interest since they are likely to improve the properties of polymers, even when they are introduced at minor amounts [1]. Among these nano-particulates, nanoclay has gained acceptance as a viable commercial material and is being used in products such as food packaging materials and automobile semi-structural components. A series of pioneering work conducted by Toyota Research Labs [2-4] introduced the application of nanoclay to reinforce conventional polymeric resins. The problem of nanoclay particle agglomeration in polymers is overcome by surface modification of the originally organo-phobic surface of the nanoclay platelets through cation exchange reaction [2]. Later, the organo-philically modified nanoclay in Ref. 2 is mixed with ε-caprolactam, the monomer for nylon 6 [3]. Upon polymerization, the resulting nanocomposite is examined by x-ray diffractometry (XRD) and transmission electron microscopy (TEM) for the changes in gallery spacing of the nanoclay. The results revealed over 600% increase in basal spacing of the nanoclay due to combined effects of insertion of ε-caprolactam into the gallery spacing and its swelling during polymerization [3]. Kojima et al. tested various mechanical properties of the nanocomposite fabricated in Ref. 3. Despite slight decrease in impact resistance, tensile and flexural properties improved by as much as 122% over pristine nylon 6 with the addition of 4.7wt.% nanoclay.

Following the work done by Toyota research group, several researchers implemented both modified and unmodified nanoclay in various polymeric resins. Most commonly, these studies focus on possible improvements in thermo-mechanical properties of polymers [4-16]. For instance, Lan and Pinnavaia [5] prepared nanoclay from Na^+-montmorillonite by an ion exchange reaction with alkylammonium chloride or bromide salts. The resulting nanoclay was then introduced to EPON 828 epoxy resin at loadings ranging from 2 to 23.2wt.%. Both x-ray diffractometry (XRD) and transmission electron microscopy (TEM) results indicated complete exfoliation of nanoclay platelets in epoxy matrix. Consequently, tensile testing confirmed up to 12- and 18-fold increase in tensile stiffness and strength, respectively. However, with the choice of poly(ether amine) as the curing agent, the fabricated nanocomposites had sub-ambient glass transition temperatures. Lan and Pinnavaia [9] also report that the improvements in mechanical properties for systems at glassy state were rather marginal. Similarly, Wang et al. [6] mixed three commercially available nanoclay types: Cloisite® 20A, Cloisite® 30A and Nanomer® I30, with various thermoplastic polymers. Although XRD analyses indicated increased basal spacing for nanoclay platelets upon polymerization, the improvements in mechanical properties were rather limited. 2.7-fold increase in elastic modulus is followed by 39% and 87% decreases in tensile and impact strengths, respectively for polystyrene/nanoclay systems [6]. Abot et al. [7] observed a similar behavior for epoxy polymer reinforced with organically modified nanoclay. The authors reported up to 31% increase in elastic modulus as the tensile strength deteriorated by as much as 28% over the nanoclay loading range of 0 to 20wt.%. In addition to deterioration in tensile strength, Abot et al. [7] reported up to 28% reduction in glass transition temperature as determined by dynamic mechanical analysis (DMA). On the other hand, Shen et al. [8] were able to simultaneously improve strength and stiffness. Authors in this study used an organoclay modified from montmorillonite specially for applications of nylon 6 and nylon 6,6. Akin to Kojima et al. [4], nanocomposite is prepared by melt compounding using a twin-screw extruder. With the aid of a nanoindentation technique, the authors measured the strength and stiffness of nylon 6,6 reinforced with 5wt.% nanoclay. Compared with pristine polymer, the results indicate 15.2% and 27.9% increase in strength and stiffness, respectively.

The large variations in the mechanical property improvement with the addition of nanoclay may be due to inadequate dispersion and exfoliation of nanoclay particles. In particulate reinforced composites, the effective particle dimension is of particular importance as it dictates the mechanical properties for a given loading [17-22]. Singh et al. [17], for instance, investigated the effect of aluminum particle size on the mechanical properties of polyester/aluminum composites. Aluminum particles of three different dimensions (i.e., 100nm, 3.5μm and 20μm) were added to liquid polyester resin by mechanical blending at loadings ranging from 1 to 10wt.%. Overall stiffness of the composite at a given loading is observed to be independent of the particle size, whereas strength is found to decrease monotonically with increasing particle size. Correspondingly, Cai and Salovey [18] used polystyrene particles of sizes ranging from 0.315μm to 1.250 μm to reinforce polysulfide matrix. In the range of particle sizes studied, 10.2% improvement was observed in stiffness versus a decrease of more than 47% in strength. Degradation of strength with an increase in stiffness was also observed by Wang et al. [6] and Abot et al. [7] for nanoclay reinforced epoxies. Consequently, one can conclude that the reduction of strength with the addition of nanoclay may be due to agglomeration of nanoclay particles and their lack of dispersion into individual platelets. Nonetheless, compared to post-dispersion changes in thermo-mechanical properties, dispersion characterization did not receive adequate attention. In order to have predictive capability over the mechanical properties of nanoclay reinforced composites, it is essential to be able to characterize nanoclay dispersion at multiple length scales.

Among the small number of studies devoted to nanoclay dispersion [23-24], Park and Jana [23] studied epoxy aided dispersion of nanoclay in PMMA matrix. Transmission electron microscopy (TEM) and wide angle x-ray diffractometry (WAXD) were implemented to compare the state of dispersion of nanoclay in PMMA with that of a ternary system epoxy/nanoclay/PMMA. The results indicated that a priori mixing of nanoclay in epoxy is more likely to produce exfoliated clay structures. Park and Jana [24] also approached the problem from a rheological point of view. The authors attribute the increase of basal spacing between nanoclay platelets to the elastic forces exerted by the polymer matrix as the cross-linking takes place. Furthermore, it was concluded that the expansion in gallery spacing takes place as long as the ratio of storage modulus to complex viscosity is over 2-4s^{-1}.

Traditionally, the characterization of dispersion as well as intercalation and exfoliation of nanoclay is performed by using two methods: x-ray diffractometry (XRD) and transmission electron microscopy (TEM). X-ray diffractometry is preferred by the majority of researchers to describe the intercalation and exfoliation in a quantitative manner. In this method, a well characterized x-ray (most of the time Cu-Kα) is sent onto the surface of interest. Based on the angle of diffraction of the x-ray from the surface, the basal spacing between the nanoclay platelets is calculated through Bragg's Law [26]. Although X-ray diffractometry enables precise nanoclay basal spacing measurements at Ångström scale, it is prone to certain shortcomings. According to Kornmann et al. [27], broad distribution of nanoclay basal spacing may lead to indistinguishable intensity peaks and thus may lead to inaccurate conclusions on the state of dispersion. On the other hand, transmission electron microscopy, due to its capability of high magnification imaging, is suitable for qualitative analysis of dispersion. However, its high magnification limits the size of imaging area and thus the obtained results may not be representative of the whole sample. Especially, if the spatial variation of dispersion state is large, such as presence of local tactoids, TEM would be a poor choice of characterization [28].

As an alternative to the above-mentioned traditional methods, researchers gradually used rheological techniques in the characterization of dispersion [28-30]. For instance, Wagener and Reisinger [28] studied rheological characterization of dispersion in poly(butylenes terephthalate)/clay nanocomposites. Based on scanning electron micrographs and tensile properties of the nanocomposites, the authors concluded that the shear thinning coefficient may be used as a semi quantitative method in describing the state of dispersion. However, the setback of rheological methods is that the measured quantity is a bulk property of the sample under consideration. Therefore, the state of dispersion obtained through rheological methods does not yield information on spatial variation.

The current study investigates the effects of mixing temperature on the state of dispersion of nanoclay particles in epoxy matrix. For this reason, 5wt.% nanoclay is mixed into epoxy resin at three different temperatures, (i.e., 30°C, 50°C and 75°C) by sonication. The resulting epoxy/nanoclay compound is then used to fabricate center-gated disks to be used in analysis of nanoclay dispersion. To characterize the dispersion of nanoclay as a function of cluster size and spatial position, a novel method combining scanning electron microscopy (SEM) and wavelength dispersive spectrometry (WDS) is implemented [31]. Scanning electron micrographs taken at various magnifications indicated the presence of nanoclay clusters of various sizes. Thus, a sample is cut in the radial direction of the disk and its through-the-thickness plane is analyzed for nanoclay clusters. Nanoclay clusters larger than 1.5μm are analyzed by performing digital image analysis on the scanning electron micrographs taken at 50x magnification, whereas, clusters of smaller dimensions are analyzed by wavelength dispersive spectrometry. Temperature dependence of the radial distribution of nanoclay sizes and shapes are also presented.

2. Experimental Studies

2.1. Materials

Cloisite® 25A of Southern Clay Products (Gonzales, TX) is mixed with EPON 815C epoxy resin (Shell Chemicals) at a loading of 5wt.%. This particular type of nanoclay is modified by the manufacturer to increase the organo-philicity of its gallery region, thus resulting in better dispersion in various types of resins. EPON 815C is a low viscosity resin with a room temperature viscosity of 0.74Pas (740cp) that is primarily preferred in molding applications. It is also well known that addition of nanoclay into polymeric resins result in sharp increases in viscosity and adversely affects the processibility. The epoxy resin used in this study is especially suitable for mixing nanoclay particles due to its low viscosity. The epoxy/nanoclay compound is cured with Epi-cure 3282 curing agent from Shell Chemicals at a weight ratio of 5:1 of resin to curing agent. At this particular mixing ratio, the gel time is approximately 20 minutes. In this study, the mold cavity is filled under 10s, well before the cross-linking starts.

2.2. Mixing of Nanoclay in Epoxy Resin

Nanoclay is mixed into the epoxy resin with the aid of a 42kHz, constant amplitude sonicator. Initially, the resin is placed into a beaker which is immersed into the sonicator filled with water. Then proper amount of nanoclay is gradually added into the resin. To help dispersion of large aggregates, 5 minutes of hand mixing is applied before the sonication starts. Total sonication time is chosen as 60 minutes, beyond which a visual change in the resin/nanoclay compound is not observed. The amount of nanoclay added into the resin is determined by accounting for the curing agent needed during molding stage, such that the final nanoclay weight fraction of 5% is achieved.

In order to investigate the effects of the mixing temperature on the state of nanoclay dispersion, nanoclay is mixed with epoxy resin at three different temperatures of 30°C, 50°C and 75°C. A cupper tubing connected to a constant temperature water bath is placed into the sonicator to keep the water surrounding the beaker containing the resin/nanoclay compound at the desired temperature.

At the end of sonication, a thin layer of small air pockets are formed on the surface of the resin/nanoclay compound. As these air pockets would weaken the final properties of the nanocomposite and might affect the dispersion state, the compound is kept aside for degassing for an additional hour before molding.

2.3. Molding and Sample Preparation

Samples used in investigating the effects of mixing temperature on the dispersion of nanoclay are fabricated by a custom made molding setup. The schematic representation of the setup is given in Figure 1 and described in detail elsewhere [32,33].

The two hollow cylinders on the molding setup serve as the reservoirs for epoxy/nanoclay compound and Epi-cure 3282 curing agent. The inner diameters of the cylinders are machined to 55.47 and 25.43mm which yield 4.7:1 volumetric ratio for the resin and curing agent, respectively. A 80-kip hydraulic press is utilized to force the epoxy/nanoclay compound and curing agent out of the cylinders via two plungers. Outflows from both cylinders are then combined by a tee-connector and passed through a static inline mixer with 32 alternating helical elements placed in a polypropylene tube to provide thorough mixing. Well mixed nanoclay/epoxy compound and curing agent are injected into a mold that is positioned inline with the system. The constant speed of the ram results in a volume flow rate of 5.32cm^3/s during mold filling.

The mold is composed of three main parts, two mold walls and a spacer plate. The 228.6mm x 228.6mm spacer plate is a 3.175mm (1/8in) thick square with a 152.4 mm (6in) diameter circle cut out from the center. The disk shaped cavity is formed by placing the spacer plate between 6.35mm (1/4in) thick aluminum mold walls. The resin/nanoclay/curing

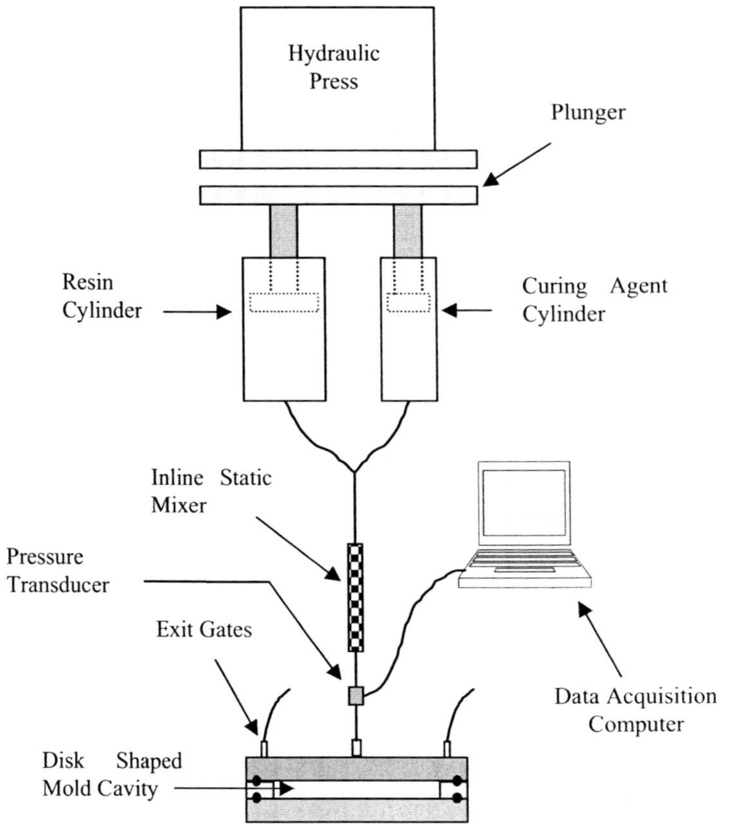

Figure 1. Experimental molding setup used to fabricate center-gated disks.

agent mixture enters the mold cavity through a fitting, mounted at the center of the top mold wall. Other than the inlet, four exit vents are placed symmetrically at the outer edges of the top mold wall. The injection is continued until the mixture comes out of the exit gates, after which the press is stopped. The molding is then completed by sequentially clamping the exit gates and the inlet gate. Since some amount of post-fill pressure improves the part quality [34], the press is operated for an additional second before clamping the inlet gate to apply a modest packing pressure.

A total of three disks reinforced with Cloisite® 25A nanoclay are fabricated. The resin/nanoclay compound used in each disk is prepared at different temperatures, i.e., 30°C, 50°C and 75°C. A sample is cut along the radius of each disk (i.e., 76.2mm long) as depicted in Figure 2 and radial variation of dispersion state is analyzed on through-the-thickness surfaces of these samples.

2.4. Quantification of Dispersion

Preliminary microstructural analysis of the nanocomposites is carried out on a JEOL-880 high resolution scanning electron microscope. The images obtained from scanning electron microscope indicate that the nanoclay exists primarily in the form of clusters of various sizes.

Further analysis at magnifications ranging from 100X to 25000X revealed that there is a continuum of cluster sizes from nanometer scale up to 50μm. A sample microstructural image taken at 2500X showing various nanoclusters is depicted in Figure 3.

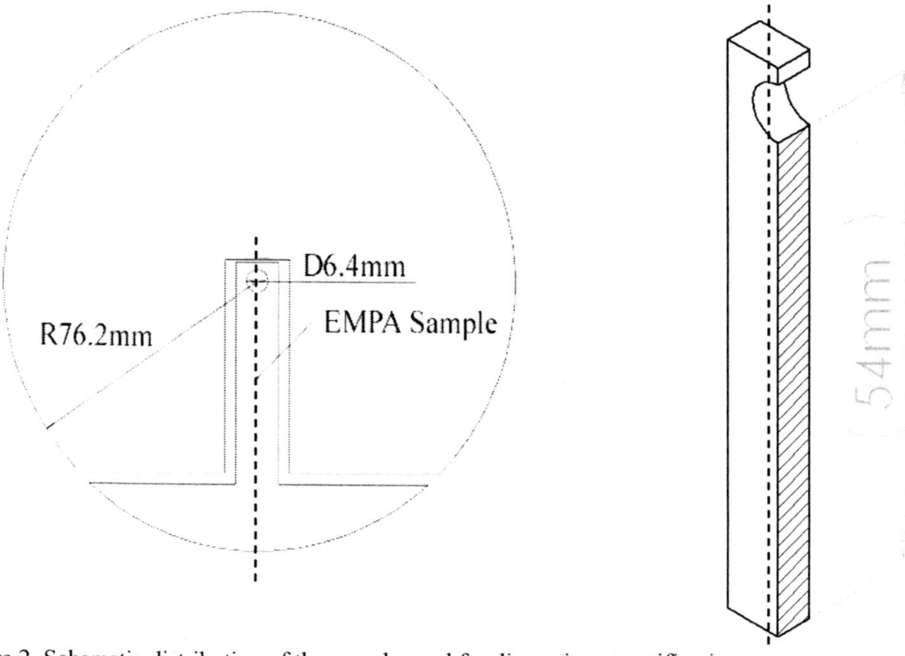

Figure 2. Schematic distribution of the sample used for dispersion quantification.

To characterize the state of dispersion accurately, one needs to consider nanoclay clusters at all relevant scales. The traditional methods of dispersion characterization are lacking spatial coverage and are usually inadequate to characterize large nanoclay clusters. In nanoclay composites, nanoclay most likely exists in the form of clusters. In such cases, spatial coverage of the method used to characterize dispersion is especially important, as it is well known that thermo-mechanical properties of the material strongly depend on the cluster size and their spatial distribution. To assess the required spatial and dimensional coverage, we utilized an electron microprobe analyzer (EMPA) and characterized the dispersion at various radial locations of the molded composite disks.

The dispersion state of the nanoclay composites is characterized using Cameca SX-50 electron microprobe analyzer (EMPA). This particular EMPA, in addition to its imaging capability through scanning electron microscopy, is capable of performing detailed compositional analysis via wavelength dispersive spectrometry (WDS) and energy dispersive x-ray analysis (EDXA). In particular, five wavelength dispersive spectrometers positioned around the column are capable of detecting elements with atomic numbers 5 and above with properly chosen diffraction crystals. Both imaging and compositional analysis of the EMPA are provided by a PC-Based SAMx data acquisition system.

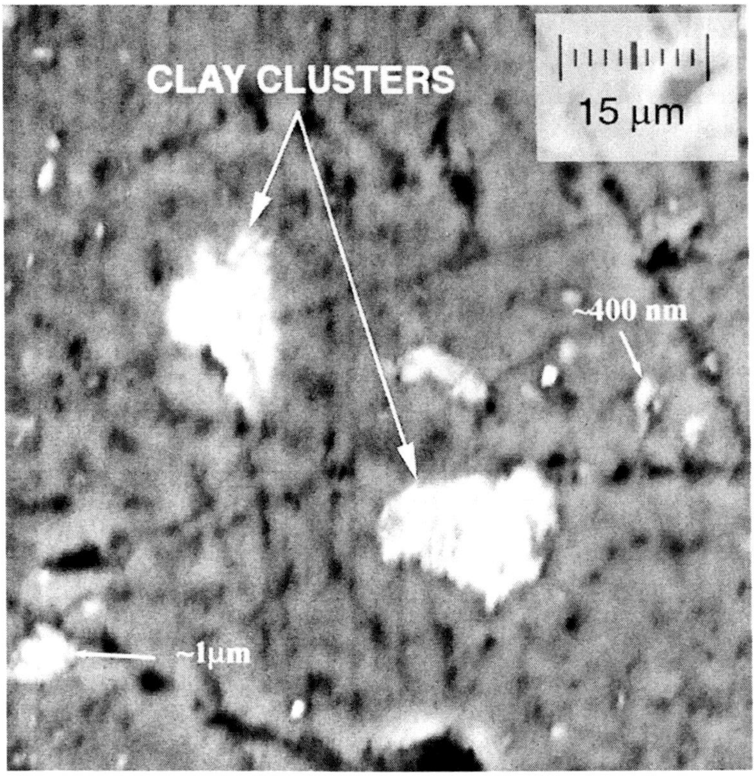

Figure 3. Scanning electron micrograph of the nanocomposite micro-structure taken at 2500X. Clusters of various sizes are indicated.

One sample from each disk is cut radially from the inlet gate at the center to the outer edge of this disk. These samples are then embedded into EMPA sample holder sidewise such that the through-the-thickness surface is exposed for analysis. To cover a wider range of nanoclay cluster sizes, the dispersion analysis is carried out in two categories. Nanoclay clusters that are visible at 50X magnification scanning electron micrographs are quantified by performing digital image analysis. At the utilized imaging resolution, one pixel at 50X magnification is equivalent to 1.5μm. Hence, nanoclay clusters quantified by digital image analysis are larger than 1.5 μm. This category of nanoclay clusters will be referred to as *micro-scale clusters* throughout the article. The nanoclay clusters that were not visible at 50X magnification are analyzed by wavelength dispersive spectrometry (WDS) and will be referred to as *nano-scale clusters*.

Digital image analysis is utilized to quantify the *micro-scale clusters*. For each of the three approximately 56mm-long samples, scanning electron micrographs are gathered along the center line of the surface of interest at 4mm intervals. A total of 72 images are captured in the back scattered electron mode at an accelerating voltage of 20kV and a beam current of 5nA. Images are then stored into 1024X1024 pixel arrays and subjected to digital image analysis using UTHSCSA Image Tool® software. The first step of digital image analysis involved a thresholding process, thereby converting the originally 8-bit grey scale images to binary images. The thresholding process is repeated 7 times in order to quantify and reduce the uncertainties involved in the image analysis. Figure 4 depicts a thresholded image that is further used in quantification of *micro-scale cluster* dispersion. All these binary images are later analyzed to obtain nanoclay cluster content, number of nanoclay clusters and nanoclay cluster roundness.

Wavelength dispersive spectrometry (WDS) is preferred for quantification of *nano-scale clusters*. Prior to WDS analysis, compacted Cloisite® 25A nanoclay is analyzed by energy dispersive x-ray analysis in order to determine its constituent elements to be targeted in WDS analysis. The major elements are determined as silicon, calcium, magnesium and iron. These elements are targeted by wavelength dispersive spectrometers of the electron microbeam analyzer along the cross-section of the sample at 500μm intervals. Along the length of the samples, a total of 320 locations are analyzed by WDS. A pristine epoxy polymer is also analyzed by WDS and used as background corrections for the quantification of *nano-scale clusters*. Prior to data collection, a trial sample is analyzed at various beam conditions in order to determine the optimum beam condition for maximum precision and minimum beam damage on the analytical volume. As a result, all analyses are conducted at a beam current of 5nA and a spot diameter of 20μm.

Figure 4. SEM images are thresholded to discriminate the nanoclay clusters from the matrix. The image depicted is taken at 50X magnification.

3. Results and Discussion

3.1. Dispersion of Micro-Scale Clusters

Dispersion and exfoliation of micro-scale nanoclay clusters down to sub-micron size are particularly essential since existence of nanoclay aggregates is often encountered and is known to extensively affect the final mechanical performance of the nanocomposites. In that respect, we investigated the phase fraction and morphology of nanoclay present in the form of aggregates in epoxy matrix as a function of temperature.

Researchers often attempted solving the problem of agglomeration by changing parameters such as temperature, during mixing of nanoclay into the polymer matrix [35,36]. However, the effects of mixing parameters are quantified either by the dispersion characterization methods mentioned earlier, which are lacking spatial coverage, or by elaborating on the final thermo-mechanical properties of the nanocomposites. Investigation of micro-scale nanoclay cluster dispersion by the method implemented here provides information that was previously unavailable as it contains complete spatial coverage of the sample.

Radial distribution of *micro-scale cluster* content is depicted in Figure 5 together with 95% confidence intervals for each of the three different mixing temperatures studied. Each data point in Figure 5 is formed by determining the phase fraction of nanoclay from the images captured by scanning electron microscopy starting from r=3.2mm (r is radial distance). Figure 5 indicates that volume fraction of *micro-scale clusters* do not display a significant change in the radial direction, regardless of the temperature. The average micro-scale cluster content is calculated as 2.8, 3.4 and 4.0vol.% for mixing temperatures of 30, 50 and 75°C, respectively. The increase in micro-scale cluster (clusters larger than 1.5μm) content with the increase in mixing temperature indicates the presence of lesser amounts of nano-scale clusters at higher mixing temperatures. Based on these results, a more effective dispersion of nanoclay seems to take place at lower mixing temperatures. It should be noted that the nanoclay content calculated by digital image analysis is expressed as volume fraction rather than weight fraction since the density of nanoclay is unknown at its current degree of compaction.

This trend may be attributed to the higher viscosity of the epoxy resin at lower temperatures. It is believed that shear forces developed during mixing are responsible for cluster breakdown and improved dispersion of the nanoclay. Since the mixing is performed with a constant amplitude and frequency sonicator (i.e., constant strain rate), lower viscosities of the resin/nanoclay compound would result in lower shear stresses acting on the nanoclay clusters. Thus, as observed in binary SEM images, average micro-scale cluster content is higher for the higher mixing temperatures. This trend is observed by Park and Jana as well [24]. The authors argue that the lower resin temperatures result in higher viscous forces and therefore yields higher levels of exfoliation. In a recent study, Lertwimolnun and Vergnes [36] investigated the effects of several mixing parameters on the degree of exfoliation of polypropylene/organoclay nanocomposites. Cloisite® 20A is mixed with polypropylene in an extruder at two different temperatures: 180°C and 200°C. Although the XRD peak positions are not affected by the mixing temperature, rheological observations revealed that the degree of exfoliation is considerably higher at 180°C compared to 200°C.

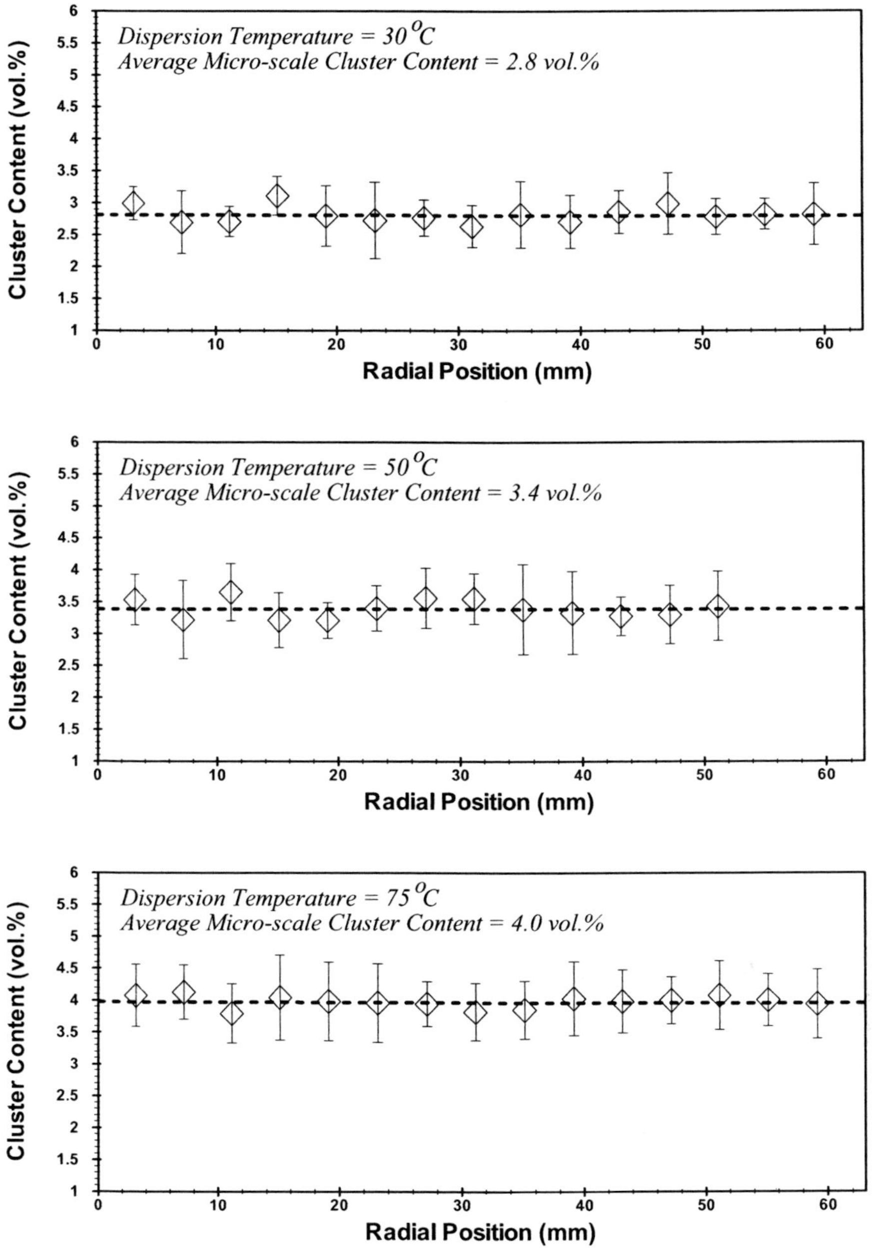

Figure 5. Micro-scale cluster distribution along the radius for the mixing temperatures of 30, 50 and 75°C.

As Figure 5 indicates, *micro-scale cluster* content remains constant along the radius of the molded disks, yet nanoclay clusters may exhibit a preferential size distribution. During filling of the disk-shaped mold cavity, nanoclay particles are subjected to shear forces due to narrow gapwidth and compressive forces due to decelerating flow [37]. These forces may result in cluster breakdown and consequently, preferential variation of nanoclay cluster sizes. If there is such a variation regardless of constant nanoclay content, the nanoclay cluster density, i.e., number of nanoclay clusters per unit area, should vary in the radial direction.

Figure 6 shows a distinct variation of cluster density in the radial direction for all three disks. At the outer edges of the disks, *micro-scale cluster* density is observed to be as much as 50, 70% and 44% higher than that of the inlet for 30, 50 and 75°C, respectively. Knowing that the *micro-scale cluster* content remains constant along the radius, increase in the *micro-scale cluster* density indicates that nanoclay clusters are becoming finer close to the edges of the disks.

The breakdown of nanoclay clusters into smaller particles may be further demonstrated by the change in percentage contribution of *small clusters* (i.e., $A<3\mu m^2$) to the overall nanoclay cluster content at various points along the disk radius. Figure 7 depicts the percentage contribution of *small clusters* as a function of the radial position and mixing temperature. At all mixing temperatures studied, the percentage contribution of small clusters increases by as at least 8% towards the outer edges of the disks.

These results indicate that nanoclay clusters are preferentially transported and/or broken down along the flow direction due to the viscous stresses. A more thorough analysis can be performed by identifying this preferential distribution for a broader range of nanoclay clusters. For this reason, nanoclay clusters are categorized into four groups based on their area, A. These four nanoclay cluster groups are: *i)* $A<3\mu m^2$, *ii)* $3\mu m^2 \leq A<20\mu m^2$, *iii)* $20\mu m^2 \leq A<50\mu m^2$ and *iv)* $A \geq 50\mu m^2$. Percentage change of contribution of different cluster sizes are calculated with respect to the first data point, i.e., r=3.2mm. To illustrate the reduction of nanoclay cluster size, percentage contribution of each nanoclay cluster group at a particular radial location is divided by the percentage contribution of the same nanoclay cluster group near the inlet (i.e., r=3.2mm).

For example, at the mixing temperature of 30°C, clusters with $A<3\mu m^2$ make up 35% of the total clusters at the inlet, whereas same size clusters make up 41.3%, 43.3%, 49.7% and 45.5% of the total clusters at r=19.2, 31.2, 43.2 and 55.2mm, respectively. Thus, as shown in Figure 8, the percentage contribution ratios of small clusters is, 18.1, 23.7, 41.1 and 30.2% , respectively. The percentage contribution ratios are calculated for all four nanoclay cluster size categories and three mixing temperatures. It should be noted that the analyses for nanocomposite disk with a mixing temperature of 50°C is performed on three radial locations due to smaller length of this particular sample compared to others. The percentage contribution ratios are represented in Figure 8. One can deduce that percentage contribution ratio of all cluster sizes are reduced compared to the inlet except for the small clusters with $A<3\mu m^2$. Therefore, at the outer edges of the disk small clusters are a greater portion of the nanoclay clusters compared to the inlet. On the contrary, larger nanoclay clusters are decreasing radially along all disks. The results presented in Figures 6-8 clearly depict a preferential variation in nanoclay cluster size in the flow direction. This spatially non-uniform cluster size variation may have been caused by two factors. First, smaller clusters are more mobile and may move faster with the flow during mold filling and accumulate at the outer edges of the disk. However, small cluster sizes and viscous nature of the resin result in creeping flow with negligible inertial effects. Thus, the local flow is dominated by viscous effects and all clusters move with the flow. Second and more likely explanation is the breakdown of nanoclay clusters due to the viscous stresses formed by the flow kinematics. It is well known that the small gap thickness causes high shear stresses that are dominant over the planar stresses. In addition to high shear rates acting on nanoclay, the circular disk geometry causes decelerating flow and forms compressive stresses on the nanoclay particles suspended in the flow. The combination of shear and compressive stresses are likely to affect the breakdown and transport of nanoclay clusters.

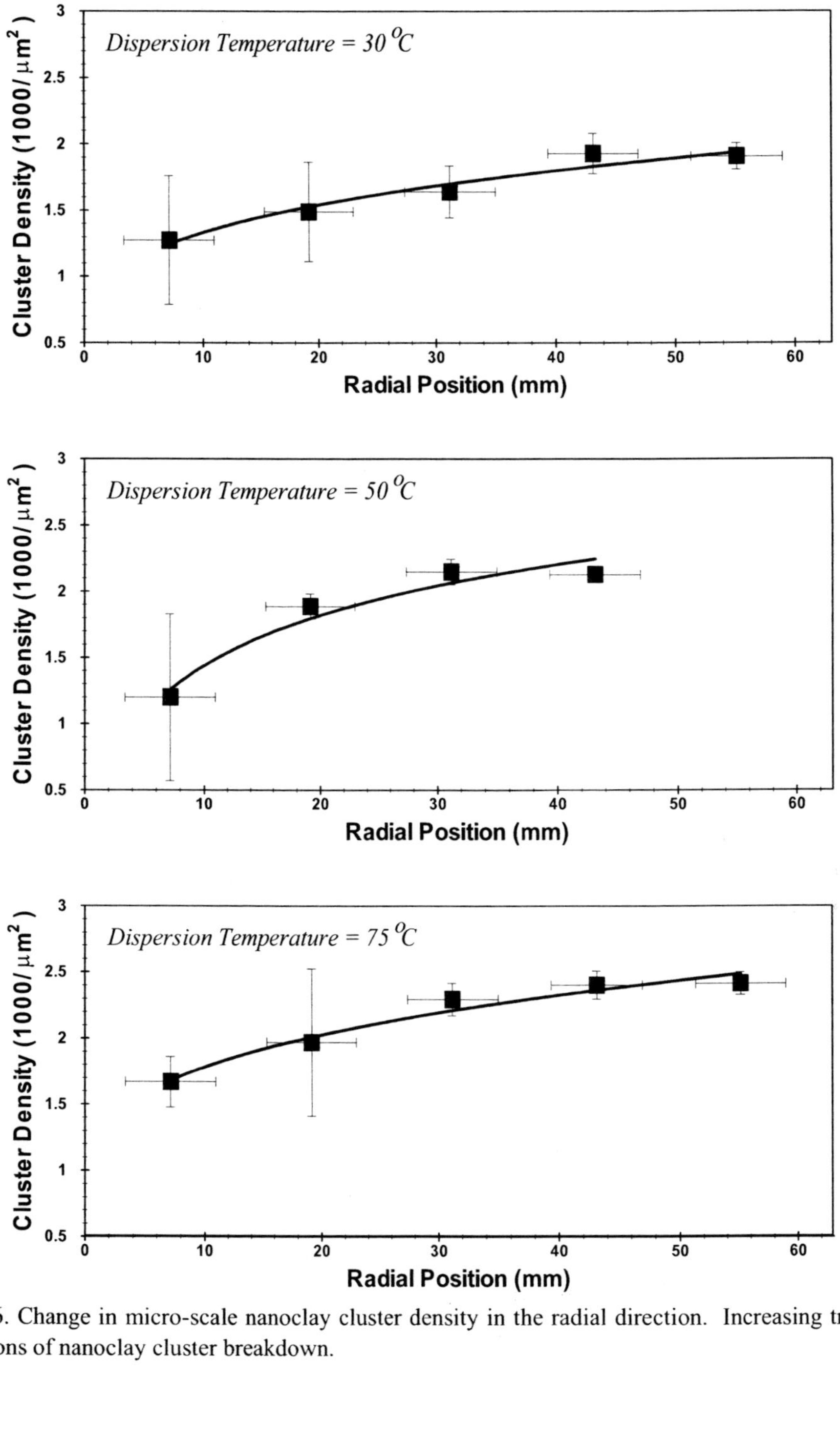

Figure 6. Change in micro-scale nanoclay cluster density in the radial direction. Increasing trends are indications of nanoclay cluster breakdown.

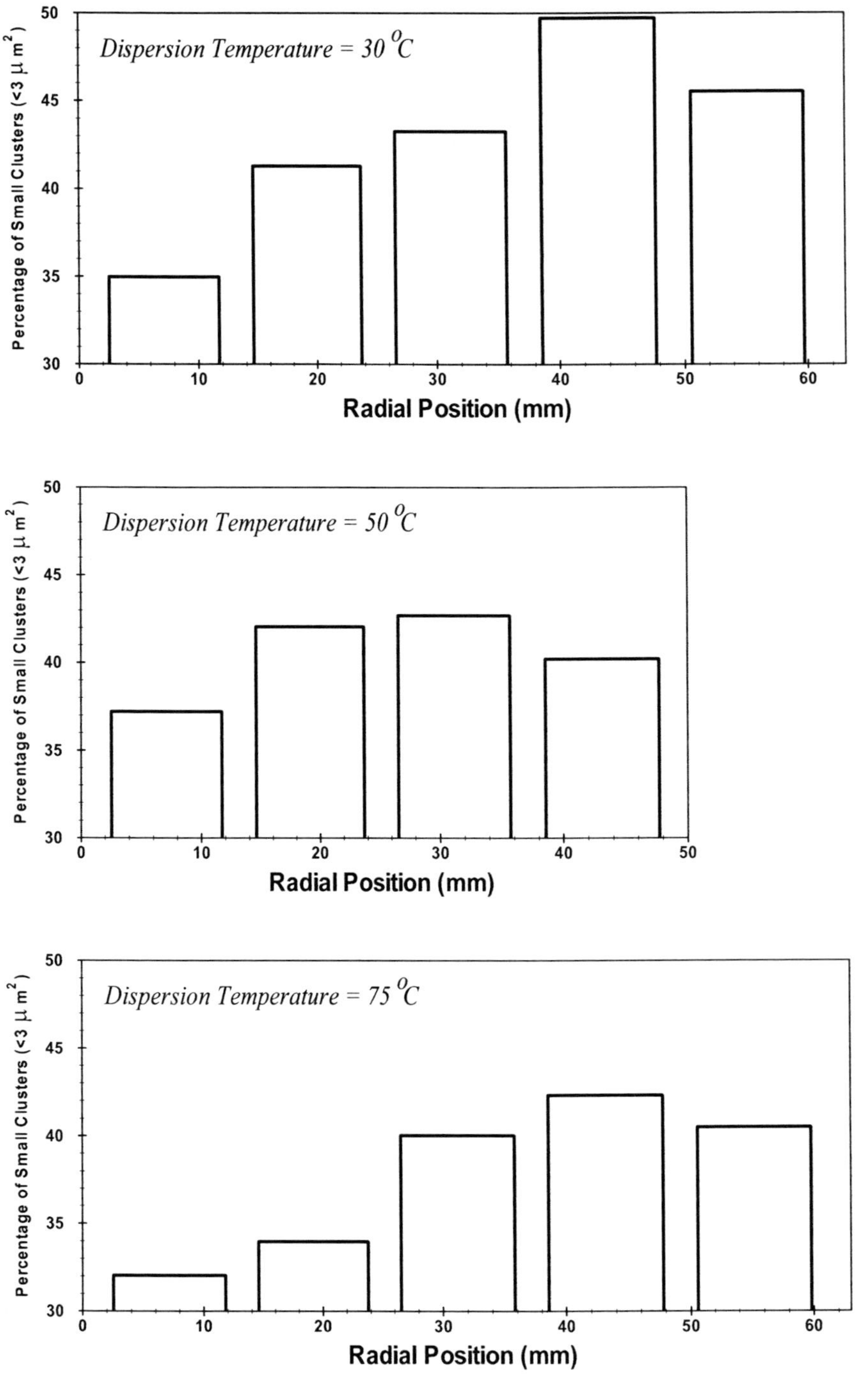

Figure 7. Percentage of small nanoclay clusters (*Area*<3μm²) in the flow direction.

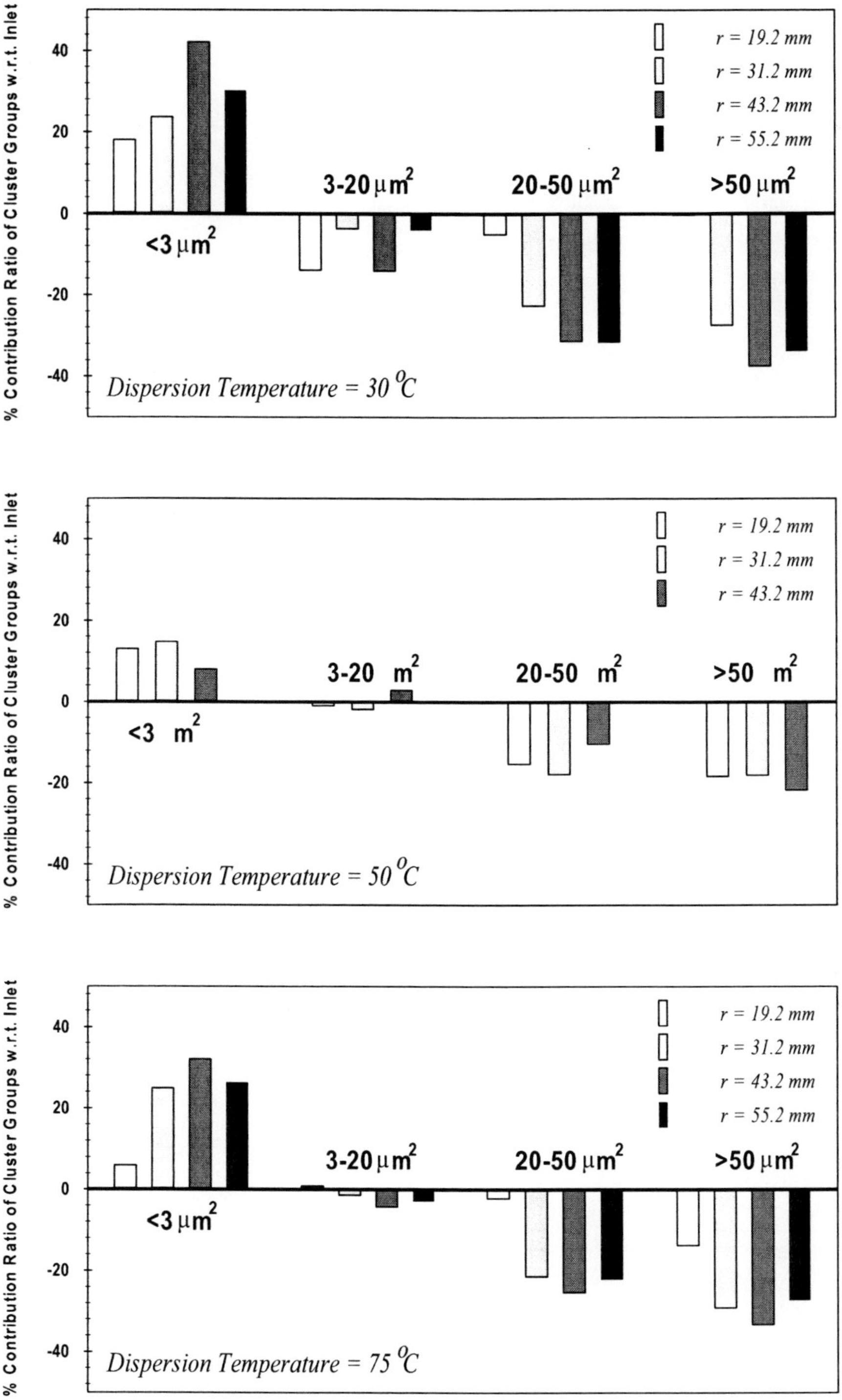

Figure 8. Percentage contribution ratio of nanoclay clusters of different sizes along the flow direction calculated with respect to the cluster size distribution near the inlet.

As the nanoclay clusters are broken down, it is expected that their shape characteristics would change as well. To investigate the shape change of nanoclay clusters along the flow direction, the average roundness at near the inlet and at the outer edge of the disk are calculated. In this study, roundness of a nanoclay cluster is defined as,

$$\frac{4\pi \times Area}{(Perimeter)^2}.$$

When defined according to the above equation, the roundness varies between 0 and unity. A roundness value of unity indicates a perfect circular shape, whereas irregular, elongated shapes assume a roundness value that is closer to 0.

Figure 9 depicts the roundness distribution of the nanoclay clusters in the first and last image taken along the disk radius. The locations of data bars of both inlet and outlet data are slightly shifted for the clarity of the plot. The solid and dashed lines, on the other hand, are quadratic fits to these data points which identify the distribution peaks clearly. At all mixing temperatures, the peak is observed to shift toward smaller roundness values, indicating that the nanoclay clusters are becoming less circular as they move and break into smaller clusters in the flow direction. It should as well be noted that the nanoclay clusters analyzed for roundness are the ones that are larger than 60pixel^2 (i.e., A>140μm^2) which make up of at least 18.5% of the nanoclay content. Using roundness values for smaller clusters would not be representative of the cluster breakdown as the number of pixels used would be insufficient to quantify the changes in cluster shape.

Figure 10 depicts the effects of mixing temperature on the state of dispersion of nanoclay. Percent contribution of small (A<3μm^2) and large (A>50μm^2) nanoclay clusters to the overall nanoclay content are depicted for mixing temperatures of 30, 50 and 75°C. As the mixing temperature is increased from 30 to 75°C, percent contribution of small nanoclay clusters decrease from 43.3% to 40.8%, whereas that of large clusters increase from 8.9 to 10.4%. Due to the lower viscosity of the resin at high temperatures, the shear stresses that are breaking down the nanoclay aggregates decrease and result in less favorable nanoclay cluster size distribution.

3.2. Dispersion of Nano-Scale Clusters

Dispersion of nanoclay clusters smaller than 1.5μm is analyzed using wavelength dispersive spectrometry (WDS). Prior to compositional analyses, a compacted nanoclay sample is analyzed using energy dispersive x-ray analyses (EDXA) to determine the major constituent elements of the nanoclay. The EDXA spectrum of Cloisite® 25A is depicted in Figure 11. Interpreting the intensity peaks and their energy levels, the major constituents are determined as magnesium, aluminum, silicon and iron. Presence of these elements is targeted by WDS. At least 102 locations that are 500μm apart are analyzed along the radius of each sample. After background corrections using the data obtained from a pristine polymer sample, the weight percentages of nanoclay clusters that are smaller than 1.5μm are depicted in Figure 12.

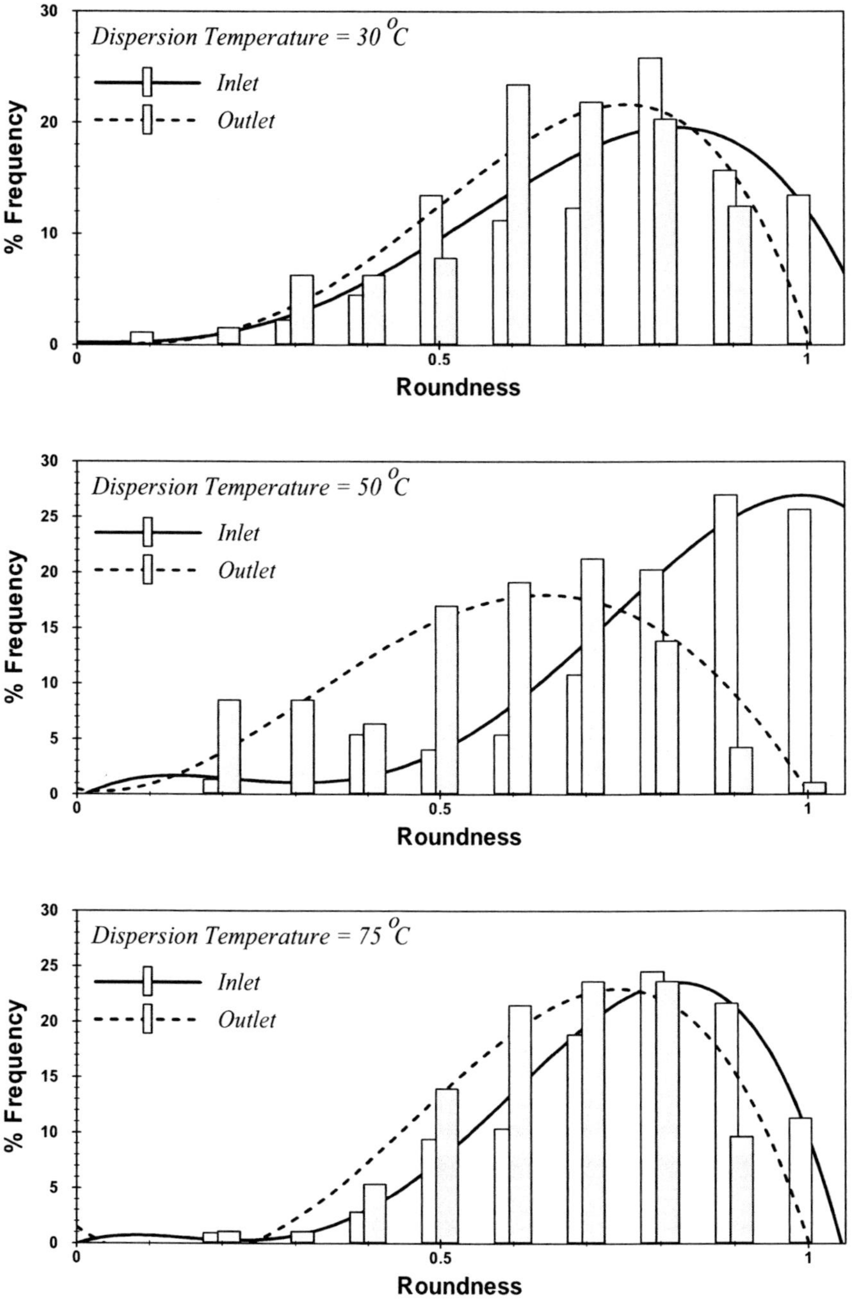

Figure 9. Roundness distribution of nanoclay clusters at the inlet and outer edge of the nanocomposite disks.

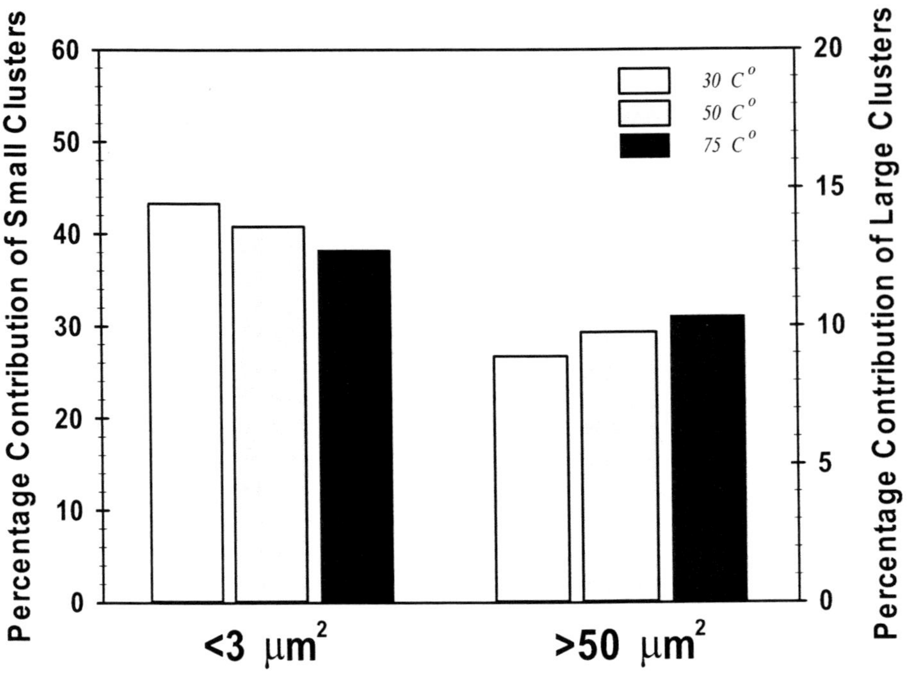

Figure 10. Overall percentage of small (*Area*<3μm^2) and large (*Area*>50μm^2) nanoclay clusters as a function of temperature.

Akin to dispersion of micro-scale clusters, nano-scale cluster content did not indicate dependence on the radial position. An average nanoclay content of 2.5, 2.2 and 2.1wt.% are obtained for mixing temperatures of 30, 50 and 75°C respectively. Since the total nanoclay contents are equal for the three mixing temperatures investigated here, the increase in micro-scale cluster content with increasing temperature is corroborated with the opposite trend in nano-scale cluster content. The points that are targeted with microbeam for WDS analyses are carefully chosen not to include micro-scale clusters that are visible on the surface. However, the finite analytical volume of WDS is formed by the penetration of microbeam 5μm below the sample surface. Therefore, invisible micro-scale clusters below the surface may have contributed to the variations in nanoclay content shown in Figure 12. In fact, the spikes in Figure 12 that reach up to 6wt.% may possibly be the points with invisible nanoclay clusters that are beneath the sample surface.

For the given beam current and analyses time, 3σ minimum detection limits (MDL) are determined for the targeted elements. For magnesium, aluminum, silicon and iron, the MDL's are determined as 0.02, 0.02, 0.03 and 0.04wt.% respectively. Since the nano-scale cluster contents reported here are much larger than the MDL's, it can be concluded that the peak to background intensity and counting times were adequate throughout the study.

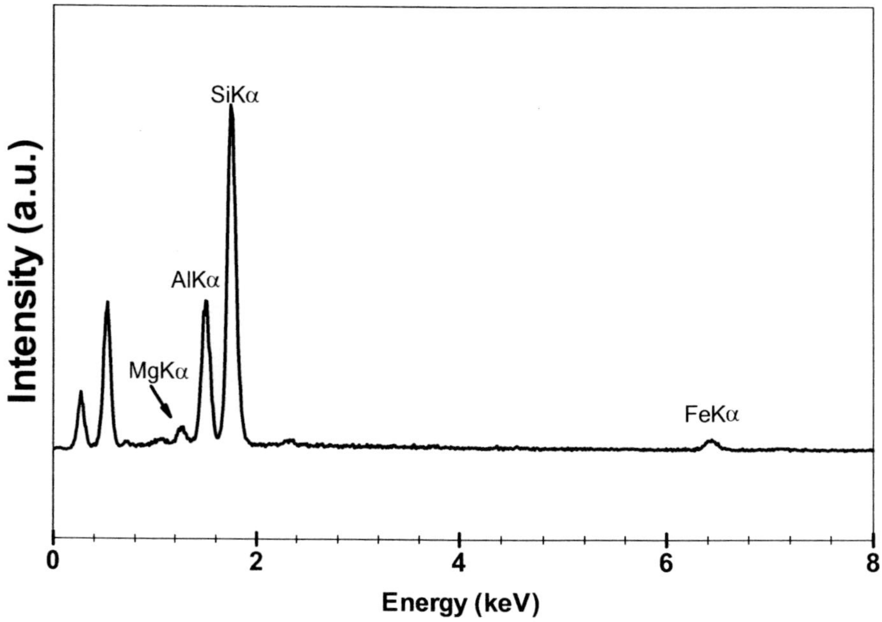

Figure 11. Energy dispersive x-ray analysis (EDXA) spectra of Cloisite® 25A used to identify the constituent elements.

4. Conclusion

Effects of mixing temperature on the quality of dispersion of Cloisite® 25A in an epoxy resin are investigated by combining scanning electron microscopy (SEM) and wavelength dispersive spectrometry (WDS). For each mixing temperature, a disk-shaped nanocomposite containing 5wt.% Cloisite® 25A is fabricated. One sample along the radius of each disk is cut and its through-the-thickness cross-section is analyzed to quantify the dispersion state. Nanoclay clusters larger than 1.5μm are analyzed by performing digital image analyses on the scanning electron micrographs taken along the radius, whereas smaller clusters are analyzed by WDS.

It is found that increasing mixing temperature results in larger nanoclay clusters. The contribution of nanoclay clusters smaller than 3μm^2 to the overall nanoclay content is observed to decrease from 43.3 to 40.8% when the mixing temperature is increased from 30 to 75°C. In the same mixing temperature range, contribution of large nanoclay clusters (i.e., A>50μm^2) is increased from 8.9 to 10.4%. This observation is attributed to the lower viscosity of resin at higher temperatures, which in turn causes reduction of shear forces responsible from the breakdown of agglomerates during mixing.

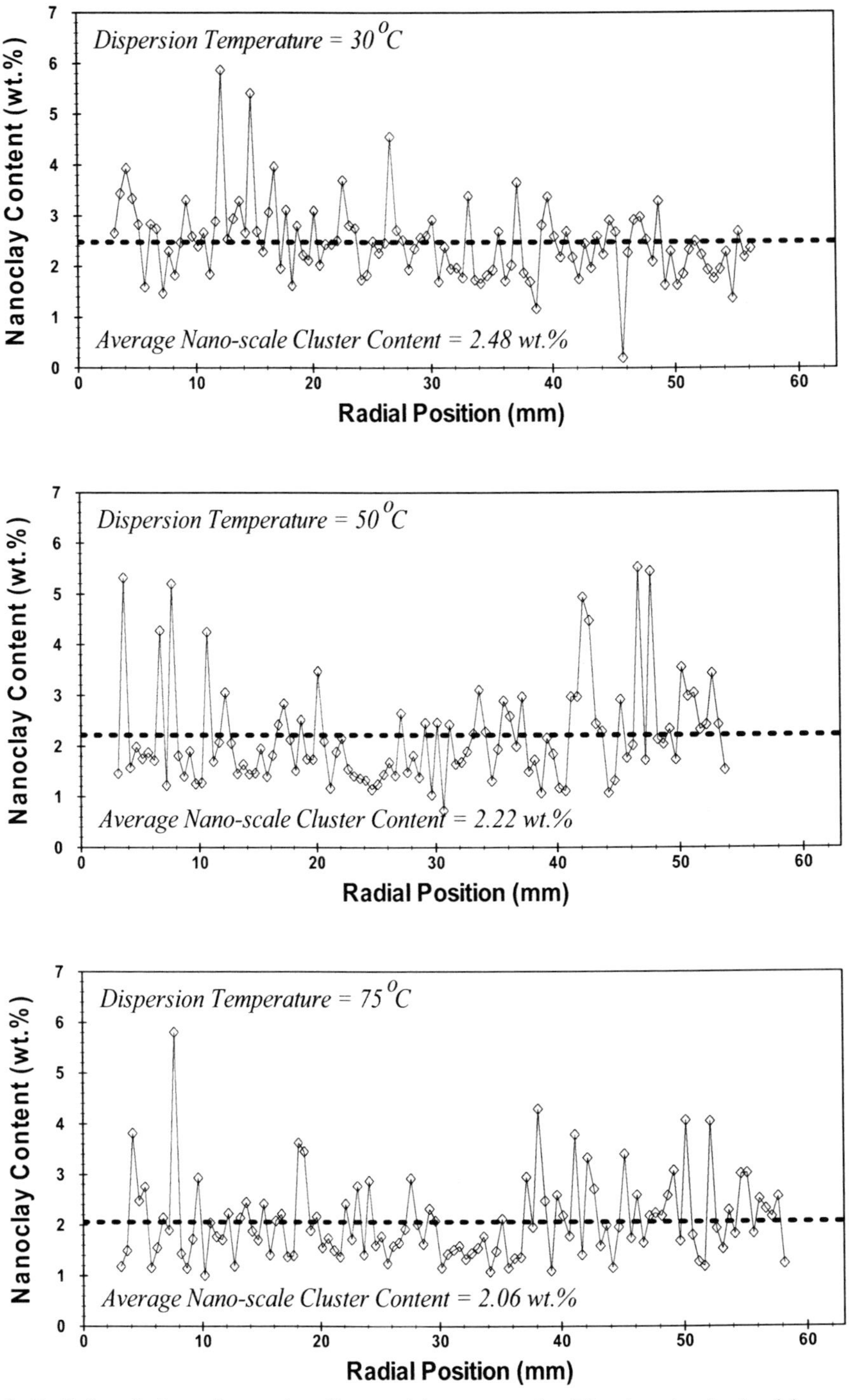

Figure 12. Radial variation of nanoclay dispersed in nano-scale. The data is obtained by wavelength dispersive spectrometry (WDS).

Size and shape distribution of nanoclay clusters along the radius of each disk are also analyzed using the binary SEM images. It is found that nanoclay clusters are broken into smaller clusters along the flow direction and form smaller nanoclay particles at the outer edges of the disk. For instance, percentage contribution of small clusters (i.e., $A<3\mu m^2$) increased by as much as 30% in the flow direction due to cluster breakdown. It is believed that the cluster breakdown is induced by the viscous stresses due to the small cavity gapwidth and by the compressive forces due to the flow deceleration during the filling of the disk-shaped cavity.

5. References

[1] Ahmadi, S. J.; Huang, Y. D.; Li, W. *J. Mater. Sci.* 2004, *39*, 1919-1925.

[2] Usuki, A.; Kawasumi, M.; Kojima, Y.; Okada, A.; Kurauchi, T.; Kamigaito, O. *J. Mater. Res.* 1993, *8*, 1174-1178.

[3] Usuki, A.; Kojima, Y.; Kawasumi, M.; Okada, A.; Fukushima, Y.; Kurauchi, T.; Kamigaito, O. *J. Mater. Res.* 1993, *8*, 1179-1184.

[4] Kojima, Y.; Usuki, A.; Kawasumi, M.; Okada, A.; Fukushima, Y.; Kurauchi, T.; Kamigaito, O. *J. Mater. Res.* 1993, *8*, 1185-1189.

[5] Lan, T.; Pinnavaia, T. J. *Chem. Mater.* 1994, *6*, 2216-2219..

[6] Wang, H.; Zeng, C.; Elkovitch, M.; Lee, L. J.; Koelling, K. W. *Polym. Eng. Sci.* 2001, *41*, 2036-2046.

[7] Abot, J. L.; Yasmin, A.; and Daniel, I. M.; *Mater. Res. Soc. Symp. Proc.* 2003, *740*, 162-177.

[8] Shen, L.; Phang, I. Y.; Chen, L.; Liu, T.; Zeng, K. *Polymer* 2004, *45*, 3341-3349.

[9] Pinnavaia, T. J.; Lan, T.; Kaviratna, P. D.; Wang, Z.; Shi H. *Polym. Mater. Sci. Eng.* 1995, *73*, 117-118.

[10] Yasmin, A.; Abot, J. L.; Daniel, I. M. *Mater. Res. Soc. Symp. Proc.* 2003, *740*, 75-80.

[11] Becker, O.; Varley, R. J.; Simon, G. P. *J. Mater. Sci. Lett.* 2003, *22*, 1411-1414.

[12] Kinloch, A. J.; Taylor, A. C. *J. Mater. Sci. Lett.* 2003, *22*, 1439-1441.

[13] Isik, I.; Yilmazer, U.; Bayram, G. *Polymer* 2003, *44*, 6371-6377.

[14] Xu, Y.; Brittain, W. J.; Xue, C.; Eby, R. K. *Polymer* 2004, *45*,3735-3746.

[15] Dazhu, C.; Pingsheng, H. *J. Comp. Mater.* 2003, *37*, 1275-1287.

[16] Kashiwagi, T.; Harris, R. H.; Zhang, X.; Briber, R. M.; Cipriano, B. H.; Raghavan, S. R.; Awad, W. H.; Shields, J. R. *Polymer* 2004, *45*, 881-891.

[17] Singh, R. P.; Zhang, M.; Chan, D. *J. Mater. Sci.* 2002, *37*, 781-788.

[18] Cai, J. J.; Salovey, R. *J. Mater. Sci.* 1999, *34*, 4719-4726.

[19] Siviour, C. R.; Gifford, M. J.; Malley, S. M.; Proud, W. G.; Field, J. E. *J. Mater. Sci.* 2004, *39*, 1255-1258.

[20] Mani, G.; Fan, Q.; Ugbolue, S. C.; Eiff, I. M. *AATCC Review* 2003, *3*, 22-26.

[21] Liang, Y. M.; Zhoa, J. H. *J. Mater. Sci.* 1999, *34*, 2175-2181.

[22] Cardoso, R. J.; Shukla, A.; Bose, A. *J. Mater. Sci.* 2002, *37*, 603-613.

[23] Park, J. H.; Jana, S. C. *Polymer* 2003, *44*, 2091-2100.

[24] Park, J. H.; Jana, S. C. *Macromolecules* 2003, *36*, 2758-2768.

[25] Pattanayak, A.; Jana, S. C. *61st Annual Technical Conference-Society of Plastics Engineers* 2003, *2*, 1424-1428.

[26] Bragg, W. H.; Bragg, W. L. *Proceedings of Royal Society of London (A)* 1913, *88*, 428-438.

[27] Kornmann, X.; Lindberg, H.; Berglund, L. A. *Polymer* 2001, *42*, 1303-1310.

[28] Wagener, R.; Reisinger, T. J. G. *Polymer* 2003, *44*, 7513-7518.

[29] Wagner, N. J.; Bender, J. W. *Mater. Res. Soc. Bull.* 2004, *29*, 100-106.

[30] Akkapeddi, K.; Facinelli, J.; Worley, D. *61st Annual Technical Conference-Society of Plastics Engineers* 2003, *2*, 2240-2244.

[31] Aktas, L.; Hamidi, Y. K.; Altan, M. C. *Plastics, Rubbers and Composites* 2004, 33, 267-272.

[32] Aktas, L.; Hamidi, Y. K.; Altan, M. C. *J. Mater. Process. And Manuf. Sci.* 2002, *10*, 239-254.

[33] Barraza, H. J.; Aktas, L.; Hamidi, Y. K.; Long, J Jr.; O'Rear, E.A.; Altan, M. C. *J. Adhes. Sci. Technol.* 2003, *17*, 217-233.

[34] Olivero, K. A.; Barraza, H. J.; O'Rear, E. A.; and Altan, M. C. *J. Comp. Mater.* 2002, *36*, 2011-2028.

[35] Wang, D.; Zhu, J.; Yao, Q.; Wilkie, C. A. *Chem. Mater.* 2002, *14*, 3837-3843.

[36] Lertwimolnun, W.; Vergnes, B. *Proceedings of Polymer Processing Society 20th Annual Meeting* 2004, Paper No: 229.

[37] Altan, M. C.; Rao, B. N. *J. Rheol.* 1995, *39*, 581-599.

In: Nanomaterials: New Research
Editor: B.M. Caruta, pp. 219-235
ISBN: 1-59454-369-0

Chapter 7

SYNTHESIS OF THIOL-DERIVATIZED GOLD AND ALLOYED GOLD-SILVER CLUSTERS WITH CONTROLLED MORPHOLOGY

G. Carotenuto*, B. Martorana[1], P. Perlo[1] and L. Nicolais

Institute of Composite and Biomedical Materials. National Research Council.
Piazzale V. Tecchio, 80 - 80125 - Napoli. Italy.
[1] FIAT Research Center, Strada Torino 50 – 10043 Orbassano TO. Italy.

ABSTRACT

Thiol-derivatized gold clusters (thioaurites) are nanostructured materials potentially useful for a number of technological applications mainly in the fields of optics, non-linear optics, electronics, catalysis, etc. However, the technological exploitation of these nanoscopic objects requires perfect control over their morphology and structure. In this paper, a recently developed chemical route for the controlled synthesis of thiol-deriatized clusters of pure-gold and gold/silver alloyed clusters is described. This synthesis scheme is very simple and may allow preparation of high-purity gold cluster compounds having a tunable metal core size and different types of alkane-thiol shell.

1. INTRODUCTION

Thiol-derivatized gold clusters play an important role in many different research and technological areas. For example, they can serve as model systems to experimentally probe the effects of quantum confinement on electronic, catalytic, and other properties. They have

* Istituto per i Materiali Compositi e Biomedici (IMCB). Consiglio Nazionale delle Ricerche; Piazzale Tecchio, 80 – 80125 Napoli (Italy); E-mail: giancaro@unina.it

also been widely exploited for use in catalysis, biological labelling, photonics, optoelectronics, surface enhanced Raman scattering (SERS), etc. The unique properties of a nano-sized metallic phase are mainly determined by size, shape, composition, crystallinity, and structure (solid versus hollow). In principle, one could control each one of these parameters to fine tune the characteristics of nanostructures and working devices based on them. However, still limited are the synthesis schemes available for the preparation of thiol-derivatized metal crystals that may offer a complete morphological control (i.e., type of organic shell and metallic core size, shape, and composition).

Alcoholic reduction of metal ions in presence of poly(vinylpyrrolidone) (PVP) as a protective agent is one of the oldest and simplest chemical routes to produce colloidal noble metals (e.g., Ag, Au, Pt, etc.). In addition, co-reduction and step-reduction of metal ions allow to produce bimetallic clusters with controlled composition and core/shell structure, respectively. The cluster growth stage can be simply end by addition of a non-solvent liquid (e.g., acetone, tetrahydrofurane, etc.) to the reactive mixture, since polymer flocculates and clusters are isolated in a polymer-embedded form [1]. Consequently, a complete control over cluster size and core/shell structure is possible. Recently, the possibility to use this synthesis scheme to produce metallic nanoparticles of controlled shape has been also investigated [2]. In particular, it has been shown that the preferential absorption of PVP molecules to different crystal faces may direct nanoparticles growth into various shapes by influencing the growth rates along the different crystal axes. Nano-spheres, nano-rods, nano-wires, nano-cubes, and nano-prisms of silver, gold, and platinum have been obtained by alcoholic reduction of metal ions at room or slightly higher temperatures.

In this paper, the possibility to obtain thiol-derivatized metal clusters by extraction of gold and alloyed Au-Ag clusters from the protective PVP matrix simply by treatment with alcoholic solutions of thiols is described [3]. Alcoholic reduction of metal ions in presence of PVP followed by thiol treatment represents a very powerful synthetic scheme for the controlled preparation of these special cluster compounds. Details on the spectrophotometric (UV-Vis) approach to control the size of produced thiol-derivatized pure-Au clusters or the composition of thiol-derivatized Au-Ag alloyed clusters are given.

2. Traditional Synthesis

Colorful aqueous solutions of gold colloids date back to Roman times and were known to the medieval alchemists as aurum potabile [4]. In most cases gold particles were charge-stabilized in an electrolyte solution, and hence their isolation as a pure product without significant irreversible particle coalescence was not possible. The notion that gold sols indeed contain small metallic particles was first expressed in 1857 by Faraday [5], who conducted a very elegant and simple study of the optical properties of thin films prepared from dried colloidal solutions. He observed reversible color changes of the films upon mechanical compression. Under pressure the films appeared green, like thin continuous gold films, while they became bluish-purple when the pressure was released, resembling more the gold particle solutions.

Important aspects in nanoparticle research are: (i) control of particle morphology during synthesis in order to fine-tune properties, (ii) manipulation and study of individual particles, and (iii) assembly of two- and three-dimensional materials and structures in which nanoparticles are closely packed. The chemical stability of nano-sized particles is a crucial point to avoid degradation processes such as partial oxidation or undesired sintering. In the past, the lacking of sufficient chemical stability of metal nanoparticles has impeded the development of real world applications of these nanostructured materials., and it represents the reason why gold, as a relatively inert metal, has played an important role in pioneering experiments. The stability of naked gold clusters has been improved by development of clusters compounds like thiol-stabilised gold clusters, from which new opportunities for fundamental and applied studies have arisen. Probably in the future a large variety of metal clusters will be handled and used in such passivated form.

The first paper concerning thiol-stabilised gold nanoparticles appeared ten years after the discover of self-assembled monolayers (SAMs) of organosulphur compounds on gold surfaces, in the 1983 [6]. In this study, gold hydro-sols were capped with alkane-thiols to make them soluble in a non-polar solvents [7]. Then, the particles were deposited electrophoretically onto a carbon specimen holder for inspection by transmission electron microscopy (TEM). Two-dimensional hexagonal super-lattices in a fully reversible deposition process were found. In addition, the interparticle spacing was found to be adjustable with molecular precision by the choice of alkanethiol ligands of different lengths. A simple preparative method for bulk quantities of thiol-stabilised gold particles was developed one year later [8] and it become very popular as a starting point for a broad range of nanoparticle studies. This chemical route involved the phase transfer of an anionic Au(III) complex from aqueous to organic solution in a two-phase liquid/liquid system, followed by reduction with sodium borohydride in presence of the thiol-stabilizing ligand. Dark brown solutions of moderately polydisperse particles in the size range of 1-3.5 nm, containing from 100 to 3,500 gold atoms can be obtained by this chemical approach. The typical ruby-red color of colloidal gold emerges with particle sizes above ca. 3.5 nm. This is due to the plasmon absorption of free electron gas which is absent in smaller particles. Detailed studies of particle shape revealed that the truncated cuboctahedron is the predominant structural motif, but other geometries such as decahedra, dodecahedra, and icosahedra are also present in the obtained product. The particles can be purified and kept in the solid state under ambient conditions for months without showing significant aging effects. However, not all types of thiol ligands lead to the same extraordinarily high degree of stability that can be achieved by the use of alkane thiols with a hydrocarbon chain length of C_5 to C_{18}. Hydroxo-functionalized particles stabilized by 4-mercapto-phenol, for example, are somewhat less stable and degrade slowly over several weeks under ambient conditions. The same trend is observed if shorter (C_2 to C_4) thiol molecules are employed as stabilizers.

The principal disadvantage of this preparative method is that in some cases (e.g., ω-substituted thiols) an excessive product purification is required since a layer of the ammonium surfactant covers the thioaurite compound. A solution to this problem has been the one-phase synthesis developed by the same research group and carried out in methanol as solvent and sodium borohydride as reducing agent [9]. Gold nano-particles covered with 4-mercaptophenol have been successfully prepared and this compound has been modified by successive reactions on the shell surface, broadening the application of thiol-derivatized gold nano-particles from a stable but chemically inert compound toward a truly functional reagent. However, owing to solubility issues, methanol is not the ideal solvent for the broad variety of alkane- or arene-thiol compounds. Such a fundamental restriction prevents a full exploitation of this synthesis scheme. Chemical functionalities can be introduced in the alkyl shell by a post-synthesis place-exchange reactions, but this strategy is employed only to obtain multifunctional ligand shells since the synthesis of homogeneous thiol shells and inert n-alkyl derivatives requires direct introduction of thiol molecules. A further disadvantage of these synthetic schemes is that a growth stage is practically absent in the cluster formation, and therefore the core size in the resulting material can be only lightly modified by adjusting the amount of gold salt. The thioaurite compounds properties (e.g., color, electrical conductivity, etc.) are strictly size-dependent and the possibility to fine tune the metal core size is of a fundamental importance from a technological point of view.

3. Size-Controlled Synthesis

An alternative technique for the synthesis of thiol-derivatized gold particles is based on a well-known approach for colloidal gold solutions preparation, i.e., the alcoholic reduction of ionic gold in presence of a polymeric stabilizer (e.g., poly(N-vinylpyrrolidone)) [10]. The primary polymer function is to avoid cluster sintering, but it also allows particle size control by co-precipitation. In fact, polymer absorbs on particle surface, making possible their separation from the reactive mixture by addition of a non-solvent liquid. The obtained polymer-protected nanometric gold particles may dissolve in alcoholic solutions of thiol molecules that promptly remove polymer from particle surface, giving a hydrophobic thioaurite product. Such hydrophobic compound can be easily isolated, purified, and fractioned by size-selective precipitation or Gel Permeation Chromatography (GPC). The synthesis route is interesting principally for the possibility to prepare particles of controlled size. In fact, since the reactive medium is perfectly transparent and it slowly develops a ruby-red color during the metal phase separation, cluster nucleation-growth process can be *in situ* on-line monitored by optical spectroscopy and the growth process can be end at the required size value by co-precipitation with polymer.

For example, the preparative scheme for the synthesis of gold clusters protected by dodecanethiol involved the mixing under stirring of a poly(N-vinylpyrrolidone) (PVP, Aldrich, M_w=*10,000 a.m.u.*) solution in ethylene glycol (stabilized at a temperature ranging from 60°C to 110°C) with a little quantity of a concentrated tetrachloroauric acid ($HAuCl_4$, Aldrich) solution in ethylene glycol. In particular, the first solution was prepared by dissolving 4g of PVP into 20ml of ethylene glycol and the second one by dissolving 5mg of $HAuCl_4$ in 1ml of ethylene glycol. After gold nanoparticle formation the solution had a ruby-red color. In order to end the reaction, the reactive mixture was cast into a large amount of acetone (250ml) and the system was sonicated for a few minutes to allow for the ethylene glycol removal from the Au/PVP nanocomposite. The product was washed several times with pure acetone and then dried at room temperature under vacuum. The obtained solid Au/PVP system was dissolved into a dilute ethanol solution of normal dodecanethiol ($C_{12}H_{25}$-SH, Aldrich, 98%). Dodecanethiol is able to produce a continuous protective mono-layer on gold clusters. These molecules bonded the gold surface much stronger than PVP side-groups, and therefore the polymeric stabilizer was completely removed from cluster surface. Thiol molecules were chemisorbed on the gold surface according to a red-ox reaction. After a short time, the exchange reaction was completed and the hydrophobic thiol-coated nanoparticles were easily separated from the PVP/ethanol solution by centrifugation. In order to remove all thiol excess, the product was accurately washed with ethanol. A waxy, purple solid product was obtained. This material can be handled like a simple chemical compound (for example, it can be dissolved and dried several times without decomposition) and it is stable for months in air at room temperature. Thiol-derivatized gold clusters have a hydrophobic nature and consequently result very soluble in aliphatic and aromatic hydrocarbons, chlorine solvents, and ethers; moderately soluble in styrene; and insoluble in esters, acetone, alcohol, and water.

A number of high-nuclearity thioaurite compounds have been equivalently obtained by treatment of PVP-embedded gold clusters with alkane-thiol solutions in alcohols. In particular, thioaurites based on octadecanethiol and hexadecanethiol were prepared too.

4. Product Characterization

4.1. Morphological and Structural Characterization

The microstructure of both gold clusters embedded into a PVP matrix and thiol-derivatized gold clusters has been accurately investigated by Transmission Electron Microscopy (TEM, Philips EM208S). As visible in Figure 1a, all particles had a pseudo-spherical shape, which in some cases corresponded exactly to a polyhedron, and aggregates were not present in the samples. When the reaction was performed at a temperature of 60°C for 20min, the particle size was moderately poly-dispersed and a monomodal distribution approximately described by a Gaussian function with μ=7nm and σ=5nm resulted (see Figure 1b). Reaction time and temperature affected the particle size distribution, however the average particle size was widely controlled by varying the tetrachloroauric acid amount.

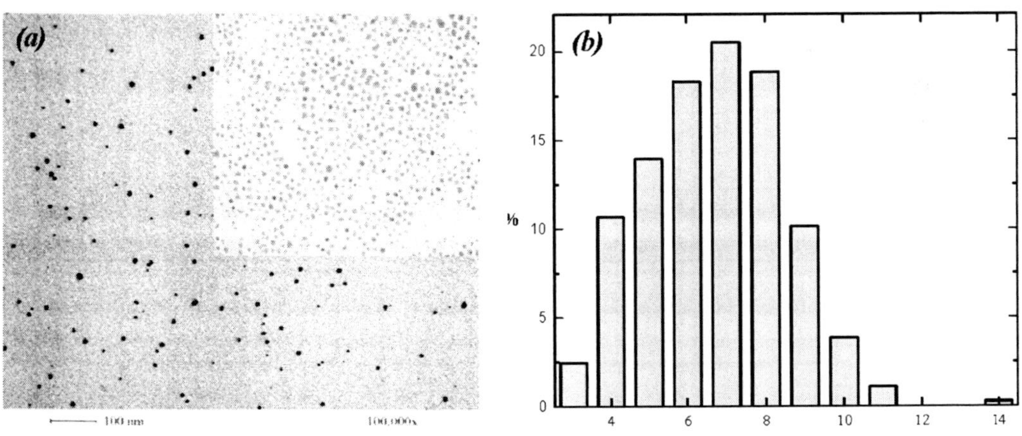

Figure 1. TEM micrographs of PVP-embedded gold clusters and thiol-derivatized gold clusters (insert) (a) and related histogram (b).

Heptane suspensions of gold particles passivated by normal dodecanethiol spontaneously produced self-organized submicron-sized domains of hexagonally close-packed nanoparticle arrays after solvent evaporation (see insert in Figure 1a). Clusters aggregates produced by sintering of the metal cores were not contained in the final product, and thus the ligand-exchange process was complete and effective.

Thioaurite compounds were structurally characterized by X-ray diffraction (XRD, Rigaku DMAX-IIIC goniometer), using Cu-K_α radiation (λ=0.154056 nm) and a pyrolytic graphite monochromator. The XRD-pattern of Au/PVP nanocomposite is reported in Figure 2. The typical peaks of a face centered cubic (fcc) gold lattice are well-visible superposed to a background produced by amorphous PVP. The obtained lattice parameter of 4.077(2) Å coincides with pure bulk gold value, indicating that nanoparticles were not subjected to lattice distortion due to interstitial impurities. The average crystallite size derived from peak broadening analysis always resulted quite close to the nanoparticle diameter obtained by TEM measurements, suggesting that nanoparticles were single-crystals.

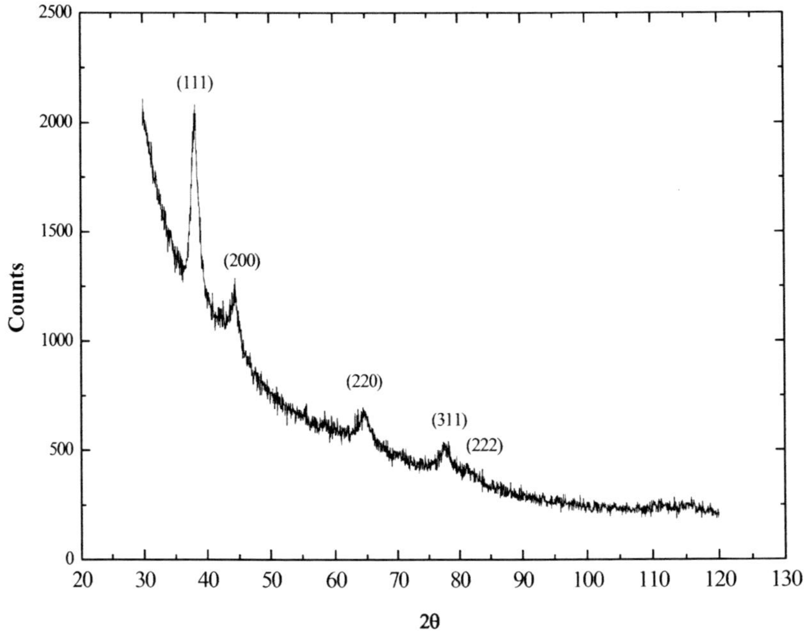

Figure 2. XRD spectrum of PVP-embedded gold nanoparticles (65s at 80°C). The Bragg peaks of fcc gold are labeled.

4.2. In Situ On-Line Spectrophotometric Sizing

The formation-growth process of gold clusters in the reactive liquid mixture was monitored by UV-Visible spectroscopy, looking at the very intensive surface plasmon absorption resonance that characterized the nano-sized metallic phase [11]. Absorption spectra were obtained under isothermal condition at stepped reaction times by using a diode-array UV-Visible spectrophotometer (HP-8453 UV-Vis spectrophotometer), equipped with a

Peltier apparatus to control the reaction temperature (from 0 to 100°C with accuracy of ±0.1°C). The system employed a magnetic stirrer and far-UV quartz cuvettes. Absorption spectra were monitored and recorded on a personal computer connected to the spectrophotometer. Since the reaction rate increased with temperature, shorter sampling times were required at higher temperatures. For example, at 25°C a sampling time of 120s was selected, whereas at 100°C it was of 0.5s. Typical UV-Visible spectra at two reaction times, namely 37s and 65s, are shown in Figures 3a,b respectively.

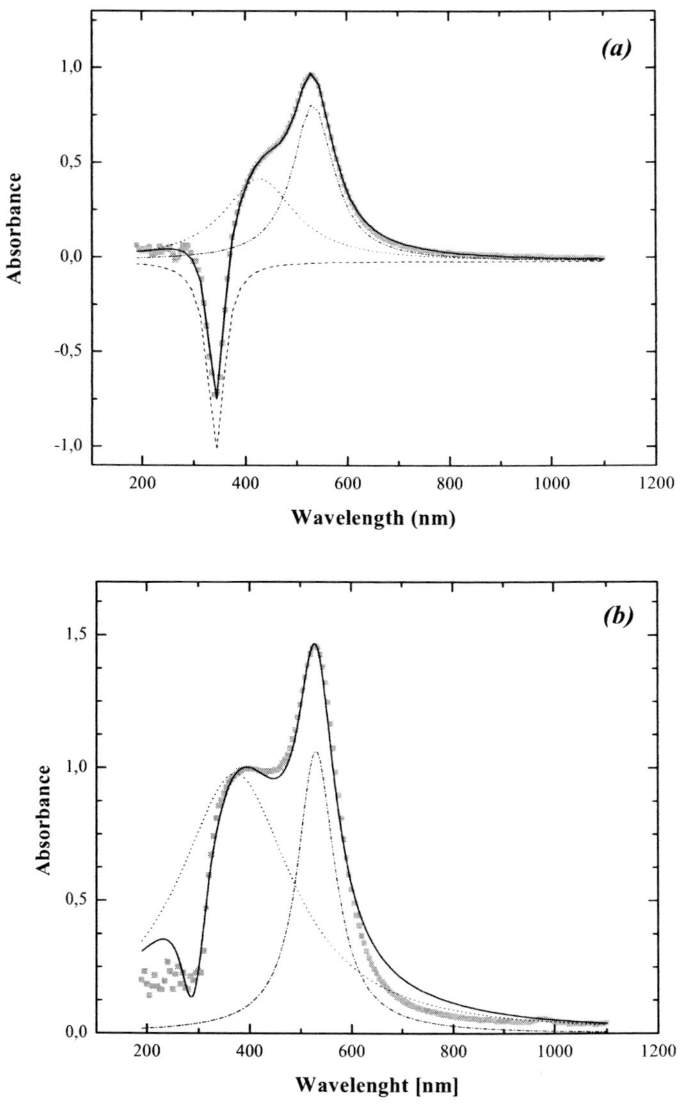

Figure 3. Optical spectrum of a gold mixture corresponding to a reaction time of (a) 37s, and (b) 65s. The curves obtained from data convolution are also plotted, dashed lines are the three contribution (i), (ii) and (iii), while the grey squares represent their sum.

The shape of recorded optical spectra is determined by combination of three main absorptions: (i) that produced by glycolic Au^{3+} complexes, (ii) the $5d \rightarrow 6sp$ interband transition of gold clusters, and (iii) the surface plasmon resonance band of gold clusters. An example of spectra convolution by Lorentzian functions is reported in Figures 3a,b. Since Au^{3+} ions are reduced to the zero-valence state, the peak intensity (proportional to the Au^{3+} concentration) becomes more and more negative during the reaction. Spectra convolution allows accurate determination of plasmon peak parameters, *i.e.* maximum absorption wavelength, full width at half maximum (FWHM), integral absorption, etc. Gold clusters sizing can be obtained from these plasmon absorption parameters. In particular, there are theoretical models [12] that allows correlation between plasmon peak characteristics and morphological-topological information concerning the gold nano-particle systems. As visible in the TEM micrograph, gold particles are spherical in shape and aggregate-less, consequently the particle formation-growth mechanisms can be predict from the simple Mie's theory. Such theory predicts, that optical absorption, A, is dependent on the number, N, and the size, R, of clusters and such dependence is governed by a simple proportionality law, $A \propto NR^3$, where N and R change continuously during reaction. The nucleation process increases the N value and different particle growth mechanisms may affect in a different manner the temporal evolution of radial growth, R. Therefore, the behavior of the cubic root of measured absorbance *vs.* the reaction time is clearly indicative of which mechanism is dominating in particle growth [12]. A quantitative analysis of optical spectra in terms of cluster dimension can be performed under the hypothesis that the number of clusters in the solution do not change during the reaction. This condition is achieved when nucleation rate is high enough, and nucleation and growth processes are separated stages. In other words, if temperature is high enough, clusters are approximately of the same dimensions since all metal nuclei are generated at same time and grow simultaneously. In such experimental conditions, the temporal evolution of cubic route of absorbance can be directly related to the cluster size evolution. Two different kinetic mechanisms for particle growth maybe involved: (i) diffusion-controlled and (ii) deposition-controlled. The dominant mechanism being the slowest one. Under a diffusion-controlled kinetic mechanism, the radial development of clusters should scale according to a $t^{1/2}$ law, whereas it should result linear with time in the case of a deposition-controlled kinetic mechanism [13]. Data shown in Figure 4 clearly suggest that a deposition-controlled mechanism is the predominant one at reaction temperatures above 70°C. While, at temperatures below 70°C, absorbance cubic root *vs.* time curves do not follow a linear behavior, that can be explained on the basis of a continuous formation of new nuclei during the reaction.

TEM analysis demonstrated that the nanoparticles average size grew linearly with the reaction time at temperatures above 70°C (see Figure 5). This behavior confirms that a surface-deposition controlled kinetic mechanism should be involved in these experimental conditions. Similar behaviors have been also reported for gold cluster formation in formaldehyde-based systems [14]. Finally, *in situ* optical spectroscopy represents a very good approach for size-monitoring during nanoparticle synthesis, because it allows accurate control of final average dimension.

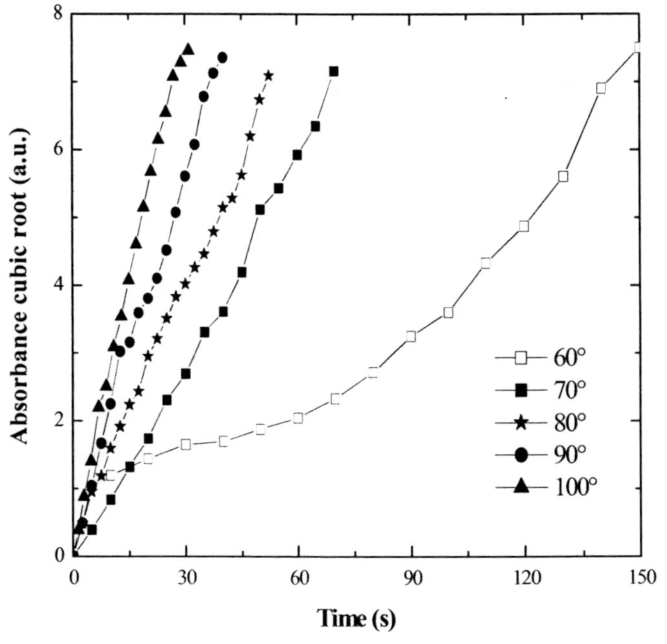

Figure 4. Time dependence of the cubic root of the absorbance at different reaction temperatures.

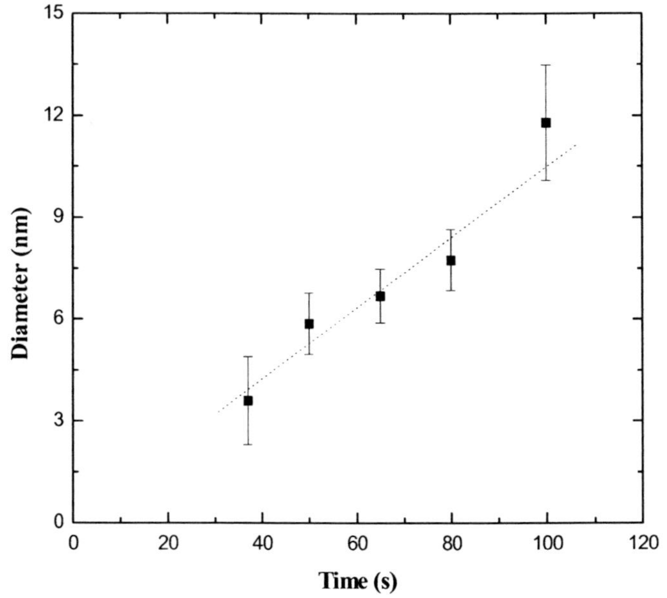

Figure 5. Nanoparticles diameter measured by TEM *vs.* reaction time for a sample obtained at 80°C.

4.3. Thermal Characterization

The thermal stability of dodecylthioaurites was investigated by Thermogravimetric Analysis (TGA, TA-Instrument Mod.Q500). The TGA-thermogram (performed at 10°C/min, under fluxing nitrogen) showed two signals: a first intensive weight loss occurring at a temperature of ca. 250°C and a second small signal was located at 400°C (see Figure 6a). Such weight-loss was probably caused by the evaporation of organic shell decomposition products. When unpurified products were investigated by TGA, a further weight loss was detected in the thermograms at ca. 200°C, probably due to the evaporation of free thiol molecules present in the samples.

Important structural information about thiol-derivatized compounds at solid state were obtained by Differential Scanning Calorimetry (DSC, TA-Instrument Mod.Q100). As visible in Figure 6b, the DSC-thermograms showed the presence of a thermal transition corresponding to melting of crystalline regions produced by interdigitation of thiol chains [15]. When the product was not accurately purified, a further endothermic peak appeared in the thermograms, owing to the presence of pure thiol crystals. Pure dodecanethiol melts at -7°C, while thioaurites showed a very intensive endothermic transition at ca. 30°C. DSC-thermograms obtained on cooling runs of samples previously heated up to 100°C, showed the presence of one exothermic peak produced by the formation of interdigitated n-alkyl chain crystals. The crystallization temperature resulted inferior to the melting point value and cooling rate dependent, owing to super-cooling effects.

5. Thiol-Derivatized Alloyed Au-Ag Clusters

Metal clusters characterized by surface plasmon absorption can be conveniently used as pigments in the fabrication of plastic optical limiters (e.g., colour filters, UV-absorbers, polarizers). However, the possibility to control the frequency of the plasmon absorption is of primary importance for such a kind of application. The absorption frequency of plasmon-based pigments can be finely tuned by alloying metals characterized by surface plasmon resonance located at different frequencies (e.g., Pd-Ag, Au-Ag, etc.) [16]. For a complete control of absorption frequency between the limit values of pure metals, the two metals should give solid solutions in the full composition range. Plasmon resonances in a wide spectral range (430-530nm) can be achieved by alloying gold with silver. Thiol-derivatized Au-Ag clusters of different compositions are very promising as pigments for colour filters, these hydrophobic compounds can be mixed with a number of optical plastics to fabricate advanced optical devices.

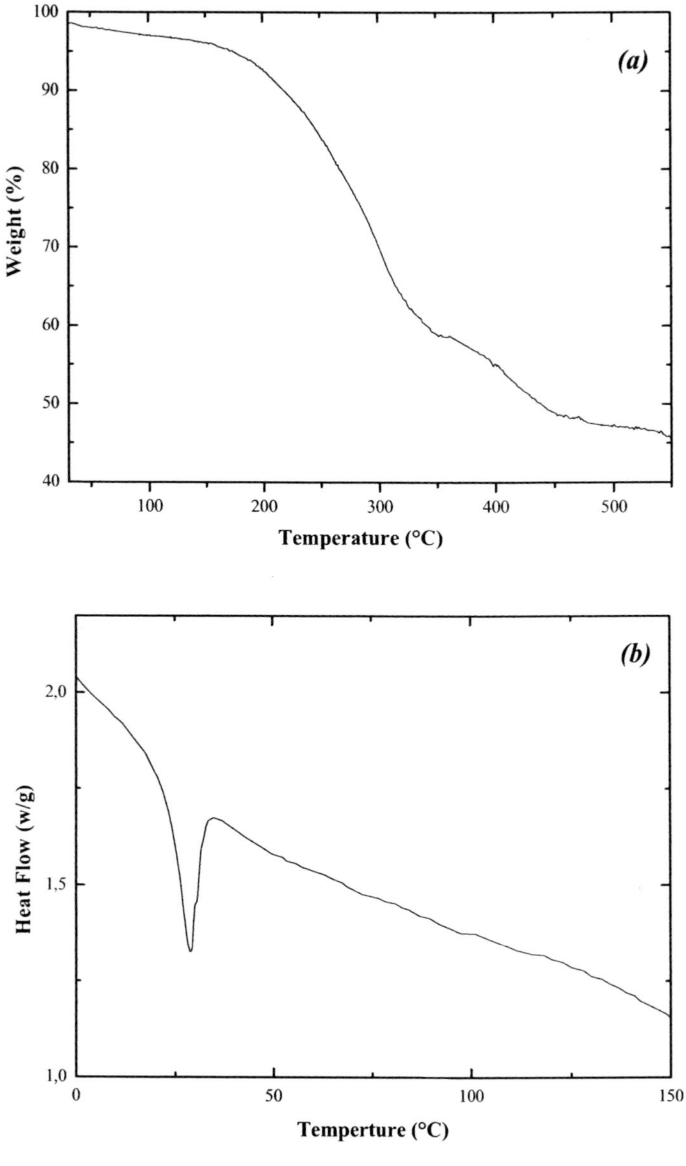

Figure 6. TGA-thermogram (a) and DSC-thermogram (b) of a gold dodecylthiolate sample.

Thiol-derivatized Au-Ag clusters can be obtained by the above described chemical route. In particular, gold and silver ions can be simultaneously reduced by ethylen glycol in presence of poly(vinyl pyrrolidone) as sterical stabilizer to produce alloyed bimetallic nanoparticles. Since Au^{3+} and Ag^{+} ions have similar atomic radius and crystal structure (cubic face centered), Au-Ag solid solutions can be obtained in the full composition range simply by modifying the quantities of two ionic precursors. The obtained Au-Ag clusters can be isolated from the reactive mixture by co-precipitation with acetone and, analogously to PVP-embedded pure-Au clusters, they can be treated by alcoholic solutions of thiols to give thiol-derivatized clusters. Since the reduction of gold ions by ethylene glycol in presence of PVP has an induction time (due to the initial reduction of Au^{3+} to Au^{+}), typically the reaction was done by mixing a solution of $HAuCl_4$ and PVP in ethylene glycol with a freshly prepared silver solution in ethylene glycol. Since silver require the presence of PVP for reduction, the silver reduction-precipitation process starts just after mixing of two solutions. Cluster growth was end by addition of acetone to the reactive mixture, and the isolated PVP-embedded Au-Ag clusters were dissolved in the alcoholic solution of thiol (e.g., dodecanethiol/ethyl alcohol). Dodecane thiol-derivatized Au-Ag clusers is a stable hydrophobic product that can be easily isolated and purified from the reactive mixture and stored for months without degradation.

Since both silver and gold have optical absorptions in the visible spectral region, important structural information (temporal evolution of average composition) about the growing clusters system maybe obtained by *in situ* on-line spectroscopic monitoring of their formation-growth process. Such analysis is based on the measurement of the wavelength of maximum surface plasmon absorption band of alloyed Au-Ag clusters during their formation process. In particular, the optical absorption spectrum of gold-silver alloyed clusters does not correspond neither to monometallic silver nor to monometallic gold cluster spectra. Both shape and position of alloyed cluster absorption band is exactly an average of two characteristic bands. The exact position of absorption band is related to the cluster composition, and it can be used for such measurement. Since plasmon absorption depends exclusively on the cluster surface composition, the temporal evolution of cluster composition should correspond to radial one if a linear growth law is valid.

In particular, it is known that the frequency of the surface plasmon absorption of pure metal clusters, ω_{sp}, is proportional to the plasmon absorption frequency of the bulk metal, ω_p:

$$\omega_{sp} \propto \omega_p \qquad (1)$$

and that:

$$\omega_p = (4\pi n e^2/m)^{1/2} \qquad (2)$$

where n is the electron density (i.e., ratio between the conduction electron number and cluster volume), e is the electron charge, and m is the effective electron mass. Since the electron density of alloyed Au-Ag nanoclusters, n_a, depends on the metal composition, □ (gold volume fraction), according to the following expression:

$$n_a = \phi\, n_{Ag} + (1-\phi)\, n_{Au} \qquad (3)$$

the maximum wavelength of the alloyed clusters, $\lambda_{a,max}=2\pi c/\omega_{sp}$, can be written as:

$$(1/\lambda_{a,max})^2 = x/(\lambda_{Ag,max})^2 + (1-x)/(\lambda_{Au,max})^2 \qquad (4)$$

Where x is the molar fraction of gold in the alloy that coincides with gold volume fraction, ϕ, since gold and silver have similar values of the molar volume (10.2 cm^3/mol for gold and 10.27 cm^3/mol for silver). Equation (4) can be used to obtain x from experimental measurements of $\lambda_{a,max}$.

The temporal evolution of Au-Ag cluster composition for different reactive mixture composition calculated according to (4) is shown in Figure 7a. According to the experimental determination of surface plasmon absorption of pure Ag and Au clusters produced in a PVP/ethylene glycol medium, the value of $\lambda_{Ag,max}$ and $\lambda_{Au,max}$ have been taken equal to 430nm and 530nm, respectively. Such behaviour may correspond to the radial one if cluster radius develops according to a linear law. As visible, at beginning of reaction the gold content in the clusters is zero, then cluster composition changes, gold amount grows and stabilize on a constant value. Probably, since the two metallic phase have a different nucleation rate (silver nucleate faster than gold), the phase separation process starts with silver core formation and then the co-precipitation of two metals follows according to a heterogeneous nucleation process. During co-precipitation, the alloy composition may slightly vary because of the different consumption of two metals. Consequently, the radial composition of clusters is not uniform, but gold amount slowly decreases during the process. Figure 7b shows the correspondence between the reactive mixture composition (expressed as molar fraction of gold, Y) and the cluster composition (expressed as atomic fraction of gold, X). As visible, the percentage of gold in the cluster increases quickly with increasing of gold salt amount in the reactive mixture. Probably, the nucleation stage is faster for a pure silver phase but the rate of gold atoms deposition at cluster surface is higher than that of silver atoms.

6. Applications

Thiol-stabilised gold and Au-Ag clusters prepared by the above described chemical techniques can be used for a number of technological applications. A short description for the prominent potential application of these materials follows.

Thin films of self-organized thiol-stabilized gold clusters have been shown to change their electrical conductivity rapidly and reproducibly in presence of organic vapors [17]. This effect is based on the reversible swelling of the material upon gas absorption, which leads to an increase in spacing between the metal cores. Since the typical electron hopping conductivity in these materials depends very sensitively on such distance, the absorption of organic vapor leads to a strong decrease in electrical conductivity. This phenomenon has been exploited for the development of novel gas sensors [17].

Films of gold nanoparticles exhibit strong optical anisotropy if nanoparticles are aligned into parallel rows. Transmitted light polarized parallel to the rows will be absorbed as if it were passing through a continuous thin metal film, while light polarized perpendicular to the rows will interact with individual particles. This effect can be exploited for polarizing filters for displays. Two different approaches have been developed to align the particles. In the first method, gold nanoparticles have been deposited onto friction-transferred lines of PTFE on glass substrates and optically anisotropic windows were obtained after subsequent drastic heat treatment close to the melting point of the plastic material [18]. In the second method, similar effects were achieved by mechanical stretching of polyethylene films previously loaded with nanoparticles [19]. The particles were found to align parallel to the stretch direction producing 'neck-lace' like structures. For example, for silver-based systems, the perceived color of the transmitted light was yellow if polarized perpendicular to the rows, and red if polarized in parallel.

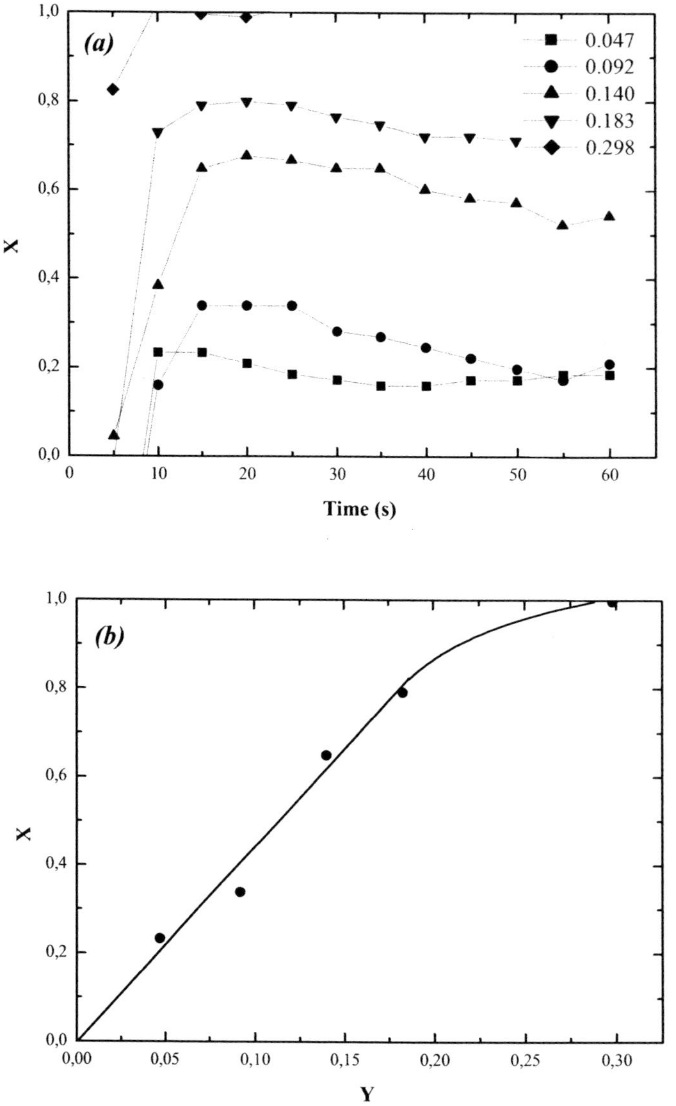

Figure 7. Temporal evolution of Au-Ag alloyed cluster composition for different reactive mixture compositions (a), and correspondence between cluster composition, X (molar gold fraction), and reactive mixture composition, Y (molar gold fraction) (b).

Aggregation of gold nanoparticles produces a color change from ruby-red to blue. This has been exploited to develop extremely sensitive colorimetric methods of DNA analysis, capable of detecting trace amounts of a particular oligonucleotide sequence. This approach also allows to distinguish between perfectly complementary DNA sequences and those that exhibit different degrees of base pair mismatches [20]. The relations between structure and optical properties in these systems have been studied quantitatively [21] by electrodynamics calculations involving aggregates of a large number of particles.

Applications of thiol-stabilized gold nanoparticles in catalysis include asymmetric dihydroxylation reactions [22], carboxylic ester cleavage [23], electro-catalytic reductions by anthraquinone-functionalized gold particles [24] and particle-bound ring opening metathesis polymerization [25]. These catalytic applications have in common the exploitation of carefully designed chemical functionality of the ligand shell, rather than the potential catalytic activity of a nanostructured clean metal surface.

One of the most important potential long-term applications for metal nanoparticles coated by a thin dielectric layer is the development of new, ultimately small, electronic devices. Several promising attempts to construct devices have already been reported, based on gold nanoparticles and Au_{55} clusters [26]. In particular, the single electron transistor action has been demonstrated for systems that contain ideally only one particle in the gap between two electrical contacts separated by only a few nanometres. This central metal particle represents a Coulomb blockade and exhibits single electron charging effects due to its extremely small capacitance. It can also act as a gate if it is independently addressable by a third terminal, for example, the substrate itself, or an appropriately positioned STM tip.

Recently, it has been demonstrated the possibility to fabricate an electrochemically addressable nano-switch based on a single gold particle attached to a gold surface via a small number of dithiol molecules containing a redox-active viologen moiety [27]. It was shown by *in situ* STM that electron transfer between gold substrate and gold nanoparticle depended strongly on the redox-state of the viologen, which could be switched electrochemically.

6. Conclusion

Thiol-derivatized pure-gold and gold-silver clusters are nanostructured materials useful for a number of technological applications. The few synthetic methods available in the literature do not offer enough control over thioaurite structure which is of fundamental importance for properties tuning. Consequently, the availability of new chemical routes for the controlled synthesis of these materials result of primary importance. Alcoholic reduction is a well-known technique for preparing colloidal noble metal solutions. This technique is also used in the synthesis of layered core/shell and alloyed clusters. Cluster growth can be monitored by optical spectroscopy and the presence of a polymeric stabilizers makes possible to isolate metal clusters by co-precipitation with polymer with a non-solvent liquid (e.g., acetone), thus allowing size control. Clusters stored in a stable polymer-embedded form can be used as precursor for thioaurite synthesis. The composite solid is alcohol soluble, consequently gold clusters maybe treated by thiols in an alcoholic medium. The thiol molecules chemically adsorb on the gold surface through a red-ox reaction (S-Au bond formation), removing polymer, and the hydrophobic thioaurite product spontaneously separate. This novel synthesis scheme has been investigated for a number of alkanethiol molecules and it can be utilized also for the preparation of alloyed Au/Ag clusters. The main advantages of this chemical route lies in its simplicity, low toxicity of reactants used, high product purity, and complete control over the compound structure (both nature of the organic shell and size of the metal core).

References

[1] G. Carotenuto, Appl. Organomet. *Chem.*, 15(2001)344-351; G. Carotenuto, S. De Nicola, G.P. Pepe, L. Nicolais, *Eur. Phys. Journal B* 24(2001)437-441; G. Carotenuto, S. De Nicola, L. Nicolais, *Journal of Nanoparticle Research*, 3(2001)467-473

[2] Y. Sun, Y. Xia, *Science*, 2002, 298, 2176-2179

[3] G. Carotenuto, L. Nicolais, *J. Mater. Chem.*, 2003, 13, 1038-1041; G.Carotenuto, L.Nicolais, *Composite: Part B* 35(2004)385-391

[4] W. Caseri, *Macromol. Rapid Commun.* 21(2000)705-722.

[5] M. Faraday, *Philos. Trans. R. Soc. London* 147(1857)145

[6] R.G. Nuzzo, D.L. Allara, *J. Am. Chem. Soc.* 105(1983)4481

[7] M. Giersig, P. Mulvaney, *Langmuir 9*(1993)3408

[8] M. Brust, J. Fink, D. Bethell, D.J. Schiffrin, C.J. Kiely, *J. Chem. Soc., Chem. Commun.* (1995)1655

[9] D. Bethell, M. Brust, D.J. Schiffrin, C.J.J. Kiely, *Electroanal. Chem.* 1996, 409, 137-143

[10] F. Fievet, in *Fine Particles Synthesis, characterization, and mechanism of growth*, ed. T. Sugimoto, New York, 2000, p. 460-496

[11] J. Turkevich, P.C. Stevenson, J. Hillier, *Discussion Faraday Soc.* 11(1951)55-75

[12] U. Kreibig, M. Vollmer, *Optical Properties of Metal Clusters*, Springer-Verlag (1995)

[13] V.K. LaMer, R.H. Dinegar, *J. Amer. Chem. Soc.* 72(1950)4847-4854

[14] R. Zsigmondy, E. Hückel, Z. Physik. *Chem.* 116(1925)291-305

[15] R.H. Terril, T.A. Postlethwaite, C.H. Chen, C.D. Poon, A. Terzis, A. Chen, J.E. Hutchinson, M.R. Clark, G. Wignall, J.D. Londono, R. Superfine, M. Falvo, C.S. Johnson, Jr., E.T. Samulski, R.W. Murray, *J. Am. Chem. Soc.* 117(1995)12537–12548; T. Prozorov, A. Gedanken, *Adv. Mater.* 10(7)(1998)532–535

[16] H. Remita, J. Khatouri, M. Treguer, J. Amblard, J. Belloni, Z. *Phys. D* 40(1991)127-130

[17] H. Wohltjen, A.W. Snow, *Anal. Chem.* 70(1998)2856; S.D. Evans, S.R. Johnson, Y.L. Cheng, T. Shen, *J. Mater. Chem.* 10(2000)183

[18] A.H. Lu, G.H. Lu, A.M. Kessinger, C.A. Foss Jr., *J. Phys. Chem.* B101(1997)9139

[19] Y. Dirix, C. Darribere, W. Heffels, C. Bastiansen, W. Caseri, P. Smith, *Appl. Opt.* 38(31)(1999)6581-6586.

[20] J.J. Storhoff, R. Elghanian, R.C. Mucic, C.A. Mirkin, R.L. Letsinger, *J. Am. Chem. Soc.* 120(1998)1959

[21] A.A. Lazarides, G.C. Schatz, *J. Phys. Chem. B* 104(2000)460

[22] H. Li, Y.-Y. Luk, M. Mrksich, *Langmuir* 15(1999)4957

[23] L. Pasquato, F. Rancan, P. Scrimin, F. Mancin, C. Frigeri, *Chem. Commun.* (2000)2253

[24] J.J. Pietron, R.W. Murray, *J. Phys. Chem. B* 103(1999)4440

[25] M. Bartz, Jo¨rg Ku¨ ther, Ram Seshadri, W. Tremel, Angew. Chem., *Int. Ed. Engl.* 37(1998)2466
[26] T. Sato, H. Ahmed, D. Brown, B.F.G. Johnson, *J. Appl. Phys.* 82(1997)1007; S.H.M. Persson, L. Olofsson, L. Hedberg, *Appl. Phys. Lett.* 74(1999)2546
[27] D.L. Gittins, D. Bethell, D.J. Schiffrin, R.J. Nichols, *Nature* 408(2000)67

INDEX

A

B

C

D

E

F

Q

R

S

T

U

W

X

Z

The New Geography of Consumer Spending

This book is dedicated to Ceri and Michael

The New Geography of Consumer Spending

A POLITICAL ECONOMY APPROACH

Alan G. Hallsworth

Belhaven Press
LONDON

Copublished in the Americas by Halsted Press, an imprint of
John Wiley & Sons, Inc., New York

Belhaven Press
(a division of Pinter Publishers)
25 Floral Street, Covent Garden, London, WC2E 9DS, United Kingdom

First published in 1992

Copublished in the Americas by Halsted Press, an imprint of
John Wiley & Sons, Inc., 605 Third Avenue, New York, NY 10158–0012

British Library Cataloguing in Publication Data

A CIP catalogue record for this book is available from the British Library.

ISBN 1 85293 2007 (in the UK only)

Library of Congress Cataloging in Publication Data

Hallsworth, A.G. (Alan G.), 1947–
The new geography of consumer spending: a political economy approach / Alan G. Hallsworth.
p. cm.
Includes bibliographical references and index.
ISBN 1–85293–200–7. – ISBN 0–470–21930–0 (in the Americas only)
1. Consumption (Economics) – Europe. 2. Finance – Europe.
3. Retail trade – Europe. 4. Japan – Economic conditions – 1945–
I. Title.
HC240.9.C6H34 1992
339.4'7'094–dc20 92–24767
CIP

ISBN 0470–21930–0 (in the Americas only)

Typeset by Mayhew Typesetting, Rhayader, Powys
Printed and bound in Great Britain by Biddles Ltd, of Guildford and Kings Lynn

Contents

Acknowledgements

This book has been a long time in the writing, and during its production my thoughts have been influenced by a large number of friends and colleagues. There are too many to list individually, but inspection of the references will reveal either their names or the books they will recall advising me to consult (sometimes both). It is, however, just possible that neither will appear for there are those – whose comments were every bit as valuable to me – who advised against adopting paradigms that they felt were unfashionable or, occasionally, 'not politically correct'. This latter group may very well have been right, but I feel that my remit (to attempt an explanation of contemporary western consumerism and the wider economic factors underpinning it) is so vast that there is scope for many interpretations.

This particular interpretation is a highly individual one that seeks to conflate many seemingly irreconcilable influences, hence the adoption of a very broad paradigm, International Political Economy, as the cornerstone. I gained much enjoyment from writing the book and I shall count it a success if there are at least some who enjoy reading it. It must by now be clear that the usual disclaimer that I accept total responsibility for the content and any errors therein is particularly apt.

I am most grateful to my family for tolerating the disruption caused by my working on the book, to Lynn Ward for the bulk of the typing, and to Iain Stevenson for allowing himself to be persuaded into publishing it. John Ashby of PION is particularly thanked for allowing me to reuse material that was originally published in *Environment and Planning A*.

A LITTLE TRIP DOWN MEMORY LANE

One enduring characteristic of the British is said to be their fondness for the status quo. The essence of conservatism is the mistrust of change for its own sake. Foreign visitors probably find confirmation of this solid sameness whenever they walk down the 'Great British High Street'. They will soon realise that one high street looks much the same as any other. Here is Marks and Spencer, there J. Sainsbury, over there is C&A, Woolworths, Boots or W. H. Smith. All comfortingly the same. Hard to imagine much change going on here. Terribly, well, British (except, of course, that C&A is not . . . whilst Woolworths wasn't - but now is).

Locals with long memories might tell a somewhat different story. We all have to eat, and not too long ago you could shop for food at Lipton's, or Keymarkets, or Maypole. You might even have had the chance to shop at Dickie's Discount or Hillard's or International Stores. Perhaps you particularly liked Fine Fare or Lennon's or Mainstop or Dee. The list of foodstores that you might once have used, but can no longer, could go on for most of the rest of this page. No matter what the locals may have thought, no matter how well the store manager performed his tasks, those once-familiar names have disappeared without trace.

TAKE A LITTLE INTERNATIONAL TRIP

Why is it that there are literally thousands of out-of-town shopping malls in the USA, spreading inexorably outwards to cover tens of thousands of acres of land? Why, on the other hand, are there very few such large developments in the UK? Is it perhaps traceable to the relative disposable incomes in the two countries? There are more Americans and they have much more disposable income - but not so much more as to explain the disparity in shopping provision. The next most probable response to the question would be that the UK has imposed far more restrictive land-use planning controls than the US. But why? Relative to the thousands of unspoilt acres of rolling British countryside, a few shopping centres dotted here and there would really make very little difference. Could it possibly be that the two countries have really quite different systems and philosophies in respect of land? Whilst the dogged preservers of rural England are now the professional planners, on whose behalf are they restricting the supply of urban land whilst preserving the unspoilt countryside? Indeed, trusted and professional though the planners may be, is it not a little odd that central government itself has usually remained the final arbiter of land-use planning decisions?

Would it not be a fine position for one to be in, to own protected rural land and enjoy its beauty? At the same time, ideally, to own precious urban land in the knowledge that its investment value would not be diluted by the conversion of agricultural land into urban uses? Such a property-ownership profile happens, quite by coincidence, to mirror that of the Duke of Westminster. The Duke is often referred to as the richest man in England, and there is no reason at all why this should surprise us, given British attitudes towards land. Coincidentally, there is no shortage of rhetoric on the viewpoint that industry, the rootstock of mass employment, hence mass wealth and mass consumption, has too often been regarded by British entrepreneurs as little more than a stepping-stone towards the ultimate goal of land-ownership and social position.

Major power-brokers in the USA, conversely, may have had much to gain from sub-urban sprawl in a country too big to dominate simply by owning a high percentage of the land. It is possible to arrive at a conceptualisation of Fordism that goes far beyond factory-based mass-production of cars. Henry T. Ford was interested in producing workers as well as cars. Henry T. realised that the mass production of cars implied that there had to be mass consumption of cars. Where better to start the consumption process than in one's own factory? High wages led to the concept of the 'social wage', with the worker's wife well able to afford to stay at home and produce more little consumers. Where better to locate that home than in a sprawling suburb? How better for the worker to get to and from that suburb than in one of Henry T. Ford's own cars, consuming the product of his own labour? As it happens, there was plenty of demand elsewhere for Ford's cars - but the principle is easy enough to comprehend. And so it went on. Until Japan came on the scene. But that is another part of the story that this book seeks to tell.

1

The roots of change

This book is about the power of consumption and consumerism. It was inspired by the changes taking place in the retail sector of the UK economy. Whilst the nation that led the first industrial revolution was collapsing headlong into apparently irreversible manufacturing decline, its retailers were being lauded as the best in the world. Business gurus were describing retailing as one of the very few things that Britain did at all well. Retailing, however, does not operate in a vacuum, and there are as yet no instances of a national economy that has been led to a world prominence via its retail sector alone. The sector depends upon there being products to sell and consumers willing to buy. How could this be sustainable in a country verging on industrial collapse? How could a country forget how to produce and yet remember how to consume? After a decade of rule by the most forceful politician in the world, the country sat much as it had done a political generation previously . . . with unemployment, interest rates and inflation all apparently beyond the capacity of politicians to control. Or, rather, if one were controlled, something rather unpleasant tended to happen to one or both of the other two.

Was there, then, some fundamental flaw, some mote in the eye of Britain that condemned it to a cycle of decline? This, despite the legendary inventive brilliance of so many of its citizens. Self-evidently, there had to be wider factors at work. Theories to explain the sort of 'deep background' to national economic performance may be found in the body of work characterised as International Political Economy and which I shall refer to throughout as IPE. One especially attractive aspect of IPE is its concern for the roots of power. A sub-text of the book, then, will be power: how it changes, who holds it and what the intended (and unintended) outcomes may be. The aim is to delve into the deep background in order to identify factors driving consumerism.

To continue our tale, then, Thomas Lipton can be seen as one of the great early innovators of British mass retailing and the origins of his company are hardly shrouded in mystery. After four years in the USA Lipton returned to his native Glasgow and began to import cheap foodstuffs that could be sold to a rapidly-growing urban population that was acquiring genuine purchasing power. The growth that took Lipton into the first rank of retailers was founded on a major stake in the tea trade. Such was Lipton's impact on the tea trade, that when he took the London market by storm in 1899, most regarded him primarily as a tea merchant. The tea and the bulk of the other foodstuffs came from the colonies and were inextricably linked with Britain's status as an imperial trading power.

Liptons prospered and grew to over 500 stores by the end of World War One. War and its effects are a prime concern of IPE, and the direct threat to the independence of Liptons was the boost that wartime demand had given to the influence of the technology-driven British margarine industry. As suppliers of a staple retail product and with overcapacity to worry about, the margarine companies were dangerous power-brokers. They were dangerous to retailers because they wished for assured product outlets, they knew they had to diversify and they had the financial power to achieve it. To this extent they mirrored the position of tobacco companies that have also sought to diversify out of single-product dependence. Before long, amalgamations forced by the margarine companies gave rise to Allied Suppliers, which continued to trade under the banner of some of the retailers that had been swallowed up – including Liptons. The links between the single entrepreneur and the store bearing his name had soon enough weakened . . . yet one could shop at Liptons during most years of this century. Allied Suppliers went on using the Liptons store name for many years, but eventually became part of the Cavenham Foods empire controlled by Sir James Goldsmith, who based his success on financial power. The motivation for Sir James to trade in any of the countries in which his General Occidental group was present seems largely to have been a function of his current perceptions of the stability and growth potential of that country.

As befits a finance-led operation, Cavenham was an early British purchaser in the USA with the takeover of Grand Union in 1973 at a time when Sir James was clearly unhappy with the UK operations. This led to divestments in the UK, and the roots of the total disappearance of the Lipton name from British high streets.

The British divestments paled in comparison with Sir James's disenchantment with the democratic decision of the French electorate to install President Francois Mitterrand in 1981 – against the trend of 1980s right-wing or centre-right leaders in OECD countries. Funds from the Goldsmith operations joined a general flight of capital (and a range of more transportable possessions) heading for the French border. The economic policies of the sovereign state of France were soon reversed – not least as a result of capital flight flowing from a failure of general confidence and, as we shall see below, a misreading of US economic policy.

We have covered such concepts as states, sovereignty, takeovers, power (in the spheres of purchasing, finance and technology), empire and war. Though it is often taken for granted, an important benefit of the USA is that it offers a politically stable environment, hence the flight of capital to the USA in times of crisis. Unless we have been misinformed, rebels are not poised to take over the White House. Certainly, retailing in the USA is a safer investment than Safeway made in its Kuwait operations.

Crisis? What crisis?

Perhaps, then, the simplest way to emphasise the fundamental difference in approach between this and more conventional studies of consumption is to consider the oil crisis of the early 1970s. The first reaction of retailers was to speculate on the knock-on effects of higher fuel prices on consumer mobility. Would consumers abandon their cars and revert to public transport where possible? Would the oil crisis, then, adversely affect prospects for out-of-town retailing?

An alternative perspective is to take the oil crisis and ask instead what happened to the windfall oil revenues accruing to the OPEC states. What influence did this vast transfer of capital from western/OECD countries to OPEC countries have on the global economy? How did the changed conditions affect the prospects for national economies and for the consumers living there? Substantial passages of the book will be concerned with matters of finance as essential underpinnings to the changed nature of consumption.

This more indirect approach is certainly convoluted, and speculation is still rife about just exactly how circuits of capital work their way through the system. The analysis is unlikely to be straightforward, and alternative viewpoints may be found. Indeed, there is a need to range widely, and large parts of the text will relate only indirectly to retailing. Certainly, it is not true to suggest that researchers have totally ignored the wider socio-economic environment – it is simply that the conventional view of retail consumption is one in which mercantilist or globalist perspectives are rarely discussed. In recent years the 'wider retail environment' has increasingly come into focus – but the basis of analysis has often been neo-classical and the aim profit-maximisation.

A common viewpoint held by those involved in the marketing of consumer goods in the UK was that retailing was simply the end point of the distribution channel. Yet channels of distribution have broken down as vertical integration has taken place. Wholesalers, in particular, have been 'squeezed' by the wide scope of activities undertaken by the retailer. At the same time, manufacturing operations such as Benetton have begun to take in retailing via the franchising system. Whilst one trend has been towards a blurring of distinctions between manufacturers, wholesalers and retailers, another trend very much promoted the interests of UK retailers. This was the abolition, in 1964, of Resale Price Maintenance (RPM) – a bulwark of manufacturer power. Large British retailers were soon able to exert power over the manufacturers in order to obtain better terms on larger orders. The prohibition of such deals was the substance of 1936 US legislation – the now widely ignored Robinson–Patman act.

Some of the most interesting retail research in recent years has focused on how legislation on mergers, monopolies or trusts has impacted on retailing in the USA and the UK.

At first, the effect of RPM on how power-relations could be changed was generally relegated to secondary status. What was felt to matter to the 'sovereign consumer' was the implication for prices in shops – that was 'the bottom line'. It should, of course, be noted that the power shift also tipped the balance in favour of large British retailers, against the interests of the smaller independents and co-operatives. The retail system inexorably became more concentrated – especially in the grocery sector – and power likewise. Yet so long as the big retailers ventured to use their power to offer apparently low prices, then the attention focused on the prices – not the power. In this book, it is power, not price, that counts.

From the mid-1960s onwards, then, as the balance of power tipped more towards large retailers, so the problems that preoccupied retailers also moved to the forefront. In a very mechanistic way, the problems of how to cater to an increasingly mobile population were solved by developing larger food-stores with car parking and in off-centre locations. From this point onwards, concern with the retail environment grew.

The spatial fix

One area where much attention was required was the field of land-use planning. If UK retailers were to maximise profits from suburban, mobile consumers, then a series of land-use planning battles would need to be fought. The retailers duly engaged in a series of land-use planning 'inquiries' where 'objective' data were provided in order to achieve the 'right' outcome. At this point we can see why retailers must have, if anything, more regard to the changing nature of society than must manufacturers/product marketers. The bulk of retailers have to accept that one major facet of their operation – the geographic one – is fixed. Analysis of the locations of Harrods in London, Eatons in downtown Toronto, Galeries Lafayette in Paris, or Bloomingdales flagship store in New York shows that many of the current locations are also the historic locations. This point has been reinforced by May (1981). The likelihood that a certain shopper type or segment of the national consumer market will patronise a given store is largely a reflection of the extent to which that group is likely – or constrained – to be in the vicinity of the premises of the retailer.

If the retailer, committed to a fixed geographical location, finds that trade is falling, then there is a tendency to internalise the problem. What is the retailer 'doing wrong'? Why are the rich, high-spending patrons no longer in evidence? It may perfectly well be that the retailer is doing as well as could reasonably be expected, given that such patrons may have abandoned usage of his city-centre location and now shop 'out-of-town'.

In a more general sense, if the economy goes into decline, the purchasing power of the retailer's typical patrons may decline. Conversely, the advent of leading national retail outlets may upgrade a centre (see Agergard *et al.*, 1970), and thus fortuitously improve the retailer's trading prospects. Thus, whilst the nature of modern society has brought forth the 'yuppy' and given the marketers a new target, such a customer-type may be seen as irrelevant to the trader in the declining urban centre. Except, of course, that this is too short-sighted a view. It may be that, as purchasing power passes to the yuppy, it does so at the expense of the residents of declining urban centres. The need for a more holistic approach to retailing becomes evident — yet, classically, such approaches have not often been taken. One of the few transpositions of the retail *problematique* came from Coelho and Wilson (1976), who tried to maximise consumer welfare rather than retailer profits.

As we shall see, there are good reasons why retailers should seek short-term profit growth and the general thrust of studies continues to turn this way. The theme of a 'changing retail environment' is one where the retailer must be responsive to new opportunities, lest they be exploited by others and turned into threats. With time, the retail scene changed so dramatically that retailers who had 'cost leadership' in one decade might quickly lose it the next. What, then, were these continuous threats/opportunities? One major change that started to impact on retailers came in the demographic structure. The 1960s were seen by many as having been a golden age. It was a time when teenagers had money to burn and they were extremely interested in burning it in retail shops. As the teen market dwindled, it dawned on the more astute retailers that this demographic cohort was ageing, and taking its tastes and spending power with it. Other changes were afoot (Hallsworth, 1987, chapter 2): the whole nature of the family unit was changing, and retailers felt the need to respond. Again, the emphasis was on reaction to new markets, or stopping the threat of the loss of old markets.

In the 1980s, as Michael Poynor put it (1987, p. 106), 'profit and money are no longer dirty words in most circles'. The city salary and the yuppy had arrived. Consumption was back in fashion — but why? The rôle of the retailer was not to ask such questions; merely to react or, ideally, to anticipate. 'Hit and miss' seemed to be the underlying trend.

Cost factors, however, remained dominant. Where the types of products permitted, large-scale retailing, taking advantage of off-centre locations and ample parking, brought benefits of scale-economies. It was a trend extensively experienced in the USA and in Europe. Product sourcing also reflected the need to control costs. The ability of the Japanese to offer competitively-proved consumer electronics made them an ideal source for cost-conscious retailers.

New preoccupations for retailers

The 1970s appeared to offer further new opportunities for British and European retailers. These came from the possibilities of expansion into the USA. There was a clear perception in Europe that population growth was slowing and their oligopolistic market structures were creating other pressures (see Hallsworth, 1990a) for a fuller description). Attention turned to the USA for several reasons. It appeared that the US market was characterised by regional groupings of stores, some of which were small enough to take over. In the 1970s in particular, most European countries found that the $US was in decline and so purchases of US companies would be cost-effective.

At roughly the same time, retailers became more preoccupied with new technology. It was discovered in the USA that laser scanning offered the real possibility of cost savings. The initial focus lay with better control of costly staff. Laser check-outs were said to be faster and, supremely, the operators would not ring in the wrong prices and cheat the till. Furthermore, the laser scanning system removed the need to price individual items and so labour costs would be saved in that area also. We will later discuss some of the wider ramifications of in-store technology — not all of which were initially anticipated.

As power shifted to the retailers, so they began to take on some of the rôles of the product marketers. Attention was turned to the key questions of why people shopped at particular stores. Maslow's (1970) basic needs model was increasingly used, though many researchers felt retailers to be broadly ignorant of why customers used their stores. Academic work on store choice continued apace, but probably the most successful applications lay with mathematical modelling of store locations. Doubts remained as to the relevance of the less accessible academic work on store choice, but retailers seized on certain apparent changes in shopper behaviour. For example, many surveys in the 1980s tended to show that 'the shopper' was less concerned about price and more concerned about convenience of location. This was often perceived as showing that increased wealth had reduced the price emphasis and allowed more subjective factors to come into play. It seemed to reinforce the need to be in the 'best' location. It has been noted (Hallsworth, 1991a) that this type of finding (which may have motivated many operators to move into food superstores) may not be totally straightforward. Retailers also began to use the type of lifestyle data most commonly associated with product marketers. Geodemographics became a concern for British retailers in the mid-1980s, not least because such techniques were being employed by direct marketing organisations in order to segment retail groups.

If we then summarise this 'British view' of recent retail change we see an emphasis on 'challenges' allied to the need to retain existing markets or seek new ones. Most innovations have been cost-oriented and market share has traditionally been bolstered by merger or organic growth (or both) and scale-economies have been sought. We should not be too critical of this generally passive/reactive role of retailing. The retail companies are under the same pressures as other sectors to perform profitably in order to meet analysts' expectations and to be judged on the stock market. Losing control of costs is as good a route as any to trading disaster.

We have attempted to show how retail research can take a wider perspective. Next we shall consider how retailing and IPE can be put together, and how IPE offers a framework for the widest possible remit in retail analysis.

2

Retailing and International Political Economy: Shared Issues

Retailing as a subject of formal academic study is in its infancy in the UK. The first chairs of Retailing in British universities have been established only in the last decade or so. This is not to suggest that the topic has totally been neglected – simply that there has often been no comprehensive view of who might be interested in retailing or why. Yet retail studies have been undertaken by geographers, economic historians, psychologists, anthropologists, marketing analysts, economists, statisticians, sociologists, quantity surveyors and many more. Even semioticians would feel aggrieved at being left out. Each would come up with a different working definition of retailing – and some would not bother. To some, retailing is clearly a study area worthy of attention in its own right. They are studying retailing *per se* and seeking answers to questions that carry implications for the practice of retailing and for wider society. Others see themselves as pursuing academic issues in their own established discipline, and retailing becomes merely a topic of interest or a handy peg on which to hang another application of their favourite model.

Looking at the subject matter of retail researchers, we find that much effort is devoted to either predicting the revival of the small shop or to lamenting its total demise. The balance of evidence is that in the context of mass, westernised retailing, the small shop is its 'basic unit of accounting'. Some of the concern for small shops does not derive from interest in their retailing characteristics, but focuses on loss of community in rural areas should they close. Wherever fixed-unit retailing is known, so the small shop is known. Hypermarkets are far from ubiquitous, whereas the small shop is a concept everyone can easily grasp. Most fixed-unit retail outlets are small shops. Other retail work ignores any unit of accounting at all and considers the changing character of consumers, channels of distribution or types of consumer markets. Where retailing is an adjunct to academic enquiry, the range of research topics is almost endless, and it would be pointless to attempt a catalogue of them.

This brings us to the topic of International Political Economy (IPE) – a term which now requires definition. One may argue that, as a discipline, IPE has several parallels with retailing. In IPE, the historical basic unit of accounting is the state itself. That said, there are those who would regard analysis of the state as too restrictive a remit. As with many of the small shop supporters, so defenders of 'the state' only appear when some exogenous threat is perceived – when something comes along to threaten its sovereignty. For many, that something was the Multinational or Transnational Business Corporation (MNC or TNC). In some factions of IPE, then, only truly global issues are deemed to be worthy of study. To others still, IPE may as well not exist; the premises that IPE espouses – states and their wider relations – are seen as irrelevant to processes that are universal by virtue of being part of normal business practice or economic functioning.

There is, however, a contrast in respect of how IPE and retailing are viewed in terms of their academic significance. IPE has a problem of acceptability that is the mirror image of that facing retailing. The weighty matters with which it deals are undoubtedly worthy of academic consideration. Because this is so, the economists, political analysts and others seem rather reluctant to let go of the reins and concede that their models and ways of thinking should be subordinated to another discipline. It is less that, as with retailing, the subject matter of the IPE is regarded as too trivial to be accorded status; rather, it is seen as too important a field to be lost by other disciplines. Advocates of the IPE approach have done themselves few favours by setting the widest possible boundaries to discourse. The most usual approach taken by an aspiring new discipline is to set up clear boundaries in order to have grounds for legitimating its viewpoints and for consolidating the position of those prepared to adhere to the tenets being so quickly set in stone. IPE seems to have done little of this, and accordingly suffers from sniper attack from those who have found what they perceive to be more solid ground.

What IPE allows

It is clearly not satisfactory to leave the reader in limbo by stating that IPE allows everything, or by suggesting that IPE is about the state or threats to the state from transnationals. Yet that is the first impression that may be gained from some of the literature; Tooze (1984), for example, is about as catholic about IPE as is humanly possible. For this reason, his work offers a reasonable starting point, through both Gilpin (1975) and Strange (1988) provide excellent definitions. A first concern is with the types of issues that might fall within the remit of IPE. Tooze earmarks such matters as international trade, international monetary relations, TNCs, global economic problems, and others – including the foreign economic policies of states. This latter topic means that work in

IPE has often been devoted to the roots of war. War is certainly one of the more extreme outcomes of state policy, but is still only part of a wider political process as Clausewitz's dictum long ago demonstrated. At root, IPE seeks to clarify the issues of power-relations that lie behind the policies of states and which sometimes lead to war. What states claim to be doing (such as 'defending democracy') occasionally is at odds with what the more cynical believe they are doing (such as defending oilfields), as events in the Middle East have recently highlighted.

My own perspective rests solidly with that band of work in IPE that stresses the pursuit of power by (usually) sovereign states for hegemonic ends. However, I wish to modify and extend the remit into the whole issue of economic growth. Indeed, I wish specifically to examine the effect of a push for growth upon individuals. To emphasise growth may be a little *passé* in these ecological times, but recall that our sub-text is power. No government has yet been elected on a no-growth platform, and I wager that none ever will. A key aspect of power is to acquire the mandate, albeit passive, of the masses. The problem for those who wield power is that outcomes are never quite what was expected, as the (surviving) architects of the events of 19—22 August 1990 would testify. Essentially, the very act of embarking upon the road to a desired outcome may of itself be sufficient to ensure ultimate failure. In particular, Hymer (1975) and Hirsch (1977) have stressed that we may desire an outcome, but in achieving — or even pursuing — that outcome, we change the initial conditions upon which we based our desires. Such considerations will be important in a book that considers the fundamental nature of the demand that retailers claim to exist to satisfy.

Hirsch stated:

> Considered in isolation, the individual's demand . . . can be taken as genuinely individual wants . . . acting alone, each individual seeks to make the best of his or her position. But satisfaction of these individual preferences itself alters the situation that faces others seeking to satisfy similar wants. . . . What each of us can achieve, all cannot . . . if everyone stands on tiptoe, no one sees better . . . to see total economic advance as individual writ large is to set up expectations that cannot be fulfilled, ever. (Hirsch, 1977, pp. 4—9)

Just contrast Hirsch's hard-edged words with the utopianism that prevailed in some quarters in the 1960s. Were we not all on the edge of a lifetime of leisure? Every whim catered for by the miracle of robotics? Ordinary people, it was averred, would soon escape the drudgery of routine (Fordist?) work. Yet where is the utopia? It has failed to appear because the utopians themselves saw the solution as feasible within the bounds of technological change and neglected the social aspects of 'needs and wants'. They forgot that, for the masses, work was not an end in itself, but the only realistic route to fulfilment of needs, many of which had been externally and artificially created. The crucial question that was never asked was this: who would decide what standard of work-free living each work-free individual would command? And how would those who said, 'Please, sir, I want more' ever come to be satisfied? The work of Hirsch addresses such matters – as did the New Right political regimes of Thatcher and Reagan.

We may note that, in defiance of Hirsch, one of the basic false premises of the Thatcher/Reagan years was that, just as companies or nation-states should act as free agents in the pursuit of wealth, so should individuals. The problem is that the rationalist thesis (that aggregate benefit stems from the accumulation of individual self-interest) is patently false. Many social situations may be outlined where individual self-interest detracts from the aggregate outcome. One such is the dollar auction, where collective losses typically outweigh any individual gain – unless the participants actively collaborate. The Prisoner's Dilemma and several other social traps warn us against simplistically assuming that the world is an objective, economic environment. The whole field of game theory exists to explore alternative scenarios, some of which are inherently unstable. Much more fundamentally, rational/maximising responses fall foul of the problem that real-world information is not, and sometimes cannot be, perfect. Wolpert (1964) demonstrated this in a farming context – since when could farmers predict the weather?

There thus has to be considerable irony in the fact that Hirsch's reworking of the earlier ideas of Harrod (1958) was published just as Thatcher and Reagan were poised to promote the notion of individual entrepreneurship/self-interest to new heights (or depths, depending upon your viewpoint). Reagan, of course, was associated with a remarkable cold war arms bill that writ large his hegemonic intentions. There was also the small matter of $3,500bn. worth of national debt. The problem for aspiring hegemons is the likelihood that even more subtle means to hegemonic ends than blatant military might will be resisted by rival states shrewd enough to surmise what is going on. All too soon there is a recipe for contradiction and confusion. This book is about how those contradictions and confusions have impacted upon even something so apparently parochial as retailing. We will return many times to Hirsch and especially his ideas on the search for status or 'position'.

Superpowers

For the time being, however, let us spend a little time playing with the concept of IPE . . . and those confusions. If the hegemonic paradigm within IPE can be accepted, then it is natural to write about superpower states: that such a label can be attached and understood is a clear sign that IPE has a legitimate focus. The implication is that the former USSR and the United States of America ought to have been attempting to make hegemonic moves on all possible fronts. Given that premise, we can concentrate on interpreting how the USA may have been dispersing its interests worldwide via the military, monetary and economic/trading spheres. (The focus here is western, so we ignore Third World issues from this point onwards). We can find a clear example of what we can call hegemonic confusion by considering the superpower arms race. To tolerate a situation whereby one power (however benign it perceives itself to be) has total military superiority is a recipe for instability. The lack of good information about the actions of the enemy – and there always has to be an enemy (Hallsworth, 1987a) – leads to an arms race.

However, the awesome destructive power of nuclear weapons brings problems at home. Oddly, some citizens cannot help being afraid of nuclear destruction and so protest begins. In the event of the nuclear option having become a party-political issue, those who sought global hegemonic power by military threat could have found themselves usurped by democratic protest. The ultimate irony is that the destructive nuclear arms race was, symbolically at least, called to a halt by Mikhail Gorbachev – a leader not troubled by the need to fight democratic elections (though always at risk from a palace coup).

With consumption as its central interest, it is inevitable that the foci of hegemonic power most central to this book will be not military, but monetary/economic and technological. Yet here again we can see that the military expenditures cannot be ignored. The defence expenditures of the Reagan years (and of Vietnam in an earlier era) profoundly affected the flexibility of response open to the USA in its monetary/economic policies. Finally, of course, there are those powers that might want to pursue their own global interests but for whom no military option has been open. Japan and West Germany have, in the post-war period, adopted economic strategies that, in the context of IPE, emerge as rational responses to the globalist perspective of others. So 'successful' has their response been that Japan will be taken, throughout this book, as the ideal-typical countervailing power to the USA.

Note that it has hardly been possible to outline the issues without outlining some of the key players in the global game. This is unfortunate, since my aim is to withdraw from IPE some general themes and then show how elements of them may be identified even in retailing. Accordingly, I shall propose that, though specific states will be named and though specific companies will be named, each should be taken merely as representative of wider general themes or trends. To this end I intend my examples to be seen as ideal-typical as formulated by Max Weber (1968). The work of Weber will be alluded to on more than one occasion, not least because Weber has articulated issues both of power – one half of the power and value alluded to by Susan Strange (1988) – and of bureaucracies, through which dominant values are enforced.

Key themes in IPE

What are these general themes that we might seek to identify? For this we can again turn to Tooze, who seeks to outline the perspectives from which, he argues, authors have approached IPE (Tooze, 1984, pp. 15–18). Drawing upon the work of Gilpin (1975) and others, Tooze outlines the liberal, mercantilist (or neo-mercantilist), structuralist, world systems, and Marxist and radical viewpoints. Tooze reinforces the view that there is no value-free political science. All work has to be read in the context of the perspective of its author. We may call this the Mandy Rice-Davies viewpoint since, when someone first clearly lays out their general perspective and then we hear what they have to say, we are usually able to utter, 'Well, he would, wouldn't he?'. For precisely the same reason, unexpected findings that run counter to what we would expect from that source usually carry more weight.

Tooze, on my reading of his 1984 work, by giving weight to the requirement that researchers clarify what academic baggage they are carrying around with them, rather risks throwing the baby out with the bathwater. IPE covers ground that is important to most disciplines and can be tackled from many disciplinary perspectives, but it can also be denied. We should be able to see that those who appear most vehemently to deny IPE usually do so because of a belief that what IPE regards as issues are merely by-products of the normal functioning of the system. That natural system is usually an economic system driven by neo-classical constructions of market liberalism. Yet I would argue that everything is socially constructed around accepted visions of the world, and those visions also vary between nations or groups of nations and with time. Risk is a social construction; health is a social construction (after all, in the western context, illness is dichotomised between 'fit for work' and 'not fit for work'). The approach in this book will not be to sift the five viewpoints for useful perspectives and generalities, but to take as a starting-point the operating philosophies of world trade. It soon becomes clear that two stand out. Liberalism/globalism and mercantilism will be the twin planks of most of this book. Most of Tooze's viewpoints, of which liberalism and mercantilism are the first two, are familiar to anyone working within the social sciences. The liberal formulation I am often going to refer to as 'globalist' — a term already utilised in the military/hegemonic discussion above. Tooze's liberalism is a perspective that sees harmonisation of economic purpose across the globe as a logical, indeed inevitable, consequence of the undeniable benefits of capitalism, free trade and comparative advantage. All problems stem from failures to implement the necessary economic policies that will lead to advancement through growth. Such a perspective views the state as having a role for purposes of national defence and as a facilitator of free trade via the removal of obstacles to this holy grail. Globalists are the great seekers of the 'level playing field' who refuse to concede that, in reality, the international public park (an impure public good) only has swings, roundabouts — and a seesaw. The seesaw appears to be level — but step on one end of the level seesaw and the other end shoots into the air.

The second vital concept — and one to which substantial reference will later be made — is mercantilism. Here, the interests of the state are set much more centrally, with the economy as a handmaiden of national interest. Put simplistically, the economy should be at work to ensure an equilibrium in the balance of payments with a view to keeping the country solvent. Ironically, this good housekeeping philosophy has sometimes been pirated by those whose viewpoints are far from mercantilist. We shall also see, as a double irony, that much of what motivated the *laissez-faire* writings of Adam Smith was a revulsion against the petty mercantilism of Britain in the sixteenth century. That earlier version of mercantilism ossified inefficiencies at home, rather than allowing in goods that could more easily be produced abroad.

The latter-day neo-mercantilist group of states is generally populated by those who were perched on the other end of the economic seesaw when a fat guy suddenly sat down. In future, they are playing all games on the home ball park, and if the game gets too rough then they will just simply take their ball home. Others of a mercantilist persuasion are staying home and, believing fit to be better than fat, are taking the Charles Atlas course until they are fit enough to come back and push the fat guy off the seesaw.

The remit of this book does not extend beyond OECD countries, so no attention will be paid in this book to the poor people who could not even afford to enter the playground once the monetarists decided they had to pay their way financially. For reasons of completeness we should return to Tooze's other three themes where he goes on to outline how structuralist, world systems, and Marxist perspectives can be read as IPE approaches – though I suspect that many of the practitioners in these fields would see IPE as subordinate to their wider/superior viewpoint. For this additional reason I intend to take them no further.

Alternative paradigms

It should be evident that I am stepping back from certain other approaches that might well have been adopted. There is a burgeoning literature on regulation theory, post-Fordism (and post-modernism) and flexible specialisation. Frequent reference is made therein to Japan, either as empirical case study or in ideal-typical mode. I deny neither the overlap with this book, nor the value of the research that has emerged. What I do have is reservations about all these alternative approaches (and even with the suggestion that all are totally distinct). Indeed, what is so exciting about social theory at the present moment is its very state of flux and lively debate as exemplified by the exchanges between Scott (1991) and Lovering (1990).

As the researchers weave their theories into ever-wider webs, it seems to me that gaps sometimes appear. Increasingly there appears to be the need for a yet wider framework. Where, on the other hand, a writer is totally confident and the work is brilliantly impressive, it is usually precisely because there is confidence in the preconstructed theoretical underpinnings (see, for example, Harvey, 1989).

Flexible specialisation could have been an approach that would have covered much of what I shall later present as evidence. The problem with that is that I have set store by taking Japan as ideal-typical. On one reading of flexible specialisation Japan can be accepted as its home – yet I do not totally accept this. Japan's rise to industrial prominence seems to me to be clearly rooted in a desire to compete in the high-volume consumer industries. What happened was that in the immediate post-war period, inexpensive capital was not available to facilitate powerful, direct competition with the then-dominant US via a one-off leap into the mass production systems associated with America. Catch-up implied new ways of work, and Japan was forced into a kind of flexible automation that was parsimonious rather than profligate with capital. Accordingly, I place the power of capital at the forefront of explanation, even ahead of technology. Technological innovations fortuitously reinforced the advantages of having eschewed the 'American way'. Only with hindsight can we say that they were certain to do so in the long run – for some of the early Japanese automobiles were of extremely poor quality. Much of what is now produced in Japan is of robot-built quality, but still all too clearly geared to volume production in aggregate terms. The American consumer market has remained the target, even if American methods were not adopted. That there were over 12 million cars produced in Japan in 1985 is what counts; it matters somewhat less that they came in all sorts of shapes and sizes.

The pressure to produce sharply differentiated models of any product can be seen as a restless search for a successful selling style in order to ensure corporate success. Beneath the skin, product standardisation – a key to cost control – goes on apace. High quality and reliable (but cost-effective, standardised and refined) components are used in order to assemble apparently diverse end-products. Furthermore, the various attempts by other countries to ape ideal-typical Japan have brought forth hybrid variants that often fail because they are inevitably influenced by local norms and behaviours. A process continues, so those variants that emerge where Fordism is pressured are themselves transformed by neo-Fordist or neo-flexible forms into a myriad of outcomes . . . or so I believe. Because I believe this, I wish to steer well clear of what could become a taxonomic nightmare. Whilst regulation theory, in a sense, tries more than most of the new orthodoxies to tiptoe through the methodological tulips in eclectic fashion, it nevertheless faces problems. Not least is the positivist slant of trying to utilise empirical evidence. Because of reservations I hold about our ability to predict the final port of call whilst still in the industrial maelstrom, I very much prefer to operate in ideal-typical fashion back at the aggregate level of IPE perspectives where Japan serves, primarily, as our mercantilist rôle-model. I am, therefore, predictably happier with the regulationist's emphasis on modes of operation, competitive institutions and norms as preconstructed underpinnings. The very essence of IPE is that mercantilism and globalism are embedded, historically-based ways of organising economies and societies. As capital and technology have transformed mercantilism and globalism, so the scope has emerged for viable research into all the post-Fordist and related themes.

That the regulationists may come to give the most coherent account of contemporary trends is evidenced by Jessop's (1990) interesting and wide-ranging account of the regulationist schools. My view remains that neither the unwarrantedly global view of the post-Fordists, nor the narrowness of the Emilia–Romagna school, nor even the overly nation-state-based approaches of some branches of regulation theory will quickly give us an explanation for all seasons. Jessop, however, does identify some regulationist approaches that transcend national regimes, and these offer the most promise.

It is amusing to suggest that one reading of IPE could help to explain why there should be the present proliferation of theories. Would not US academics, with their globalist background, assume naturally that Fordism (their dominant productive paradigm) was equally globally accepted? Would not the French regulationists (coming from an overtly centralist/Bonapartist and mercantilist state) not naturally assume that each nation works out its own regimes? (And would not Ray Hudson (1989), sitting at the edge of a great coalfield, not produce powerful evidence that 'it never happened here'?)

It is no coincidence that I specifically note Hudson's work, for the case of UK miners will serve to further illustrate how matters of position comprise a continuing theme throughout this book. Much in the manner of the regulationists (though in a far simpler way), I argue that both the national context and the stage of economic development influence the way in which position may be asserted or reasserted. The state of the UK mining industry has been well illustrated by Hudson. Bear in mind that because it is a basic extractive process, the lessons from manufacturing cannot directly be applied. However, the balance of rewards in the mining industry developed through time from a competitive piecework system that set man against man and pit against pit into a more equable wage-rate system. This was a clear result of union pressure at a time when coal was desperately needed. A consequence was that it was difficult for the younger, fitter, miner who was prepared to risk the safety issue (or too desperate to care about it) to assert position through harder work and greater rewards. That demand, however, remained latent. When the management had allayed the worst fears of exploitation and had attended to matters of safety, the union position became weaker. With the fall in demand for coal, the industry could be restructured. The militant pits could be closed and standard wage-rates attacked. Productivity was readily increased by reassertion of agreements that were inherently more appealing to the younger, fitter miner. The latent demand for the chance to make catch-up positional gains on other individuals and on other industrial sectors was made real. Inherently, because the system which had been inserted when the unions were dominant had failed to accommodate the 'aspirers to position', it was inherently unstable. To this extent it mirrored the situation in the mass, public-sector housing market.

Accordingly, then, I suggest that in all societies we see a need for individuals to assert position. At certain times, when more basic needs are satisfied in the working population, those in power in society can use this demand for position to set in train changes that will work to their benefit. The classic example is the harnessing by the Japanese of an enduring and deeply embedded system of loyalty and position to drive their economic expansionism. As global economies become more interdependent, so practices drawn from lead economies are bolted-on to other societies. The effects are more complex in individualistic societies where loyalties can more readily be bought and sold. These hybrid outcomes are what make the work of the regulationists so complex. This book suggests that meaningful insights can be made just by extracting the powerful influence of matters of position.

To return to our consideration of other orthodoxies, the term 'post-Fordism' seems to act as catch-all for the two approaches above – and more. Again, I feel that this focuses too narrowly on the fate of a generalised idea of working practices, even if I did accord it prominence earlier. There are two areas where I do have sympathy with post-Fordist researchers who regard themselves neither as regulationists nor as being in the flexible specialisation camp. One is that Fordism does seem to me to have been an ideal-typical formulation that was in tune with the dominant orthodoxies of its formative times. Second, I also believe that the spirit of Fordism (if that is acceptable terminology) is not entirely dead, whilst in some spheres it never really existed. Again, the financial and technological transformations of the post-Bretton Woods world have been responsible for the mutations that Fordism has faced. The countries where Fordism was most likely to emerge (on my reading of IPE) are in the throes of trying to work their way through more severe contradictions than are faced by the mercantilist/nationalist states for whom the changes have been more advantageous. Fortunately, since IPE issues operate at a higher level of abstraction, we need not become bogged down by enumerating instances where Fordism did or did not take root.

Because of reservations about all of the above paradigms, I remain convinced that IPE has the breadth to accommodate the diversity of issues that will be raised. We may note, for example, that the New International Division of Labour (NIDL) – though occasionally ignored by post-Fordist researchers – is entirely predictable from IPE principles. Likewise, the attitude of the Japanese towards funding for industry, allied to a faith in new and high technology (when mixed with a cocktail of unregulated pressures for growth, intense nationalism and peer-group-driven loyalties) gave the necessary conditions for their economic, if not social, miracle.

The 'taken for granted' world

I have already twice alluded to situations where attitudes and opinions could be inferred from a scrutiny of the background of their proponents. There is a genuine danger that the precepts of IPE are so obvious, so taken for granted, that they themselves become ignored entirely. It is precisely because IPE relates to the deep background of economic affairs (to the national psyche, as it were) that I find it so appealing. There is no shortage of theories that seek to transcend national boundaries . . .

from Marxism to Fordism. Yet, however weak and inappropriate the concept of the nation-state may be to tribal societies, it remains a pervasive influence on western thought. As Rosa Luxembourg asked of the workers of the world, 'But what will you do if your country goes to war?'. Whenever it has come down to a matter of the King's shilling, we have yet to record an instance of class solidarity transcending nationalism.

So, even where global finance and technology are prime, one cannot spirit away effects, treat them as causes, bolt them on to fading socio-economic structures and expect something wonderful to happen. Technological quick-fixes are not possible. The potential drag imposed by national institutions and norms, the culture of a country (as stressed also by regulation theory (see Petit (1986)) are so deeply ingrained as to be almost invisible to all but outsiders. To exemplify: the City in the context of the UK does not see itself as short-termist. There is a rational explanation devoid of overtly short-term motives for just about everything that goes on. The problem is that the system itself produces short-termist outcomes such that criticism of specific practices becomes futile.

It may be noted that Rybczynski (1988) has expounded on the links between the financial and industrial sectors. We can note in particular this statement:

> The re-structuring of an economy with a securitised financial system has come under strong criticism, and is often compared unfavourably with re-structuring in countries with a bank-orientated or market-orientated financial system, such as Japan and Germany. The main aspect of re-structuring in a securitised financial system which has been subject to detailed examination has been that relating to the market for corporate control, and especially its emphasis on the short term, described as 'short-termism'. That the working of this market does raise important issues covering technical, accounting, legal and other questions as well as those relating to its efficacy is beyond doubt. However, evaluations of this type are limited in their scope and do not extend to the inter-relationship between financial systems in different stages of economic development. They do not take account of the internationalisation of business, and they do not attempt to see this function as merely one of the elements of the working of a dynamic financial system. An assessment of the system must take into account also the working of the credit and capital markets such as the market for venture capital and buy-outs which are an integral part of the re-structuring mechanism. (Rybczynski, 1988, p. 12)

Clearly, I hope to add a little to the evaluations that Rybczynski dismisses as 'limited in scope'. At the same time, he is to be thanked for so clearly laying out the grounds on which certain types of financial system may be criticised. The point here is that these systems may be so embedded as to be impervious to change. That the old and trusted ideas are hard to unlearn can be further reinforced with reference to the theories of Adam Smith. His 'restraints on the importation of goods' were, at root, underpinned by an unshakeable belief that the costs and risks of transportation would be a natural influence keeping most investment at home. Such costs would also inhibit the importation of any foreign product that was not produced substantially more efficiently than at home. Once transport was revolutionised, most of Smith's work should have been consigned to the dustbin of history. Ironically, those who claim to adhere most strongly to his work not only are attracted by the least viable of his notions, but would also be the first to suffer if anyone ever began to take seriously his strictures on the evils of joint stock companies!

The same refusal to admit that external realities have changed is evidenced in those societies that 'attack inflation' because it 'causes' industrial uncompetitiveness. The simple reality is that inflation is a *symptom* of uncompetitive economies – not a cause. Rather than address the big issues of why a society has come to be structured in a way that makes its economy uncompetitive, it is simpler to treat effects as causes: not least, of course, because the latter approach is altogether less painful for those who are, basically, at fault. It may be altogether more emotionally satisfying to be mercilessly flogging a dead horse for having the temerity to die than it is to go about the messy business of holding *post mortems* to find out what killed it. In the long run, however, the latter enterprise is altogether more productive.

It would be extremely unwise to assume that terms such as mercantilism or liberalism come with simple, ready-attached labels. There is still massive disagreement about the nature of mercantilism: even over whether or not it ever existed as a coherent state policy towards trading. In France it may have emerged as Colbertism, in Germany it was seen as intrinsically state-building, and so on. An excellent debate on mercantilism is to be found in the collection of fourteen papers edited by Minchinton (1969).

To clarify my position on this I shall essentially be taking a neo-mercantilist viewpoint that sees mercantilism as a logical business stratagem. I am seeking examples of situations where, in order to bolster the home market income and thus spending power, enterprises are making heavy investment in contemporary economic efficiency in home markets – only conceding to foreign production once all domestic sources of efficiency are exhausted. Given the capital-intensive nature of modern production, this should inherently be an attractive option in any case. To this extent it rather mirrors the 'social mercantilism' of John Cary with its concern for employment, rather than the earlier crude bullion fixation that characterised some early mercantilist thought.

It is perhaps ironic that the liberal free-traders have, conversely, probably paid too little attention to the implications of removing impediments to global flows of finance rather than flows of products. Again, it is the contradictions and confusions that ensue that will concern us.

Mercantilism and globalism at all scales

Overall, then, my intention is less to adopt a liberal or mercantilist approach to writing, than it is to seek to show that it is conflict between these two main western economic policy perspectives that exacerbates existing 'contradictions' and confusions'. I shall therefore be hoping to demonstrate that free-world states or businesses can be seen as pursuing either mercantilist or globalist economic policies. On a time-scale of centuries, a particular state could at one time be pursuing globalist ends, later it may become mercantilist — or vice-versa. Some parts of a national economy may be pursuing mercantilist ends whilst other parts are functioning globally — yet more potential for confusion. Further, specific classes ('interest groups' may be a better term to cover societies less class-ridden than Britain) within society at large may control policy and decide to run a globalist economy in pursuit of their internal hegemonic interests. Clearly, when we write of 'the state', we will be making some substantial assumptions about the nature of the beast. Later it might even become clearer in whose direct interest state policy is working.

Let us now briefly attempt to insert globalism and mercantilism into the 'roots of change' section outlined earlier (see Chapter 1). In all probability, Liptons regarded itself as purely concerned with the distribution function and with ensuring profits from an operation geared exclusively to the British shopping public. However, it is hard to deny that the early successful growth of Liptons was fostered by the twin processes of globalist empire-building and free trade so strongly advocated by the British at a time when they were ruling the waves.

We will find good reasons to support the argument that, whilst external trade was fostered, domestic retail companies (rather more than industry) were protected from excess foreign competition in a way that assured their longevity. However, Liptons later fell foul of the general process of merger, takeover and agglomeration that has characterised Anglo western economies in the twentieth century. Finally, a wider process of globalism, with its roots in US policy of the post-World-War-Two period, facilitated the movement of investment capital out of certain national economies and into others. It is precisely because retailing has become deeply enmeshed in global rather than national economic systems in the last decade that this book has been written. (However, the global pressures become transformed by local circumstance into peculiarly national outcomes.) A prime aim is to articulate issues of power and value as they are perceived in the context of consumption, and show how these are linked to IPE in more ways than might at first appear evident. For the reader who is still not satisfied that the remit of IPE — at least as it will be pursued in this book — has been adequately defined, I return again to the work of Strange. Strange (1988) has offered a working definition of IPE thus: 'it concerns the social, political and economic arrangements affecting the global systems of production, exchange and distribution, and the mix of values reflected therein . . . they are the result of human decisions taken in the context of man-made institutions and sets of self-rules and customs' (Strange, 1988, p. 18). This seems to fit neatly with the type of context that we drew together when briefly discussing the fate of Liptons. Strange went on to list four roots of structural power as security, production, finance and knowledge. War was certainly a factor in creating the power that sank Liptons as an independent organisation. It fell to the Van den Bergh margarine group – with a power base in wartime production – in 1927. Yet Van den Bergh's interests were ultimately less significant than those of the financial power of Cavenham: and Cavenham itself was expendable in a wider financial context. I venture to suggest that, as this book is rooted in retailing in OECD countries, it is Strange's latter two power-influences – finance and knowledge – that are the most relevant to this study. Not only that: they will increasingly be the factors that create the competitive edge in the future. We can already hardly ignore their influence on security and production issues.

As confirmation of this, Strange goes on to note: 'finance – the control of credit – is the facet which has perhaps risen in importance in the last quarter century more rapidly than any other . . . its power to determine outcomes . . . is enormous' (Strange, 199, p. 30). Strange adds that the most sought-after form of knowledge is technology – a point reinforced by Williams (1984) who has written the 'International Political Economy of technology'. In what may effectively amount to an International Political Economy of retailing, I shall take Strange's working definition of IPE but concentrate on the two major and growing power issues: finance and technology/knowledge.

Power

As the themes of IPE are played out, a considerable amount of this book will concern itself with power. Most researchers of the UK retail scene will readily identify powerful retailers. These retailers can bring about change that reinforces their position – often in respect of suppliers. This is not the time to look in detail at such matters. What is essential is to reinforce the point that aside from such introverted views of power-relations, retailers face other wider power pressures.

We learned above from Susan Strange that students of International Political Economy are concerned with issues of power and value, so often neglected in neo-classical economics. These two issues will form a subtext throughout this book. I seek to show that, in large part, issues of power are either poorly articulated by retailers, or are ignored entirely. When power-factors are addressed (usually by the retail chains that have already achieved power) they are frequently miscast. Power factors are usually addressed in the economic mode: strictly as operational factors. There becomes a preoccupation with simple market share/market power in the home economy and with little else.

What, if anything, do retailers already know about wider issues of power? Many retailers in the UK will have faced the power of the state in its regulation of spatial outcomes through its town and country planning powers. I made this point above in the context of attitudes towards land. Other law-making powers affect aspects of employment, safety and financial dealings and so on. In the future, UK retailers will face more and more EC legislation. The USA imposes, or has traditionally imposed, perhaps even more blanket trade regulations covering many aspects of retail practice.

We will constantly seek evidence of one particular manifestation of power. This is the ability to control working practices, in particular to insert or speed up 'rat-races' by feeding on the aspiration to position (identified by Hirsch) that is latent in individuals or groups in society. In most organisations the key debates are not about practice, but about power. As Giddens averred (1984, p. 283), 'power cannot be regarded as a second-order consideration in the social sciences. Power cannot be tacked on, as it were, after the more basic concepts of social science have been formulated. There is no more elemental concept than that of power.' The ruling elite most readily controls power for its own ends when the criteria for positional gains is as ill-defined as possible. I will later argue that it is no coincidence that the criteria for allowing or denying the lucrative gains from planning permissions are, in most societies, extremely loosely defined. One cannot think of a developed country that employs a rule-book of criteria that, if met, will in all circumstances guarantee acceptance of a development proposal. To employ such a rule-book would be to throw away the direct hands-on power to deny as well as to confer benefits. The most worthwhile power, to those who seek it, is that which cannot be denied because its key criteria are hidden. Thereby, any decision can be justified in a *post hoc* manner. The history of women's struggle for equality is littered with instances where the individual best qualified for a position in hard objective/quantifiable terms was eventually denied. Nor was it ever difficult for those who had denied the access to position to later justify their previously hidden criteria. In most societies there is no great evidence of a diminution in the extent to which key decisions are taken behind closed doors by a limited number of powerful individuals.

In many cases retailers find that, in pursuing normal business, they have to face the fact that they are subordinate to state power. This book warns that there is an increasing risk that retailers, whilst concentrating on their core business, will face exogenous pressures – often unwelcome ones – from financial power. I argue that the extent to which retailers can be sheltered from such pressures is a function of the relations between the state and those global pressures. It begins to become clear that we will need some background on these power-relations. I believe that once the pressures are at least outlined (albeit briefly), then it should be clear that strategic responses by retailers become necessary.

What, then, is power? The over-arching conception of power that will be adopted is that proposed by Max Weber. The reason for this is that it makes quite specific points about the power of the state and how that power is legitimated. As a basic point in consideration of power, then, I take Weber's (1948, p. 180) classic statement: 'We understand by "power" the chance of a man or a number of men to realise their own will in a social action even against the resistance of others who are participating in the action.' Note, here, that Giddens (1976) has discussed the importance of including the word 'even' which is sometimes omitted (either by translators or by Weber himself). In this version there is a clearly coercive nature to power. The state, naturally, seeks to legitimate its coercive powers. The fact that state power quickly becomes solidly entrenched, generally accepted and fully legitimated, can be ascertained from this alternative, revolutionary viewpoint: 'This country . . . belongs to the people who inhabit it. Whenever they shall grow weary of the existing government they can exercise their constitutional right to amend it, or their revolutionary right to dismember it, or overthrow it.'

Or, as Camus put it, 'Power . . . settles everything', and he also had thoughts on how: 'The truth is that every intelligent [man], as you know, dreams of being a gangster and of ruling over society by force alone . . . one generally relies on politics and rushes to join the cruellest party. What does it matter, after all, if by humiliating one's mind one succeeds in dominating everyone' (Camus, 1963, pp. 35, 42).

What is crucial is that the public accepts the legitimacy of state/government powers: the dissenting revolutionary passage above was, of course from Abraham Lincoln's inaugural address of 1861! Most expressions of power in everyday life are substantially less confrontational than Lincoln's US conception. Nor did Lincoln's revolutionary ideas last long there: as C. Wright Mills long ago noted in respect of his 'power elites' (1956, p. 269): 'changes in the power system of the United States have not involved important challenges to its basic legitimations'. Incidentally, the 1991 Gulf conflict is a classic example of societies clashing not least because, as Weber would have defined it, one legitimated power in rational-legal fashion, the other via charismatic legitimation. How can we see rational-legal legitimation in action?

This book was introduced with a reference to contrasting attitudes between the UK and US in respect of land. This deserves some elaboration in respect of its direct relevance to retailing – and power will serve as a link. The post-war period in Britain has been characterised by rising property values. There are many reasons for this, some of which may be traced back to the Barlow Report of 1939, produced as a reaction to regional disparities and the unchecked sprawl of buildings into open countryside. The mutual national sacrifices of World War Two made interventionist political initiatives somewhat more acceptable than was to prove the case forty years on. There was a feeling that the nation had acted in concert during the war and should, in a rather paternalistic way, be offering benefits and improved living standards to all as reconstruction began. Needless to say, it was not the expectations/aspirations of the ordinary man that were to define standards. The way in which this manifested itself in land-use planning has been outlined by Hall *et al.* (1973). A theme was restraint and urban containment. It was assumed that the masses were consumed by the desire to view unspoilt countryside. A restricted and expensive land market was the result. Despite periodic collapses due to over-accumulation, property development in Britain has almost always been a potential passport to riches (intercepting the surplus of capitalist and worker alike, as Marx would have noted).

An increasing number of retail companies, to the confusion of the corporate balance-sheet, have frequently found it rather more easy to make money from dealing in retail property than from retailing itself – at least until the 1990/91 property crash. The same can be said of office and hotel properties. A key part of the attraction of corporate merger and/or takeover has always been the lucrative potential of surplus head offices for sale. To take a few case studies, aside from growth generated by newly-acquired subsidiaries such as B&Q, the holding company that took over the ailing British Woolworth empire (now Kingfisher) generated substantial early property income via its subsidiary, Chartwell Land, which began trading in surplus Woolworth stores. Literally, Woolworth was worth more dead than alive.

Crucially, the development programmes of retail chains that are aggressively expanding have often been funded by 'sale and leaseback'. The whole concept of sale and leaseback is predicated on the asset value of property, and on the assumption that such value (which must be extracted over a long payback period) should not be jeopardised. That property development produces so many millionaires suggests that the system has succeeded in this aim of retaining/storing value. It also forces us to consider the rôle of the ultimate appeals arbiter – the Department of the Environment.

The splendidly Weberian bureaucracy surrounding the activities of the Department of the Environment (Hallsworth, 1988; Norris, 1989) defies all attempts to find a logical rationale for final decisions – and rightly so. The planning appeals process has become an excellent example of Weber's rational-legal argument-formation leading to judicial/adversarial processes. This leads perfectly on to the type of ad hocery in respect of planning permissions described by Cole (1986). Accordingly, a major part of the construction of scientific models of retail impact, of trade area, or of market share/sales is merely a rôle-play. It is a necessary part of the play-acting of argument-making. Indeed, this type of procedure is explicitly regarded thus by some participants. Officials of the Ontario Municipal Board in Canada, when officiating on a disputed planning application, once stated that the aim of the contesting parties was quite simple. Each had to show that their mathematical model, or planning argument, or whatever, was the only believable model. The rivals' expert testimony had to be ridiculed. The playing-out of this type of game was experienced in Manchester in the 1980s where Roger Tym and partners were commissioned to study the impact of various possible shopping centre schemes. Much of the effort of those experts whose clients' plans were not favoured by this exercise were soon engaged on the full-time business of proving that the Tym work was objectively wrong. Such behaviour is entirely predictable from Weber's work on power-legitimation and the rôle of the state.

This view of the value of legitimate adversarial argument-making may run counter to the views of those who believe that mathematical modelling in the social sciences has some right to be regarded as sacrosanct because it is objective. They might usefully employ some time contemplating Godel's theorem – or the work of Sayer (1978), who offered a realist critique of mathematical models. Sayer stated:

> A definition is invented; it is then set equal to something else and the illusion is produced that we have established how something is determined. This form of definition of variables at one end and the same time, both precise and ambiguous, is a great aid in the construction of elegant, analytical, mathematical models because non-identical phenomena can be defined as identical, and troublesome disequilibrium quantities can be excluded and non-linearities reduced. As a means of understanding real processes, it is a marvellous form of technocratic mystification. (1978, p. 45)

Technocratic mystification is the basis for objectifying in rational-legal fashion what are, at root, political decisions about land and its value (see also Wynne 1982; Smith and Wynne, 1989). Mathematical modelling for purposes of argument-making in public inquiries is, in the UK, a power-process in a quasi-judicial procedure that will confer at least partial monopoly power on the victor. It should be seen as, exclusively, a political participation exercise. Mathematical modelling is valid and powerful in the context of repetitive, systems-like situations. It can be, and has been, successfully used where trading data can be fitted into feedback loops (Penny and Broom, 1988).

All that need really concern us here is that, as a result of planning controls, the UK has about one-third of the per capita retail floorspace of the USA. This leads to a much more protected market. Whereas in Western Canada, for example, superstores gain planning permission in pairs that they can fight out a local market and avoid monopolies, the UK norm is for one major development to have the exclusive right to dominate an area. The over-provision fear (leading to dilution of value) is accorded more weight than the fear of monopoly power. Let us remind ourselves again that the US monopoly-phobia derives from the Constitution. That document was put together as the antithesis of UK socio-political practice.

The UK planning system, then, with its Bumble-like granting of exclusive market areas, assists in conferring power. This is not to say that there are no merits in controlling sprawl or over-provision. We should not, however, lose sight of the fact that the issuance of planning permission confers immediate windfall benefits on landowner or developer or both. The disastrous UK Community Land Act of the 1960s totally failed to come to terms with this phenomenon. We see the consequences of this incrementalist approach being played out daily under the guise of planning 'gain'. Everyone accepts that planning confers commercial gain; it should not, then, surprise us that, in the UK, land property is both a route to, and a symbol of, wealth.

A further and clearly related major thrust of this book is that to Mills' already lengthy list of power elites, the eighties added yet one more: the money men. They will be seen to be far more powerful than the ordinary individual of whom Mills wrote in his classic critique of democratic behaviour.

We should not, however, become bogged down in the macro-levels of state or governmental power. In general, everyday relations, one individual, or firm, stands (or is perceived to stand) in a position of power relative to some weaker individual or firm. The success of enterprises has immutably been linked to the ability to control – through power – those variable factors that influence success or failure in enterprise. Standing at the other extreme from coercive state power is, for example, the power of persuasion – a form of non-coercive power. Both Wrong (1979) and Galbraith (1984) place considerable emphasis on non-coercive power. Galbraith's strictures against advertising are well known in this context. Wrong (1979), by including persuasion as a form of power, noted how significant it was that media power was concentrated in a few powerful hands. Wrong wrote powerfully on power – especially the persuasive power of mass culture. I shall later argue (somewhat in the manner of Hirschman and Stampfl, 1980, and Hirschman, 1981) that retailing itself can be a powerful producer of popular culture. All but a very few individuals regularly interface with the retail industry. There is an in-store learning process about product availability and desirability. Indeed, where choice can be seen to be exercised, so the choice of retail store signifies something about the consumer. The marketing industry spends massively on advertising, yet one of the most common points of contact with the advertised product is beyond their power to control – the retail outlet. Equally, too, retailers cannot always respond to the ever-accelerating power of the media to influence lifestyles. The power of the media is, however, beyond the scope of this book.

When Strange's four roots of power were considered, financial power and technological/knowledge power were seen as pre-eminent. Certainly, much attention will be given to both in later chapters. What we have seen, though, is that just by considering levels at or above that of the state one also brings in wider problems of power and its legitimation.

Power: an example

Lest all this appear a little too abstract, consider a hypothetical example of the manifestation of power through one key facet of retailing – price. The mythical item to be offered for sale will be a health product. Initially, the manufacturer has to persuade the major retail chains to accept the product.

Perhaps this particular item is initially regarded by the grocery retailers as too esoteric. They have the power to refuse to stock the product altogether. It may then be taken to the health-food chains where the manufacturer perhaps holds some power through other products being currently supplied. (This could also be a lever with the grocery chains.) In the health food store the product may have a high 'skim' price because health-food faddists will pay a premium for such a product. There is a 'unique selling proposition' (USP) to be exploited. If the market fails to grow, the product can be kept in that 'niche'. If a more general demand is identified (and the health market is nowadays far more general), then a premium price can soon be charged for the 'market leader' status. Armed with powerful sales information, the manufacturer is now in a much stronger position in respect of the major grocery chains who now positively demand the product.

The product can be treated by the manufacturer as a 'cash cow'. Market demand means that the manufacturer also has the power to insist on keeping prices high. The next crucial point is the uniqueness or, alternatively, copiability of the product. If the product is inimitable – perhaps produced by a unique, patented process – then power should stay with the manufacturer. At least, that is, until the general interest in the product wanes (subject to possible relaunch), at which point there will be an erosion of power. If, however, generic products can be produced by rivals, then manufacturer power will erode, especially if the retailers move to 'own brands'. Defences against copiability include unique packaging or (especially in the child market) a link with a television character or personality. (The links to lifestyle will be elaborated upon later.)

It becomes clear from this highly simplified and idealised example that as the product develops, so the power relationships between the manufacturer and the retailer move back and forth – and these are just in the context of pricing a single product. Most individuals involved in sourcing and in price negotiations are aware that they are in a power struggle. The simplified version given above deliberately underestimates the extent to which negotiation and power-relations are brought into play, in order to emphasise power rather than the mechanisms of power. Any text on buying or pricing will elucidate the myriad facets of special discounts, overriders, credit, promotions, special supply/pricing deals, coupons, equipment and other standard negotiating ploys. The bottom line is that attention must always be paid to how power is won or lost.

To conclude with a generalisation, there is growing evidence that global economic (if not military) power has, in recent decades, increasingly been lost by those economies (led by the US and UK) that have most actively sought free and open markets. Within both economies, likewise, there has been an internal shift of power from manufacturers to retailers. The rise to prominence of the retail and service sectors in advanced economies should not surprise us. The capacity of these economies to meet basic needs of food and shelter has long passed. The USA alone could solve all the global problems of famine and disease, had it but a mind to. We are beyond needs and into wants. Equally, there remains the eternal pressure for growth. As Galbraith has many times stated, the hungry man has no need of advertising to tell him that he needs food. In the West, however, the hungry man has long ago lost any power. The entrepreneur, conversely, does need to know what the affluent want. Better still, wants can be created. New societal mores give rise to new needs and wants and thus give the promise of growth. Ideally, the new product, in its scarcity, becomes the hallmark of status and position.

In a fast-changing society, new rôles and statuses must signify their place. A universal yardstick is required. Goods, houses, possessions, holiday locations all feature in the semiology. Should it really, then, surprise us that retailing is a central element of the circuits of capital? Equally, as their worth and status have grown, so retail firms have themselves become targets of those wishing to ground their accumulated capital in real value.

There are no new ideas here, for Marxist thought has long examined the ability of capitalism to extend growth via new products and new markets. Recall, though, that not all capitalists welcome this constant treadmill of innovation. Some would wish to pause, take breath and capitalise. Further, what is new is often just different. Your job replaces my job, your factory replaces my factory, your shop replaces my shop. That the system cannot permit of a pause is reinforced by the analysts whose job it is to advise the holders of capital as to where it should, albeit temporarily, be parked. At root, economic growth is but a surrogate for dividend growth. Not the least problem for theorists of the new social and economic order in the post-Fordist era is the sheer pace of change. As Don Janelle (1968) noted years ago, there is a time–space convergence. Even as the globalist nations changed priority from production to consumption (Reagan's 'feelgood factor'), so Japan accelerated its move into their place as producer-in-chief to the consumers-in-chief. Clearly, then, we need to look at Japan. The crucial point in respect of Japan is this: Japan is cast as ideal-typical of a mercantilist philosophy. To behave in a mercantilist fashion requires investment at home as a first option in every sphere of life. In a period of technological advancement, this too must attract investment. The question is, then, what evidence is there that Japan has invested at home and has benefited from so doing?

3

Japan: The Rising Power of the Rising Sun

I have already emphasised that the study of Japan, and many other examples/case studies will be taken as what Weber would have seen as ideal-typical representations. That is, they will be presented in an idealised way, and it must be accepted that certain aspects of the concepts will not exactly fit present patterns of retail consumption in OECD countries. This is an important caveat, for there are good reasons why ideas and business practices should not simply be pirated from another country and used out of context.

Indeed, the deification of Japanese business practice by those who wish to decry UK practice is itself ideal-typical. The position to be taken in this book is that practice without context can be meaningless.

Now, bringing in our IPE concepts, we can surmise that there are several ideal-typical ways to market advantage. One is to undercut the opposition with cheap imports: globalism. Another is to seek increased domestic production efficiencies: mercantilism, and a third (in conjunction with both) is to utilise new technologies to increase market information. The successful retailer would probably attempt to use all of these and certainly many others in the pursuit of market power. The point is that these isolated examples are all manifestations of wider trends at work in modern society. It may be possible to clutch at one of the business practices in isolation and apply it randomly, but it is far better to consider the wider processes of which such practices are a part. So, what sort of modern western society?

A tilt at modern western society and post-industrialisation

We might readily imagine that the service sector (of which retail is part) has already been set in societal context. Indeed, some studies have looked at modern western society exclusively as post-industrial. This is not a difficult soubriquet to apply to the UK since many regions have yet to recover from the massive deindustrialisation of the early 1980s. All, however, is not quite as it seems and, when looking at retail change, we should beware of being content with the term post-industrial, as I earlier argued when justifying my choice of the IPE approach. Yes, retailing is a service sector activity, but the service sector is far from uniform. The greatest interest has, rightly, been shown in producer services that are closely allied to the wealth-creating sectors. Furthermore, Japan (the ideal-typical model for many business practices) has been intimately devoted to manufacturing, not services. Lewis (1988) reinforced the theme that will form the first part of this book. He praised an important series of papers on producer services (Marshall, 1988) but added, in a piece entitled 'Employment matters':

> the theoretical context about the development of producer service should not be the 'post-industrial' versus 'deindustrialisation' accounts of structural change . . . far greater insights are to be gained by relating to . . . the debate on 'productive decentralisation' and 'vertical disintegration' . . . This approach accounts for well-known empirical trends such as the declining size of firm, growth of subcontracting and 'flexible specialisation' by particular enterprises. (Lewis, 1988, pp. 270–72)

This warning reinforces the need to set retailing – a service industry – in its proper, wider, context, as I hope to do.

Retailing, as a labour-intensive industry, has learned many lessons both from manufacturing and from producer services in respect of its labour practices. Note, too that in the terminology of 'economic base' studies it also tends to act on internal wealth, rather than create wealth from abroad. Yet if retail is reactive, we surely must see more clearly to what it is reacting: social and economic pressures determined in large part by leading nations – and Japan is in the front rank of those nations. Gow (1988) warned against the quick fix approach that can stem from trying slavishly to follow the lead of Japan and has, instead, called for a more measured appreciation of Japanese innovation in business. Consideration of Japan's industrial development, however, allows us to see why the West is pressured.

Japan and export effort

In emphasising, perhaps context more than culture, Gow showed how Japan, stripped of empire, had to have reconstruction based round export effort. This was an ideal seedbed for neo-mercantilism. The USA, supporting Europe by other means (as we shall see) was happy to assist as a means of staving off Communist influence. The USA 'pressured Japan's former enemies to open their markets' and 'based on a banking system designed specifically to assist rapid, forced development, Japanese corporate planners, operating relatively free from shareholder pressure, have been able to plan longer-term strategies for economic success at home and abroad' (Gow, 1988, p. 18).

This one passage lies at the root of many topics to be raised subsequently.

Gow noted how, because the welfare culture has been internalised as 'company culture', Japan (having fought off external competition in the 1950s and 1960s) has a fiercely competitive internal market. With seven leading car companies alone, merger-mania is clearly not a factor. Perhaps more precisely, horizontal merger is less of a factor than a sort of vertical merger that created the great trading corporations. The ultimate testimony to Japan's mercantilism is that its initial position was so weak, that the early days of the post-war period saw some Japanese pointing out the futility of trying to take on the US car producers (who, they said, had so many natural advantages!). Mercantilism won the day and emerges, too, in Japanese restrictions on low-priced imported goods.

What we discover in Japan is a rather schizophrenic industrial structure and Wolferen (1989) roots this in 'the system'. This, industrially, produces core industries in targeted manufacturing sectors that offer a lifetime employment/company culture plus a vast array of peripheral suppliers often with rather shorter lifespans. These latter are geared to subcontracting, and the whole fits together as the 'flexible firm' (Atkinson, 1984). Implicit in this concept has been a whole series of spatial and operational strategies. In simplified form we see the opposite of lumpen labour. The core is protected by the buffer of the peripheral workers, whose labour is first to go in a downturn. Gow has identified other key strengths of the 'Japanese way' and it is useful to outline these. One is that, within the medium- and small-sized firm sectors, there is a high failure rate. Bankruptcies are tolerated as no bad thing outside the realms of core industries. This fear of failure is sometimes seen simply as a major stimulus to entrepreneurship. However, it may more appropriately be seen as evidence that someone has come up with a new method for producing goods more cheaply. Since Japanese (and German) companies rarely make hostile take-over bids, a new, cheaper production process will force competitors to the wall. Fewer bankruptcies, then, would probably be read as a bad sign — probably of complacency. With specific reference to mergers and acquisitions in Japan, Cooke (1988) stated that for many years they 'were regarded as being immoral' (Cooke, 1988, p. 303). Japan, too, like West Germany, has benefited from pushing its R&D effort into commercial consumer areas rather than into defence. Defence spending has remained at around 1 per cent of GNP, unlike the UK and USA. Like Napoleonic France, or Germany of the Junker period, government has suffused itself in production/engineering industry. A key element of the economic (if not social) success of Japan has been the rôle of the Ministry of International Trade and Industry (MITI) which has often been a catalyst for change. Note the use of the word industry. Japan has also had the advantage of being a follower or late-developer, able to adapt technologies derived elsewhere (notably in the USA).

Roots of the Japanese system

In Japan, family, class, or parental status play less of a part in securing success than does circumstance. We can trivialise this as 'being in the right place at the right time'. Just occasionally, chance meeting by someone of lowly birth and someone of position will be the hook that guarantees success for the former. Few successful societies get far by chance, however. Once one accepts the primacy of the large corporations as the ideal place to be employed, then examination of their employment practices reveals where the right place and time will be found. If seniority, loyalty and succession – rather than birthright – are the prime criteria for ultimate success, then simply getting a foot on the bottom rung of the ladder may be all that it takes. So, if the key posts of the future are with certain key companies and those companies recruit on merit, knowing who they recruit and from where is vital. At root, Tokyo University can be seen as a fount from which most good things of the future flow. Western observers are occasionally surprised by the relative lack of diligence of Japanese university students. This has to be seen in the context of the fact that few students will see the university itself as their lifetime employer. The lifetime employer will recruit them from the university and offer thorough training in 'the company way'. Since companies differ so markedly, there are few generalities (of practice) that can be taught. It is access to the university, rather than academic success once there, that has secured a foothold on the gravy train. The real stress, strain and cramming come from school, as Wolferen confirmed (1989, pp. 82–90). Japan, then, has been forced, through a particular context – reinforced by a lack of energy resources – to be mercantilist in outlook and to seek externally-oriented growth. Japan has been in catch-up mode through a period of technical/technological advancement. Japan's philosophy is that the core of workers can be protected – even in a period of global economic decline – provided Japan gets a growing share of the world market. Japan, however, now has to be a front-runner. Fortuitously, future growth will be in high-cost capital-intensive sectors where, typically, Japan, the USA, West Germany and even France have been prepared to invest, unlike the UK. There may be a technological distance factor that will create an industrial super-elite of nations in the twenty-first century.

Core-workers and 'Just-in-Time'

The distinction between loyal core-workers and the rest is a crucial one. We should never allow ourselves to forget that Japan's envied industrial peace is founded upon some extreme confrontations with organised labour. The idea of idyllic industrial relations is a result of many Japanese finding security only within the confines of a company structure in a manner that would be anathema to most westerners. Japanese success is predicated on the workforce having a very great deal to lose from not being part of a successful industrial elite, for the business corporations have the key power. Indeed, Japanese society as a whole is encouraged to have a rather Hobbesian view of a paternal state apparatus. That said, the system being based on seniority is very transparent. The players, mostly, know the rules of the game. We will later see how the exercise of power *within* western organisations may lead to unproductive dissent.

Rooted in this period of Japanese growth is the symbiotic growth of technology and its uses. Robotics and information technology combined to give Japan a massive cost advantage over conventional mass-production rivals. Porter (1990) studied ten nations in his search for their comparative advantage. He ranged from Singapore, with its 2.6 million people at a density of 10,833 persons per square mile, to the USA with 243.8 million and a respective density of 66. Of interest to us here is his confirmation of Japan's catch-up mode. The first Japanese robots, for example, were imported from the USA in 1967, and production began the next year under licence. The Japanese began to adapt and improve the US designs, especially in respect of reliability. Nissan was installing Kawasaki-made robots by 1970, and robots were seen as the solution to skill shortages and overtime working. In other words, the Japanese were not content to let production levels fit the availability of skilled labour; they extended the powers of skilled labour. Crucially, Porter noted that the German/French/Japanese emphasis on engineering had produced technically-competent managers. They were not threatened by the advance of robotics. By the early 1970s, Japan had installed 60 per cent of all the robots in use globally, increasing to 66 per cent by 1984. Robots in Japan have not displaced Japanese workers; they have displaced workers in countries that cannot compete with Japan.

By instituting 'Just-in-Time' techniques, Japan has saved massively on stockholding costs. Some Japanese entrepreneurs have been heard to utter that stocks are evil, that buffer stocks hide production imperfections. Clearing out stocks forces improvement in production processes and engenders massive savings in stockholding and attendant costs. The 1970s and 1980s have provided the technology to achieve this: cometh the hour, cometh the robot.

Electronic data capture, stock re-ordering and attendant procedures have been suffused into Japanese business practice. Under Just-in-Time, warehouses should be empty. Just-in-Time and robotics together have led to shorter product runs (again cutting stocks), new products arriving on a shorter time-scale, and there is a demand for fewer (i.e. core) but multi-skilled workers. This type of production process brings such inherent cost advantages that others have been forced to follow suit. Estall (1985) gave some idea of the scope of the stockholding problem: in 1982, US manufacturing inventories were worth $512bn.! To reinforce that Japan is merely being used as a model, we can note that as far back as 1979 it was suggested that even by copying German stock control techniques of that time, UK manufacturers could have saved some £20bn. The costly inventory problems in the US were seen, by contrast, as a legacy of Fordist mass-production processes. Again, it is fortunate that we do not need to spend long on Fordism. Contrast, for example, the viewpoints of Sabel (1982) and Piore and Sabel (1984) with those of Murray (1987). If there is disagreement over the basis of industrial organisation in a region of Italy, why should we be surprised at the extent of global disagreement and debate? (Reference may be made to the exchanges between Schoenberger (1989) and Gertler (1989), where many of the relevant issues are again raised.)

In large part this reinforces my decision to cast this book in an IPE mould. As evidence bounces back and forth, so one is left with the basic question of how it is that *some* regions, *some* national economies have managed to thrive (whatever that means). Pascal Petit (1986) drew together many strands of evidence to show that the post-war social and economic experience of nations must vary. It cannot be overstated that nations do not all come equal to the economic fray. At the most basic level this can be influenced simply by the size of the national economic base. This is by no means the same as pitching into comparative advantage. The reality of the late twentieth century is that most of the products (bar natural resources) that make or break the national trade figures could be produced almost anywhere. The IPE approach offers some basic ground rules. Certain ideal-typical attitudes have benefited from the financial and technological revolutions of the last thirty years in a self-reinforcing way. Other formulations seem eternally doomed to fail. The explanations, it seems to me, lie further back — not further forward.

So, in contrasting Japanification and Fordism, the ideal-typical contrast is between Ford Motor Co. under Henry T. and the Kan-ban system developed at Toyota by Taichi Ohno. All other considerations apart, the Fordist system was geared to the financial imperatives in the USA as Ford experienced them, just as the Kan-ban system was geared to Japan's prevailing financial imperatives. Fordism called for long production runs and substantial stockholding. With the USA as a growing financial power, the costs of keeping stocks was not prohibitive for an expanding industry in an apparently endlessly expanding market. Even a poor model (the Edsel apart) would probably, eventually, use up a cost-effective percentage of components.

Post-war Japan was desperately short of cheap money. It would not have been feasible to initiate industrial growth with the same financial profligacy of Japan's rich rival, the USA. It is not too fanciful to state that it was financial pressure that pushed Japan down its now-successful route. Too much emphasis is often given to technological push and late-developer/catch-up factors in Japanese success. That cheap money (lack of it) was really at the root of pushing Japan should come as no surprise to students of IPE.

In the long run, two further factors worked in favour of Kan-ban-type cost-efficiency. Money everywhere became expensive. Second, what had been a necessity (short, demand-driven production runs) became a marketing virtue. Fordism presumed manufacturer power, mass tastes, mass values, mass purchasing power. It presumed a million buyers for a million identical cars at a good price. We should not forget that part of the attraction of Taylorist mass production was that Henry T. Ford could thereby find a way to produce his cars at an affordable price. The Japanese short production runs would have had far less of an inherent advantage if the mass markets had prevailed. Fortuitously, modern tastes changed just as Japan was into its export stride. Everything came together for Japan – and fell apart for more inflexible, less cost-effective modes of operation.

If we seek a final irony it is surely this. Ford, classically seen as just a car manufacturer, also happens to be one of the world's largest consumer credit organisations, with $120bn. of business globally.

For Japan, there was a further logic in investing in robotics and in outsourcing. If the large Japanese firm was going to offer lifetime employment to its core workers, then it wanted this generous offer to apply to as few people as possible, and for those workers to be of the highest possible quality. It would be unrealistic not to note that certain Japanese concerns have only been kept alive by utilising production methods that involve overseas cheap labour operations. Woronoff (1984) is one who illustrates the wider scope of Japanese practice. This should not detract from the fact that such procedures (like 'transplants' to avoid trade restrictions) are generally a last rather than first resort for mercantilist nations.

Japan, its banking system and MITI

Whilst Gow warns against reading too much into Japanese culture, the work of Gibbs (1980) is of interest. He too noted how, in Japan, relatively high proportions of lower income groups obtained places at the prestigious national universities. (Shortly afterwards, Charles Handy bemoaned: 'It is some sort of national disgrace that 44 percent of Britain's young people go into a job today with no qualifications at all compared with 6 percent in West Germany' (Handy, 1984, p. 99). Clearly, the Germans, like the Japanese, saw education as a worthwhile beneficiary of investment at home. Gibbs observed that though there were then 300 private fee-paying universities in Japan to which the rich could send their offspring, these universities had less prestige, higher pupil/teacher ratios and paid lower salaries than the 108 publicly-funded universities. Gibbs reinforced the view that loyalties are vertically oriented within the family and within the firm. This had 'beneficial effects . . . in terms of flexibility, lack of job demarcation, loyalty and enthusiastic support' (Gibbs, 1980, pp. 20–21). Gibbs also noted that, at the time of writing, Japanese firms favoured debt financing over equity: the supporting role of banks was especially noted. Large corporations had a lead bank which was in effect a subordinate creditor. Gibbs noted: 'The difference from the behaviour of UK banks could scarcely be more marked' (Gibbs, 1980, p. 33). So, whilst the British system has forced banks to see industry as a cow to be milked like any other, the Japanese banks believe in keeping the cow fed and watered and letting the milk take care of itself. We will many times return to the problems which emerge when one treats effects as if they were causes.

In Japan, the big players — the winners — are backed to the hilt, long-term: less so the smaller industries. High debt-equity ratios among Japanese firms exposes them to inflationary pressures. This is a likely root of the fabled aversion of Japanese (and German) societies to inflation *per se*. The need to service debt and to offer career growth opportunities pressures the large Japanese firm to seek sufficient growth to meet these liabilities and ambitions. Only big firms can have the flexibility to move people around.

Bluestone and Harrison (1982) related the 1980s mania for small firms to this peripheral group of Japanese-style operations. They noted that, in the US as well as Japan, the birth and death rates for small manufacturing enterprises were high. They looked critically at the link drawn especially by US Republicans that goes: small firms = independent firms = non-union firms = entrepreneurial firms = good firms.

Sadly, many small firms prove to be incapable of providing stable long-term employment and most are under-equipped for innovation in the technological age (Scott, 1982). Small firms do not invest in biotechnology or microchips. What really counts is that major corporations have become smaller, hiving-off subsidiaries in order to create the Japan-style core. The businesses that once were divisions of the parent corporation then become the peripheral supplier. This is a route to Japanification. Like Gow, Harrison and Bluestone noted that the much-vaunted power of MITI really rests in its advisory capacity. Japanese firms co-operate with MITI because MITI is seen as having their long-term interests at heart. Bluestone and Harrison, like Gow, also referred to long-term attitudes in Japan:

> The Japanese can afford to take the long-term view because the private market is not perpetually hovering over each firm and demanding it make a profit and return to a regular dividend. Hitachi, Matsushita, and Toshiba were able to turn themselves into major semiconductor suppliers in this way, while in the United States General Electric, Westinghouse Electric, and RCA grew impatient with the slow payoff on their semiconductor investments, cut back, and never fulfilled their early promise. (Bluestone and Harrison, 1982, p. 216)

They also shared Gow's view of the lifetime employment phenomenon in Japan, seeing this, too, as a key to training, long-termism and loyalty — as well as flexibility and the ability to move around within the firm, if not outside it.

Note, however, that this must also pressure firms to foster growth internationally. If one expects to inherit dead men's shoes, this is easier in a time of expansion than in one of contraction. This may partly explain Wolferen's perception that the Japanese system is running out of control. A point to reinforce again: the lifetime-employment phenomenon is a product of the large, stable firms. It does not apply in the smaller (majority) of firms — nor in society at large. The low level of security benefits acts as an incentive to join the lifetime elite.

The Japanese dimension was succinctly observed by Handy (1984, pp. 90–95). He accepted that some Japanification of business practice was under way, but feared some possible consequences of offloading corporate responsibility on to minor subcontractors. Worries are clearly well founded. Though some store is set by the employment opportunities offered by Japanese transplants to the UK (and USA), it is all too clear that most prefer to subcontract with Japanese enterprises that are themselves transplants. Not for nothing have we stressed the globalist/mercantilist dichotomy. A Japanified UK conglomerate might feel obliged to continue trading with an offshoot that it had shed, but cheap outsourcing and hands-off relationships would probably remain the UK norm.

It is tempting to suggest that Japan approximates a form of meritocracy. That would, one suggests, be going too far. We have already noted some of Wolferen's observations on the complexities of Japanese social structure, and meritocracy is not a term that quite fits. Note, however, that whilst Wolferen does not emphasise mercantilist pressures, he does suggest that the Japanese production machine is unregulated — there appears to be no supreme authority to urge a slowdown. In contrast, the mass of the population appear powerless. It has been suggested that one negative aspect of any true meritocracy would be that, secure in its self-legitimation, it would be difficult to regulate from below. Perhaps Japan shares that feature of a meritocracy — and one which has its production accelerator jammed open.

Terms such as meritocracy are easy for outsiders to use. But a prime concern of this book is to penetrate the taken-for-granted world. So, just exactly how does one describe UK society? Meritocracy certainly would not fit!

Distilling the 'Japan effect'

As a rôle-model, Japan is far from simple to understand. What is essential is to distil out certain key characteristics. These would include a devotion to education and to industry, and an emphasis on promoting and protecting large, important firms in targeted growth sectors. Great value is placed on education over 'background' and on securing employment in and maintaining loyalty to the key core firms. Technology is seen as a key to cutting costs and thus as a key to long-term profitability. This long-termism is perhaps the vital point. From a low point in 1965, average company profits, though dipping in 1974, have shown good growth in the UK. In Japan, profit growth has consistently been substantially less (the USA has steered a middle course). This suggests that the Japanese have been much more tolerant of slower growth and of the re-investment of capital. This inevitably brings us back to the tolerance of Japanese funding agencies which (like their German counterparts) have not forced short-term profit growth. Clearly, the rôle of banks will have to be a central issue in this book.

All the evidence, then, is that the economic future will be dominated by a handful of major players with enormous assets and involvement in new technologies where the costs will act as barriers to entry for all latecomers. There is little evidence that, internationally, the UK will have much of a part to play. All the indications suggest that early involvement in major technologies have been eschewed both by companies and by the government. The USA and Japan continue to dominate with their enormous Research and Development budgets. In 1985, second only to the USA, Japan spent £34bn. on R&D, three-quarters of which was contributed by industry – a ratio well ahead of the USA and Europe. At this point we note again the fact that the ratios are biased by the low level of research for military applications. Kaldor *et al.* (1986) have shown convincingly that there is a strong relationship between military spending and poor economic performance. Were the UK to produce cars of the quality and technical sophistication of its fighter aircraft, one might see a world-beater. Too much should not be made of the sale of the Rover group to British Aerospace. There may be some technology transfer, but post-Gorbachev diversification was a more probable motivation.

This leads us on to another vital point. There is no necessary relationship between pure technical innovation and commercial success. By 1987 it was estimated that there had been nearly thirty-five times more American than Japanese Nobel prize winners in science. Indeed, the UK, with a much smaller population than either, ranked fifteen times more strongly than Japan. There are, of course, distortions in such figures. The USA is a more open society, with a greater likelihood of US winners having immigrated. What really counts is that Japan is able to apply the 'brilliant technology' to market successful products. The current evidence that Japan is filing more new patents does not dent my argument – many patents surround foreign inventions. The UK image of the self-taught innovative genius damages the perceptions of formal education and masks the fact that innovation does not equal sales. The classic UK example is to contrast the relative status of technology-led Sinclair with market-led Amstrad. Both required immensely sophisticated technology, but in the case of Sinclair, this became dominant. Amstrad, on the other hand, followed Henry Ford's concept of producing to a price that would sell. The tragedy is that, for decades, such lessons had been there to be learned. The fact that Amstrad's owner was not the product of a management school, but had in a sense re-invented the wheel, merely reinforced the UK's charismatic view of entrepreneurial success.

Japanese retailing

Whilst the main purpose of this chapter has been to outline how Japan has come to pressure the West economically, it is a little unfair to leave Japan without briefly considering the retail structure. To westerners, however modern and superbly staffed they may find the department stores to be, actual Japanese retail channels appear very confused, even outmoded. Why should this great industrial nation be serviced by a plethora of small shops dealing with proportionally small wholesalers? The small shop has been under pressure in the West for decades. How can it possibly survive in super-efficient Japan?

We need to consider the community as well as commercial viewpoints. Hendry observes: 'persons seeking employment are only regarded as unemployed if they are not able to work even one hour a month, and helping in a family business counts as employment' (Hendry, 1987, p. 142). Given the stigma attached to unemployment, we should not wonder that the family economic base offered by the small shop is valued – nor that the shopkeepers may offer gifts to regular customers at certain times of year. Whereas in times of unemployment UK industry often over-employed, that task (consciously or not) fell when necessary to the small shop retailers in Japan.

Writing in 1979, Beaujeu-Garnier and Delobez also attributed the survival of the small shop system to the endurance and power of the large trading houses or *shoshas*. The complex hierarchies of transactions, which we can readily attribute to convention or custom, make levels of sales at the wholesale level much higher than those at the retail level. Often, products pass through two or three stages, where many western operations would favour direct retail–manufacturer dealings. Bear in mind that, historically, the road infrastructure has been very fragile and the population less mobile than in many parts of the West. There is common sense in having several regionalised break-of-bulk points. Furthermore, the apparent total domination by wholesale channels is confused by the fact that the *shoshas* also deal with manufacturer–export relations. These would not commonly be accounted for as part of the domestic retail/wholesale system in the West. The position is further confused if we note the preponderance of industrial suppliers with their merger-resistant corporate structures. Operating via the *shoshas* can save duplication of manufacturer-based systems. More bluntly, Wolferen stated: 'The distribution system is not complicated. It is rigged' (Wolferen, 1989, p. 393). It is widely suggested that Japan is one society where retailers remain solidly under the thumb of the manufacturers – a source of assured outlets for Japanese manufactured products.

The preponderance of small shops serving localised markets (and offering employment to family members) has, then, a deep social as well as commercial significance. Since such an important social duty is performed, and since retailing is part of the dependent sector of the economy, it can safely be left to work out its own solutions. Recently this has involved a technology-driven small-shop revolution based on the 7–11 chain which has found the protection afforded to small shops to be very useful.

As an aside, we can also find mercantilism, at a firm level, exhibited by West German food retailers. As in the UK, the prices of goods supplied for resale by manufacturers up to the 1960s were in some way or other fixed. The abolition of Resale Price Maintenance in the UK in 1964 symbolised the end of this practice. In West Germany, the Albrecht brothers, trading in the Frankfurt area, began to ignore the prices fixed on to products by the suppliers. That the prices were attached in the first place testifies in part to the latent nature of demand in post-war Germany and also to inflation-aversion. There is little point in printing prices during inflationary periods.

The point is that their deep discounting attracted inflation-averse customers and began a virtuous circle of increased volume efficiencies that was soon copied by rivals. Now, in the German/Japanese tradition of family control, this cost-cutting (in effect a price war) was not diluted in its intensity by the need to keep shareholders happy through dividend payments nor by pressures for contested bids for rivals. Profits in the Albrechts' firm – and in family-run rivals – were ploughed back in a frantic search for market share and cost-leadership. This was the motor behind driving 100,000 outlets out of the market by 1990. The effects on underlying inflation of this vicious price-orientation were electric. Some food products barely rose in price (Deutsche-Mark for Deutsche-Mark) between 1970 and 1990. The effects on the overall German economy should not be underestimated. As in Japan, too, such a self-reinforcing system finds it hard to back-off from aggressive market-seeking.

Avid believers in mercantilism, of course, would suggest that any evidence of *inefficiency* also supports the view that Japan is, indeed, mercantilist. Japan is *so* anxious to produce everything that it tolerates inefficiency at home rather than import from abroad. The classic example of this mercantilism is found in rice production. Rice can be produced more cheaply abroad, but the Japanese insist on growing their own, compromise with the US only being reached in January 1991. We have mentioned that the small shop sector has been abetted by government in its fight for survival. The department stores and other larger retailers have been hedged about with restrictions. The long-established department stores created a major presence before the small-shop-orientated communities realised that they had to react. Mitsukoshi department store opened in 1904 and others followed in the 1930s, whilst the small shopkeepers fought back in 1937. The ensuing legislation to protect the small merchant was scrapped after World War Two, but was replaced in 1956 with more protective legislation on new stores and on opening hours.

Supermarkets generally managed to evade the restrictions placed on department stores and proliferated in the early 1960s and 1970s. In many cases they avoided direct conflict with the traditional small shop by opening in burgeoning suburbs with no previous retail infrastructure. There are good reasons for the growth of Japanese suburbs, for whilst the staggering post-war rates of natural increase were not repeated in the 1960s, they were still running at nearly 7 per cent (in 1968 the rate was 6.8 per cent as compared with the England and Wales rate of 5.1 per cent). Indeed, the respective rates of natural increase had rarely been so close (compare 21.8 per cent with 7.0 per cent in 1948 or 6.1 per cent with 0.2 per cent in 1978). The rapid population expansion that has given Japan such a comparatively low dependent population and has fuelled the workforce also created those new suburbs for the supermarkets to serve. By 1974 the small shops felt it time to curb their activities – the small shop sector was beginning to face losses as in the West – and more legislation was enacted. A main thrust of the legislation was to control the opening hours of department stores and supermarkets in excess of 1,500 sq. m. This legislation was toughened again in 1979 with the ceiling lowered to 500 sq. m. To a large extent this has consolidated the position of existing department stores and supermarkets, but it also happened to be very useful for Japan's 7–11 stores. Note that the modern store sector has been even more assiduous in its use of point-of-sale technology than has the West. In a technology-oriented society, this should be no surprise.

Beaujeu-Garnier and Delobez (1979) identified supermarket group Daiei as market leaders in 1972 with turnover of 744,000 million yen. Terasaka (1985) confirmed Daiei as leaders in 1983, with turnover up to 1,226,624 million yen. Commenting on Daiei's preparedness to sell imported goods, another observer once commented that this was 'close to a mortal sin in a land where generations of businessmen are weaned on the credo that Japan, to survive, must produce and export only'. Quite so.

Summary

This brief consideration of Japan has highlighted how a determinedly mercantilist approach can pay dividends, at least at the level of the balance of trade, but initially at the expense of the domestic consumer who would like to buy cheap imports (though, in the long run, the rising value of the Yen means that import prices fall). Technological influences, our second power-facet, were very much to the fore. Supremely, however the culture or society of Japan was fertile ground for such approaches. As working practices develop, so does financial strength: these in turn alter society. This influences the consumers, their behaviour and spending patterns. If Japan (and Germany) are to be the lead nations of the future, their success will itself affect the prospects – and social outcomes – in other nations. It is easy to overestimate the Japanese influence, concentrating as it does on industrial organisation. Nevertheless, in late 1990 the Massachusetts Institute of Technology (MIT) produced a wide-ranging survey that suggested that, worldwide, no industry would escape the effects of Japanification.

If retail is to remain a secondary-player in the economy, then it is indirectly at the mercy of anything that happens to front rank industries. If Japanification kills UK jobs, then it kills UK spending power and kills UK retailing as surely as if the Japanese had revolutionised retailing practices.

Finally, have we really distilled out what forced the Japanese into their particular flexible work patterns? Probably not, since there is a great temporal as well as spatial complexity in the matter. The Japanese were able to make fast advances because the crucial unions were smashed (Wolferen, 1989), but also because the technology was coming on stream just as they needed it. They were saddled with fewer inefficient relic industrial forms. The inertia that stems from a commitment to other working practices (which we may as well highlight as Fordism) was not there. Japan did not become a major car exporter until long after World War Two, so the structural inefficiencies of Fordism had not been built in. Japanese flexibility, it turned out, had major cost advantages (for those starting up in industrial production – not for those tied-in to earlier production systems). The Japanese could seek cost efficiencies that Fordist economies could not adopt without throwing out Fordism too.

4

Bringing mercantilism to the High Street

We have had little enough difficulty in identifying Japan as a mercantilist nation. The widely-held belief that Japan has made all possible moves to keep its markets closed merely reinforces this. Far from espousing a free-trade/comparative advantage approach, Japan internalised business practice wherever possible. My claim was, however, that mercantilist approaches might be adopted by specific retail firms, and liberal/globalist perspectives by others. Can this claim be substantiated? What happens to firms that adopt such approaches? Can a mercantilist stance thrive in countries like the UK and USA, which are archetypal liberal economies?

A natural mercantilist

A good place to start would be with Marks and Spencer – often characterised as Britain's most successful retailer. K. Tse (1985), in a passage headed 'St Michael patriotic?', outlined Marks and Spencer's renowned policy of buying from British sources. At the time that Tse was writing, this had been Marks and Spencer policy for decades and Tse was forced to remark how surprising this was given the cheapness of comparable goods from Far East sources. Tse edged around the question of whether or not such a policy constituted patriotism. It should not be lost on us that it constitutes mercantilism, especially when Tse highlights the Marks and Spencer relationship with its major supplier, Corah. From the discovery that Corah had an ability to undercut one of Marks and Spencer's other suppliers resulted a debate on how the price differential might be employed. In the event, the capital was reinvested in the production process in order to give an even better product. The better product went on to make better sales. The economies of scale from longer production runs gave further cost-cutting benefits: pure, nationalistic mercantilism. For the record, Michael Marks, founder of M&S was intensely patriotic and was said to feel a moral obligation to provide employment. The fruits of that employment would, in all probability, find their way into expenditure at M&S stores – a mutually beneficial cycle. Tse offered further examples of the recycling of short-term profit into longer-term investment in productive capacity and the beneficial effects on quality and volume of trade that M&S then went on to enjoy.

Such examples as this offer us a real and clear parallel with Japanese practice. Many of the apparent examples of Japanese dumping of products are, in reality, simply the end-product of controlling costs. If costs are controlled by improvements in capital equipment, then two possible strategies open up. The cost efficiencies may be creamed off in extra profits, dividend payments or emoluments to directors. Alternatively, the price of the product may be cut, in order to increase market share. As the examples of Marks and Spencer (and myriad Japanese companies) showed, there is a double benefit in the latter stratagem. The increased volume of trade, assuming, of course, that the market is sufficiently elastic, leads on to further economies of scale. Consider these comments from the founder of YKK zip manufacturers and quoted in Stopford *et al.* (1980):

> Now suppose that we succeed in reducing the cost of a certain product to Y50 while other companies make the same product for Y100. Then, we will pass on two-thirds of the balance of the cost saved to consumers and related industries, and we will retain the remaining one-third ourselves, which we will use as much as possible for future investments. This is my idea of profit. Savings make the difference between human beings and animals. Inventiveness and savings are the two indispensable wheels for human progress.
>
> I would say that those people who make money without working but just by raising prices in a concerted way, as you have seen recently, are committing a sin against society. Some people are said to have earned as much as Y100 million by merely buying and selling stocks of the companies for which they are not working. In my view point, this is one of the shortcomings of capitalism. As I cannot favour speculation to make money from shareholdings in companies which are not your own, YKK does not put its stocks on the market; we are trying to give YKK stocks to YKK employees as much as possible.
>
> We can rely on our own excellent production facilities. Our investments since the 'Nixon shock' alone amount to Y80 billion. But our wages have not been on the high side in the country and some of our people wanted larger price increases and bigger bonuses. I admonished them and reminded them, making money by buying things at low prices and selling them at high prices is not compatible with the YKK's principle because that money is not earned by our own efforts and toils. I told them that now was the time for the YKK group to exert itself to serve society better by keeping prices as low as possible even if we were to use up the last bit of our stockpile. (Stopford *et al.* 1980, pp. 344–5)

An important and enduring difference between mercantilist or liberal ideals is that there is only one question being asked: are you in this market for the long term or the short term? All the evidence is that, nationally, the Japanese and the Germans play long-term (the UK and the

USA look increasingly short-term). In describing their move into the USA in the middle of a pronounced decline in the US retail market, Lord Rayner of Marks and Spencer suggested that a key part of their reasoning was that they were in the market for the long term. This should not surprise us, given the import of Tse's work.

We may now reinforce how important it is to identify, not just a price to which costs can be cut, but also an actual 'price-line'. We saw that this policy largely accounted for much of the early success of Ford – and of Amstrad in the UK. The early Marks and Spencer stores clearly had a policy on price-lines. When Michael Marks first started in business he did so with the Penny Bazaar. Tse identified as of fundamental importance Michael Marks's innovation of the unit pricing at one penny. Possibly just an early example of price-lining, it made a massive difference to his customers. Goronwy Rees emphasised this fact: 'it was striking and simple and easily understood . . . working-class customers, then largely illiterate . . . satisfy their domestic needs at a low price'. As confirmed by Santink (1990), Timothy Eaton founded his Canadian store empire on just this principle: the classic Woolworth 'five and dime' strategy. I would argue that the price was not material. The price-lining could have been twopence or a half-penny, for this was the mass market, not the rarified positional good. What really mattered was that the customer, however gauche, could purchase items comfortably. The store was half-way to being self-service. The customer need not enter into complex arguments with the staff, possibly thereby revealing a lack of social command. Purchasing at a unitary price also meant giving nothing away about one's total income. There was no risk of embarrassment (as in stores where haggling took place) if one realised that the price was unaffordable. The result was comfortable shopping without the risk of feeling inferior or powerless, and it was offered by Marks and Spencers, Eatons and Woolworths. Part of the reason why Harrods is not inundated by the general public, given that its doors are open to all, is not simply that they cannot afford the goods on offer, but more that they would feel socially out of place. The whole edifice is making a statement about the type of people who shop there. We need no expert in semiotics to tell us the attractions of a Macys or a Harrods shopping bag. This merely confirms that we will not at any stage be able to ignore the state of development of society.

New social realities were part of the early success of Next in the UK. Sparse displays and an open layout specifically attracted a confident type of shopper. This experience is best described by reference to the alternative formula. There is no shortage of outlets catering to the mass youth-to-twenties market, and here the ambience is quite different. The outlets are crammed with racks brimming with merchandise. There is a two-fold message. First: shop here and you are almost certain to be able to self-select something from one of our many displays; you can then take this to the check-out and pay. Second: if you are undecided, there is a mass of stock behind which you can, quite literally, hide until you have made your decision or have left the store empty-handed – perhaps after you discover there is nothing that you can afford. The shopping experience is as easy as it was for Michael Marks' first customers. Such was not the way with Next. Entering the store implied a degree of intentionality to purchase, a willingness to discuss purchases with the staff and, if needs be, having the confidence to march out empty-handed. Leaving this type of store empty-handed certainly did not imply a lack of funds. Again, the outlet made a statement about the customer (leading one top director of Next to complain that at one stage the shops were more like art galleries than stores).

This brings us back to the whole question of the mass market. The decline of mass employment in low-pay, low-skill jobs (albeit allied to a rise in unemployment) has eroded both the traditional confines of class and the concept of a mass market in the UK and USA (Steinberg, 1983). Aided and abetted by the ubiquitous TV set, social change has given rise to an expectation of individualism. It is an expectation in that there is no clear evidence that the necessary underpinning of individual decision-making has developed alongside the purchasing power of the employed. The mass market has become a malleable mass of potential individualists seeking outlets that will allow them to safely express a comfortable degree of individuality.

It is for this reason that I have chosen to intersperse throughout this book a consideration of the work of Fred Hirsch. His observations on, primarily, social position have successfully been transposed into consideration of positional goods. This is logical. As traditional rôles break down in a fast-changing society, how does one establish status? An easy route is to acquire the material goods that are trappings of a social position or lifestyle that one seeks to emulate. The visible symbols of success are so much easier to replicate than the more subtle indicators such as language, social contact or style. In such a way, even classless societies can keep the engines of economic growth going full tilt. Yet it is growth that is led by consumption, not production. How people spend, and from which countries they buy, will define the ultimate economic outcomes. The notion of position posits a relationship between individuals and a formalised status that is evident to others. It signifies a particular place in the pecking order, the structure of society. It is, therefore, not difficult to accord it a rôle in the ongoing debate over 'structure and agency'.

Accordingly, we are not simply dealing with consumption as a transaction, but as a key underpinning to society at large. The centrality of matters of position in society is reinforced by a vast collection of phrases. We hear of 'keeping up with the Joneses', whilst goods are produced 'for the man who has everything'. Society may be 'dog eat dog' with 'one-upmanship' and 'blow you, Jack, I'm alright'. One vastly important term in the context of Hirsch's theories is the 'rat race'. The human in the rat race may run ever faster — but still ends up precisely in the same place. The essence is that there is the incentive, the belief, that with just a little more effort, everyone in society can 'make it'. Some, however, believe with Hirsch that if all stand on tiptoe, none sees better, that the donkey never actually catches up with the carrot. It is these issues that are ultimately so central to the future of consumption.

The essence of the best positional goods is that they must be in short supply. Marx was not unaware that scarcity was a boon to the monopoly capitalist, and that shortages could be manipulated. It is, then, essential never to flood the market with a good that has become a positional good.

To return to our present theme, Marks and Spencer seems to have appeared as a very 'Japanese' company. In essence, of course, it was the Japanese who did the copying – as another element of the company philosophy shows, for Marks and Spencer set up its welfare department in 1934, early evidence of commitment to staff. Staff services such as access to doctors and chiropodists, even hairdressers, symbolised the M&S attitude. In the workplace this emerges as loyalty and training. Adapting to extended opening hours and part-time work has still meant that staff retain pro rata entitlements to benefits on pensions, sick pay and discounts. Such policies, initiated in 1975, predated most of the pressures for part-time working.

There is a fundamental problem with this approach. Staff welfare would appear to directly affect profits and this stands in direct contradiction to the once-fashionable stance of monetarism. F.A. Hayek has stated that ideally, one should: 'tie management much more effectively than is now the case to the single task of employing the capital of their stockholders in the most profitable manner and would deprive management of the power of using it in the service of some "public interest"', and has quoted approvingly Milton Friedman's great dictum: 'If anything is certain to destroy our free society, to undermine its very foundations, it would be a wide-spread acceptance by management of social responsibilities in some sense other than to make as much money as possible. This is a fundamentally subversive doctrine.'

Sadly for the Hayek/Friedman axis, Weitzel *et al.* (1989) showed that, after store size, the key determinant of sales levels in retail stores was quality of service offered to the customer. And what was the key determinant of good service? . . . the way that the company itself treated its staff! Petit (1986) drew on Durkheim to refute the reductionist view, beloved of the New Right, that there are no wider social and economic relations to employment. Whilst Adam Smith and Herbert Spencer may have taken a more fundamental Social Darwinist position of workplace relations, the balance of evidence is that social interrelationships at work and elsewhere are fundamental to the human condition.

Globalist aspects of UK retailing

The close symbiotic relationship between Marks and Spencers and its suppliers clearly mirrors the close manufacturer–supplier relationship of Japanese mercantilist flexible production. Yet we have noted that the UK is one of the archetypal, liberal globalist economies. Sure enough, we find that Marks and Spencer is the exception rather than the rule among UK retailers. The UK has been identified as a once-great trading nation (with a once-great merchant navy of which Adam Smith would have approved) and a long-term import fetish. At one time, fashion, style and position could best be demonstrated by the ownership of something foreign and preferably exotic — ostrich feathers, perhaps. More crucially, in times of rising inflation, a keen price can lead to increased sales. One quick-fix solution is to resort to imports — of cheap rather than of exotic goods.

It has been suggested that the UK menswear group Fosters adopted this classic stratagem when market pressures grew. They were quickly able to exploit their purchasing power to acquire low-cost products from the Far East in a manner that smaller rivals would find hard to replicate. This is, in effect, an example of retail participating in the New International Division of Labour (NIDL). (For a wider analysis of NIDL, see Henderson, 1989.)

The Fosters example gives us two key points with which to work. The first is that there was an instant quick fix in terms of reduced costs. The lower labour costs in the Far East — at least for routine work in the clothing industry — gave an overall cost advantage in a shrinking world where transport costs are not the factor that they were in Adam Smith's day.

The second point is confirmation that this policy can be seen as one that confers market power. There is a clear strategic implication to this sourcing policy. It immediately undercuts on cost the rival who is still sourcing from the UK. To generate comparable savings, there would have to be substantial long-term capital investment on the model of Marks and Spencer. Note that Porter suggested both strategies (1990, p. 609): 'A firm must be willing to source products or equipment from foreign firms if they are superior at the same time as it works to upgrade local suppliers.' How many UK or US firms worked on the upgrading, and how many just took the superior (i.e. cheaper and more profitable) goods from abroad? When they saw the low price, how many of the consumers in the 'throwaway society' cared over-much about the lower quality? There need be no real surprise that companies with quite different trading philosophies can co-exist in a country pursuing policies that may favour one above others. So much of business practice is part of the taken-for-granted world that company culture is often only identifiable to outsiders. Company culture, like managerial style, is often invisible to those concerned. How many managers will have analysed their own style (in the manner of Makin *et al.*, 1989)? If we then insert the style of the manager into the style of the company and on into the national economic and social climate, we can reasonably expect a proliferation of outcomes. Some will be substantially more pleasant for the workforce than will others. Such complexities are at least as fraught as those concerned with predicting if parts of the economic base of a nation are, were, or could be Fordist.

Consideration of Strange's other route to power — technology — is also fruitful in the context of retailing. Many instances can be found of

UK retailers using the best available technology in order to seek trading advantage. A name to note here is Shoppers' Paradise. Shoppers' Paradise makes an excellent case study in retail change. For much of the earlier part of the 1980s this chain was seen as a pioneer of EPOS systems and was well positioned to exploit the lower end of the UK grocery market. Store layouts were basic and on cheaper secondary high street sites. Shoppers' Paradise was described by Soloway as:

> the largest and leading users of scanning equipment in the UK food retailing industry. The attractions of scanning were seen as checkout speed and the chance to increase range. Shoppers' Paradise had placed scanning in 150 stores in just 15 months and range had been increased by 650 to a maximum of 1500 lines. The datachecker system operating through 500 scanning lanes was not envisaged for stock control. (Soloway, 1985)

This certainly appeared to be a strong platform for growth, led by IT. Note that Kwik-Save were perhaps even more indebted to IT. For some time they had been relying on the ability of their checkout operators to remember every price in the store – with dire consequences for those with poor memories! Once laser scanning became feasible, the pressure was off the assistants and the range could be increased. Why, then, when IT was such a boon to progressive retailers, has Shoppers' Paradise not thrived? The answer lies, as we will see later in more detail, in the fact that Shoppers' Paradise *per se* simply no longer exists. This is the strongest possible warning that the retailer may be making all the right trading moves, and yet still become extinct.

Summary

With the foregoing examples we can identify most of the important trends that this book will follow. There is the contrast between mercantilism and globalism. There is the use of technology and also recognition of pressure from Japan. If UK firms are to be pressured into Japanese-style working, what does this do to UK society? More to the point, how real is the notion of post-industrialism raised earlier?

5

THE POST-INDUSTRIAL 'PROBLEM'

In 1977 Gershuny fired a warning shot across the bows of Daniel Bell and certain other advocates of the concept of a post-industrial society. What Gershuny had noted was that much of the evidence put forward in support of the post-industrial notion (Bell, 1974) was based on the inter-sectoral shift of employment from agriculture, through manufacturing *per se* to service-type occupations. What Gershuny argued was that this merely meant that fewer people were needed to produce the goods and more could be liberated to service the related transactions. What remained was the primacy of the manufactured product – a point forcefully emphasised by Cohen and Zysman (1987). My point is, that what is vital is how the product is consumed.

Retailers should never underestimate the wider symbolic nature of the products they supply. Veblen (1899) was an early observer of patterns of consumption – much of it conspicuous consumption of highly visible products (services seem to be a far less visible token of status). We can argue that Veblen lives on in the recently-observed phenomenon of status (of a sort) being acquired through the wearing of particular types of outrageously expensive sports shoes (murder/mugging for such shoes is now apparently not uncommon in the USA) whilst it has been suggested that in Lambeth, London, the *main* reason for muggings is to steal designer sportswear. What the sports shoes clearly represent is a Hirsch-type positional good. Retailers have to react to the social/cultural environment that they face.

The primacy of the product

We dare not underestimate the significance of the manufactured product. Taking a tight definition of service occupations, Gershuny (see also Gershuny and Miles, 1983) was able to confirm that the primacy of the manufactured product was as strong as ever: indeed, growing. Were not laundries being superseded by the home-based washing machine? Had not people deserted the cinema for the more durable pleasures of TV? The old-style notion of service (related to servitude) was declining at the expense of the manufactured product. The consumption process was becoming home-based, internalised. Gershuny went on to note the rise of a self-service, do-it-yourself type of society (see also Hallsworth, 1987b) that has been propounded, too, by Pahl (1984).

One can easily find more evidence to back up Gershuny. Expenditure on durable goods may tend to show a fall-off through time, but that would certainly not have been the case if the average TV set of today retailed at the same relative price as when they first appeared. The famous East German Trabant is a good example of what simple consumer goods might cost if manufacturing efficiency and the mass market had not slashed the real prices paid by western consumers. If we flip over to actual ownership levels, we see consumer goods that once were luxuries now being regarded as the necessity that everyone must have — and most do.

A reaction to these types of observations was to redesignate many production-related service occupations as 'producer services' (Daniels 1985): a much more realistic description. We should note that Gershuny was really making two telling points. The first is the continuing primacy of manufacturing and manufactured goods in our daily lives. The second is that, as individuals, we are home-centring as much as we can. Why subsidise the cinema or the laundry for no net long-term benefit when you can acquire a long-term, home-based asset? Why employ the expensive labour of a painter or decorator when you can, with the advent of advanced, easy-to-use manufactured goods 'do it yourself?' The contrast between this and the other-centredness of services such as dining out and holiday travel is one we should not neglect. Foreign travel is an early casualty of any spending downturn. Families in financial difficulties will, on the other hand, often seek solace in the purchase of new items for the home or person.

In the UK, increasing home-centredness ran counter to the post-war trend of supplying low-cost (and often low-quality) rental housing through the local authority. Whilst Castells could see the hand of the economic elite in the provision of low-cost housing, there were positional problems for the residents also. In many advanced countries in the post-war period, depersonalised, uniform, system-built high-rise housing replaced drab, unsanitary but often individual and humanised well-established private sector rental properties. The older housing had often had distinct sub-markets, social interlinkages and pecking-orders. At a stroke, such relativities were replaced by assigned housing, with government officials acting as gatekeepers. The old orders were disrupted. Families with spatially-linked kinship networks were pitched into housing alongside complete strangers. The ability to express position through housing was suppressed. Uniform and uniformly drab mass repainting in standard colours reinforced the point that the inhabitants were 'all the same'. The powerlessness of the workplace was cemented by powerlessness even to control the colour of one's own front door. The incoming Thatcher government of 1979 tapped into a deep well of resentment against depersonalised housing.

It may well be that the 1979 UK general election was won on the desire to increase home-centredness. The sales of carriage-lamps, ornamental shutters, new front doors and other positional indicators bears eloquent testimony to this possibility: between 1980 and 1988, 1.4 million UK council houses were sold off. Seeking a more general context for home-centredness, we can probably regard the home increasingly as a refuge from the *anomie* of wider social life. The problem, for society, lies in the circularity that this implies. Withdrawal from society implies a reduction in general standards of civic life, thereby reinforcing increasingly the desire to withdraw. For the more wealthy and mobile, increased spatial segregation becomes possible with, especially, a retreat from inner urban areas. Increasing egocentricity also makes it politically acceptable to cut areas adrift: the suburbs refuse to fund the city. We seem entirely likely, except when inner-area riots intrude, to be reworking the old class arguments. Does spatial segregation lead to ignorance of, and thus neglect of, the problems faced by the bottom strata of society? But let us not go too far down the road of interfacing product and consumer, without first considering the effects that spin off when mercantilist countries such as Japan expand their markets. What happens to marginally less efficient producers such as some found in the UK? In what different ways, impacting upon society, do the threatened producers react? Perhaps more crucially, in what ways are economies devoted to the globalist/comparative advantage approach, *constrained* to react when faced with powerful competition from mercantilist producers?

The post-Fordist dilemma of how to create more demand when mass employment is in decline is exaggerated not only by resource-depletion. The inter-sectoral shift of employment from primary, through secondary and tertiary and on to quaternary modes is beginning to creak. Classically (and related to technological shifts), a new wave of employment comes along whenever advanced societies face employment difficulties. The problem is that declining levels of employment in lower-order sectors has been related to the efficiency of available technology and to labour-cost factors. Indeed, wherever profits have been squeezed by labour costs, so labour-shedding has taken place. Fortunately, something has always turned up to save the day.

Now, more than ever before (despite the strong claim of the original Luddites), there seems to be less and less hope for those who can but offer physical strength in the job market. The reason for this is not just related to the increasingly technological nature of employment. That costs in aggregate/societal terms in advanced societies are often weighted by the size of the public sector means that this is a sector under threat at present. The public sector, despite claims to the contrary, soaks up many menial jobs. But being low-cost and menial offers no defence against the cost-cutters. More and more employers found cost-pressures a useful excuse for shedding employees in many tertiary and quaternary occupations. We might note that the UK has a particular problem in how to soak up the residue of surplus labour. When we studied Japan, mention was made of the resistance to rice-importing. Japan still tolerates many low-paid individuals in traditional agrarian roles. Nor should we forget that the agricultural policy of the EC has been influenced heavily by the subsistence/peasant bloc in many EC countries. Yet Britain cleared its peasants from the land centuries ago. A return to the land is one last resort that is denied to the one country that puts such a premium on land.

Restructuring

As pressure increased from Japan and other cost-efficient producers, so less efficient societies retrenched and two stratagems offered themselves. One was collective belt-tightening, heavy investment and greater efficiency; the other was to maintain profits by cheap imports and by cutting costs whenever and wherever possible. The latter approach was soon evident in the UK.

Some evidence of cost-cutting practices in the UK manufacturing sector was advanced by Massey and Meegan (1982). They specifically related changed production practices in a sample of industries to both job loss and deindustrialisation. They studied what they termed 'technical change', 'intensification' and 'rationalisation' as elements in the equation. Technical change was seen in the context of (often substantial) capital investment. In some instances robots replaced jobs. In the example of the synthetic resins industry (Massey and Meegan, 1982, p. 65) output rose by 43 per cent and productivity by 79 per cent, but employment fell by 20 per cent between 1968 and 1973. Intensification generally involved no major investments, nor change in capacity. It was reorganisation of work practices that made the difference. They noted: 'These methods go by such titles as "increased flexibility", "changes in work practices", introduction of labour-saving devices and "reductions in over-manning".'

We are basically looking at productivity gains through greater worker effort – letting labour take the strain. The context was quite different from that of Japan's mercantilist and export-driven efforts of earlier years. There were hints of multi-skilling and longer working hours – the 'Japanese' phenomena. All too often, the process was one of de-skilling and longer working hours. Of necessity, rationalisation, the third trend detected, does relate directly to disinvestment by plant closure. In many circumstances, also supported by evidence from Bluestone and Harrison (1982), plants that were closed were not easy to divorce from the existence of mergers/conglomerates. The single-plant firm is either profitable or it is not. In the multi-plant firm there is always going to be one plant that is the worst performer. That plant is vulnerable, even though it may be far more profitable than other plants in its local economy.

Precisely this situation arose in 1990 when a multinational food producer announced that it was to close one of its Yorkshire factories. The factory was not only profitable, but one of the best and most profitable factories in Yorkshire. This is the flipside of the international division of labour. Wherever labour costs are a key factor, there will always be some newly-developing country that can find labour more cheaply than it can be found in the West. This phenomenon was sadly unknown to Hume when he wrote:

> Suppose four-fifths of all money in Great Britain to be annihilated in one night – what would be the consequence? Must not the price of all labour and commodities sink in proportion and everything be sold as cheap as they were in former days? What nation could then dispute with us in any foreign market or pretend to navigate or to sell manufacturers at the same price which to us would afford sufficient profit? In how little time therefore must this bring back the money which we had lost and raise us to the level of all the neighbouring nations? Where, after we have arrived, we immediately lose the advantage of the cheapness of labour and commodities and the further flowing in of money is stopped by our fullness and repletion. (Hume, 1752)

By 'we', Hume did not mean the labouring classes who would bear the true burden of wealth loss. Yet the Japanese and South Korean workers have joined the US and UK workers in refusing to work for the price of a bowl of rice. It is noticeable how one keeps returning to the nature of the structure of industrial organisation when seeking to explain the fate of particular plants. The significance of rationalisation lies also with the whole concept of disinvestment in which, in Japan, MITI has also been heavily involved, so that decline as well as growth is managed.

Company culture

If other societies are to travel yet further down the Japanese road, then an increasing amount of attention will need to be paid to company culture in the key core enterprises, and this will not be easy. The Japanese companies achieve their edge by having quite different cultures: this is a factor, too, mitigating against mergers and takeovers. Quite simply, cultures do not mix – and cultures are important. Growth is achieved at the expense of other, less cost-efficient companies. The rivals are not taken over and absorbed: they are ruthlessly driven from the market. A fierce price war is often necessary, as in low-cost German food retailing. The whole system creates business failures where companies do not fall – they are pushed. The cost-effective victors will, inevitably, also be very cost-effective globally. At the same time, the Japanese employment system operates in a clear way. There is an emphasis on career prospects through merit and education (especially university education). Once established in a key and hopefully invulnerable company, the graduate will move around horizontally, absorbing the culture. US and UK retailing may find this hard to copy – and not all of it will be the fault of the retailers. UK graduates rarely analyse the corporate ethos before joining a company. They tend to be theory-orientated and to assume that they will know better than a superior who does not hold a degree. In turn, the barrow-boy-turned-manager can feel threatened by this, so one resort is recruitment before university. This Jesuitic approach allows the company to acclimatise the young individual. It also partly explains the lack of graduates in UK enterprises. Only when retail (and other business) entrepreneurs feel happy with graduates as subordinates (and the graduates feel happy as subordinates) will the position greatly change. Ironically, the stronger the company culture, the more likely is the Jesuitic approach.

This all offers a rather depressing outlook for countries like the UK in particular, and we have to ask ourselves how this has come about. One powerful explanatory factor is the nature of the control of financial matters in the UK. It is at this point that we truly start to examine the roots of merger-mania and short-termism. Much of what follows is based upon the work of Ingham (1984) and Greider (1987), and aims to expand the debate outlined by Rybczynski (1988).

The City and industry

Porter (1990) has a chapter entitled 'The slide of Britain' that begins:

> Britain has been losing competitive advantage in industry since well before the second world war. From a position in industrial dominance in the nineteenth century, Britain began a long slide that only recently shows signs of being arrested. Britain has been plagued in the postwar period with a high unemployment and pressure on living standards . . . the growth in productivity and per capita income in Britain have, along with that of the United States, been at the bottom of the nations we studied. Unlike the United States, however, Britain was not far ahead of the other nations to start with. One by one, most advanced nations have overtaken or passed her . . . Yet Britain possesses national competitive advantage in a range of industries and enjoys a vast pool of accumulated wealth. (Porter, 1990, p. 482)

This carries the implication, in Porter's industry-orientated world, that a 'vast pool of wealth' should be an advantage for industry. I seek to argue that it could as easily represent the ability to consume what others have produced. Indeed, most analysts of national and global economic change are familiar with wave cycles. Economists have made a healthy living down the years from the theories of Kontratieff and other wave-cycle analysts.

Librarians are familiar with another wave-phenomenon. This is the ebb and flow of books dealing with the issue of why UK industry is not adequately supported by the City – the repository of that vast pool of wealth. Wave peaks followed the Wilson report (of 1980) and another can be expected imminently as the topic resurfaced again in mid-1990. What is the more remarkable is that for all the column-inches devoted to the topic, nothing has actually changed, for it is part of the taken-for-granted world. The futility of railing against the inevitable was long ago demonstrated by King Canute. Ingham (1984) offered a well-known critique of the relationship between industry and the City. He drew on diverse sources to emphasise the split between capital and industry in the UK. He emphasised that, despite the status conferred on Britain as the first industrial nation, it retained a weak industrial bourgeoisie when compared with the power of the elite or ruling class.

A nation of shopkeepers

I argue that, in essence, the industrial revolution in the UK was a mistake. In reality, the UK is a nation of shopkeepers. The industrial revolution represented an aberration, a temporary distortion of class values that turned the agricultural peasants into a lumpen industrial workforce but little affected the 'mighty oaks' of society. The true industrial revolution came in those societies better equipped to exploit it . . . by virtue of a more internalised and often dictatorial culture. The process of industrial production in the UK is as unlike that of Japan as are a carthorse and a racehorse.

Ingham quoted Sir Keith Joseph as having commented on Britain's lack of a capitalist ruling class and went on to outline the views of Anderson and Nairn as critics of industrial decline. Ingham's viewpoint was that the industrial revolution came too soon in Britain and was always second-best to Empire and the power of the City as a financial power-base.

This idea was confirmed by Short (1984), who suggested that Britain became the first industrial economy but never became an industrial society. In essence, then, the City pre-dated industrialisation in Britain and subsequently either ignored it or treated it as any other investment vehicle whilst pursuing its financial goals. Far from the Japanese model of banking as an underpinning to a central industrial core, the City has never seen itself as subordinate to any other sector. Ingham reaffirmed Nairn's work on the close links between the City, the Treasury and the Bank of England. He saw links with the aristocracy in what he saw as 'archaic policy'.

It is not difficult to find other evidence to support the view that there is a kind of City—Treasury—Bank of England triumvirate. In 1964, Sam Brittan confirmed the familiar role of the Treasury in the period 1951–64. The Treasury, 85 per cent of them Oxbridge graduates, was the elite of Whitehall. Its finance group, stated Brittan, has as its most important responsibility the defence of £ sterling. To shore up the reserves, suggested Brittan, one suppressed home demand in order to cut imports. It is not difficult to see how one can increase imports! Brittan conceded that the Treasury debates were complex, adding: '(The homely analogies sometimes used by Chancellors in their television chats — "the nation is like a family and can't spend more than it earns" — simply confuse the issue and are invented after the real decisions have been taken)' (Brittan, 1964, p. 39). In other words, little has changed since Hume's day. When government speaks of our 'having to take painful economic medicine', one can usually read 'you' for 'our'.

Of the triumvirate of the establishment – the Treasury, the Bank of England and the City, Brittan wrote that the Treasury had to work through the Bank to influence the financial markets. This led to a situation where bank rates were within the gift of the Chancellor. The Bank of England was seen as sitting between the City and the Treasury. In respect of the Bank of England Brittan felt that it perhaps too closely upheld City values – perhaps because in 1964 it was still practically recruiting direct from the public schools. Brittan described the central banker role of the Bank: 'talking round a hardened Swiss or German Central Banker . . . convinced in his innermost being that Britain is engaged on a rake's progress at someone else's expense' (Brittan, 1964, p. 63).

For present purposes, the most crucial observations are probably these:

> The Bank of England has two main jobs that are important for policy-making. It is responsible for managing the foreign exchange market and for running the market in government securities. Just as its responsibility for restraining government spending is a better clue to how the Treasury will behave ninety per cent of the time than any more highfaluting theory, so these two functions of the Bank enable an outsider to predict many of its attitudes.
>
> The Bank is more interested in whether foreigners are buying or selling pounds, and less in theoretical calculations about the balance of payments than the Treasury. (Brittan, 1964, pp. 63–4)

To return to the work of Ingham, it has to be said that much of his subsequent work is set in the context of explaining the exceptionalism of UK industrial development in the context of Marxist expectations. He did, nevertheless, offer a solid analysis of the City and its institutions, noting 250 years of supremacy, and added that the City regarded its best defence as being its contribution to the invisible balance of trade. In essence, of course, detractors quickly argue that the very level of invisible earnings is a measure of the true extent to which investment in Britain has been neglected in favour of investment abroad.

Nothing seems to have changed

Lest it be felt the neglect of UK industry by the City is a recent phenomenon, Ingham in one of his more well-known passages averred that even when Britain was 'the workshop of the world', our balance of trade was in deficit, showing a steadily worsening picture between 1865 and 1913 (Ingham, 1984, pp. 40–41). The activities of the City alone were what made the shortfall into a surplus. Those activities included marine insurance, banking, finance and dividend repayment. We will later see that there is more to all this than immediately meets the eye. The rôle that the £ sterling played in world markets carried with it some deficit implications. Nevertheless, the concept that the City was somehow moving in an opposite direction from that of industry is hard to dispel. If all British industry had the very best of machinery – and a strong machine-tools sector to stay at the technological edge – then it would be churlish to also criticise the City for reinvesting surplus capital in lucratively oiling the wheels of international trade. All the evidence is that such has not been the case. Even if defenders of the City would claim that industrialists never came forward to request the necessary capital, that would only be part of the story. The ethos of the City, we shall see, is of trading in assets. Industry was quite naturally regarded as a tradeable asset like any other. When excess global capital flowed round the world in the 1980s looking for assets to acquire, then other countries, and other sectors besides industry, were to discover the folly of thinking long-term in a market that was acting short-term.

In the final quarter of 1989, the UK invisibles were in deficit for the first time since the Napoleonic wars. Borrowing sterling at 15 per cent to finance a trade gap in manufactured goods was a large part of the reason. Remember, again, that manufacturing has traditionally offered the strongest prospect for mass employment and hence mass expenditure in the UK. The country is still living with the effects of the manufacturing 'shake-out' of the early Thatcher years.

For the moment, however, we should leave this analysis of short-termism and look to the wider financial trends to which the City sees itself bound to respond.

6

THE FINANCIAL MARKETS

In this chapter we attempt to assess financial power by examining the rôle that financial markets see for themselves (especially those of the UK and the USA). A look is then taken at how financial matters have resolved themselves, and emphasis is placed on the interlocking relationships between the great global manufacturing nations. It fills out some of the work on the City introduced by Ingham. Consider now this quote: 'Brokers' and jobbers' . . . fundamental crime lay, according to their critics, in their habit of buying, fictitiously and purely for the sake of speculative gain, stock for which they had no capital to pay' (Wilson, 1965, p. 326). But for the date of the reference, we might imagine this to be a critique of contemporary affairs, but it is, in fact, a record of the early days of the UK stock exchange at the turn of the eighteenth century. In reference to Weber's characterisation of rational-legal bureaucratic processes, Ingham (1984, p. 129) observed: 'The eighteenth century treasury was the antithesis of the rational-legal form of bureaucracy. The officials were recruited through patronage, worked minimal hours and were frequently corrupt . . . the wayward younger sons of the leisured classes.' Ingham went on to suggest that the dominance of City interests had been inherently tied up with the consolidation of the British aristocracy. This seems plausible. The City will not generate enough income to keep the whole country afloat, but it should always continue to do very nicely for the already wealthy: not least because all its instincts are to conserve wealth already created rather than to institute any new wealth. The eighteenth century also consolidated the Bank of England. With a renewed charter from 1708 and housed in Threadneedle Street from 1734, its power and profits were based on its intimate connection with the government. This connection was cemented by war: Britain's imperial glories cost money, and the government had to raise debt. By 1763 the National Debt stood at £132.1 million – mostly as a result of the Seven Years' War. A crucial preoccupation became the raising of debt and the associated contrivances to make that debt as secure as possible. Wars fuelled speculative booms and later led to rising prices – now graced as 'inflation'. Loans to government came largely from the East India, Royal African or Hudsons

Bay companies, which were great beneficiaries of the naval/imperial power that their loans bought. Throughout the eighteenth century then, though dented by the infamous South Sea Bubble, the City saw itself as immersed in affairs of state and in foreign relations – but above all in the need to raise financial resources to service debt. Anything, however absurd, would suffice as a vehicle for investment, for the only really important question was this: could the government actually pay? (This was a question raised again in the 1980s as the US government ran up almost unimaginable debts.)

Early mercantilism

One focus of financial matters was mercantilist thought associated with the work of Mun. Mun's work, much of it hard to comprehend, was based on his experiences with the East India Company. Essentially, the mercantilists wanted what they defined as beneficial trade. Without spelling such matters out, Mun thought that East India trade was acceptable because it was essentially exploitive and one-way. The prevailing perception that mercantilists were preoccupied with bullion flows rather puts the cart before the horse. Mercantilists wanted beneficial trade and that was defined as profitable trade and thus found its bottom line in bullion flows. In some ways one is reminded of Friedman's famous strictures on how to control growth in the car industry. Too much mercantilist thought ended up being about controlling effects rather than controlling causes. Gradually, and this emerges (albeit slowly) from developments of Mun's convoluted earlier work, there was a reappraisal of what the desired ends might be in the context of national interest. Slowly, the feeling grew that the development of manufacturing industry might be important. For that reason, attention turned anew to the balance of trade. Issues of national security and power began to take a less significant role in thoughts about trade. It is possible, however, that those whose opinions really mattered never came to terms with the need for industrial employment. If not the bullion-fixation, then the capital-fixation never really ever went away, however much the Bank was immersed in trade, imperial power and government debt. If anything, the nineteenth century served even more to consolidate the position of the City at the expense of industry.

The Pax Britannica

This was the period of the Pax Britannica. The growth of international trade, either through, or facilitated by, the City of London, was always significant relative to the total share of the economy generated by manufacturers. London had an unassailable global position and a global perspective: manufacturing did not. Rivals such as France and Germany could copy manufacturing, but they could hardly copy the City. Whilst, in Britain, systematic effort was put into analysing and perfecting financial mechanisms, the foreign opposition concentrated on treating manufacturing professionally. Whereas the City was all sophistication and mystique, manufacturing industry was for gifted idiots from the lower classes. No sooner did industrial prowess bring wealth than the entrepreneurs sought the company, the habits and the lifestyle of the City men. They aspired to become 'landed gentry'. If the City helped industry, it did so by securing foreign markets — a rôle model we shall see again later. It was vital to such interests that the pound sterling be regarded internationally as the currency for payment, and gold convertibility assured this. This is the financial trading structure with which the UK still has to live, even though the interests that were meant to benefit from Pax Britannica have long been in decline.

One of the predictably enduring problems for Britain is that, having created wealth through Empire, it has singularly failed to cope with the contradictions of loss of Empire. The home demand that was fed by the imports from Empire, and which included — lest we forget — the cycle of the slave trade, created early consumerism. Other nations share the problem of high-living that has come before its time. Canada created a wealthy nation fit to consume with the best of the industrialised nations, except, of course, that any industrialisation that took place came after wealth had been created by the more primitive mechanism of resource exploitation and trading.

We should not lose sight of the fact that the Pax Britannica bulldozed a level playing field that was inherently suitable to the interests of the City. It may very well be that the current obsession with 'level playing fields' is some kind of throwback to this golden age. Germany and especially Japan have found that level playing fields are anything but necessary for industrial success. As Britain was reinforced as a supreme imperial power, so foreign trade was reinforced as was the power of the City. Adam Smith's free trade heresy was more at home with trade than with production, and inevitably the pound sterling became the world's reserve currency. The legacy that this exalted status for sterling has conferred on the UK economy should not be underestimated. London remains part of the great international financial triumvirate, with New York and now Tokyo.

Old skills have not been forgotten. The currency arbitragers, in the halcyon days of the gold standard, would ship gold from London to New York in order to balance out the currency fluctuations. They learned early how to sell one currency and buy another in order to show profit. Soon, it was argued, the 'natural' price for a currency would fall into line with economic performance. We should not forget that only sterling and the US dollar have held reserve currency status. This suggests that we will need to pay close attention to the Federal Reserve Board, 'The Fed', which was created in 1913 as a lender of last resort to the US banking system. Space does not permit a full exposition of the fate of sterling over nearly three centuries, but suffice it to say that the aftermath of World War Two left most European states weakened, and the stage set for a new era of financial power. It is also an appropriate starting point, not least because the absolute volumes of finance capital that could truly be described as international or 'footloose' are largely a product of the post-war period.

A new world order

As the end of World War Two approached, the supremely powerful USA was ideally poised to enact its vision of a new economic order. Indeed, perhaps here we find the crux of the problem for the UK and the USA. Their central banking systems have always had a global, hegemonic perspective — for structural reasons, the UK more so than the USA. Britain's days of Empire carried an outward-looking legacy at the expense of affairs at home. The US post-war view was determinedly expansionist. As a buffer against Communism the USA perceived a global duty in its 'new order'. US industry had good reasons not to be reluctant to join in this rush abroad.

Strange (1988) was one who noted that there were push factors behind US industrial expansion abroad. She drew on the observations of Ralph Nader, who showed that the inherently open US society required strict observance on the reporting of company accounts and other affairs relating to stockholder's rights. This did not appeal to the robber barons, nor to many other sectors of growing US corporate power. By the 1890s, smaller states of the Union moved into 'chartering', and offered companies more secrecy and managerial control. As the great steel and oil conglomerates grew in power, and that power was increasingly held by key individuals, so Congress acted. The Sherman anti-trust act was passed in 1890, to be followed by other legislation against the corporate giants. This insistence on competition effectively prevented monopoly power (if not oligopoly) within the USA. The power of these great industrial giants in overseas markets was, by comparison, unlimited. They had to be wary of affecting US home markets via acts of their companies abroad — and so kept them under tight rein from the USA. We should not, therefore, underestimate the knock-on effects of US legislation upon the world at large. Often, US domestic policy has had quite unforeseen consequences that take a great deal of time to work their way through the system.

Breathnach (1988) pointed out how transnationals' tax debts may be offset with the connivance of states seeking advantage at the expense of other states. Not all states can, however, play this game. The Japanese in particular set great store by stability and the likelihood that their investments will be protected.

A further point of confusion involving the rôle of sovereign states concerns the transnationals' cross-border dealings between branches of the same company. It is not difficult to see how this plays havoc with national systems of accounting for imports and exports — the whole balance of trade. A classic example is Canada where the national accounts are dominated by cross-border trade with the USA. The extent to which sovereign Canada trades with the US is blurred by the vast amount of trade going on between US corporations that have operations on both sides of the 49th Parallel.

It should be becoming clear why we should seek to link policy in the UK and the USA. Most would agree, surely, that inflation has been a major preoccupation of twentieth-century economic life. Calleo and Strange have points (similar to ones made by Rueff) to make here too:

> Few countries, of course, have lacked strong inducements for inflationary policies. The principal difference between American inflation and that of other major capitalist countries lies less in the cause than in the consequences. For under both the fixed-exchange rates of Bretton Woods and the subsequent floating regime that prevailed afterwards Americans have been able to run balance-of-payments deficits without external restraint, and hence to 'export' a good part of the consequences of their inflation.
>
> Under fixed rates, surplus countries were more or less compelled to augment their domestic money supplies by absorbing America's excess dollars into their reserves. The shift to a global structure of more flexible rates did not make America's deficits any more subject to external restraint. Quite the contrary. Surplus countries could continue as before, and go on supporting the dollar through 'dirty floating'. Otherwise, they could either revalue – not a popular course for countries heavily dependent on exports – or else watch the dollar depreciate, with the same generally deleterious trade effects. The logical response to this dilemma would have come from a European bloc protecting itself against American money and goods. But in a divided and dependent Europe this was not a likely option. Not until the late 1970's did a European–Arab coalition finally succeed in forcing the Americans to defend the dollar and hence to control domestic inflation. Thanks to Khomeini, the Americans entered the age of Volcker. (Calleo and Strange, 1984, p. 112)

But this is moving too far ahead. The immediate concern is with the new economic order. That new order began, in effect, at Bretton Woods, Canada in 1944. Much attention has been paid to post-war economic reconstruction (Strange, 1986; Calleo and Strange, 1984; Scammell, 1975), but most start with Bretton Woods when the IMF and World Bank were founded. By September 1949, US pressure forced a £ sterling devaluation to $2.80. The USA was also a massive beneficiary of the Suez Crisis of 1956 that also became a sterling crisis. Gold weakened as the status of the USA (an oil state, of course) was enhanced, US bonds were in demand and the rôle of the dollar firmed: just as with the very early days of the Iraq/Kuwait dispute of 1990. The USA decided to call the tune at Bretton Woods as its price for funding the reconstruction of its trading rivals. Open markets for US goods, overflowing the borders of the USA, was one obvious price. The hidden hegemonic agenda, then, included the spread of US influence worldwide. It is of interest to note that Bretton Woods only became fully operational by 1958. Quite simply, the USA chose to run a deficit in the 1950s for specific geo-political purposes. The general feeling that it was time the rest of the world fully pulled its weight under Bretton Woods came after 1958, when a record gold loss was recorded by the USA. Loans from the IMF were not permitted to countries receiving Marshall Aid. This is a further reason why the full Bretton Woods system only worked for around a decade from 1958. Supremely, we see a post-war world economy kept afloat by the outflow of funds from the strong US economy. The problem had to come when the USA 'owed' more than its gold reserves could repay.

The God Almighty Dollar

The US pumped defence dollars into Europe, and US corporations pumped corporate investment dollars into Europe. Europe was the first destination, outside North America, for multinational corporate investment. Before formalising itself as a new international division of labour (Henderson, 1989; Dicken, 1986), US corporate moves were as likely to be forced by US anti-trust legislation at home as by any other pressure. The need for secure markets has long been at least as significant as the pressure for cheap out-sources. In the case of the USA, the patriotic duty to spread US products world-wide in support of the 'God Almighty Dollar' (Greider, 1987) was at least as strong as any patriotic pressure to keep production at home. Such a policy bears an uncanny resemblance to British policy of the nineteenth century. One might almost conclude that nations pay most attention to employment at home when they are not engaged (or are prevented from engaging) on a pursuit of empire. Such has been the significance of London down three centuries that the City has never really lost empire of one sort or another. The crux is that, as US overseas investment and defence spending (not least on Vietnam) went on during the 1960s, the grudging gratitude of the free world allies wore thin. There was supposed to be the dollar–gold parity. Yet the USA was exporting more dollars into the world economy than could be redeemed for gold. Surely the dollar had to be worth less, the more that were printed?

These worries were not helped by US domestic policy of the 1960s which, under Kennedy and Johnson, saw a push for growth, full employment and the Fed under pressure to print money — so much of which, as we have seen, leaked abroad to cause inflation there. Once Johnson finally turned off the tap in 1969, the federal budget was for once not in deficit, but the result was a stagflation and an election boost for Richard M. Nixon. Nixon's solution was, in essence, a reaction against 1969, not the decade that went before it, so it was back to more expansion, more dollars, and an internationally weakened dollar. Worries about the dollar continued on throughout the 1970s as various schemes were invented to save it from itself. It finally dawned on US policy-makers that a policy of decade-by-decade deficits and a capital outflow was not endlessly sustainable. The relationship between the effects of Japanese trade policy and world fluctuations should not be underestimated. It was the US trade imbalance with mercantilist Japan — amid suggestions of dumping – that preoccupied observers in 1971. If one tries to look at matters objectively, the Japanese mercantilist outlook seems a sensible reaction to the US policy of seeking global hegemony. Narrow national self-interest, if it can be harnessed economically and with the collusion of the banks, seems, on balance, to have been a logical response by Japan – or Germany, or other mercantilist states.

As the 1990 Uruguay round of GATT confirmed, the comparative-advantage free-traders inherently depend upon persuading – or forcing – all the others to come out to play. In 1971 the USA was anxious to send warning shots to Japan and a possible devaluation of the dollar was in prospect. In fact, by May 1971, both the Dutch guilder and Deutsche-Mark had been floated. The US wanted a better relationship with the Yen and a more modified one with the European currencies. When, over 7–8 August, the Reuss sub-committee suggested a dollar devaluation and it was revealed that Fort Knox was then down to its last $10 billion of gold, the scene was set. With the Deutsche-Mark floating upward against the dollar, the markets had anticipated something afoot. To effect its devaluation, especially in respect of the Yen, the US government floated the dollar and 'closed the gold window' at the Fed on 15–16 August 1971. A deteriorating trade situation in respect of Japan had removed the USA's room for economic manoeuvre. The dollar/gold relationship had to go. The era of floating interest rates had arrived.

Contradiction and confusion

This was a classic playing-out of a contradiction that had plagued the UK. It is extremely difficult to sustain a global reserve currency rôle and protect one's own industry. This was always resolved in the UK by pretending that UK industry did not exist. Hard upon the heels of the 1971 float came the 1973 oil crisis. We have noted that the classic retailers' reaction to the oil crisis was to analyse what this might mean for distribution costs, and personal mobility to stores, whereas our question is, what happened to the surplus dollars in OPEC hands? Mostly, of course, they went into the dollar-recycling chain. Not all of it found its way back to the USA, not least because the route to gold convertibility was lost in 1971. There is every reason to suppose, indeed it has often been suggested, that the oil states were amongst those least happy about the August 1971 float, as it increased uncertainty as to the value of their assets. Libya was the first to propose an oil price rise to match dollar devaluations. Certainly, it is convenient to blame the oil crisis and not the financial moves that preceded it for the chaos of the early 1970s.

Most OPEC states had less interest in industry than in armaments, and there was for a while a real concern over where they would put their money. In the event, they placed their money in Euro-dollars, and this was then recycled into the Third World, going on to cripple small economies by saddling them with monstrous debt burdens (very often just the type of countries with which OPEC countries so often professed to sympathise). In so far as they were agents of this Third World investment, the UK banks were in the process of repeating a mistake they had made in the 1890s. The Baring Crisis of that year saw a potential disaster only just avoided (Barings had been too heavily involved in Argentinian securities).

In the view of Calleo and Strange (1984), a major cause of inflation in the USA was the attempt simultaneously to pursue the policies for full domestic employment and the world leadership previously identified. One might reasonably conclude from this that one consequence of attacking inflation would be an attack on full employment, but for that we need to await Ronald Reagan. However, as the dollar-based assets homed in on Europe, it was virtually inevitable that 200 years of global financial sophistication would make London the natural home. Instead of just circulating UK government debt, the sophisticates of the City could recycle endless amounts of offshore US debt – accelerated from 1973 by the oil windfall.

Euro-dollars

The system for manipulating the dollar market that was operating offshore became the Euro-dollar market, centred in London, which grew inexorably from £3 billion in 1960 to £75 billion in 1970 and £1,000 billion by 1984. The implications were obvious: the City needed UK industry less than ever before. With the home dollar effectively cut loose in 1971, why bother with the USA either? The Euro-dollars could be recycled, debt could be raised against them and investments plotted, all outside the control of the Federal Reserve Board, or the Bank of England. Note, too, that the tax haven countries – Switzerland, Luxembourg, *et al.* – hold at least $700bn. of foreign investments. Indeed, the UK offers useful evidence to contradict the suggestion that national economic systems are closed. This can readily be refuted by examination of an atlas. The UK is surrounded by islands, such as Jersey (where corporate tax is 40 per cent lower than the UK) and the Isle of Man, which offers tax exile opportunities. Even other member states of the EC (notably Ireland) have traditionally offered a tax exile base for those making their money from the UK economy.

Looking globally at tax shelters, there are many familiar names, from Switzerland to the Cayman Islands. Aside from the $700bn., the value of these tax shelters can also be gleaned when one compares the amount of profit some trans-national companies make from their global operations with the total amount that they remit in taxes. It is perfectly possible to make millions of pounds in clear profit from operations in a country, and yet return nothing to the tax base of the same country.

Tax lawyers can advise on how to declare losses in those countries that offer tax credits and profits in those countries that do not tax profit. The only prerequisite is the desire to avoid taxation and the necessary scale of operations to make it worthwhile.

Meanwhile, back at the formal money markets, London became an off-shore piggybank for international capital. London became natural home for the oil money, to be used as the global bankers saw fit. In essence, they saw an unmissable opportunity to make heavy loans to Third World countries, especially those with potential oil assets. After all, would not oil prices escalate for ever? One could also speculate on the newly-floated currencies. Basically, then, the financial structures that existed in London had been in mothballs for a few years, yet they flourished again as the ideal, natural, purpose-built machinery for the Euro-dollar. Note that in the period of their quiescence, the UK for once toyed with the 'white heat of technology'.

It is no surprise that this emotive phrase was coined by the then Prime Minister, Harold Wilson, in the 1960s. The bases of the UK manufacturing decline were well in place, but not terminally so. The UK was still turning out about as many cars as Japan. Wilson tried to initiate an industrial policy that would sustain the regions in the long term (and failed). By the time 15 August 1971 came around it was too late. The financial muscle of the City had a much better toy with which to play. This has been noted also by Zysman (1983) who observed that UK governments could not manipulate interest rates for industrial development, because the rates were already being manipulated for purposes of financing debt.

All the evidence is that, post-1971, the old ideals of the gold standard – when arbitragers actually shipped gold between London and New York – completely gave way to new principles for making the markets move. Money flowed into currencies such as the DMark or Yen and out of weaker currencies, largely on the basis of market sentiment. Dow and Saville (1988, pp. 52–3) have commented on this by noting how 'fickle and uncertain' the markets are, and confirming the existence of band-waggon effects. Expectations based on the very latest news rule the markets: but what news, whose expectations? Dow and Saville suggested that what matters is whether or not state policy appears to the market-makers to be credible. They could offer few guidelines on what would destroy confidence or when! There is a strong body of theory within retailing (consider Uncles and Ehrenberg, 1990) to suggest that levels of sales of a product can be deduced from market share and that little else counts. A much worse situation seems to apply with currencies. Currencies are strong because the markets believe they ought to be strong. Sadly, this offers little comfort to those with weak currencies and who hope to make them stronger. At least the retailers who want to increase sales know that they should look to market share. Though perhaps all is not lost, and something can be learned. The strongest currencies – the ones that floated upwards rather than sank – have been in low-inflation countries like Germany, Switzerland and Japan. Not too difficult to deduce that inflation must be the market's talisman, rather than the modernity of productive plant, quality of management, research investment or some other such frippery. So much simpler to tackle effect rather than cause! Without much consideration of why the exemplar nations had low inflation, much of the 1980s was devoted to conquering inflation *per se* in other, weaker, economies.

Beating inflation

In this context it should hardly surprise us that in total contrast to Wilson's 1960s, UK policy during the 1980s was prepared to sacrifice employment, and especially manufacturing employment, on the altar of beating inflation. Such was not, however, the preoccupation in the 1970s. After 1971, and soon boosted by seemingly limitless oil revenues, there was one problem. There was more money than ever before, but what was it worth? There was certainly now a usually high and rising price to be paid for gold, but gold was not readily linked to currency. A crucial link in the chain had been broken.

Capital is, at root, worth only what it can buy. In the 1970s the boom industry lay in predicting worth. Speculation became rife in works of art, and in any potential Third World scheme – all essentially geared to finding worth. If any product, or share issue, was perceived by the market-makers as being 'good as gold', then surplus capital rushed in. In the UK this became just part of the 'Barber boom'. A popular destination was property, or oil, or futures of any sort. The City had not stood still and, with a whole new era of financial mechanisms just in place, money had chased assets. Not surprisingly, the price of those assets went up. Nor, if we accept the age-old truism that wars are inflationary, should we forget the US involvement in Vietnam. It has been suggested that Lyndon Johnson understated the real cost to the USA of Vietnam. There are many reasons why we should not disregard wars as sources of inflation. Wars can be seen in many cases as sources of impetus towards social equality. Returning soldiers have all too often been promised a better deal: a greater share in the wealth of the nation that they and their fallen comrades have fought to protect. This gives rise to inflationary spending pressures once the economy is in shape to respond. The US context, of course, was that the Second World War made the USA. Work was plentiful in wartime factories, overall spending power was given a boost, and the new industrial capacity and spending power were not dimmed by the need to reconstruct cities after any bothersome carpet-bombing. Later, the 1970s became the prime era of price inflation. No-one need be surprised. The last link to reality – the gold window – had been closed and Vietnam pitched in its best efforts. To save themselves from being swamped by petro-dollars, governments printed more. The cautious oil states occasionally spotted this happening (and fled currencies such as the pound in the year 1976). The oil states had good reason to look sceptically at what happened to their windfall profits. Strange observed:

> over the last fifteen years there has been substantial divergence between the 'real' price of oil and its nominal price. While the nominal price, denominated (as oil mostly still is) in US dollars, went from under $4 in the early 1970s

to $34 and over in 1979, the inflation and the consequent depreciation in the value of the US dollar meant that the real price rose only to about $15. (Strange, 1988, p. 194)

Inflation, then, was a double-edged sword. It was partly caused by the events of August 1971, themselves in part caused by US fears about Japan. Equally, inflation was a way of diluting the effect of the dollars that had to be paid to OPEC for re-priced oil (the dollar deflation that the OPEC states detested was a problem too). As assets were upwardly valued in a sea of money inflation, it forced everyone to readjust their horizons. In an inflating world, the least sensible thing to do was to save. For the ordinary worker, in the inflationary and generally high-employment seventies, borrowing long-term to buy assets that were growing in value even in the short term was an extremely sensible policy. After all, wages could be relied upon to rise. Later on, wage-driven inflation came to be seen as the culprit, and the cart was duly put before the horse. The classic UK investment example was the 1970s housing market, which saw two remarkable price inflations. If money was to be worth less, then assets, hard tangible assets, just had to be worth more. An excellent analysis of this phenomenon and its later turnaround is offered by Greider (1987).

The threat to the bondholders

The work of Greider offers the chance to expand more fully the role of the Federal Reserve Board. Greider offered graphic evidence of the soft effects of monetary policy in the inflating seventies. Consumerism in the USA was given a substantial boost. It had not taken the street-wise long to realise that the longer one waited before purchasing, the higher the price went. The USA, already a credit-prone society, accelerated its live today/pay tomorrow attitudes. Credit brokers and retailers were the major immediate beneficiaries. Greider quoted the research director of Gallup as believing that the brakes to spending were off. UK home-owners were under even more pressure than their US counterparts during the 1970s. The more sophisticated UK financial sector ran mortgages, typically, on variable interest rates. As market rates rose, the lender was able to raise the rate to the borrower with immediate effect (a policy that worked wonders for Third World debt also). The US home-owner, on a fixed rate mortgage, had the fateful date postponed a little longer – until he or she moved home.

The money markets fuelling the 1970s boom on Wall Street echoed the City. Though limited by the Glass–Steagall Act, banks were nevertheless big, and half of the sixteen biggest were in New York. Citibank with 1979 assets of $70.5 billion ranked only behind San Francisco's Bank America at $86 billion. More to the point, investment houses also inhabited New York. Merrill Lynch had $70 billion in money-market accounts, and sat alongside Salomon Brothers, Morgan Stanley, First

Boston and Goldman Sachs. The 1970s inflationary spiral may have reduced real interest rates for borrowers, but for long-term savers/ investors it could have been a disaster. The worst affected were those in the bond market, whose progenitors had floated the South Sea Bubble. On a thirty-year time scale, erosion of real assets over a full decade was extremely bad news. It was from this sector, inevitably closest to the government whose bonds it held, that pressure for an end to inflation would come. Basically, it took the bond markets about a decade to regret the events of 15–16 August 1971.

The essence of the 1970s explosion in capital can be demonstrated quite clearly by the state of markets in the USA by 1979. Greider shows that corporate equities stood at a value of $1.2 trillion, but the value of the money markets was far higher, at $4.2 trillion. Even though long-term debt made up the bulk of the money markets, the short-term end of the market was still the equal of stocks.

To put government back at centre stage we can refer again to Greider (1979, p. 31), who showed that, at the start of the Reagan years, the greatest debtor on Wall Street was the government itself with nearly $1 billion in bond debts. The image of the USA was, in the eyes of key foreign investors, measured in large part by the value of those bonds. The decline of the US dollar by 1979 also worried most of Wall Street. The spendthrift seventies had one important corollary. Like most people in most countries, the ordinary citizen was not a bond-holder. Overall, the ordinary citizen was a long-term debtor even if that was, prudently, only in the form of a house mortgage. More than 80 per cent of net financial assets were held by just 10 per cent of the US population. Greider showed that this top 10 per cent owned 51 per cent of short-term financial paper, 72 per cent of company stocks and shares, 70 per cent of bonds, 86 per cent of tax-exempt municipals and 50 per cent of all the real property. To place the ordinary citizen at a further remove from the markets, the basic reality is that a handful of financial decision-makers controlled the markets in which the assets of the rich were parked.

To put matters crudely, during the 1970s the fast-spending masses caught up on the rich. By spending fast, they were using their growing purchasing power wisely whilst the position of the rich was apparently eroding. There was too much power in the wrong hands and no question as to the culprit – inflation. But what was inflation? Not the least of the problems of inflation was its measurement. This varies from country to country, and in the UK the mix of goods on the Retail Price Index (RPI) is subject to debate.

Two major aspects of inflation to be highlighted here are the underlying characteristics of inflation and its malleability. First, let us be clear, societies cannot easily have a low-wage and a low-inflation economy. Inflation in Germany and Japan is linked to their status as high-wage economies and as major investors in technology. Keeping costs low via cheap imports – the alternative strategy – leaves far less scope for control.

High inflation in low-wage economies cannot surprise us, and nor should low inflation in high-wage economies. A country like the UK can ill afford to complain about high inflation when it also brags that industrial wages are half those of West Germany and one-third below the level in France. As regards the malleability of inflation figures, we should not forget that inflation concentrates on the rate of increase of prices and that this is often within the gift of governments.

The Fed fights back

Pressures against the 'live today' individual – essentially the wage-earner with the ability to earn tomorrow what he or she spent today – were reinforced by those on fixed incomes. The demographic pressures towards an ageing population showed up, even in the USA, as a growing percentage of people on pensions. They too had real reasons to fear rampant inflation. In reality, everyone feared inflation, but not everyone could see the short-term as well as the long-term reason why it had to be controlled. The short-term reason was clear for the long-term investor in bonds. At least twice in the US, real interest rates (market rate minus inflation) had fallen as low as −4 per cent.

With Paul Volcker installed at the Fed, a monetarist policy was invoked. The high interest rate policy pursued by the Fed from 1979 – just before the election of Ronald Reagan – had exactly the opposite effect from the 1970s inflation. It hit 'the weakest, smallest players first, and most severely, whilst the largest and more powerful enterprises could evade the ill-consequences' (Greider, 1987, p. 137). The individuals and corporations in higher tax brackets had more tax allowances to set off against real interest rates. The poor had less of a cushion. So the 1979/80 flip-over from easy money to tight money advantaged those with long-term invested wealth and crippled those with high borrowings. It became a clear new money versus old money/poor versus rich battle. The old-established and the rich won hands down, and soon displayed the fruits of victory.

Mason (1981), writing at the advent of the Volcker/Reagan/Thatcher years, discussed at length the phenomenon of conspicuous consumption. That consumption he clearly saw as rooted in the structure of the society in which it took place. The need to consume ostentatiously, even to waste ostentatiously, relates to a statement about status and position. Adam Smith saw the required role of the rich man as involving his having a table sufficiently groaning as to generate droppings on which the inferior classes might feed. This can be extended to a role-model aspirational function of encouraging work and wealth-accumulation through a desire to emulate. Mason referred extensively to Veblen and to Shenval's view of American life at the turn of the century: 'enormous wealth . . . beyond the dreams of avarice . . . has descended upon a tiny group of persons . . . To the second generation is given the spending of it . . . there are no communal responsibilities of social obligation . . . It is a society organised from top to bottom on a money basis with everything else as a sideshow' (Mason, 1981, p. 89). Shenval's disapproval might have paralleled the attitudes of High Tory Conservatives to the *arriviste* products of the Thatcher years. Mason, having documented some earlier revulsion against positional/conspicuous spending, noted that general opposition to the phenomenon could be seen as in decline by the late 1970s. One reason was that there seemed to be no real risk of great social disorder if the rich became a little richer. He also noted that the obvious manipulatory power of the rich that had been evidenced in years gone by was muted by the political/democratic process. A further erosion of resistance to conspicuous excess was seen as stemming from the rise of anonymous corporations with anonymous executives — taking over from the obviously and publicly rich founder/owner/boss. Finally, Mason saw the welfare state eroding the most basic of inequalities. A general rise in life-styles removed the worst worries of everyday existence; basically, no-one was too evidently better off than anyone else.

This left Mason with the impression that an aspirant upper middle class might best exemplify conspicuous consumption, using it to make a statement to those adjacent in the social order. This statement was about moving up or, as Hirsch would have said, believing oneself to have moved up.

It becomes clear that 1979, the year that gave the UK Margaret Thatcher and the US Paul Volcker, was the watershed. The inflationary effects of 1971 were coming home to roost. The employed masses had seemed to benefit for a decade, cashing in on the redirected oil money. Their betters, suffering positional losses, could take it no longer. The time was ripe for the New Right.

It is not difficult to see that, having tapped into a latent demand for some social mobility, the Reagan/Thatcher revolution was bound to release conspicuous consumption. This hardly helps those whose relative position is in decline to accept the new changes readily. Hence a possible reversion to earlier manifestations of social unrest. It then also becomes necessary for those at the very top to find some means of distinguishing themselves from those whose conspicuous consumption is alerting the world to the fact that they are socially on the move. There becomes a preoccupation with 'taste' and with subtleties of signifying established position. The massive amounts of capital slushing around the system in the 1980s may have made 'staying top' a very expensive proposition. For producers and retailers of status goods, the eighties were a splendid time, and it should not surprise us to see jewellery sales performing exceptionally well.

7

The New Right

One effect of the advent of the New Right was soon felt. By December of 1982 there were 12 million unemployed in the USA, some 3 million in the UK. Fledgling companies in the USA went bankrupt in droves – the worst period since 1933. Those living on accumulated wealth or wishing to acquire smaller rivals by merger never had it so good. Everything was for sale cheap – labour, small businesses, farmland – as the high interest rates shook out those 1970s borrowers not robust enough to face the new realities.

Of such realities Pollard once wrote:

> one is still struck by the sheer impudence of the demand by the City advisors that tens of thousands of large wage contracts should be re-fought and re-negotiated; that inevitably in the process the weak (and the unsheltered industries) should have their wages further reduced as against the strong; that loss of profits, bankruptcies and unemployment should be deliberately provoked; and that incomes should further be re-distributed from the active and the poor, to the rich (the bondholders). (Pollard, 1970, p. 9)

Pollard was writing about the British return to the gold standard in 1925 at an over-inflated pre-war rate! Greider was another who suggested that greater inflationary periods followed wars, when, as he put it (1987, p. 100), 'government did what it would not have dared to do in other times – it spent far beyond its means'. It may then seem odd that a high interest rate money squeeze should be implemented by a President – Ronald Reagan – who was fighting a costly war against an 'evil empire'. The effects were there, though, as a massive budget deficit and inflation exported abroad. The link between defence spending – as during wars – and inflation has a long history. How it exactly works, however, is in debate. In a real war the economy goes to work, growth takes place, shortages occur, prices inflate. We can call this the 'classic outcome'. The cold war scenario of the 1980s was rather different. The Reagan arms spending tended to be high-tech. The feedback effects or 'trickle down' are rather poor for defence spending anyway, but are dreadful for high-tech defence spending. By one estimate, the defence dollars, diverted to education, would create 800 per cent more jobs. The benefits of this economic stimulation were, in the 1980s, overtaken by the realities of government borrowing by bonds. This raised the dollar and deflated the economy.

The usual way out of this was for the Fed to dilute the wartime-type borrowings by printing the money and accelerating the inflation. The 1970s stagflation resulted because of the poor feedback from defence industry. Volcker prevented any dilution of the problem by money supply means, leaving a debt-driven recession, but no inflation, during the period of the early 1980s. Reagan was on his own with his deficit. The tightened money policy pursued by the Fed in the USA from 1979 was, however, full of holes. The global US banks, as we have seen, had access to the Euro-dollar markets. This money could easily flow into the US system and take advantage of the high interest rates there – or more accurately, take advantage of those who actually had to pay the high interest rates. Precisely the same effect was experienced in the UK, where the Thatcher government had itself decided on a high interest rate policy and had abolished exchange controls in order to make footloose capital even more footloose.

The debt cycle

Greider demonstrates how the global industries, like the banks, were induced to evade the Fed's strictures on money supply. Multinationals could borrow from foreign banks, or foreign branches of US banks. This money could then be re-lent, within the company to the US parent division: yet another example of how interest rate policy hit unevenly. Whilst there was internal chaos in the USA, monetarist-inspired stop–go policy at the Fed did boost global confidence in the US dollar. The US dollar began to recover on world markets.

The really telling point in respect of the global flow of capital is that it is, on all the evidence, controlled only by a herd instinct and market sentiment. Dow (1989, p. 226 observed): 'So long as an exchange rate policy appears credible, the authorities appear to have great power over the rate. On the other hand, if their policy ceases to appear credible they can rapidly become almost impotent.' So the exchange rate, that which governs international competitiveness, is demonstrably at the mercy of a market whim or fad, and can be sent into a tailspin by an ill-chosen word. Those who doubt this need but look at the period prior to Britain's entry into the European Exchange Rate Mechanism (ERM) when positive voices sent the pound up and dissent from Prime Minister Thatcher quickly caused the reverse. A most fascinating way to run the economy.

Consideration of sentiment was further reinforced by Dow and Saville when they looked at interest rates: 'interest rates are determined by expectations of future interest rates . . . operators operate chiefly on a short-term basis, and are influenced by what they expect the opinion of other short-term operators to be' (Dow and Saville, 1988, p. 217). Were it not for the fact that the New York situation is much the same, one might conclude that international finance was still dominated by the thought processes of the wayward younger sons of the landed gentry. The high interest rates stabilised a currency that should have been pulled in the opposite direction by inflation. The other secondary beneficiary of this painful treatment was the UK.

In the 1890s, US domestic policy had helped set in train the great transnational corporations seeking to find abroad the dominance that Congress denied them at home. In the 1980s, Volcker/Reagan policies set in train another internationalisation process – the recycling of debt. The revised global flows of credit and capital that followed were of a quite dramatic magnitude. The world financial markets had been in confusion since August 1971. Burgeoning inflation, ballooning money supply and Euro-dollar markets were all ready for the new unreality. The *pièce de résistance* was financial deregulation. Soon the massive assets of US Savings and Loans would be let loose upon an uncertain world. We have already seen that France, allegedly believing that avid tax-cutting by Ronald 'Laffer curve' Reagan, would cause a real sustainable boom in the USA, ignored the interest rate message and prepared to expand the economy as a springboard for export effort to the USA. French capital, already worried about the first socialist President, took flight when the evidence came in that the smart international money was flowing to London and New York. The French franc went into rapid depreciation, unemployment rose: Mitterrand had found it impossible to kick against the pricks. To achieve a monetarist paradise in the UK there were some small sacrifices to be made. The lambs that were led off to the slaughter were UK businesses, especially large and small manufacturing businesses. Great swathes of male, full-time, unionised employment in industry and elsewhere disappeared almost overnight. It was, at the same time, pointed out by the highly-paid that those less well off could save their jobs by working for less. The industrial decline was extreme; in 1979 there were 155,000 manufacturing apprentices in the UK, but by 1989 there were just 53,000.

This clarion call of the 1980s – that inflation could only be beaten if workers' wage settlements were moderated – never had any great appeal to the UK labour force. There are several good reasons for this: not least was widely-accessible media coverage of the staggering emoluments that many company owners and directors awarded themselves during the 1980s as they reasserted position. The exhortation to 'do as I say, not as I do' had even less appeal when it was noted that those rewards were magnified by falling tax rates at the highest levels. It may even have been that the owners and managers were relatively restrained before the 1990s simply because the marginal benefits of higher rewards were always diluted by the taxman. The 1980s made rewards at the top worthwhile because, at last, you really could take most of it home with you (or, most likely, abroad). The fallout from the worker-restraint versus conspicuous consumption battle has claimed victims wherever it has emerged. In Australia, pressure has increasingly been put on the national wage bargaining system that sought to preserve relative position for groups of workers (Clark, 1991). Such a system can hardly withstand the pressures placed upon it by the conspicuous consumption of those falling outside its remit. The society-page antics of the Alan Bonds and Donald Trumps merely reinforced the view that the rich were carting away money by the barrow-load. Why did the common worker deserve less? This reinforcement of attitudes would be as self-evident to Hirsch as to any Japanese entrepreneur. The Japanese team ethic only works if the management seem to be taking the rough with the smooth, like the workers. Ostentatious spending by the captains of industry is not the Japanese way, and it seems to work: they get rich anyway.

We again see how success relates to internal organisational cultures and not simply to copiable technology inventions. Nakane (1970) emphasised key aspects of Japanese business organisation. One is the role of the leader – a concept difficult to adequately describe in a country where the team matters more than the individual. She stressed that, unlike the US business leader, he (it is usually a he) need have little hands-on experience of the minutiae of business operations. His function is to ensure loyalty – to keep the workers happy and entrust them to perform their allotted tasks. The leader stays in touch through knowing the workforce without necessarily knowing everything that they do. This shared experience means, that, according to Nakane: 'an effective demonstration of leadership informs employees that even the leader shares hard times with them' (Nakane, 1970, p. 73). The workforce are often conceptualised as 'collaborators' – not the type of relationship to emerge from Huw Beynon's *Working for Ford* (1973). If we accept for the moment the structuralist viewpoint that society replicates itself in the workplace (and vice-versa), then many UK industries seem wonderfully class-ridden. Dare we go a step further and suggest that some of the battles to retain family control of companies – or the breakups that are family-instigated once the patrician founder has departed – reflect a conception of business as a personal milch-cow to provide family income? It would be interesting to know how many Japanese entrepreneurs sell out at the height of a company's growth simply in order to withdraw personal equity. Adam Smith was adamant that joint-stock companies were evil. Each individual should control his or her personal destiny – but for what ultimate personal motivation? These 'soft' indicators of industrial progress reinforce the attractiveness of the IPE paradigm in which a national ethos is prime. Indeed, in the UK, as thoughts of social justice have become twisted by detractors into 'the politics of envy' it surely must be conceded that envy grows where that which is enviable is blatantly flaunted. It ill-befits one to complain of the negativities of envy when the apparent sole motivation for any individual endeavour is the old stablemate – greed.

Finally, the cult of individualism and the demise of collective bargaining, so roundly supported by UK governments of the 1980s, also worked against voluntary wage restraint. The theory of social traps again applies. Just as it is the other chap who should make an orderly exit from the burning building – or support the corner shop, or use public transport – so wage restraint is for someone else. The staggering tolerance of mass unemployment through the 1980s suggested that there was almost no limit to the amount of suffering that we were prepared to let someone else bear. Nor should we neglect the benefits to the employed from the downward pressure on inflation that unemployment brings. The early 1980s were a time of bargains and fire-sales as de-stocking and labour-shedding took place. Rarely had there been a better time for the employed person to buy a house or car or TV – the cast-offs of someone else's failing lifestyle. This is a scenario that can be re-run and re-run. The most likely victims of any new round of squeezed-out employment in the 1990s will be the public sector. Industry in financier-run economies like the US and UK will still be under some pressure (from the threat of takeover or failure to get the product to market) to pay wage increases and retain productive capacity. The public sector (already under privatisation pressures in the UK) has no product to sell. There is virtually no limit to the pressures that can be placed on public sector wages – at very little political cost.

Rewards at the top

The essence of executive remuneration is that these days it is more difficult to hide, and there are more researchers looking. The workforce increasingly know the levels of reward that the top people are organising for themselves. *Labour Research* of October 1990 devoted two pages to the lucrative directorships obtained by former government ministers. Indeed, perhaps the most visible self-contradictions of government come when serving MPs disclose that they can manage to take on several highly-paid directorships whilst admirably fulfilling their duties to their constituencies. The linkages between former MPs and high salaries have been especially highlighted when the new employer turns out to be a company with which the MP was associated when in public office. The 'Caesar's wife' school of thought has clearly been relegated to the mists of antiquity. *Labour Research* also highlighted how divided payments, rather than simple salaries, can be the true source of serious money for directors. The magazine showed that annual dividend payments to Robert Maxwell and David Sainsbury exceeded £20m. A further twenty-four directors of companies received in excess of £1m. in dividend payments. It is, of course, the board of directors that approves the level of dividends to be paid out. Clearly, many of these individuals also had substantial directors' salaries to add on to these payments.

It is arguable that as long as the organisations for which these people work are good employers, reward their workforces proportionately as well as they reward their directors and generally contribute to the well-being of the nation, then there is nothing wrong with such payments. To be so foolish as to think otherwise would invite suggestions of envy – still a deadly sin. It is, however, by no means always the case that the great stalwart companies of the national economy are also those that are heavy on the directorial largesse. Indeed, should a financially-troubled group suddenly appear riding high on the list of those offering lavish emoluments, then the workforce might well suggest that rats were preparing to leave the sinking ship.

Massive emoluments to directors was not solely the province of companies involved in the spectacular collapses in the high interest rate period of 1988–91 in the UK. In May of 1990 the *Independent on Sunday* published a list of eighty leading UK companies that showed the salary of the top director and also the earnings per share (EPS) of those companies. One might reasonably assume that the salary of the leading director would track that of EPS quite closely, or, if the salary was fixed, it would track average earnings. Not so. Only twelve top directors listed (15 per cent of the sample) showed less than a 100 per cent salary increase over a five-year period. Only sixteen (20 per cent) of the directors took an increase that either tracked or was less than the rate of corporate growth as measured by EPS. (Nine directors fulfilled both criteria, though the list revealed nothing about dividend payments or other perks.) Accordingly, 80 per cent of directors were paid, or chose to pay themselves, a greater increase in salary terms than the EPS justified. Many banks, inevitably, showed large decreases in EPS (that did not stop one bank from giving a 548 per cent increase in salary to its top director). Likewise, these figures mask the phenomenon of the holder of multiple directorships who may simultaneously accept several substantial pay rises.

Such behaviour would stand in marked contrast to our ideal-typical Japanese business leader. It is also out of tune with recent US opinion polls. In October 1990 *Business Month* claimed that executives in a recent poll had voted 2,025 to 25 in support of long-term business strategy over quick profits. On page 32 of the same edition the summary of another poll response was phrased thus: 'Before the greedy Reagan era, multimillion dollar managers were rarer than the spotted owl. Now, they're everywhere. Small wonder that 90% of you complained that American Chief Executives are grotesquely overpaid.' In the early 1980s such revisionism was unthinkable. No-one seemed to care that, as Strange pointed out, the UK rush to Friedmanite policies came at the expense of employment and infrastructure. Tightening up the UK economy meant cutting spending, liquidating assets, and generally running down the economy. At the very same time, a government-promoted rise in home-ownership restrained any industrial activity or strikes that might cause an individual to lose his or her job. For job losses now meant loss of the home: in times of high real interest rates, few debts attract the priority that is accorded to the mortgage on the home. No single policy could so perfectly have encapsulated the aims of Thatcherism and, equally, the true depths of any UK recession now has an excellent barometer – the level of home repossessions. A year later, the 1991 scandal centred, not around politicians, but focused instead on the ballooning salaries of those placed in charge of the privatised state monopolies.

The fate of the worker-consumer

In the context of retailing, and in particular retail demand, it is worth looking at Greider's references to former Fed chairman Marriner Eccles. Eccles had felt that mass consumption implied distributed wealth but that, by 1929–30 too much wealth was in too few hands. 'By taking purchasing power out of the hands of mass consumers the savers denied to themselves the kind of effective demand for their products that would justify reinvestment in new plants' (Eccles in Greider, p. 307). Eccles' views were clearly Fordist/Keynesian. It is not all that difficult to see that the 1970s was the heyday of the mass markets, and that the period 1979–80 was the key to cementing a polarised or segmented market. The decline of mass employment, as I have emphasised, led to a decline of mass consumption. Throughout the analysis of the 1970s/80s flipover, the one factor overrides. What were the real inflation-adjusted interest rates? In the 1970s they were often negative — a real loss to the lender. Throughout much of the 1980s, even in those post-recession periods when interest rates could be kept low, they were positive: a strain on the borrower and a boost to lenders.

Congdon (1988) has structured a book around the threat posed by high real interest rates. His *The Debt Threat* is subtitled *The Dangers of High Real Interest Rates for the World Economy*. By his estimation, 1973, 1974, 1975 and 1977 were years when the 'implied real interest rate' in the USA was negative. For both 1974 and 1977 it was down to −3.9 per cent. The significant factor is less that rates began to soar from 1979, than the fact that the interest rates took off as price rises slowed. By 1982 the real interest rate was a staggering 10.4 per cent and, in figures to 1986, the lowest real interest rate since then has been 8.9 per cent in 1985! To simplify, lenders were asking for around 10 per cent more in interest repayments than borrowers might reasonably be expected to recoup just from selling products at prevailing prices — or from their labour.

Another beneficiary of the 1970s and fuller employment had been the trade unions. The Volcker/Reagan recession and the emphasis of the rôle of the individual soon reduced such powers. Much the same happened in the UK where mass unemployment greatly reduced the membership lists and thus the financial assets of the trade unions. The bulk of those who suffered unemployment were union members. The sector in which the pain was greatest, both in the UK and USA, was in traditional heavy industries. As they declined, so Japan, Korea and other rival countries picked up their markets. The job losses were heavily concentrated in certain geographic areas. Mass employment, mass values, mass purchasing power, gave way to mass unemployment, split and segmented values and markets. We have seen how Massey and Meegan (1982) described the new working patterns based on much lower costs that were set in train. The trend to part-time and often largely female labour was accelerated. Union pressures were avoided in the US and the UK alike by moving enterprises to new regions with little tradition of organised labour. New patterns of work followed, as did new patterns of consumption. Unions of the traditional ilk were not invited to the party.

Note that Hymer (1975) had already predicted the end of collective bargaining and grave troubles ahead for organised labour. Internationalisation of production set the workers in one country against the workers in another, with the work going to the lowest bidder. Labour in advanced societies could improve its position at the expense of other workers in the same country. In effect he was describing a Paretian situation with no group able to become better off without leaving another worse off. This led Hymer to point out that increased standards of living were predicated upon not everyone achieving them, as Hirsch had also noted. Even offering higher education to all merely served to devalue its currency. It is simply not possible for everyone to gain access to top jobs; by definition, they would not then be top jobs. We cannot overstate the point that modern western society is rooted in the principle of the donkey following the carrot. If the donkey comes too close to the carrot, the pole must be made a little longer — this is one interpretation of the switch in fortunes for organised labour in the 1980s.

Yet again, wider financial policy was having an effect on employment at home and exaggerating the effects on the heavily-indebted Third World. In the US the deficit sucked in money, forced up the dollar, and then sucked in imports too. Those who, say, worked in the auto industry, survived the lay-offs, took a wage cut, and had to economise. Maybe they bought a cheaper car — maybe a Japanese import — and bought themselves out of a job.

Yet more debt

'The global recession induced by the Federal Reserve had collapsed Latin economies in the first place, rendered their swollen debts unsustainable, and put the major banks at risk. It was perhaps the gravest price that the world — and the United States — would pay for Volcker's zealous assault on inflation' (Greider, 1987, p. 547). Debt crises are an endemic feature of growing nations (the US itself had such problems in earlier days), but the post-1970s Third World debt dwarfed all but the Reagan deficit. Western banks with heavy exposure to such loans were at risk of going under. Even today, many bank balance sheets do not bear too much close scrutiny. In the end, this was what forced a turn in policy at the Fed. Paul Volcker's involvement with Mexico's affairs marked the beginning of widespread awareness of the debt crisis. By 1988, Latin America was remitting £21.7bn. to the West; this rose to £27.2bn. in 1989.

For the short term, however, the early part of the 1980s was a good time to be in employment, and a better time still to be able to make loans at high real interest rates. Some long-standing loans, contracted in the inflationary 1970s, became punitive to service. In the 1980s recession, oil was a major loser, and it was not just individuals and companies that lost out. Canada bought back its own oil at 1970s prices — only to see oil prices fall and interest rates rise from 1979. The Canadian deficit soon dwarfed even that of the USA on a per capita basis.

We have clearly seen how interest rates rose as capital flowed around the financial system in the 1980s, seeking to ground itself in real assets. Some financial sectors could not compete in the search for windfall returns by virtue of already being grounded in real assets and by being rather closely tied to their true worth. Leading among such financial institutions were the US Savings and Loans, or 'Thrifts'. The Thrifts, tied to personal property mortgages, could not speculate beyond the financial limitations of the ability of ordinary Americans to pay for their homes. They simply could not compete in the 'casino'. At this point, two things could have happened. The banks could have come down to earth in their loan and interest rate policies, or the Thrifts could be set free to play in the fantasy world of surplus capital. Predictably, the Reagan administration chose the latter option. In October 1982, the Thrifts were loosed from their grip with reality, except that the US taxpayer was committed to guarantee any loans made. Three-quarters of a trillion dollars and thousands of land-flips later, the true scope of the disaster can still only be guessed at.

Soon, in addition to bailing out Mexico, the American taxpayer, via the Fed, would directly be bailing out its own banks – and the Savings and Loans scandal was yet to come. In the USA, as in the UK, government that would never step in to save lame-duck manufacturing industries nevertheless happily pumped money into failing banks. It was the banks' own folly, then, that forced Volcker's change of policy in the mid-1980s. Note that the supreme irony of the early days of monetarism at the Fed, and in the Reagan administration, was that the tight money policy that induced the recession also doubly benefited Japan. As bond holders (recycling worthless dollars back to the USA to fund more imports of Japanese cars), the Japanese gained from the increased real interest rates. Secondly, as US industry collapsed, the US purchaser found it even simpler to buy Japanese cars. Greider used two speeches by Lee Iacocca, head of Chrysler, that are relevant to this point:

> The fact is, without a strong industrial base, we can kiss our national security goodbye [Iacocca warned]. We can also kiss goodbye to the majority of this country's high value-added jobs. It was the middle class that made this country great in the first place. Take away America's $8-to-$12-an-hour industrial jobs and you undercut the country. If we don't watch out, I'm afraid we're going to find ourselves armed to the teeth – and with nothing left to defend but drive-in banks, video arcades and McDonald's hamburger stands.

and:

> People in this town better start realizing that buried somewhere in those numbers, between the highs and lows of these [dollar] swings, are things like 140,000 bankruptcies, three million jobs going overseas and 100,000 fewer farmers, most of whom lost their land. These aren't just bell curves from a textbook. These are real people – human beings trying to eat and buy shoes for their kids and pay off the mortgage. (Greider, 1987, pp. 601, 651)

We are back to the central question. Manufacturing matters – but to the economy, not to individuals. Manufacturing is therefore easy to sacrifice in the short term when so many fewer people actually work in the sector and so many influential people can live the rest of their lives on capital already accumulated. Let us return to Shenval. Perhaps the lesson of 1971, worked out in the 1980s, was that accumulation was for earlier generations. As far as the USA and UK were concerned, it was now time to consume. The battle centred on which sectors of society would get the lion's share.

This is a good point to summarise some of the lessons learned from the Volcker/Reagan experiment of the early 1980s. One is the inevitable critique of monetarism in action – especially in a country where the executive and the legislature are separate, and enactment of the President's wishes cannot be assured. (The US budget crisis of October 1990 again led people to ask if this was any way to run a country.) Congress and the Fed were pulling in opposite directions and neither could directly influence the other. Yet, for many years previously, both Reagan and Volcker had been assumed to be united in the same purpose. Eventually, fearing the worst on the banking front, the Fed changed its policy out of pure expediency.

Monetarism on the run

The monetarist proposition had clearly been unwound in several ways. One was that the post-1971 floating dollar had eroded any clear idea of what money was actually worth (much more so than did the 1930s abandonment of the gold standard). Second was that monetarists held to the belief that money supply was somehow leak-proof or globally controllable. The Euro-dollar markets gave the lie to this. Finally, the monetarist influence had come at a time when, because of inherited wealth, more and more people were immune to the short-term vagaries of money markets. Fourthly, the deregulation of finances in the USA and UK in particular meant that there was now no clear idea of how much ready money there was in the national economy.

In the context of the UK, Dow (who spent ten years at the Bank of England) wrote: 'in this country, monetary targets have been largely abandoned. Some proclaim that this kind of monetary policy is dead . . . our view, as it has developed, is that it ought never to have been believed possible or useful in the first place' (Dow and Saville, 1988, pp. VI–VII). The greatest value in the work of Dow and Saville comes from the explicit recognition that banks do not represent a black hole into which capital disappears, never to re-emerge. Banks do not do the economy some great favour by vacuuming up all the money that the naughty citizenry had planned to spend on items appearing on the Retail Price Index – for example, food.

Dow and Saville conceded that when high interest rates impoverish borrowers from banks they simultaneously enrich those already rich enough to lend money to banks. Though we must concede that in the UK most lenders are institutions, Dow has tried to tackle the question of how inflationary it might be to make the rich richer. Note that, as we have left it, the retail mass markets must decline as spending falls, but retail specialist markets catering to the rich should rise. Dow's rather splendid response is that probably the spending of the rich will not suddenly take off, because they were never especially constrained in their spending in the past. Good point (though Thrift and Leyshon (1990) believe they see excess capital heading into personal house property). But how do we maximise this anti-inflationary breakthrough in the national interest?

It would seem most logical to use the banks to systematically impoverish those already poor enough to have to borrow from them. That is clearly anti-inflationary. The repayments of interest to those already rich enough as to have surplus capital should now be prevented from creating inflation in domestic markets. Perhaps the ancient vision of the entrepreneur using banknotes to light his cigar was an early, patriotic, anti-inflation gesture?

Ironically, once Volcker eased up, one implication of the crisis was a slowing-up in banks' own willingness to be seen lending. Volcker had to act to stimulate the markets by easing interest rates and bailing out the banks. Banks were in a Catch—22. With high real interest rates they had in a sense been cashing in, provided the loan repayments came in at all. Volcker presumably felt that lower interest rates would bring in less profit, but from more sources. (This tiny blip was probably enough to re-elect the media President, despite his deficits which, after all, were for future generations to worry about.)

Grieder quoted Robert O. Anderson of Atlantic Richfield Oil Company on the new recovery, and it largely reflected the first Reagan realities. The white-collar worker was benefiting, but blue-collar industry was still in decline. Anderson's message was clear, and applicable in many OECD countries. This was that some individuals and groups were reflating the economy whilst others were still suffering from recession. Curbing the spending of one sector would add more misery to the other.

At root, we see that (since no political party has yet put systematic impoverishment of the masses into its manifesto) large groups of those who could spend would have to stop spending. The political (i.e. real-world) decisions all basically focus on whether it is to be the rich or the poor who are to curb their appetites. The eighties have left little doubt as to which groups UK and US governments have been most keen to restrict.

Junk

With no controls on credit, the US government (like the UK government to follow) relied on financial good sense. If the banking experts had the good sense to loan to Mexico, Brazil and downstream to the likes of

Penn Square Bank, what better could be expected of the general public? After all, President Reagan had been elected twice on his assurances that things were good and getting better. Confidence breeds confidence: but there was also a more sinister problem. At a corporate level, asset purchases were in vogue. Surplus cash (or, more accurately, surplus credit) could be used in the form of junk bonds to relieve corporations of their assets. As repayments became due that could not be met, new, less secure, higher interest loans were taken on in order to meet short-term needs. Grieder was of the opinion that control of credit via interest rates simply did not work, for exactly the same reasons put forward by Dow and Saville. One man's crippling debt burden consists of paying the interest rates to the person who made the loan to him, or to his bank. Finally, as Greider (1987, p. 684) put it:

> Milton Friedman, the intellectual father of modern monetarism, was more grudging in admitting defeat. 'I don't feel there has been any repudiation of the theory,' Friedman insisted. 'After all, it's a science in which theories must be tested. So, if we've been wrong about some things, they have to be corrected.' After years of self-confident predictions and caustic criticism for his opponents, this was as close as Milton Friedman could bring himself to acknowledging that, in the real world, his theory did not work. (Greider, 1987, p. 84).

The essence of the US experience was that the regulators behaved as if the system was closed when, in fact, it was open. The money-creating mechanisms (such as government borrowing) careered through the system without ever stimulating the industrial sector (as the tax-cut policy said it would do).

The system was open for imports to intercept the cash (aided and abetted by high exchange rates attracted by high interest rates). The money, having by-passed the manufacturing sector, flew into the banking sector to stimulate ever-more-ludicrous ventures. In essence, virtually the same critique of Friedman's monetarism was made by Calleo and Strange (1984) from their hegemonic/geopolitical perspective in which they clearly stated that monetarism ignored global issues at the expense of domestic ones. The dollar problem was solved in 1985. Finally, the Fed had to heed the administration on the value of the dollar, and on 22 September 1985, the Plaza accord was reached whereby the Yen and the dollar were realigned. Dollars became instantly worth less in relation to the Yen.

Feeding the goose that laid the golden egg

The only problem was that Japan still had good reasons to keep the US economy afloat, but Government Treasury bills (T-bills) were equally immediately less attractive as the Yen appreciated overnight. Under the swings and roundabouts principle, the hard $US had become hoist by its own petard. When it was rising in value on the back of high interest rates, the payouts to those who were bankrolling the Reagan party (Japan) had become all too real: the US deficits ballooned. Once the dollar was set on its revised (downward) path, the Japanese became uneasy. Just as their industries had been direct beneficiaries of the strong dollar *and* they had gained from the T-bills, so they now feared a double loss. Having been strongly involved with the US trade balance disaster, they feared they might now have to pay for it. As the T-bills became less attractive and the Yen rose, so US imports into Japan would become cheaper. The problem was that mercantilist Japan was not at all interested in buying anything from the US, not even cheap rice. On the other hand, what if US industry suddenly reawoke on the back of a more competitive dollar and began to compete with Japan in other markets? For the Japanese, the solution was obvious – to use the strong Yen to buy into this possible success story, and so they did. Interestingly, the Japanese, with their reverence for seniority, have a special affinity for brand names. They will often pay a considerable market premium for famous names (sometimes discovering that those who held the rights to the name had substantially less respect for it). The Japanese can presumably afford the odd such blunder since they own 55 per cent of foreign bank assets in the USA and four of the top ten banks in California. By late 1990 Japan had come to own nearly $300bn. of direct and portfolio assets in the US.

The direct effect of the Plaza accord was that instead of funding America, there was an accelerated trend to buying it, or what bits were worth buying. Inevitably, with the 1980s still awash with cash, the market analysts have become ever more supreme. The decision on where to park excess liquidity becomes ever more competitive. Hot money flows endlessly round the globe; market tips, when not exactly insider trading, are immensely valued. Because of the structure of the US and UK system, the analysts can make or break companies by the strength of their praise or criticism. Even with major corporations, a lack of praise from a securities house can cost millions in share values. This passage from the *Independent* illustrates the general point.

> *Kitcat profit revision dims GEC's lights*
>
> Shares of the powerful General Electric Company were dull yesterday as securities house Kitcat & Aitken cut its profit forecast for the second time this year. Analyst Chris Tucker lowered his expectations for the year ending this month to £850m. He was previously shooting for £875m. In its last financial year GEC achieved £797m.
>
> The Tucker cut has been provoked partly by GEC's controversial takeover of the Plessey electronics group. GEC, partnered by the West German Siemens group, acquired Plessey last year after a fierce, long-running battle.
>
> Many analysts still expect GEC to top the £900m mark. Some are looking for around £925m. GEC has this year made a number of City visits. The general reaction has been to leave forecasts unchanged. Mr Tucker believes GEC shares, down 5.5p to 202.5p, are, despite his profit revisions, a long term buy. (*Independent*, 14 March 1990)

The current players are virtually helpless pawns in a game devised long before any of them was born.

So the problem of where to park all the capital that was flowing into the banks under 1980s real interest rates was growing. Even if they were still in deep trouble with their Third World loans – and perhaps because of that – the banks needed good returns on the money invested elsewhere. It soon became apparent that this was not going to be easy. Third parties were happy to intervene and offer exceptionally good deals.

Grounding 'worth'

As Chase Manhattan found out when Drysdale securities went under owing $2 billion, and then Penn Square Bank collapsed, not all such investments were totally gilt-edged. US and UK banks found themselves under increasing pressure – especially since the Japanese and German banks, which had eschewed major Third World exposure, were now asset-rich. It was extremely fortunate for UK lending institutions that the incoming Thatcher government created a whole new batch of individuals seeking home loans: loans secured against tangible and recoverable assets. The 1980s became the supreme era of financial manipulations to secure real assets on home, not foreign, markets. Rather than just merger-mania, the theme became buy-outs or buy-ins on proven assets of existing corporations.

As investment capital was sucked in to the UK and USA, it had to be parked somewhere. New possibilities were needed, so an old favourite made a comeback – takeovers and mergers. These were soon justified by blaming poor management for failing to respond to the disasters that the financiers had created. One possible explanation for the choice of the poor management justification for 1980s raider activity was the failure of the immediately preceding phase of merger activity in the 1960s. If we look back to the 1920s wave of merger activity, we see that it followed US antitrust legislation of a few years previously. This legislation was far less strict on total takeover than it was on shareholding in rivals in the same line of business, and so empire-building via takeover was accelerated. The 1920s saw activity to create great combines in specific businesses to the fullest extent that antitrust legislation would allow.

The great 1960s merger waves had been different in scope. For here the process featured great single-business enterprises desperately trying to diversify out of overdependence on one industry. A classic example was British American Tobacco (BAT). BAT, in seeking to move out of tobacco, bought up a diverse range of companies including foodstores. It was generally felt that this had less to do with creating synergy within the new conglomerates than with portfolio management. The short-term pressure to seek after rewards by investing in a range of companies (on the assumption that one at least must thrive) is precisely what has bedevilled any UK or US fund manager or company that might prefer to be more long-term. It would be absurd to state that the trend to takeovers of cognate businesses ceased entirely in the 1960s. After all, the 1960s saw much management research stressing the benefits of market share – so the fight for bigness was on again. Even later, the 1980s saw the rise to power in the UK of companies like the food chain Gateway, as we shall later see in more detail.

Gateway sought market share by a phenomenal range of foodstore acquisitions, but can be seen to have had no greater success than BAT in making its giant company work, even with the synergy of 'like businesses'. Gateway and BAT were 1980s targets of 'unbundling'. Unbundling may represent a sort of second attempt to get it right. To that extent we can perhaps seek after a merger/unbundle/merger cycle. We need, however, to question the basis on which a corporate raider knows better than incumbent management what it is that must be done the second time around. Almost the only generalisation that can be made is that raiders seek a leaner workforce – which means localised job losses and localised drops in demand, already made acceptable by the recession of the early 1980s.

Government-provided investment opportunities

The most efficient production line left in the UK was the government privatisation programme that provided an endless stream of investment opportunities. In the USA, as corporate America was bought up, in and out, so stocks rose dramatically. Members of the House of Representatives sub-committee on Telecommunications and Finance are involved with the workings of the Securities and Exchange Committee (SEC). One such member Edward J. Markey of Massachusetts, attended a conference on 15 October 1987 where he stated: 'volatility in the market . . . could trigger a response . . . that could . . . create a near free-fall situation.' Most of us can recall what happened to the Dow Jones index on 19 October 1987, just four days later. It might be worth noting other comments from so prescient an individual, such as: 'We all know people who live only for today. . . . This is a bad philosophy for an individual, and a disastrous one for a nation' (Markey, 1989, p. 121). Yet that philosophy was built-in by the system just as certainly as the long-termism of Japan is built-in to their system.

From 1987 onwards, the Japanese showed an increased tendency to store wealth at home in an ever-more classically mercantilist fashion. The over-stocking of assets, especially in the property sector, caused a 1989 mini-crash on the Nikkei index in which London and New York, for once, stubbornly refused to join. Yet property values remained a keystone of the process, as had been the case in earlier merger waves. Towards the end of 1991 there were rumblings that the overheated Japanese property market might, predictably, collapse.

From the foregoing we see that the role of the Federal Reserve Board was crucial to the pattern of 1980s America. What is also clear is that, with virtually direct responsibility for the deficit, Ronald Reagan does not emerge with over-much credit. It took World War Two to switch the USA from the role of global debtor to global creditor; Ronald Reagan fully reversed the process.

Reagan contrived the classic double of fiscal and current account deficits. In the context of reserve currencies (under the liquidity concept), deficits *per se* are not remarkable, as Calleo and Strange confirmed. They used evidence from the work of Triffin and Rueff to demonstrate that running a reserve currency virtually ensures a balance-of-payments deficit, not least because there is no effect upon domestic money supply. What is costless can also appear worthless, and conflicts arise between the need to appease foreign holders of the currency and the need for domestic harmony. The peculiar talent of Ronald Reagan was that he managed to make a total mess of both aspects of the economy.

Laffer curves speed up the consumption treadmill

There are two possible interpretations of Reagan's move to augment the spectacular budget deficit with import-boosting tax cuts. One is that he genuinely believed in Laffer curves. This is hinted at by Shaw (1988, p. 135): 'It would appear that the Reagan administration displayed touching if naive attachment to the concept of the Laffer curve and sincerely believed that a programme of tax cutting was possible without incurring fiscal deficits.' Indeed, the Reagan experiment would probably not have taken place but for the coincidental promotion of the theories of Arthur B. Laffer of the University of Southern California. In timely books such as Jude Wanniski's *The Way the World Works* (1978), Laffer's theories were lauded. Government, they alleged, stifled initiative and 'the will to work'. Laffer curves, applied to taxation, claim a link with the will to work. The concept is that if taxes are cut, more people will work harder (it being worth the extra effort). This will generate more *total* income in the economy. The lower tax rate thus now has a higher taxable amount on which to operate; accordingly, it still generates the same gross revenue for the Treasury . . . in theory. Regrettably, it doesn't work. Whilst Laffer curves clearly implied an equilibrium (strictly, two points of equilibrium) at which tax revenue and the will to work were in balance, in reality no-one who subscribed to such views had any doubt. The untestable Laffer curve theory might have indicated that taxes were too low, but the supporters naturally chose to read it only one way – taxes must be too high. 'Cometh the hour cometh the man': here was Arthur B. Laffer, an economist, with the one thing that politicians the world over craved. Arthur had a theory that legitimated the policy that conservative politicians had been praying for – the chance to cut taxes. Arthur was ideal. Arthur was an academic; best of all, Arthur was an economist – the most socially-acceptable form of academic. The legitimation cover was fireproof. Arthur was the lender of last resort in the theory bank – if it all went wrong, blame him, not Ronald Reagan, or later, Nigel Lawson. For those with an interest in the Laffer curve we may note that it has two poles. Taxation may be set at 100 per cent, in which case no-one works because there is no incentive. Taxation may, alternatively, be abolished, in which case work is equally impossible because no funding exists for government and so social order cannot be maintained. Like the collected thoughts of Adam Smith, this is a classic product of its time. Middle-class college professors reflect on contemporary life and its motivations. If taxation were only a little lower, then rational economic man would work harder: it would be worth it. There would be extra gains in productivity, all from tax cuts: the ultimate in motivation.

How odd it is that for the ordinary working man such motivations disappear like mist. His marginal tax rate from working harder is the greatest of all, yet this is the last tax band ever to rate attention. Is this because, as we have seen, a greater motivation presents itself to workers in the fear of unemployment? 'Work for yourself' becomes degraded into 'work or else'? Of course, the two poles of the Laffer curve are purely theoretical. If everyone were left with no motive to work, they would not simply stop. Starvation, ever-present in too much of the world, would see to that. No, the Laffer curve is a bourgeois toying with the middle ground of taxation.

But wait, I should not be so droll about the work of Laffer. Am I not arguing that each turn of the positional wheel (or mode of regulation) is a product of its time? For many centuries, theories such as Laffer's would have had no relevance. They simply could not be applied to the prevailing modes of work or taxation. Laffer curves were the touchstone for those in power in the aftermath of August 1971 to again use positional aspirations among the masses to create favourable outcomes. The mood of the times had been signified by the 1978 'Proposition 13' vote in California. That, as much as Laffer, give birth to the rallying cry of 'no more taxes'.

Another reason why we should take note of Laffer curves is that, like the work of Hirsch, they interface between the economic regime and human motivation. They are important, then, to the Regulation. Laffer curves are to the rich what Hirsch is to the poor/aspirers. Laffer curves take for granted the motivation to work harder. Only Hirsch points out that, ultimately, this is futility. Why Laffer mattered to the rich is that the rewards for them were immediate: taxes were cut. For the poor/aspirers, this speeded up Hirsch's treadmill. There were greater rewards promised at the top (the tax cuts were real/concrete), but because the hoped-for revenues had to come in down the line, the risks of failure were greater. The welfare safety nets were cut to pay for the good times for the rich: staying put was not an option. Those who had found, in the post-war world, a niche that satisfied their moderate needs soon discovered that their lifestyles were levelled downwards.

Laffer's 'carrot' came with success; the 'stick' only applied to those who failed and were left with substandard houses, schools, and less of the hoped-for material things. Accordingly, Laffer curves could be used to speed up the consumption treadmill. The aspirers would produce more work *now* for the promise of reward *later*.

The Laffer curve was the ideal tool since it did redistribute wealth from poor to rich (which was, of course, the second and more transparent of Reagan's possible reasons for liking it).

> The 1981 tax legislation proved to be regressive in a more fundamental way, hardly noted at the time. It became the pretext for a vast redistribution of incomes, flowing upward on the income ladder, through another powerful channel — interest rates. The price of money determined how the fruits of capitalist enterprise would be apportioned — the division of shares between creditors and debtors, between investors and entrepreneurs, between the old and the young, between workers and owners. The immediate consequence of the 1981 tax bill, virtually from the moment it was enacted, was higher interest rates. Paul Volcker's warnings proved correct. The division of wealth was tilted toward the top — a larger share would flow to those who already had accumulated wealth. There would be less for everyone else. (Greider, 1987)

The whole Laffer system depended on the revenue from the new money exceeding the losses on the old money. Since the old money had practised ways of avoiding taxation and the new money was adept at losing some in the black economy, the sums failed to add up. The primacy of the dollar helped explain the ease with which the deficit could be financed. The phenomenon of the newly-enriched old money really only reached the UK context in 1988 with the famous Lawson 'giveaway' budget, beloved of industrialists from Stuttgart to Tokyo. Having avoided the Reagan trap for eight years, the Thatcher government just had to prove that if a mistake is worth making once, it is worth making twice.

Unless the further enrichment of the already rich was the sole desired end, then Laffer curves proved again that basing economic policy on the ideas of economists rarely seems to work. Nor is criticism of economists confined to other, dissenting, economists. Strange (1988) attacked the tendency of economists to regard any action as irrational if it does not accord with their theory. Not surprisingly, it was the neglect of power-relations that she most disliked. Even those economists who dally with the real world are censured for the 'presumption of economic analysis that people invariably try, first and foremost, to get everything on the cheap, and that cost is the ultimate determinant of all behaviour' (Strange, 1988, p. 35). The efforts of welfare economists notwithstanding, this is an important criticism. Throughout this book I am attempting to show that, in the long run, no decision is ever purely economic. The economic decisions taken by politicians work their way through and are felt by real people in real situations. The thrust by the logical positivists to be as scientific as the pure sciences has, in the long run, done a tremendous disservice to society. Decisions that appear to be objective are both lauded and more easily legitimated, but they are distanced from reality. It is of signal importance that Hirsch juxtaposed the human with the economic. At the same time, it can hardly surprise us that those whose prime aim is to legitimate power-decisions are happier with the distancing effects of objectified research. This distances the politicians from the social consequences of their actions. As Wynne (1982) demonstrated, a 'legitimation process' (as Weber would have recognised it) not only distances the politician, but can actually transfer blame to the expert whose evidence was accepted.

We see that, in practice, politicians rarely come to accept any level of direct personal culpability if individuals suffer as a result of their policy decisions (as on levels of health or safety spending). It may indeed be that the politicians provide the power-analysis and then shop around for the economic theory that fits; there is bound to be one. Laffer curves fitted Reagan's desire for tax cuts.

In fact, this is a good point at which to return to the theories of Fred Hirsch, since the theories of Hirsch so clearly run counter to those of Arthur Laffer. Under Laffer, tax-based incentive alone makes everyone work harder. Hirsch suggested, conversely, that this merely speeds up the consumption treadmill. Once success is achieved, it is immediately redefined. The struggle to own the BMW, once achieved, is transmuted into the struggle to own the Porsche. As the upwardly-mobile start to achieve the trappings of the rich, so the rich redefine what it is to be rich.

Galbraith, Mason and Hymer all identified – through the 1970s and before – a weakening of the working classes' dislike of conspicuous consumption. This is probably because the rises in their own living standards were eroding the social/psychological distance between them and their betters. It was only to be expected that the latter group would eventually use this weakening to seek to reassert their dominance. The crucial question is this: which viewpoint (Laffer or Hirsch) most encourages enterprise and/or national success? Is it the feeling that individuals alone can succeed and must be given the chance to break from the pack – or is it the feeling that all fare better via collective effort and that chasing after elusive positional goods merely creates divisiveness and envy? Somewhat disturbingly for the US and UK, urban unrest and rising crime seems to have been the response of those right at the bottom of the pack who, ten years on, know at last that success for the few is predicated on failure for the masses. Indeed, it has become necessary for the New Right to re-cast social justice as 'the politics of envy' for precisely these reasons.

Hirsch or Laffer?

It was truly fascinating to watch Margaret Hilda Thatcher, in her last parliamentary debate as Prime Minister, engaging in a battle over the theories of Fred Hirsch. Hirsch was not mentioned and it is reasonable to assume that she had not read his work. However, she berated a critic for having the temerity to suggest that the poor would be happy to be poorer if only the rich were not so rich. That is correct, and Hirsch wrote many pages proving it.

The Japanese subtlety in presenting captains of industry as ordinary citizens (whatever the closet reality of their life-styles) seems on balance to bring them a more successful outcome. This ultimately reinforces the point of the IPE approach taken in this book. Laffer-curve philosophy appeals to individual-oriented globalistic societies prepared to tolerate a lumpen underclass. The theories of Hirsch better describe a nationalistic/collectivistic/mercantilist viewpoint where obvious displays of individual affluence are subordinated to the goal of maximising national economic health.

Neither position is endlessly sustainable, however, for Japan will have to cope with the rising aspirations of the workers on whose backs the collective wealth has been produced. Furthermore, Japan has the additional problem that parking too much surplus capital at home means that it has been invested in property. Japan already has horrendous land costs and these factors alone (the ultimate irony) will force Japanese companies to produce abroad. As they travel abroad, the Japanese will see that general housing standards in particular are better in economically-backward countries such as the UK. The Laffer curve societies will have to cope with the fact that, as the attraction of positional goods starts to pall, and as public service provision declines embarrassingly, then even the successful will be forced to ask if it was all worthwhile. Hirsch's work offers fascinating parallels with Japanese society – which is obsessed with respect for position and status and which recognises the humiliation should one be passed over by a subordinate. The more individual-oriented norms of western society mean that position is actually best paraded if it has come at the expense of someone else. The desirability of any position or product depends at least in part upon the quality of those who have failed to hold it or own it. Exclusivity implies that others of worth desire or envy what you have. This may be why westerners sometimes wonder how Japan can succeed when even the brightest have to wait for dead men's shoes. Yet, perversely, this system is the very engine of national growth and export effort. The chances of high office are greatest in a large and growing company. It suits everyone to make it grow. As the USA exported its inflation, so Japan has exported its unemployment. Top jobs in Japanese car plants have come from grabbing the export (and home) markets of UK car executives. National economic expansionism leads to individual rewards in the long term (and Japan is nothing if not long-term). The western-style scrabble up the positional ladder (preferably at the expense of others) is socially divisive and short-term. In a winner-take-all society, the word of the top dog is supreme. The post is envied by all. In some organisations this can lead to plotting for personal gain and undermining the boss. It cannot be over-stated that Japan's success stems from a mixture of hard technology and equally hard culture.

Western business analysts have, with some ease, identified not only those who champion initiatives, but those who act as assassins. In theory, at least, Japanese consensus management should prevent this. For some western companies there is the additional problem of how to motivate the dross who realise that they have lost out in the positional lottery. Passed over by the bosses in preference for others more favoured, they may become alienated, feeling that no effort on their part can improve their status. They can become helpless, powerless and demoralised. Examples of this abound in the UK after a decade of Thatcherism. The New Right, representing the aspirations of those who wished to break away from the collectivist pack that had caught up in the inflationary seventies, had kick-started a consumption treadmill. This was necessary for them, since they needed the political support not only of the inflation-averse but of latent aspirers from the pack. The US manifestation was real tax cuts legitimated by Laffer-curve 'voodoo economics'. In the UK there were handouts from the state, but these were usually in areas where the New Right feared the long-term tax burden as in housing and pensions. The UK tax cuts were, for the majority, more illusory than real.

The New Right, probably not much influenced by Hirsch, did not accept that the creation of new incentives for more work and more consumption (the 'carrot') was sufficient to create the necessary relative losers in the scramble for position. They also wanted some 'sticks' with which to beat those who had prospered in the seventies at their expense, doubtless feeling that a good whacking was necessary *pour encourager les autres*. In the UK, most of the predictable losers were in the public sector where the New Right perceived a need to replace notions of public service with the notions of self-interest central to kick-starting workers into a great deal of extra effort – or 'value for money for the public' at little or no extra cost. That is little or no extra *financial* cost: the hidden costs in stress and so on would be borne, as usual, by the workers. The ideal ruse was to insert incentive or performance-related pay schemes (the equivalent of piecework in the private sector). As the work of Hirsch predicted, this created no outright winners, a handful of relative winners and a mass of losers. A good example of the results of the speeded-up treadmill came with the UK tax inspectorate who began performance-related pay in 1988. These workers (or, strictly, a sample of those who had not left) were surveyed in 1991 on behalf of their union. The results were predictable. Those who had not received the performance pay were naturally dispirited. One in three believed that favouritism rather than merit was the key to success. It was also noted that linking pay to performance had created a disincentive to help colleagues; why help someone else to earn more money than you do? Quite so. Jealousies were seen as having increased, and morale had decreased.

It may be that public sector employment was a bastion of those who had read Hirsch and had realised the futility of chasing after the illusion of advancement. If so, they were a real danger to the New Right and certainly had to be brought back on to the treadmill! As we noted in the context of equal treatment for women, the exercise of real power depends upon the criteria for advancement being as vague as possible. Had all tax inspectors been given an attainable benchmark, then all might have attained it, at considerable expense to their employer. The true key to driving more work out of everyone but without actually having to *pay* everyone lies in the power to move the goalposts and create just as many winners as the budget will permit. For the workers, there is then no alternative to working at full speed lest the elusive criteria be missed.

The bond market in revolt

To return to the wider fate of the New Right, tax cuts in the US were invoked simply because they suited Reagan's individualistic ideals. Ominously for Reagan, however, the policy of tax cuts did not appeal to the US bond market as Greider has shown:

> For Wall Street, the reaction to the tax cuts was enormously hypocritical. Aside from sober investment bankers like Henry Kaufman, who had warned against the tax cuts, wealthy investors and major financial institutions were among the most ardent supporters (and beneficiaries) of the supply-side tax reductions. Yet they were the first to react negatively, once the President's legislation had triumphed.
>
> Paul A. Samuelson, an elder eminence among Keynesian economists, observed caustically: 'Wall Street, in early 1981, panted for the tax cuts simply for their favourable income effects. . . . Once Wall Street got its heart's desire, it quickly worked out the consequences'.
>
> . . . So, immediately in mid-1981, Wall Street did what came naturally. It dumped its bonds, bidding up interest rates in the process. . . .

Worse still, there is clear evidence that the Reagan administration knew perfectly well that a deficit would follow the tax cuts.

> In Kudlow's estimate, the bottom line was: the Reagan program was going to produce not a balanced budget but larger and larger federal deficits – in the range of $100 billion or more in each of the next three years. . . .
>
> If the Reagan White House had chosen to state the true consequences of its tax reductions at that moment, the 1980s might have been utterly different. Congress might well have balked at the tax cuts. Or the President might at least have been compelled to moderate his tax proposal. At the very minimum, federal deficits would not have soared to $200 billion a year, doubling the national debt in five years. The recession still would have occurred, but as Paul Volcker had warned obliquely six months earlier, interest rates might have been considerably lower. Less damage would have been inflicted on debtors generally and on the interest-sensitive sectors of the economy.
>
> Between Baker and Meese, the President's senior policy makers decided not to disclose the deficit forecast. The 'rosy scenario' would be maintained as the official version of what the Reagan program would do for the economy, at least until after the tax bill was enacted. (Greider, 1987, pp. 396–7)

Small wonder that Calleo has written of Reagan's economic goals as 'irreconcilable' . . . 'Like most Governments with irreconcilable goals (tax cuts, low inflation but a huge defence budget) the Reagan administration sought refuge in political and economic fantasy' (Calleo, 1987, p. 89) or, as one-time Reagan aide David Stockman put it:

> The trouble is (David Stockman explained) the President's thinking stops in the past. He can trace the money-supply growth all the way back to the sixties, but his money-growth numbers stop in 1980. He still doesn't realize we did the same thing to the money supply that others did. It's the same with deficits. He doesn't acknowledge our deficits. He can't understand why people keep talking about his position on the deficits. He's been against deficits for forty years. Why should anyone question that? (Greider, 1987, p. 541)

This 'living in the past' notion is of some interest. Oddly, if we recall, Ronald Reagan came to government, like Margaret Thatcher, on an anti-government stance. It was, they averred, governments that caused inflation through spending. Oddly, the monetarists' assertion that high interest rates and control of money supply alone could curb inflation was dented by, of all people, President Jimmy Carter who, just before his defeat by Ronald Reagan, told the US people to stop using credit. Astonishingly, they did. Predictably, the banks were horrified. In another rather more real attempt at solving the root cause of inflation, Carter also tried to cut America's excessive oil consumption. Inflation may have started in the 1960s and before, inspired by the US government, but for most of the 1970s it ran on under its own power. (That said, we can always reserve a little special mention for Nixon's inflationary tinkering with the monetary system.)

In essence, the Reagan/Thatcher innovation was a preparedness to try to tighten up and let (un)employment take the strain, which it did. How did Reagan get away with it? He did so by tapping a deep root of national identity. As the Scots reinforce their identity by being 'not English' and the Canadians by being 'not American', so the Americans sustain themselves in relation to an abhorrence of Communism. Reagan's aggressive defence policy was critic-proof, as was his promise to deliver, and delivery of, cuts in direct taxation. Above all, like Margaret Thatcher in the UK, he had promoted the great illusion of non-government. If government had handed power back to the people, how could the people blame government if it all went wrong? Furthermore, with hot money flowing into both countries, chasing a fast buck, why should anything go wrong for the majority in the short term? Indeed, it did not. Those who suffered the worst effects of the recession of the early 1980s were not natural Republicans or Conservatives, and thus the political damage was minimal. That said, it took the 1982 Falklands miracle to drag Margaret Thatcher out of a deep hole of unpopularity. No wonder the actual practice of early 1980s political life in the USA was uncomfortable.

> While the Federal Reserve was confronting inflation with tight money and high interest rates, the Reagan government was embarking in the opposite direction. The President's across-the-board tax reductions would be stimulating the economy, while Volcker was trying to retard it. . . . How could the supply side tax cuts pump up economic growth if the monetarists' money policy was simultaneously retarding it? How could the Reagan program lead to a balanced budget if the tax cuts were at the same time increasing the deficits? (Greider, 1987, pp. 358–66)

Greider's thesis was that the pressure cooker of tight money, high inflation and tax-cutting meant that one of those three had to give – yet there are two holes in the pressure cooker. One, already noted, is the Euro-dollar market. The second is that the contradictions could work themselves out through internal restructuring.

The charitable viewpoint is that US banks, from around 1984, shrank from Third World loans in order to shore up their corporate portfolios with less troublesome respectable loans. The problem was that the new loans were hardly much better than the old. The desire for a quick fix immediately exacerbated the problem of short-termism in the open UK and US equity markets. A further problem was that, starved of new money, the Third World was rendered even less capable of servicing its accumulated debt.

In the 1980s, this was indeed how the paradox worked out. Internally, the problem of finance was solved by redistribution of incomes from one group to another. Just as, internationally, the money flowed from weak economies to strong, so it flowed internally from the economically weak to the economically strong.

Coincidentally, of course, whilst the UK had concentrated on tax redistribution rather than tax cuts, tight money began to go out of the window in 1985, uninhibited by any credit controls. Doubtless the fears for the banking system had spread, yet the expansion was sufficient to pull manufacturing production up. By election year 1987, it had reached the same level as that last achieved in 1978 – a true measure of the Thatcher 'miracle'. Three years down the line from 1985, the 'Lawson boom' sent the trade deficit into eleven figures. We should pay special attention to how this came about.

The Lawson experience

In the late 1980s the UK economy, though still buoyed up by oil, was characterised by high inflation and a deteriorating trade balance. With taxation, credit control, and trade tariff policies all eschewed, only high interest rates were being used as an economic regulator. The expressed aim was to reduce spending, and a key indicator was to be a hoped-for drop in retail sales. Retailers might have cause to wonder why poor business for them should be seen as a success for everyone else! At such times, retailers again need to turn to the truisms of spending patterns. The poor, including those newly-impoverished by high interest rates, spend more on food, on basics, and less on discretionary durable goods purchases. This prediction was adequately borne out in the resulting trade figures.

In fact there are interesting parallels between the UK and USA balance-of-payments deficits as manifest by the late 1980s; both reached over 3 per cent of the national income. The difference lies in the fact that Reaganomics led to a comparatively gradual decline through the eighties, but the 3 per cent figure was approached by 1984 and hovered around

that level for the subsequent four years. It is ironic that Nigel Lawson, then Chancellor of the Exchequer, began to lecture the USA on the need to raise taxes in order to control inflation and spending! Having had five years to watch the collapse of the US balance of payments through excessive tax cuts, Lawson himself decided to follow suit. His £32bn. of tax cuts for the upper-rate tax payers, put together with a higher percentage of individuals in control of what they chose to pay themselves, plus the 1987 G7 decision (causing the pound to 'limbo dance under the dollar') (Hallsworth, 1990a), the lack of exchange controls and a booming house market in the south-east of England all finally ran rampant, Reagan-style. In just the one year following the 1987 G7 decision and the 1988 budget, Lawson achieved all that Reagan had struggled for four years to arrive at – that deficit of 3 per cent of national income. Remember, too, that UK costs are not factored in dollars – a double blow. The story was all too familiar. Yet another blow for the small and the weak – yet another excuse for the powerful UK multinationals to source and produce abroad.

If one wanted to invest abroad, the easiest simplest and safest bet was to join the Japanese in buying up the USA. With UK industry lacking the capacity to cope with freshly-released spending power, imports were sucked in from abroad. The deficit had to be financed, and generally it was financed by high interest rates paid by those who probably benefited least from ten years of tax restructuring. Suggestions made at the time by Chancellor Lawson that the deficit merely amounted to the attraction of foreign money to a successful economy hardly held water, especially if one holds to the primacy of manufacturing export in national endeavour.

The decision to let the pound fall below the dollar was highlighted in a 1990 TV broadcast by the eminent parliamentarian Enoch Powell. He also suggested that the 1987–8 money boom released by Lawson was a further product of the UK bowing to US pressure to keep the pound weak relative to the dollar. Again, this is but a partial explanation of a complex problem; if one needed to accept the monetarist arguments at face value, then the mistake of the late Lawson years was surely to attempt to track the strong Deutsche Mark. Lawson may have seen this as a precursor to monetary union, but with such moves a long way off it came to look rather more reminiscent of 1925. In April 1925 the pound resumed at its prewar level of $4.86. This was widely construed as a gross overvaluation of around 10 per cent. It was closely related to old City theories of trust, confidence and stability. Instead, perhaps unfairly, it was actually seen as an obvious parading of such blatantly unsustainable strength that the world suspected even worse structural weakness than was actually present in the UK economy at that time.

In 1925 the consequence was a decline in industry as the exchange rate was so uncompetitive; that same overvaluation stimulated cheap imports which further undermined the economy. The parallels with 1988 are all too obvious. Ominously, in the long run, the 1925 mistake led on to the depression of the 1930s. There has to be some irony for students of

Britain's 1990 balance of trade, unemployment and interest rate disasters, in returning to Keynes' general theory and finding his criticisms of the City in the pre-war period writ large. How, he wondered, could they have been so stupid as to neglect unemployment and attempt to control policy via the bank rate and fixed parity to foreign exchanges? Perhaps Margaret Thatcher was being Keynesian in opposing entry to the ERM in October 1990 and thus effectively reimposing that which Keynes had railed against?

Whatever the motivation, the period from late 1987 to late 1989 showed a dramatic turnaround in perceptions of the efficiency of Mrs Thatcher and her Chancellor. Just as the volte-face on monetary policy that took place in 1979/80 caught out those already ensnared in the net of debt, so the Lawson mini-boom of 1988, driven by interest rates of 8 per cent, roped in some new victims. A Powellite loss of sovereignty? . . . a misreading of the savings figures? . . . an over-reaction to the 1987 crash? . . . or simply a blatant exercise in wealth distribution? . . . all paths led the same way. Billions of once-public money flooded into the private arena just in time to utilise low interest rates and buy up the companies rocked by the events of October 1987, or buy up imported manufactured goods.

Within months, interest rates rose, debt burdens accelerated and demand collapsed. As Claude Rains advised in *Casablanca*: 'round up the usual suspects'. High wage claims by the workers (who still had yet to see their very first reduction in total tax burden) were trundled out as the stock whipping-boy for what was, in reality, the most fundamental of inflationary blunders by the government itself.

The generous provision by the 1988 Lawson budget of personal capital liquidity to those at the top of society only partially explains the resulting deficit. There also has to be a propensity to spend on foreign products. Evidence is abundant that this propensity, notably absent in Japan, is all too evident in the UK. If we can believe the figures, then savings in relation to personal incomes in 1988 declined to levels not seen since 1958, when incomes were lower and there was less available capital for saving. It would appear that the Chancellor found a ready ally in his deficit aims. The population was by no means 'running on empty', as the unreliable savings figures implied, but was ready and prepared to indulge in the import boom.

No period of UK economic life better mirrored the inherent contradiction of Thatcherism than the 'Lawson boom'. Once the Lawson boom had released a flood-tide of roaring inflation, the pressure rose to dampen it back down again. However, economic success (or income-redistribution if you prefer) having been predicted on enterprise, self-interest and the tax-cut incentive, it was politically unacceptable to put back the planks that had so foolishly been removed from the floodgates. A reversion to pre-1988 tax rates for the rich was not on the agenda. Instead, appeals were made, from 1989 onwards, for collective pay restraint: this from the very administration that had spent over a decade disparaging collectivism of any ilk. Indeed, the appeals were, if anything, even more nonsensical than is implied by my use of the term 'collective pay restraint'. For the Thatcher government and its successors were actually calling for collective pay restraint – organised individually! To understand the nonsensicality of this, one need but translate the message – as intended – to the level of the individual.

How sensible and realistic to expect a low-paid worker 'in the national interest' to voluntarily take a substantial reduction in income in order to ensure that society at large could continue to offer massive incentive tax-cuts to the rich! The pay-restraint message was delivered to the masses coterminously with the publication of swathes of evidence that the rich had never, ever, had it so good. Fines of up to £5m. for a little untowardness in the City were seen to be comfortably affordable from the small change in the pockets of *nouveau-riche* entrepreneurs. Under such circumstances, what harm could be caused by the average worker taking home a pay increase that probably did not even match the underlying real rate of inflation? A decade of reductionist thought that dragged all issues of national economic effort down to the level of the individual and to nannying chats about individual responsibilities backfired spectacularly. Just as unemployment was someone else's problem (likewise the underfunding of any aspect of civic life not directly affecting the individual), so pay-restraint was, perfectly naturally, cast in the same mould. Thatcherism had set in train the fool's errand of seeking after positional gains for the individual. It could not now revert to collectivism. Just as the Japanese export treadmill was unregulated, so was the UK's race back to inflation, and only unemployment could bring it back down again. The Conservatives would not themselves take, centrally, the only measures that could stave off the plunge into recession. Instead, as we have seen, they relied on the very collectivity of interest among the British people that they had spent a decade beating out of them. The ultimate tragedy was how little of the Lawson boom went on building up UK industry (other than those parts that were foreign-owned).

The purchase by private individuals of innumerable Japanese cars hardly signified a 'buy British' campaign. By 1990 the disaster called for a neutral budget and claims that the fiscal calamity was merely a reaction to the bad times precipitated by the stock market crash of 1987. Keegan (1990) had a slightly different perspective:

> Way back before the 1987 General Election I suggested that, if Labour won, the economic situation they inherited would bear comparisons with 'a poisoned chalice'.
>
> But when the Conservatives won for the third time in a row, and inherited their own poisoned economic chalice, the last thing any commentator seriously expected was that the Government would administer even more poison to itself. The feeble state of the manufacturing base as a whole – notwithstanding many isolated success stories – was such that imports of manufactured goods soared way ahead of exports and, with oil no longer making a dynamic contribution, the balance of payments of current account went into deficit.
>
> Not only have the basic Thatcher/Howe/Lawson economic policies failed; so has the remedy the Government applied when, while not exactly conceding

> defeat, they acknowledged that a little 'correction' was in order. The failure of the Government's professed attempt to overcome Britain's fundamental industrial and inflationary problems meant that the economy was in no shape to respond to Mr Nigel Lawson's expansionary period of 1987–88.
>
> The industrial capital stock had contracted sharply, and the oil had been squandered. While charging the Opposition, then came the famous 'tax reforming' Budget of March 1988, when tax cuts at an annual rate of £6 billion were injected into an economy where lending to consumers was rising at an almost unprecedented rate. As it is, high interest rates, and, more specifically, high mortgage rates hit an obvious section of the population but actually benefit the better off – who are net savers. In any case, the monetary policy itself is ambiguous. With one voice the Government tells us it is raising interest rates to curb spending: with another it says we should have the freedom to borrow. Any sane monetary adviser arriving from outer space would advise compulsory deposit and minimum repayments on the purchase of cars and consumer durables (we used to call them hire purchase control); he, or she, would also instruct the banks to limit their consumer lending to a certain maximum growth rate each year.
>
> Yet during this period of so-called 'restraint' and high interest rates, people cannot move for offers of zero interest rates and unlimited credit on car purchases. This Government has always placed greater reliance on 'invisibles' than the experts have advised. The backbone of the City's foreign exchange earnings is traditionally insurance, but the Government never took out enough insurance in the manufacturing base, which provides the bulk of total foreign currency earnings.
>
> Do you recall the days when we were told this did not matter, because dividends from the North Sea surplus would buttress the invisibles? The deficit on invisibles is struck after taking credit for those earnings. Meanwhile, we continue to shell out high interest payments on vast short-term deposits of overseas money in London, which are financing our excessive levels of consumption – excessive, that is, in relation to our ability to pay for them out of our own production. (W. Keegan, *Observer*, 18 May 1990)

The 'poisoned chalice' argument equally has a parallel with US experience. As Keegan intimated, the real post-industrial disaster post-1988 in the UK is the collapse of invisibles. Let us not forget Ingham's point that as a trading/retailing nation the UK has never been in surplus on visible trade. It is simply the case that visible trade had never before been so disastrously awful and invisibles so poorly placed to help. One small irony may be that having created a dual economy (of cheap labour supporting an investment-rich super-class), this may be coming back to haunt the UK. With wage rates at half those in Germany and two-thirds of those in France or Italy, the UK is in every sense cheap. An examination of hourly wage rates in peak inflation years 1970 to 1977 showed that, in local currency and inflation-adjusted, US wage rates rose 11 per cent. In the same period, UK wage rates rose 33 per cent, whilst The Netherlands saw a 54 per cent rise, West Germany 63 per cent and Italy 77 per cent.

The cowing of the British working class has attracted billions of pounds of foreign investment – the UK is the logical cheap gateway to Europe. This investment makes profit returns back to the home country and wrecks the invisible trade balance. Clearly, foreigners investing in the UK make a better fist of it than UK investors looking abroad. Why do they bother? Worse still, an additional attack on invisibles comes in interest payments on the hot money that actually funds the deficit. Clearly, Myrdal's 'circular and cumulative causation' model is lost on politicians.

As is so often the case, retail suffers both directly and indirectly from poor national economic performance. The classic example of the retail trade suffering a cold when the economy sneezes comes with home-related sectors. Groups such as Lowndes Queensway, Coloroll and Laura Ashley suffered badly in 1989/90 from their heavy dependency on increased spending on the home and especially with purchases related to house-moving. The dreadful housing stagnation produced by a policy-induced price boom followed by a policy-induced mortgage rise, scuppered the UK house market (especially in the south-east) during 1989. Individuals chose to postpone housing moves, or were simply unable to move; the depressed demand for home furnishings thus affecting Laura Ashley, Coloroll and others. The process of fitting-out new property went into decline, further depressed by interest rate rises. These two chains were further squeezed by their existing heavy borrowings and the need to repay at high rates of interest. Overall, then, the New Right governments in a globalist mould did rescue the bond markets — at the expense of mass employment and mass consumption.

The contrast between the enduring centrality of those with accumulated wealth and the expendability of the wage-earning classes was emphasised in 1991 by an editorial in *The Times* (17 June 1991, p. 15), which stated:

> British citizens are losing jobs, homes and small businesses in record numbers. But when they ask for relief, the Chancellor's reply is phlegmatic and unyielding. They are cannon fodder in a just war against inflation and their sacrifice is a 'price well worth paying'. Now a group of the wealthiest in the land, including sportsmen, actors and five dozen sitting Conservative MPs face large financial losses as underwriters at Lloyds. The Treasury snaps to attention. Politically, morally and economically, this beggars belief.

That relief for the rich was proposed (though admittedly not provided) should certainly not beggar belief, being perfectly in tune with the times.

At the same time, the Japanese production juggernaut rolls on in overdrive. Imports are pumped into economies like those of the US and UK where free market sentiments prevail. This is a route to mutual disaster. If we accept Wolferen's thesis that Japan *cannot* slow down, then we probably have to accept that the global capital markets are equally incapable of ceasing to pump investment to wherever it will maximise returns, which is likely to be Japan. Thus, the last thing that Japan will ever again be sorry about is the shortage of cheap capital that first set it on its cost-conscious way! Even as the coffers overflow, Japan and other mercantilist nations just cannot stop those little aids to industry that are, these days, so much more subtle. Whilst, for much of the last decade, the US and the UK have gone on squandering their oil assets, the Japanese have instigated yet more energy-saving policies that have made their industries ever more cost-effective.

The French, also without oil resources, promoted a car industry that specialised in diesel engines. This is now a major export booster. The Germans (again oil-free) promoted catalysed engine emissions. Naturally their domestic industry was well ahead of foreign rivals and thus the market was protected. Since oil price rises have been a key source of price inflation, it should hardly surprise us that the UK and the USA, with profligate attitudes toward this resource, have suffered worse inflation than those countries choosing, or forced, to conserve.

8

Operations of the Financial Markets

The foregoing consideration of financial change in the post-war period begs a fairly obvious question. If German and Japanese companies are so wonderful, why are investors not buying *them* up, rather than UK or US companies, given that the world is awash with capital (or junk)? Essentially, the answer lies in the fact that it is extremely difficult to make a hostile bid for a German or Japanese company, even if one could find the likely target quoted on the stock exchange of Frankfurt or Tokyo. Even before one begins to examine the foreign ownership restrictions, one is faced with a simple reality. The stock exchanges of Germany and Japan exist, largely, to facilitate the raising of investment capital. The exchanges of the UK, USA (or Australia) exist to facilitate the transfer of corporate control. Because these differences exist, the stock price levels contrast greatly. UK equities appear cheap, and control is easy to achieve. So, even with the premium to be paid for control, the UK stocks represent a bargain. One of the few ways for existing stockholders to show a good real return is to sell when the stocks are at a premium – under bid conditions. Using 'fictitious capital' to buy real firms is the link to reality – or unreality. The share price rises associated with them makes bids popular with shareholders. Concerned managers, on the other hand, want to make the company look unattractive to bids. They do not, therefore, expose themselves to risk, nor keep piles of money lying around or take costly loans for long term investment. Indeed, if they have a pile of cash it is best to dispose of it (by taking over the next chap). This risk-aversion and refusal to make costly investments can make the firms less competitive, especially in capital-intensive industrial sectors. Capital is not invested for the future, but on keeping a firm afloat. Thus, rightly, the equities are down-valued. Nationally, economic performance declines and high interest rates shore up capital inflow, which puts up costs and decreases the likelihood of investment. (Go back and start again!)

The supreme contrast between mercantilism and liberalism is that the latter offers any part of the economy for sale. The more that mercantilists refuse to play the game, the more the market-movers come under

Table 8.1 UK/USA exchange rates, first and third quarters, under Thatcherism

Year	*$US exchange rate, February & August*
1979 (3rd)	2.238
1980	2.290
	2.371
1981	2.294
	1.821
1982	1.847
	1.727
1983	1.533
	1.502
1984	1.440
	1.314
1985	1.093
	1.383
1986	1.430
	1.499
1987	1.527
	1.597
1988	1.757
	1.698
1989	1.745
	1.595
1990 (1st)	1.696

pressure from the system to move the tradeable markets. The stronger US economy has always been more attractive than that of the UK, so much so that UK liberals have themselves extensively played the US market itself.

How – as an outsider – one views the US market depends only in part on the exchange rates, but this is a useful indicator for UK investors. Undeniably there are times when the USA has looked a good, cheap buy for your hard pound. February 1985 was not one of those times. On the other hand, it was a wonderful time to be remitting $US profits to the UK. The dream scenario, then, was one of a cheap store purchase in 1979, followed by on-stream profits by 1985 (Table 8.1)

Certain star industrial performers have provided evidence of the impact of exchange rate fluctuations. It was generally considered, through the 1980s, that Jaguar car profits owed less to product characteristics than to the exchange rate. The strengthening $US in the early 1980s boosted sales as the cars became cheaper for US buyers. Fluctuating fortunes at the mercy of exchange rates, however, suggest instability for forward-planning purposes. Jaguar (given its export-dependence) should probably have considered better hedges against this via US operations. In the event, Ford took the plunge and hedged its bets by buying Jaguar.

If we return to one fundamental truism, it is this: it is the entrepreneur/financiers who most consistently seek open markets. The producers of manufactured goods are far more likely to seek protection, and to benefit from it. When Britain ruled both the financial and industrial waves, sought *laissez-faire* open markets, the gold standard and comparative advantage, it would have been economic suicide for intending competitors to expose fledgling industries to the rigours of such competition. Many went off the gold standard and set up trade barriers. When the USA was economic 'top dog' it set about opening doors for its own goods, using geopolitical financial muscle to do it. Shorn of empire, Britain in the 1980s nevertheless tried to play the global game that she had once taught the world. The City structure was tailor-made for the new realities and prospered; the industrial team went down in round one. So long as one has to accept a system of national economies and national accounting, and so long as the citizens of a country pay directly for the wisdom or folly of their leaders, then it is clearly nonsense to suggest that one paradigm of economic performance works for all states. (This realisation came to Friedrich List in 1854.) From this perspective he could conclude that English political economy of the time was an 'insane doctrine which sacrifices the interests of agriculture and manufacturing industry to the pretentions of commerce – to the claims of absolute Free Trade' (List, quoted in Ingham, 1984, p. 156). Much the same type of viewpoint was articulated by Strange (1988) in her realist conception of international politics. In this, the survival and autonomy of the state was seen as the supreme concern. The contrast was drawn between the real needs of the state and the realities of international trading. She cited Japan and France as examples of countries where government and industry linked together (mercantilists both) to forge a stronger national economic base.

The question is whether or not some wider supra-national economic interest exists. There are those who suggest that, if there is, it does not (and should not) come before interests of the state: yet Britain has so often been home to exactly the opposite view. There is abundant evidence that literally for centuries the British system has been suffused in a tradition that was inimical to progress on the domestic industrial front. The education system never geared itself (in the French, Japanese or German manner) to the needs of industry. Only in so far as the City reflects the dominant viewpoint of the power elites can this problem be laid at its door. (Ingham has, however, suggested that the Treasury was once a stumbling-block to funding of state education and of research of industrial relevance.)

Moving the markets

We have now reached the situation where speculation on possible currency rate moves has gone beyond guessing what the national policy makers might do. The currency speculators can target a currency and force changes. The real anathema to some traders is not whether there is a fall rather than a rise, but no market mobility at all. If markets stagnate, structural pressures mean that they have to be moved. It is in this wider, global financial context that the UK and the USA are constrained to make policy. The true motivations of the Volker/Reagan/Thatcher years can only be guessed at. We know that high interest rate policies were extremely good for lenders (the rich) and extremely bad for borrowers (the poor). They were also, yet again, extremely bad for industry, mass employment and mass consumption. That may have been all that they were about, yet high interest rates and hard (harder) currencies have also, always, to be read in the context of the money men. The least said about the US budget deficit the better – but it has left the USA with a tremendous problem of credibility. To keep funding the deficit, the USA must have high interest rates to suck in foreign capital. But this stifles enterprise at home (at least, that element unable to use the Euro-dollar markets to circumvent the problem). The signs of economic weakness mean that in order to maintain confidence, the USA must keep up the interest rates. There is clearly a dangerous circularity from which the USA is shielded, partly because of its reserve currency status, and partly from a self-inflicted unwillingness to deal today with what must be dealt with tomorrow. The use of the term 'confidence' in the context of the economic performance of the UK and the USA is, of course, high comedy. It is precisely because there is no confidence that high interest rate policies have been pursued in virtually all years of the 1980s (bar during the runups to elections). The direst of recessionary conditions seem to be a prerequisite to any easing of the agony for borrowers.

The basic reality is that financial markets are still in a substantial mess, and the classic solution for a bank is to grow its way out. This is yet another reason why UK and US real interest rates have been so high since 1979. The banks can re-assert themselves simply via the spread between borrowers and lenders. The only risk is saturation: small wonder that much market research is devoted to saturation in retail markets. International adventures help push back the frontiers of saturation.

The key problem with global capital flows is, as we have seen, that accounting takes place at a national level. If a country is structurally weak, like the UK, the company operating only in that country suffers the blight placed upon it by the international capital markets. Sadly, it is best to run with the herd rather than attempt to move too far into internal economic solutions. Equally, the ever-more nationalist perspective of monetarism failed at a national level (despite the ostensible support of capital markets in the USA and UK), because the national accounting levels upon which it depended were so full of holes – the biggest, blackest hole being the Euro-dollar market.

Both approaches, Keynesianism and monetarism have, in a deregulated world, come to depend on everyone staying roughly in step. Yet we have seen that the UK and USA have no capacity (or apparent desire) to stay in step with Japan or Germany (for are not scandalously low gasoline prices a hidden subsidy to US industry?). The real battle is where it has always been – between the mercantilists on the one hand and the globalists on the other. The global flows of capital just loosely bind the two. That this dichotomy endures is seen from the fact that a vision of the Japanese and Europeans as 'mercantilist chisellers' was how Calleo saw the US perception of them in the 1970s! They were refusing to go along with America's new economic order. Mostly they still do. The free trade in goods, money, assets and companies is still very much a dream of the US and UK monetarists, and of those too weak to object, as the 1990 GATT round amply confirmed.

If there is a bottom line, it is that we can hardly expect to anticipate the next twist in the tale. All we can do is see what the enduring truisms tend to be. One is that the US and the world economy will never seem to be in balance, and of the global players, only the US can generally speak of credit and blame as matters improve or decline. Everyone else, including Britain these days, is just at the other end of the see-saw.

Of the other stratagems, Japanese-style mercantilism seems to be the only independent option. This too, however, has its flaws, as export effort depends on export markets and Japan has become awash with dollars – and duty bound to keep the USA afloat. Japan, indeed, has more problems on where to 'ground' capital than any other nation, hence the market in fine art and other tradeables, and utterly nonsensical Tokyo property values. Thus, until the resources run out (at which point it does not matter a fig what currency they are denominated in), there is an allure to the USA. With the Euro-dollar market there to fund acquisitions, and the USA up for sale, the sensible short-to-mid-term strategy is to join the Japanese and get buying.

We have already observed that pressures to seek growth in any financier-driven society has given rise to a whole series of waves or merger and acquisition activity (M&A). This was seen as an inevitable consequence of the liberal/globalist position, and it is equally inevitable that Reaganomics would spawn a new wave. For this reason, M&As deserve consideration in a little more detail.

Mergers and acquisitions

One of the more interesting features of mergers and acquisitions is that there is little evidence to suggest they have anything whatsoever to do with economic efficiency. Plender (1990) referred to Keynes's casino-capitalism when he addressed the twin phenomena of mergers and short-termism. Noting the 1980s takeover boom, Plender questioned whether or not this led to greater economic efficiency, suggesting: 'on the face of it . . . the answer appears to be not' (Plender, *Financial Times*, 24 July 1990). Indeed, the late 1980s brought forward a plethora of material from various sources deriding the roots of merger mania. There was certainly no shortage of new material on 'the markets' and much of it reinforced Ingham's earlier analysis. Policy prescriptions proposed by Cosh *et al.* (1990) in order to 'throw sand in the takeover machine' included the suggestion that pension funds should pool resources and actively promote investment and innovation 'like German banks'. They also noted the 'historic preoccupation in Britain with financial rather than industrial values' (Cosh *et al.*, 1990, p. 67).

The mention of pension funds is apposite, for we should not entirely run away with the feeling that short-termism is a spirit that all players bring to the game. Some UK pension funds have long-term aims and frequently seek the advice of analysts whose interests lie with the long-term fundamental strengths of companies. The system, however, does much to frustrate even long-term players. A long-term player can find the goalposts moved by the short-termism of some other sector. Among the financial players, the pensions try to think long-term. Down the corridor at unit trusts, on the other hand, they are more geared to a shorter time-frame. The system as a whole favours the latter. Since companies themselves have a (sometimes exaggerated) view of what the City expects, they too react as they see fit.

Cosh *et al.* further noted Ormerod's 1989 assertion that the UK lags £12–20bn. behind Germany in investment terms. Comment was also made on the dual pricing of firms that results from there being a 'premium for control'. Specific evidence on Japan showed a contrast in levels of takeover activity when compared with the UK and US. Above all, few Japanese takeover bids are hostile – a situation mirroring that in Germany. Clearly, then, it is the pressures that drive firms into hostile M&A activity that should interest us.

Merger mania

We have noted that merger mania is not a recent phenomenon: Dicken and Lloyd (1981) outlined several phases of merger activity. They, too, noted the turn-of-century boom that brought US Steel, Dupont and others into existence. The 1920s were seen to have been a phase that gave rise to General Foods but above all, they noted the significance of the 1960s when:

> Almost the entire relative growth of the very largest corporations in the United States was produced by merger. The Federal Trade Commission found that, if they had not been engaged in mergers, the leading 200 companies would have enlarged their total share of total manufacturing assets from 42.4 percent in 1947 to only 45.3 percent in 1968. In fact, by very active merger activity, they increased their share to 60.9 percent . . . between 1960 and 1971, a total of $53,015 million of assets was involved in the 13,134 mergers occurring in the United States. (Dicken and Lloyd, 1981, p. 67)

It will be argued here that financial pressures to demonstrate growth, without too many questions being asked as to whether or not the growth is real, is a pressure for mergers (and, for that matter, de-mergers). Marx, of course, argued that simple competition in the market would force firms to innovate just to stay in business – not to gain a competitive edge. What is equally clear is that this market pressure for mergers is not evenly spread throughout the developed world. Clifford Chance (1989) in *Takeovers and Mergers in Europe* identified some of the trends. Whilst France was seeing more takeover activity, Belgium was still characterised by a few agreed bids and the rare contested bid. In the context of Germany they noted that the preponderance of family-owned firms in which a lead bank had major equity made companies virtually immune from contested bids.

Dicken and Lloyd suggested that capital available for mergers might have been better spent on investment. If, however, one takes a short-term view, better returns (especially on market share) might be gained by buying a competitor – and maybe closing down some spare capacity. What this can lead to is Bluestone and Harrison's 'capital *vs.* community'. Commenting on the (then) US trade deficit, they suggested that in respect to Japan the USA had been reduced to the status of an agricultural nation trying to compete with a sophisticated industrial producer, adding that companies with money to spend did so on acquisitions – not on reinvestment. They posited a figure of 32–38 million jobs lost to disinvestment in the 1970s.

Surely, though, not all available capital is destined to fund corporate mergers? One area where investment might be more growth-oriented is venture capital, and in 1987 the venture capital industry for the first time raised more finance in Europe than in the USA. The long-term trend, though, has – in the 1980s – been all too familiar: less and less capital funding start-up, and more and more funding buy-outs or buy-ins. Capital as a lever rather than capital as seed-funding has been the trend – and where have we identified as *the* classic UK destination for capital?

Many facets of venture capital, ostensibly geared to improving the industrial base, are effectively laundering money for profit in a classic monetarist way. The British Business Expansion Scheme (BES), introduced in 1983, had, within five years or so, degenerated into a means for raising capital for investment in the housing market. Initially, though, events had looked promising, with over £500m. invested in nearly 1,000 companies, many of them truly high-risk businesses. By 1988, property investments were dominating the scheme. Part of the reason for this shift to easier money in 1987 could have been the substantial cuts in the top rate of UK income tax. In the early days of BES, investors could offset any risks against substantial tax advantages. There were capital gains tax benefits, and relief could be claimed against taxable income at the top rates of tax. With the cutting of tax rates, the marginal benefit had declined. Money swiftly moved to seek the security of asset-based investment. In 1988, BES raised 96 per cent of its funds for asset-based operations, usually housing tenancies. The example of BES is useful as it opens the door to a consideration of the roots of the Reagan-led M&A wave of the 1980s in the USA. If we seek the general roots to that, we find that they lie in three areas.

Mergers and taxation

One facilitator of M&As under Reagan was that the legislation was there to enable it as never before. Reaganite policies exaggerated tax advantages that made it logical, more cost-effective, to buy a corporation than to invest in one's own corporate growth – with the risk that someone else would lever you. The tax breaks all lay with the raider. Take the classic example of a US shopping mall development. It has almost become passé to suggest that malls are built where a market niche exists. From a dominance by insurance companies, all sorts of new investors (and over-investors) can now be found. The over-investor pumps more cash in than the developers' costs – the developer walks away with tax-free dollars. Big players – disastrously – have been the pension funds and Thrifts: all encouraged by Reaganite deregulation and taxpayer-backed funding. With tax-cutting enriching the already-rich (as in the UK), wealthy individuals formed syndicates to seek tax shelters, and property has long been a favourite. Essentially, these people looked to lose money in the long-term property development rather than have the taxman take it. The heavier the debt, the more long-term, the better the tax shelter. Astute tax lawyers found ways of putting together the funding to suit everyone's tax position.

Consider the following:

> syndicators . . . these are the HOT HOT ones . . . are paying outrageous prices. They are not really looking at the economics . . . they are looking at the shelter opportunities. They are often looking for . . . two to one write-offs; you put in a dollar, you write off two in taxes . . . basically they have a very strong tax-orientation. They need very high leverage, they want to maximise financing. (Hart, 1984, address to ICS)

It is evident that the general tax position in the USA served to orient groups and individuals towards retail investment, and this extended to divestment. For example, the least tax-efficient way for the founder of a family firm to retire is to take a payoff. Many European retailers bought into family-owned US firms – why? Because this was a tax-efficient way for the victims to realise some profit. Share-swaps in particular were very tax-efficient. This is one reason why we should not exaggerate the extent to which takeover bids are hostile. Many individual entrepreneurs in the US were happy to get out and leave affairs in the hands of a solidly-run European concern. Furthermore, the liabilities of foreigners towards employees were more lax and disclosure rules less stringent. It was actually easier to sell out to foreigners, as well as being tax-efficient. As Davidson put it, 'the amount of tax savings at issue can be very substantial . . . the tax savings are in effect, a subsidy that both the buyers and sellers want' (Davidson, 1985, p. 206).

For the major corporations, it may well emerge that money otherwise lost to the taxman can be used to purchase – virtually for free – a loss-making firm that has tax credits. Note that the CEO becomes head of a larger firm and thus merits greater reward. The greenest of tax lawyers can quickly show that corporate subsidiaries sheltered by parental tax credits are a financially more efficient proposition than the new-start small firm seeking funding from pre-taxed sources.

This is a clear parallel with the UK BES example just quoted. Inevitably, US corporate matchmakers can find capital-intensive firms with investment tax credits to marry with cash-generating low-overhead companies with great tax liabilities. A good example of the latter would be a foodstore chain operating from rented premises. Merger activity can push tax liability further and further down the line, deferring payment almost ad infinitum as long as the mergers keep rolling in.

Mergers and 'churning'

There are the apologists who are pleased to see active markets and suggest that this wave of activity has been beneficial in some way; 'hundreds of billions of dollars in value have been added' is a typical cry.

Since 1977 in the USA, mergers and acquisitions are filed with the Federal Trade Commission under the Hart Scott Rodino Act. Supporters of the merger activity under Reagan deregulation often point out the figures thus gathered demonstrate that merger activity at the turn of the century and in the 1920s seemed to greatly exceed levels in the 1980s. Sadly, 1920s merger activity hardly presaged a golden age of economic stability in the 1930s. Furthermore, Reagan's deregulation of the airlines, far from allowing entry of smaller players, in fact led to more defensive mergers and created more large players in the market. The shakeouts that really mattered were in the wage packets of personnel – the real route to lower prices, lower motivation and lower standards of service.

What is unarguably evident is that shareholders of target companies benefit most from takeovers: they become personally richer (or the pension fund or controlling financial interest becomes richer). Where the acquisition involves a competing company that has significant shareholder interest, then those shareholders usually benefit too, though to a rather less handsome tune. As with equities, so with takeovers, the major players benefit just so long as the market keeps on moving.

The supporters of LBO activity – including the raiders themselves – appear to operate a simple rule of thumb. Takeovers financially benefit shareholders in acquired companies. *Ipso facto* this indicates that corporate assets have now been put to their most valuable, productive use. This indicates maximum efficiency. It also incorporates a nonsensical circularity. Shareholder benefit can only, by this argument, be proven to have occurred when those shareholdings are sold at the best price – that is, at the very point when shareholders have ceased to hold an interest in the company. The shareholders, whose traditional rôle was to invest capital in a worthwhile venture, can only be proven right in their judgement of a company after they have ceased to exercise it. The whole process begs the question of what happens to shareholder capital once it has been withdrawn from the company at the maximum price. Does the thoughtful shareholder cast about for another badly-managed lame-duck industry in which to invest, in the hope that a raider will shortly be along to boost the price? Or, if an individual, is the capital windfall invested in positional goods?

Furthermore, if we have finally found the maximum price, why are the incoming takeover shareholders investing in a corporation that has reached its maximum potential? For, if it has not, why then did the original shareholders leave? Newton (1989) in a solid critique of corporate raiders pointed out: 'if corporations are to seek for excellence in all respects they must make sure that they are not destroyed by one of these junk-bond bust-up raiders, for when you are dismantled, you cease to exist, and then excellence is very difficult to achieve.'

The result of such protests has been to pressure US states into anti-takeover legislation. Particular approbium has been reserved for the 'Saturday night special', where a tender offer is communicated to the management and to the SEC, with the markets then better placed to suck up shares in the target than the management is placed to respond. One response has been for individual states to develop anti-takeover laws; indeed, Sir James Goldsmith was probably deterred from pursuing BAT all the way to unbundling because of complications with a US insurance division of the group. If we need to take one lesson from the US experience, it is this. Japanese industry began its great revival in the absence of surplus capital. Had excess capital been available, they might have adopted the profligate production practices of Fordism. Lack of cheap capital forced them into flexibility, into controllable production runs that met tight budgets. Is it not ironic that excess capital is knocking over the traces of US industrialisation and berating it for not being more like a society that managed without cheap capital? Indeed, Japan managed so well without cheap capital that capital came into the equation in a subservient rôle. The USA not only has the cart before the horse; the cart is squashing the horse. The attendant deindustrialisation, far from making the USA more competitive with Japan, is making matters worse in the sectors that really count. Blue-collar America, the heart of the manufacturing export effort, is dying out, but the financial decision makers, as in the UK, are not affected. Sethi and Bhalla (1989, p. 209) have stated: 'In its obsession with short-term profits [US industry] has consistently ignored both people and machines. It now finds itself with a relatively inefficient labour force and obsolete plants and equipment.' For US, also read UK.

Yet the above does not tell all the story. US industry still invests heavily in R&D, and it was US industry that invented the robots that so well suited Japan's new production methods. Do we blame industry or do we blame the system? I argue that we blame the latter. Cohen and Zysman (1987) have argued that agriculture increased output by colossal amounts without going offshore — but how could it? What could compete with the great US wheat basket? The system never seemed to learn that industry was more footloose than agriculture, workers more footloose than industry, ideas more footloose than workers, and capital most footloose of all. Instead, greed has its justification as widespread profit-taking goes on — an outcome only possible if the raiders are there to 'churn up the market'. To that extent, the raiders are like the grouse-beaters whose role it is to get the grouse into flight so that the huntin' classes can pot them off from a safe distance. The raiders claim to be chasing out weak, inefficient managers for the kill, but it is less the outcome, more the chance to play the game that counts: the chance to utilise capital via enhanced stockmarket valuations, at least until the markets next collapse. For that reason, it is not the poor, weak gamebirds that are most attractive, but the fat ones with a future — that could go on to produce the next generation of grouse. (Being bigger, the poor shots find them easier to hit anyway.) Target corporations thus are flushed out and shot at, and if they do not die the gun dogs give them a nasty shaking. Goodyear, Phillips Petroleum, Union Carbide and Owens Corning all still bear the teeth marks. As Davidson stated in respect of earlier eras of merger activity, 'One important group who did not care if these mergers failed or succeeded: the bankers . . . the profits came from the merger, not the business' (Davidson, 1985, p. 173).

To the bankers we have now added the junk bond merchants and sundry other market-makers. Indeed, Reagan's deregulatory activities themselves led directly to a spate of defensive mergers, most visibly in the transportation sector (though only Chapter 11 bankruptcy could save Greyhound). One early move was to scotch any new attempts by the FTC to regulate takeover activity. Lest we forget, takeover/merger activity is virtually the natural state of US enterprise. Legislation such as the Sherman Act (1890), Clayton & FTC acts (1914), Celler–Kefauver (1950), Williams (1968) and Hart–Scott–Rodino (1976) was aimed at regulating merger activity. Each left sufficient loopholes for the process to go on. Even though the latter act impinged upon the 'Saturday night special', it could not stop the churning stock-price surges of the tender offers.

Mergers and capital

When we do seek that one great prerequisite, the great facilitator, we find the capital is there in the form of repatriated dollars to fund this once-in-a-lifetime chance to profit-take. This is the inflationary capital of the seventies, that fled abroad, was repatriated by the hard dollar and is now disappearing back either into the defence budget or into the pockets of the owners of corporate America. They let it slip way once — but now it is reserved for the right destination. In the long run, blue-collar America will disappear — or be Japanese run. The service sector will appeal more to the Europeans, with the British well in front in the retail stakes. The leveraged buyout (LBO) environment ensures that purchasers are paying top dollar for America. One can almost find a defeatism about it all. Behind closed doors they seem to be saying that if America has to go, then one may as well get rich selling it . . . perhaps that is even the hidden agenda.

To all this we may add a specifically British perspective. There are differences in accounting procedures between the UK and USA that greatly advantage UK buyers of US retail firms.

Accounting for accounting

Most retail firms comprise a substantial proportion of 'goodwill'. Tangible assets, especially where rental premises are used rather than wholly-owned property, can be difficult to find. How does one make proper accounting allowance for the goodwill that represents the entrepreneurial flair of the retailers or their brands? All the evidence is that companies can substantially differ in productivity and profitability even when trading in the same lines of goods and from similar outlets. This problem of proper accounting extends to manufacturers, who have often engaged in accounting exercises to properly value their famous brand names. One can of beans is not the same as another, and a clockwork watch that happens to have the name Rolex inscribed upon it in some Far East sweatshop suddenly increases in value on the tourist black market.

The crucial point is how proper accounting procedures in the UK deal with goodwill, and also with foreign exchange fluctuations. Consider first the US retailer who buys a UK retailer at a price well in excess of pure asset value (property, stock, etc.). At time of writing the goodwill element must appear in the profit and loss account. It will be amortised and written down over a period of, say, twenty years. As it is set against shareholders' funds, so then (because, inevitably, either direct borrowings have been involved or assets sold in order to fund the deal) the dilution of these funds when seen as a ratio to borrowings gives high gearing. Analysts will be especially interested in gearing in times of high interest rates. In other words, the acquisition appears as a short-term drag on the financial health of the company, no matter how confident it may be of long-term profits or of the true worth of that goodwill. Indeed, there is no tax relief on goodwill amortisation and this again is a drag on the share price.

Contrast this with the UK where goodwill disappears off the balance sheet into reserves (sometimes into negative reserves). The goodwill element – which can be substantial (it has been suggested that more than 50 per cent of the M&S purchase of Brooks Brothers was for goodwill) – does not appear on the P&L account to dilute earnings. There is, then, no short-term, negative effect on the apparent financial health of the new parent, and it may be possible to find tax-efficient ways of dealing with what appears to be losses.

In contrast with the USA, the calculations for Return on Capital Employed (ROCE) are quite different. The UK procedures do call for amortisation, but allow the alternative of setting goodwill against shareholder funds. Virtually without exception this latter course is taken, because this is the open door to what has been described as a 'black hole' down which evidence of such debts soon disappears (the accountants' equivalent of the Euro-dollar). To consider a direct example, the February 1988 edition of *Accountancy* (p. 26) told the following tale: 'The notes to Burton's accounts . . . provides full details . . . of its two main related companies . . . as their accounts are not included in the consolidated balance sheet . . . this shows a lower level of gearing than would otherwise be the case.' The difference was between a true total of £706.8m. and a balance sheet figure of £258.7m. In the UK, the present concern with gearing leads to other financial manipulations. Gearing can be cut by repayment of debt – perhaps through asset sales. Alternatively, one finds means of revaluing assets so that the debt burden instantly reduces as a ratio to those assets. In 1990 one UK retail pharmacist reduced gearing from 174 per cent to 84 per cent simply by placing an asset valuation on its licence to deal with medical prescriptions. Gearing can also be reduced, or development finance raised, by hybrid financial instruments that in effect lay off the debt to third parties, often via a subsidiary of the parent company as Burtons appeared to do. The aim of such instruments (another is the auction market preferred stock) is to keep all negativities out of the P&L account. Another familiar ploy is to set aside as a loss any costs that may be assumed to be about to be incurred if a takeover is completed! These instruments tread a fine line between raising of debt (a direct gearing problem) and sale of equity (an asset dilution/control problem). UK retail companies are well served by accountants who try to outsmart the financial sophistication of the City. At one time, troublesome debt could be loaded via the so-called 'diamond structure' on to subsidiaries that were apparently owned by 'White knights' – but with profits really only accruing to the real owner. Most of these procedures have been entered into precisely in order to make the accounts appear debt-free. This is one means by which firms hope to endear themselves to the City.

Mergers – and on to unbundling

To return to the issue of growth through merger, we can at last trace the final fate of Shoppers' Paradise. The roots of this lie with a 1975 merger that created Linfood holdings. The most prominent retail trading feature of this wholesale-oriented group was the involvement with the French chain Carrefour to develop a handful of Carrefour hypermarkets in the UK. Gateway was acquired in 1977 and Dee Discount in 1979. The crucial move for growth came, however, with the appointment as chairman of Alec Monk, ex RTZ, in 1981. Monk, a financial rather than retail figure, proceeded to grow the business further through acquisition. Keymarkets were purchased for £21.8m. in December 1983, F.A. Welworth for £21.8m. in December 1983, and the group soon adopted the name Dee Corporation. Basically, the financial instruments of the City were being directed into retailing as I indicated that they would, and upon which I expand in the next chapter.

The Gateway saga

The market's demands for growth at Gateway were soon met by further purchases. For £23m. Lennons came into the fold in September 1984, soon followed in December 1985 by International Stores – divested by BAT for £180m. November 1985 saw the minor (£7.8m) purchase of Lonsdale & Thompson. The major purchase of Fine Fare and Shoppers' Paradise from ABF (part of the Weston family empire) cost – by one estimate – £686m. and took place in 1986, probably as a quiet break from April/May 1986 when Woolco, Hermans and M&H were bought for £351m. This was a group that had put together impressive market share, though disposals were to follow (160 Shoppers' Paradise stores in March 1987, Linfood and Digsa in 1988). The now-renamed Gateway group was taking 11.4 per cent of the UK food market in 1988, behind only Tesco and J. Sainsbury. Asda, the superstore pioneers, trailed along in fifth place with 7.7 per cent, and the Shoppers' Paradise identity was totally destroyed. So much for all that splendid IT innovation of a few years previously.

The inevitable problem was that, in building a retail empire, the group acquired a mixed bag of store sizes and locations. Overlap of interests (more than one outlet in the same centre) was not as severe a problem as it might have been but still posed difficulties. This is the opposite of organic growth into new areas where a group is not represented at all. More than one store in a centre, possibly of sub-optimal size and facing superstore pressure from, say, Tesco, Sainsbury or Asda would not be a formula for trading success. This over-supply peaked in 1987 with the Fine Fare acquisition, that included Shoppers' Paradise. The ultimate irony is that, having subsumed so many famous high street grocery stores into its rather vague corporate identity, Gateway itself fell victim to takeover.

In 1989, Gateway fell to the Isosceles consortium which achieved majority shareholding on 14 July (an isosceles triangle was a previous corporate logo). It is probable that the inspiration for the bid came from within Gateway. In December 1987, Barker & Dobson (now Budgen) attempted a takeover of Gateway (then Dee Corporation) but failed. In putting together that bid, John Fletcher of Barker & Dobson submitted proposals for the future of Gateway. For example, the policy of branding all stores, even up to its former Carrefour stores, as 'Gateway' was not a policy universally approved of since the Gateway logo had no image. The result was that several senior staff became increasingly disaffected. Four in particular were believed to be active in negotiating with David Smith, the financial architect of the Barker & Dobson bid, via a colleague who left in August 1988. In April 1989 David Smith launched a £1.7bn bid, backed by investment bankers S.G. Warburg, for Gateway – under the Isosceles name. Gateway immediately applied an injunction on the 'rebel four' and they were suspended.

The final takeover of Gateway was complicated by the rival bidding of the Newgateway group backed by Wasserstein Perella. Newgateway,

Table 8.2 Staffing levels of the Gateway group, 1986–9

	1989	*1988*	*1987*	*1986*
Full-time staff	34,525	38,341	39,113	25,028
Part-time staff	39,138	38,090	36,646	21,954
Ratio of full-time to part-time	0.88	1.01	1.07	1.14

Source: Gateway company annual reports.

a vehicle for the US-based A&P (itself 51 per cent owned by the German Tenglemann group) had somewhat different plans for a future Gateway, and built up a share of 39.8 per cent in the company despite being bested by Isosceles. A key point of difference was that Isosceles had already pre-planned and, indeed, pre-announced a major divestiture that would cut debt. This was the sale of sixty-two superstores to Asda for around £705m. Since the Isosceles team would naturally see the stores as a separate division with probably a separate identity, it was not illogical to dispose of them and concentrate on smaller stores. Newgateway, however, felt that, since the stores represented 30 per cent of total sales, they should be retained (or selected stores sold on a regional basis). Pulling out of London, the north-west and other areas would render superfluous some £700m of assets – comprising rather more stores (perhaps 250) – though selected spatially rather than by size. Interestingly, after the Asda sale, the Isosceles management was reported by October of 1989 to also be looking to regional sell-offs of stores. The argument was that Gateway had too many stores *per se*, and many had to go.

What is clear from company records is that Gateway was following the industry trend of divesting itself of shopfloor staff and particularly full-time staff (Table 8.2). On the other hand, the incoming new management had to pay out £16m. in 'benefits' to remove the old incumbents at the top of Gateway! Following the 1987 peak, fuelled by the Fine Fare acquisition, staffing levels and thus labour costs can be seen to have been progressively reduced. None of this solved the image problem and may have tested the loyalty of those who genuinely liked their International or Fine Fare outlet. This begs the whole question of how thoroughly Gateway approached the decision to 'badge' *all* their stores as Gateway – one of the sources of internal dispute as noted above. As of October 1990, available figures for Isosceles/Gateway showed an operating profit of £113.9 millions – obliterated by interest charges to give an overall loss.

It is not just in mergers that the significance of financial performance manifests itself in the retail sector. It has been suggested that in some firms other financial mechanisms are used, not least the massaging of figures. In areas such as acquisition accounting, capitalisation of interest, property profits and off-balance sheet finance, many are wary of the figures that emerge. Retailers seeking market position have had to spend heavily on store refitting, for example. Expenditure on acquisitions is necessarily complicated by provisions for goodwill. These can be inflated in value whilst true asset value is deflated. The surplus thus released can make a useful contribution to the balance sheet. Poor disclosure, some argue, is so blatant as to actually deflate stock market ratings in the stores sector. The game, as it were, has been rumbled, and firms of analysts are now taking courses in accountancy procedures. Yet who can blame the retailers for reacting to the system?

Lest we conclude that the Gateway saga (any more than that of R.J.R. Nabisco) begins and ends with debt-funding, we should note that the 1991 turn of the wheel saw attempts at equity dilution. Corporations thus wriggle and squirm between the twin perils of how to raise capital. That is, UK and US corporations wriggle and squirm. Major German and Japanese corporations sit content in their debt funding. They do so in the knowledge that theirs are the two key bond-driven inflation-averse countries. Supremely, they do so because the banks can be trusted.

Debt or equity? Choose your poison

In choosing which fund-raising gamble to take, ideal-typical UK or US corporations find that debt looks simpler (except if the corporation actually notices high *real* interest rates) because corporate control is not diluted. Equity dilution can appear cheaper, but may lead to a dividend treadmill as shareholders demand their payment at all costs, though in some instances, debt can be tax deductible. On balance, unless the company culture favours one method over the other at all times, corporations will rebound from debt to equity whenever one looks a better bet than the other. That said, companies in cyclical businesses may be vulnerable in a downturn if too much of their equity is tradeable.

By and large, the views of the institutions and other key shareholders weigh heavily. In this context it is worth noting that UK companies currently give away around 60 per cent of residual income in dividend payments. Institutions may become aggrieved if the usual payout fails to arrive. Of course, in the UK they may be aggrieved on behalf of their clients. These are the holders of, say, unit trusts, who have entered the equity markets for regular profit.

This rather lays the myth of the individual shareholder who chooses to support a company through thick and thin and is a regular attender at annual meetings. The bulk of those who make indirect investment in UK equities have very little idea of which companies have received their investment income. What these investors *do* know is that they have put in capital and, by golly, they want a dividend at year-end! It is not difficult to see how this engenders short-termism. The ideal-typical German investor saves through bonds: the classically inflation-averse route to much longer term payoff.

At this point we have covered the two main aspects of this book. We have noticed the decline, as the Americans put it, of the middle class. Markets have segmented and individualised. As standard occupations have declined, so worth has ever more frequently been defined by possessions – sometimes by 'positional goods'. Retailers have been at the forefront of defining and providing such goods. Additionally, however, the events of August 1971 meant that there has been a global crisis of worth. The old manufacturing processes (ideal-typically of Fordism) have broken down. Consumption, however, has rolled on. The retailers themselves have thus gained in worth. They have become takeover targets – wherever for sale. I therefore argue that analyses based solely on industry cannot but be partial.

Any number of problems ensue when one focuses too heavily upon just manufacturing. Should it surprise us that the productivity levels in banking and insurance have outstripped those in manufacturing? This book places the power of capital in a position of pre-eminence (did not capital beat technology in the case of Shoppers' Paradise?). Bankers and insurers deal directly with this capital, moulding it, diverting it (sometimes illegally as in the case of the 1991 scandal at BCCI). The manufacturing route to profit is more circuitous. Fixed costs are incurred even before the product has come to market, at which point the risk is that it may fail to sell. Then it is necessary to ensure that the sales are profitable (the famous British automotive success story, the Mini, never had much of a profit margin built in).

Clearly, manufacturers are on the accumulation treadmill lest their products become substituted and profit starts to fall. The banking sector, like some individuals, merely needs to recycle finance (or credit) in order to profit from profits. Thus many powerful agents are long past the point where they personally need to produce in order to accumulate. Other imperatives, including conspicuous consumption, have become more important.

Banking: hands on capital

There is increasing standardisation of financial operations around the globe. The major difference is likely to remain the impenetrability of Japan by foreign banks. Even if Japan offers greater access, the likelihood that this will lead to a practical breakthrough seems remote, given Japanese performance in other areas. Almost the only imaginable scenario is that the Japanese will wisely allow foreign investors to expose their assets to their over-inflated property sector. A talent for buying in at the top of the market should ensure some spectacular losses in the inevitable collapses. Japanese banks are involved with takeovers of companies in other countries, whilst takeover of Japanese companies remains very difficult. This in itself should be an indication of the significance of retaining locally-controlled industry. The Rowntree Mackintosh takeover saga in the UK suggests that such lessons are hard to learn. The trouble with turning oneself into a giant corporation is the risk that one might choose the wrong target for merger or takeover. Recent evidence suggests that, for UK companies, the USA remains a land with many pitfalls. The sad experience of Midland Bank in its dealings with Crocker Bank of California is a classic case in point. Between the world wars the Midland was the world's largest bank, yet it made major errors in its choice of Crocker in 1980. By 1992, restructuring of Midland in conjunction with another bank became inevitable and staff were again in the firing line.

Banks have been well to the fore in the developments that we have seen, but valuing bank assets is an art form. All that can be said for certain (to paraphrase Keynes) is that if you owe a bank £1,000, you have a problem; if you owe £1 million then the bank has a problem; if the bank owes £1,000 million then the Bank of England has a problem. The classic UK bankers' response mirrors that of the insurance companies: if you spread the risk widely, you can operate at the level of actuarial behaviour of cohorts. How they came to value Third World debt as a better vehicle than UK industry remains a mystery, except that the required equity/asset ratios almost always force banks to try to grow their way out of trouble, and quickly.

The overall behaviour of Japanese banks, then, is relatively simple to grasp. It may be scorned as corporatism, but they supported the key sectors of industry that it had been decided would grow. They lent at low interest, were risk-averse and detested inflation. They saw their policy pay off as Japanese cars flooded into the UK and the USA. Despite the low interest rates, the pay-off was good because the Yen firmed against the pound and the dollar.

The UK and US, in paying for the tons of imported consumer goods, remitted the Japanese in relatively worthless currencies. What to do? On the one hand, the Japanese quickly got rid of excess dollars (and pounds) by wholesaling them back to the USA (and UK). However, investment in the USA had an attractive side. Japanese firms, as we have seen, are geared to growth in order to offer career opportunities to the core workers (just as they are geared to using technology to keep the core as small as possible: this is essential as the population profile ages). The banks helped by investing in production and soon realised that they had also better help with the consumption. Where would the Japanese sell, if the UK and USA became too poor to buy? The simplest bet was to pump up the US economy with capital investments and bond purchases. Japanese investment and other external interest in the US (and now the UK) is a logical consequence of open markets and corporations for sale. It does not, of course, totally insulate Japan from world recessions in which its vital markets dry up.

9

THE FINANCIAL MARKETS AND RETAIL FIRMS

Having set the scene with the Gateway example, let us now try to expand upon how retail firms in those OECD countries that espouse a globalist perspective have found themselves thrust, often unwillingly, into the International Political Economy. This is not a phenomenon widely discussed by retail researchers but some have considered the trends, notably Kacker (1985). Others have commented on the 1980s merger-wave amongst retailers: Savitt has pointed out that as major American retailers explored financial markets to pursue their own growth and development programme, they exposed their assets and operating statements to a wide variety of investors. As production gave way to consumption, so UK retailers experienced much the same phenomenon.

These investors are not difficult to trace. By 1990 receipts by British pension funds were worth £12 billion per annum and the funds owned £263bn of shares – some 29 per cent of the stock market. Pension contributions are, often unwittingly, feeding the juggernaut that is consuming UK industry, and pumping up share prices to the benefit of owners. The pension funds, in effect, by asset-chasing, are redistributing money from the poor to the rich at least as effectively as Thatcherism itself. The same applies in the USA. Again, it should be stressed that this is part of the process – the way that financial matters are structured. The funds, mostly cannot help themselves – they have to invest. Note that by putting industry first, the Japanese did not lose out in investment terms; the world's single biggest investor is the Japanese Post Office.

Speaking in 1987, Andrew Sigler, chairman of the US corporation Champion International, had no difficulty in identifying the roots of the US buyout phenomenon, nor the investors involved in it:

> takeovers wouldn't be possible without the pension money. We've gone from practically nothing to approaching 2 trillion. The pension money owns American equity today. It is totally short-term driven. Stock is priced today on a formula of what the current earnings or expectations of earnings in the next quarter are. Period . . . You borrow all the money, you go in and sell the

> assets, and you make what's in between. That's a takeover, that's how it's played . . .
>
> . . . what we are doing now is absolute madness. It has forced a short-term attitude on us . . . caused companies not to do . . . long term investment, creation of jobs, creation of wealth and R&D. All these kinds of things that we're supposed to do to keep this country strong, we haven't done'. (Sigler, 1989, pp. 87–8)

This tone contrasts strongly with the Hayek/Friedman axis and seems more in tune with the thoughts of retail pioneer and millionaire philanthropist Edward Filene who observed many years ago: 'Why shouldn't the American people take half my money from me? I took all of it from them.' Incidentally, Mr Filene funded the foundation that sponsored Fred Hirsch's work. Mr Filene would have been distressed by the moves made simply in order to facilitate takeovers. In 1981 the new issue market for bonds in the USA was worth a paltry $1.3 billion. Then Michael Milken of Drexel Burnham Lambert conflated the demands of commerce for bank-free funding with the junk bond and hooked it into LBOs. This was a lightning-conductor for grounding capital (though we should not overstate the extent to which junk was the financial instrument of first choice). Drexel/Milken was soon averaging around 60 per cent of the total junk bond market. This market soared to over $32 billion by 1986 (with total outstanding debt around $125bn.) whilst 1987 saw the record $26bn. single deal by Kohlberg, Kravis Roberts for R.J.R. Nabisco. Banks, squeezed out of the companies market to an extent by bond issues, ploughed investment into real estate in the US in the 1980s. Many of these deals have turned very sour with debtors simply walking away from half-finished building projects.

At root, we have seen that everyone in the 1980s was looking for real asset value. It became the decade when the intractable dollar problems of the 1960s came home to roost. Like the 'goldbugs' who longed for the days of the gold standard, there was real concern as to what capital was worth in the sense of what it could buy. The eighties became the decade for those with sustainable and sometimes not-so-sustainable ideas of how to make money from money.

There was a five-fold increase in the number of billionaires in the world. Many of these individuals made nothing but money, destroying the myth of industrial enterprise. Others just watched their existing assets inflate, thereby maintaining their positional status. Others still were well placed to manipulate hard assets that the inflating money-markets would value. Property was not the least such asset.

At the same time, all stockholders and stakeholders began to look closely at asset value. Corporate raiders promised better returns to investors than existing management seemed capable of. Other vulnerable companies with sizeable minority shareholdings took fright. Managers and those who had been outright owners of companies tried to buy back, 'take private', the residue of company shares from the open market. Junk bonds were raised to facilitate these buy-outs and buy-ins.

Some of the most significant beneficiaries of the buy-out ethos were the managers of sub-divisions of major conglomerates. These conglomerates, facing trading pressure, often concentrated on their core business and floated off sub-divisions. Where the managers led the buy-out and where the markets favoured the new freestanding operations, massive windfall profits fell into the hands of individuals who went from salaried management status to millionaire status virtually overnight. Indeed, a lack of a track record was positively beneficial as future prospects were hard to assess. Any new venture that promised substantial returns would attract the attentions of a bank, a deregulated Savings and Loan or other financial organisation. It was possible for capital to flow out of long-established industrial firms even as it was flung into speculative ventures of almost any sort: 24-carat 'Casino capitalism'.

The overall message should be clear: there are inherent reasons why all existing commercial assets in western countries became the focus of investment attention in the 1980s. The 1980s was also the decade when the USA and the UK in particular further opened up their markets. Capital flowed to those countries where corporate restructuring was most easy. With closed borders, capital investment would have repositioned internally rather than internationally.

Safeway

I wish particularly to emphasise that the Third World disaster focused US capital back in on itself. Figures are hard to come by, but I suggest that if we strip out from the buy-ins and buy-outs the identity of the main actor(s) and search instead for the source of the capital, we will find that it is repatriated US capital that has dominated the restructuring of its own economy. Having quickly summarised why the 1980s became the LBO decade, we can delve into two case studies that illustrate the point very well. The first company we will consider is Safeway, which attracted the attention of the Dart group run by Herbert Haft, a Washington-based corporate raider. In 1986 Haft bid $58 for $40 Safeway stock.

Safeway was spurred to take on a management buyout (MBO) after which, however, Kohlberg, Kravis, Roberts held the major control whilst Haft and others gained share options (Shrager, 1987). Maryland-based Safeway, then, became the predecessor of the new Delaware-based Safeway.

Formalities were completed on 29 August 1986, when 73 per cent of the stock of the original Safeway was bought-in for $3,105m. in cash, the remainder of the stock being acquired on 24 November that year with the merger of a wholly-owned subsidiary. This was all possible because in July 1986, KKR arranged an LBO with $4.2bn. of financing. At $67.50c a share this was a premium of more than 50 per cent over the share price just a few months earlier. It left Safeway with a total debt burden of $5.7bn. and an exaggerated debt/equity ratio. Safeway chairman Peter Magowan has suggested that with nominal equity of $130m and a debt of $5.7bn. the deal was the most leveraged in history. (Stockholder equity, of course, fell as a result of the bid: it had been $1.7bn.) Massive disposals had to be made in order to cut the debt burden quickly. It is at this point that evidence emerges as to who gains and who loses from such a process. One immediate beneficiary was Mr Haft, whose Safeway stock had greatly increased in value. The disposals tell a somewhat different story.

Magowan himself (1990) described the actions that were taken. Safeway was reduced in size by half, measured by number of stores, from 2,325 to 1,144 by September 1988. The number of employees fell from 174,000 to 107,000 and headquarters staff fell from 1,200 to 630. In two years debt was reduced from $5.7bn. to $3.1bn. In turn, operating profits rose 15 per cent in 1988 and 30 per cent in the first half of 1989. This type of process, with extensive labour-shedding, is a parallel of the fate of the industrial sector as chronicled by Bluestone and Harrison (1982).

On the positive side, Safeway was forced into selling its UK operation to the Argyll group. Argyll was aggressively managed and seeking to expand. Safeway UK had a good spin-off image from its parent and some excellent own-label products. In one of UK retailing's shrewdest moves of the 1980s, Argyll quickly began to shed its own Presto label and to convert much of the expanded chain to the Safeway logo (bar some smaller Lo-Cost outlets). Argyll had made a once-and-for-all bid for the image of a chain that had been slowly building its UK reputation over a period of years. Safeway had come to the UK on 20 September 1962 as Safeway Food Stores Ltd., essentially by taking over Gardners stores. Gardners had, in April 1962, opened Europe's largest supermarket, a 20,000 sq. ft. outlet at Wimbledon, South London. Progress was slow, with 1965 seeing turnover of £9m. but a trading loss from the 26-store chain. By 1969, however, profits had been achieved on sales of £20m., the next decade seeing the total number of stores rise to 83 and on to 100 by 1983. Sales passed the £1bn. mark in 1986 with profits of £43m. from 131 stores with 19,101 employees. This was what Argyll acquired for £681m. on 20 February 1987. This purchase led to a turnover increase for Argyll in 1985—8 from £2,128.2m. to £3,409.9m. Safeway contributed 42 per cent of total 1988 group turnover. The target for March 1991 was for 400 Safeway stores with 6.5m. sq. ft. of sales area and Safeway contributing 80 per cent of group turnover. Argyll showed a rise in 'full-time-equivalent' employees from 25,930 in 1987 to 40,028 in 1988 and 41,413 in 1989. The contrast between this shrewd success and the poor image of Gateway could hardly be more marked.

On the figures already seen, however, it is clear that the real drama lies in the detail of the 1,200 stores divested by the US operation. Supermarkets were sold in Kansas, Utah, Oklahoma, Arkansas, Texas and Southern California. Why would anyone want to buy such stores at a substantial premium over their annual profits record? Magowan considered that the stores sold for forty-five times historic earnings, whilst it has been suggested that Safeway released certain US assets on price/earning ratios of more that 100.

Letting labour take the strain

The secret of the success of the Safeway stores sell-off lies in the conditions under which they were sold, somewhat blandly referred to in the US Securities and Exchange Commission (SEC) report for fiscal 1989 as:

> an improved labour cost structure . . . through its negotiation of long-term contracts and its implementation of voluntary cash buy-out programmes for employees in several key areas. Most of the domestic operations divested had high labour costs relative to local competitors. Operating profit for 1989 was higher on a $14 billion sales base than in 1986 on a sales base of $20 billion. (US Securities and Exchange Commission file no 33, 9047 p. 2)

The above passage indicates an approximate 30 per cent reduction in the size of Safeway as measured by turnover.

The basic reality of most forms of retailing is that the greatest costs are labour costs, and in the UK this has been thrown into sharp relief in 1990 by the substantial pay rises awarded by major food retailers worried about recruitment in a demographic downturn. It was, however, exactly the opposite direction for the labour that proved to be the key in the US. Safeway, with the LBO debt burden as ammunition, went into frantic renegotiation of its salary structure. The simple fact was that the saleability of disposable stores was perceived by buyers as a function of labour costs. Magowan himself has stated that LBO funds are attracted to the grocery sector not least because threat of selling could be a strong negotiating ploy with the unions. Market analysts had concluded that in many areas Safeway was in direct competition with non-unionised firms. Safeway's image and, in many cases, its store locations were good, but labour costs were much higher. Safeway, with the unions clearly perceiving a threat of total job losses, aimed for as much as 25 per cent reductions in the hourly rate. Of course, wage parity could just as easily have been achieved by levelling wage rates upwards instead of downwards. It can be argued that the unionised Safeway workers were forced into lower, non-union, rates by the preparedness of the workforce of local rivals to work for non-union pay rates under pressures of Reaganomics.

Just how quickly the US retail markets reacted to Reaganomics and the 'death of the middle class' was evidenced by the rapid rise of cost-cutting food stores. In areas where the mood was one of decline, operations that traded on service, not price, faced decline. Alternatively, they offered the same service and cut costs by cutting wages. A typical victim in many areas was the old Safeway.

Safeway became a substantially smaller operation than previously, yet had a massive debt burden with capital repayments due in the mid-1990s. Cash flow became driven as much by the need to pay off interest charges as by the need to create profit for reinvestment. Safeway has, in effect, pulled out of those southern states where the labour market was less likely to be unionised. Business efforts subsequently concentrated in areas where Safeway already had a high market share and where competitors were paying similar wage rates. Store sizes have been increased and the range of lines carried has also grown, whilst 70 per cent of the US stores open twenty-four hours a day. The labour that is forced to facilitate an open-all-hours policy is the major loser.

The second case study to be taken appears to be a clear example of the internationalisation of retailing as it involves a Canadian intervention into the USA. In fact, as we shall see, there is more to be learned from a consideration of two of the great asset strengths of retailing – property values and 'image'. Both feature very strongly indeed in a case study that appeared to reverse the world's most common transnational investment trend (from the USA to Canada). Worthy of note is how little of the finance capital appears to have originated in Canada despite the origins of the major player, Robert Campeau. I have covered this story elsewhere (Hallsworth, 1991b), but it is worth looking again at the situation as it prevailed by 1990.

The Campeau affair

The Campeau affair was, at first sight, an example of internationalisation, for by 1986 Campeau became interested in the US retail market even though Canadian developers had experienced mixed fortunes there previously. The difference with Campeau was that the timing was perfect for highly-leveraged deals and Campeau was interested in retailers' great asset – property.

In seeking mall investments in the USA, Campeau came into direct contact with retail chains with retail property investments. He soon began to look at Allied Stores. Though owners of such famous retail names as Brooks Brothers and Ann Taylor, Allied primarily interested Campeau in respect of its shopping mall property holdings. The overall Allied group, it emerged, was showing poor profits, and the temptation soon arose to take over the whole operation as a means of obtaining the shopping malls. In October 1986, Campeau bought Allied for $3.6bn., plus assumed debt and fees – $4.4bn. in all. This, at the height of the junk boom, was financed by $3bn. in bank loans from a consortium led by Citibank; $875m. in bridging finance from First Boston, and only $300m. in actual equity, of which Campeau ostensibly supplied half. Even that did not cover the whole story. Campeau had been expected to find the $300m. personally, but proved unwilling or unable to raise the finance. In a move that evoked the whole spirit of the junk bond market, he first suggested a side deal to remortgage the Allied shopping centres and use the surplus to fund the $300m. required. This was not viewed as acceptable, and an alternative emerged whereby Citibank would loan Campeau Corp. $150m. This would cover half of $300m. needed. In fact, Campeau did use the credit to part-fund the $300m., but persuaded a third party to make up the shortfall of $150m. This third party was shopping centre developer, Edward de Bartolo. It emerged that de Bartolo had obtained his $150m. in just the same way as Campeau – in a loan from Citibank. Already, therefore, we see the Canadian developer using US finance to buy US firms.

The immediate aftermath of the Allied takeover exemplified the ethos of junk. Campeau trimmed Allied trading operations in order to pay off debt. In 1987, sixteen of Allied's smaller units were sold for a total of around $1.16bn. Long-term debt was reduced and he still held key Allied divisions such as Brooks Brothers. The acquisition strategy seemed similar to that of the Hanson Trust empire – convincing investors that he was realising assets from undervalued companies. By the middle of 1987, Campeau's apparent success led him to look at Federated Stores with an asset base that included Bloomingdales. Analysts were writing enthusiastically about the power that this would give Campeau. He had plans to open many new shopping malls and, as owner of key 'anchor' department stores, he could pick and choose his mall designs and, potentially, exclude department store chains that he did not own.

The race for Federated

Macys, one of the chains that could have been frozen out of the new malls, raced him for Federated. Once protected by antitrust laws, Macys felt itself now to be very vulnerable to Campeau's potential monopoly powers. The timing seemed perfect, since the stock market crash of October 1987 depressed Federated shares still further. In early 1988 Federated shares were trading as low as $36. Had Campeau been able to acquire Federated at that price, there is little doubt that it would have been a sound investment for the property and potential cash flow reasons.

Raiders constantly seek the corporation that has cash in the bank for long-term R&D, that is in a cyclical down-turn or that is undervalued by the market. The essential question is this: what is wrong with the market that it frowns on companies that think long-term? Where does the fault lie? With those companies, or with the system? Why should it be that the spoils go to those who are able to sell out for top dollar when the share price peaks, or at least near the top of the slippery slide back to more mundane price levels?

It is intuitively attractive to assume that had Campeau in any sense been using his own money he might have applied more strict criteria to the likely future performance of his capital, or to possible alternative investment vehicles. Instead, having pre-acquired very few shares in Federated, he launched a takeover bid at $47 per share (valuing the company at $4.2 bn). The mere prospect of a bid pushed the shares higher, with arbitragers grabbing shares and leaving little prospect of Campeau sharing in any windfall profits that had already accrued to shareholders. Campeau was expected to bid as high as $60 a share, though some advisers valued the shares as high as $70. In the end, by April of 1988, Campeau had acquired Federated – at $73.50c a share – and a total bill of $6.6bn. for the shares alone. Debts and fees added a total of around $2.2bn., to give a total debt of $8.8bn. Citibank provided another $3.23bn., whilst First Boston and two other investment banks provided short-term funding of $2.2bn. This time there was an input of $1.4bn. in Campeau equity.

Confidence

As is so often the case when one examines the operations of the financial markets, the term 'confidence' assumes great significance. Campeau's ventures with Allied were seen as a success because he disposed of valuable assets quickly, but kept the jewel in the crown – Brooks Brothers. Campeau frequently stated in the early days of the Allied acquisition that he intended to hold on to Brooks Brothers. That made the Allied purchase a good deal and the financial backers had confidence. However, extra finance had to be raised for the Federated deal, and Campeau was arranging to sell Brooks Brothers to Marks and Spencer (M&S) for $750m. The M&S deal also included a $30m. payment for future space in Campeau's malls. It did not take long for the backers of the Allied deal to conclude that the assets in which they had invested were to be sold off to fund the Federated acquisition. It appeared that their assets were being liquidated to line the pockets of Federated shareholders whose company had apparently doubled in value in four months. The inexorable upward valuation of Federated shares was parallelled by confusion over what Campeau would have to sell in order to fund his expensive acquisition. As the financial process rumbled on, confidence fell. It was one thing to be attracting junk finance to acquire such a name as Brooks Brothers – another matter again for it to be set against certain less exotic names and a number of anonymous shopping malls. To emphasise the importance of confidence – often manifested simply as a herd mentality in respect of financial decisions – one can see the Brooks Brothers brand name as a key symbol. It has been suggested that by no means all of the capital set to be raised from the Brooks Brothers divestiture was destined to fund Federated: around $200m. of a total $750m. was earmarked for this purpose. Arguably, had Campeau been more open on his plans, he would have fared better with his creditors in the Allied deal.

As soon as the Federated deal was made, Campeau began to divest assets in order to cut short-term debt. He disposed of I. Magnin and Bullocks to R.H. Macy for $1.1bn. and Filene's (Edward Filene's old company) and Foley's to Mays for $1.5bn. Another $0.5bn. was raised by the sale of other more minor subsidiaries. In some cases, the purchasers of the divisions would be offered junk bond-based financing for the acquisition. Ralph's Grocery Co. became a spin-off subsidiary funded via a separate $525m. of bank lending and with a $400m. junk bond issue. In other words, it was loaded up with debt. To put this in a wider context it has since been suggested that a majority of post-1986 junk-bond-funded deals are inherently unstable, that is, cashflow will be insufficient to cover interest charges. Ralph's may be one of the exceptions.

Another key plan was succinctly described by Bullen writing in *Fortune* magazine (August 1988, p. 54): 'almost entirely by eliminating people, he has slashed expenses by $125m. a year at Allied and $250m. so far, at Federated.' Campeau had other strings to his bow, however. *Forbes Magazine* (Saunders, 1988) reported Campeau as having a tax gimmick to avoid taxes. This involved a loophole in US tax laws on capital gains. The sales of subsidiaries were to be done by instalments to defer taxes. This was a parallel of the investor who loses tax liability in long-term property development. Tax gimmicks apart, it was at this point that more problems arose. The retail market was flat (Allied's financial results were weak) and the junk bond market was overflowing. The state of Allied's bond issues became a talisman for the Federated offer. As Allied bonds fell in value, so Federated junk became ever harder to market. First Boston were attempting to sell over $1bn. of Federated junk bonds at around 14 per cent interest and finding no takers. Some $0.75bn. was eventually traded, but at over 17 per cent interest — a substantial premium on bank rates. Note how we have again returned to interest rates and we must again emphasise that these were real interest rates. The arch-critic of high real rates, Congdon (1988), devoted chapter 7 of his book to 'The leveraging of America' and he, too, traced back the high real interest rates of the 1980s to Volcker's moves at the Federal Reserve Board in October 1979.

As a further indication of the state of the retail market, another jewel in the Allied crown, Ann Taylor, sold for less than expected. Campeau had high-interest debts and an asset base that was rapidly declining back to its post-crash valuations. The bulk of the Federated and Allied acquisitions (Ralph's apart) were not food store 'cash-cows', but were geared to more fickle discretionary purchasing patterns (and post-crash purchasing patterns). Presumably preoccupied with the financial aspects of the operation, or the divestments, Campeau paid less attention to the core businesses. If we accept the inefficient management justification for LBOs, then it would be reasonable to assume that the management of Allied and Federated were the very people who first put the corporations at risk from LBOs. Campeau's response was to put Federated executives in charge of the combined group (Gallagher, 1988). This, again, tended to shake confidence.

Campeau's ploy was to try to move away from the faltering junk market and into more solidly-based funding. His new idea was to find financial partners who would offer low-interest finance that was secured on the group's real estate holdings. This would be the mirror-image of high-interest but low-security junk: in effect, a mortgage on Allied–Federated. Had Campeau shown a track record of good performance from the rump of his business, this just might possibly have worked. Any long-term, low-interest mortgage finance still depends, however, on the security of the assets being mortgaged. Furthermore, the plan raised two further complications since cash in the volume sought by Campeau (around $3bn.) was only realistically available in the junk markets. One was that the existing junk bond holders would be undercut by the hoped-for mortgage newcomers who would acquire real equity holdings in 'their' companies. This would dent confidence in junk. The second problem was that junk was already in decline. With some of the short-term Allied financing due in 1990, the markets could not tolerate such further attacks on their confidence. Yet Campeau insisted on preferring his scheme to $1.1bn. in long-term funding offered by Citibank in the spring of 1989.

This Citibank finance would have smoothed over the 1990 Allied problem and might have restored the faith of Citibank's other junk bond holders. It would have bought time for Campeau and for the junk bond market itself. That said, junk was in trouble from other directions, with the Michael Milken saga and the gigantic Savings and Loan scandal rumbling along. In spring 1989, whilst one arm of his adviser empire, led by ex-Citibank people, was refinancing the Allied debt in more conventional manner, Campeau was still pursuing his asset-based dream. Crucially, he spurned the conventional refinancing option, preferring his far more disruptive and controversial scheme. He thereby seemed to finally and fatally dent the crucial confidence of the markets. If financial deals constitute a 'sure thing', then confidence would be less significant.

Trading trouble

The next turn of the wheel was poor performance by the Campeau divisions in the summer of 1989. Though by now a gigantic operation with turnover measured in billions, it had a crippling debt burden. As a next step, Campeau returned to Canada for advice and finance from the Reichmann family of Olympia and York (Hawkings, 1989). With a 24 per cent investment in Campeau (and holdings in other development companies), the Reichmanns were persuaded to buy in more deeply. Had the $250m. Olympia and York loan of September 1989 actually proved sufficient, it would have been another shrewd investment by a group seen at that time as famous for its 'shrewd investments'. Campeau was on the floor, and the $250m. took him into a minority position in his own group. A turnaround would also have saved the reputation of the Canadian development business already tarnished by Campeau, and boosted Olympia and York's standing with major financial institutions to which it might later have had to turn. At any other time, the Reichmann involvement would have been seen as a very positive step.

Globally involved – most notably with the Canary Wharf development in London's dockland – the Reichmanns still had a solid reputation. Had they stepped in just six or eight months sooner, the offer of refinancing for the 1990 Allied debt would probably not have been spurned. Even a 38.4 per cent holding in Campeau by Olympia and York did not bring back that vital confidence, however. Olympia and York's price for involvement – the sale of Bloomingdales and strong equity pledges – failed to help (Labich, 1990; Mason and Weiner, 1990). Shares in Campeau Corp. were soon quoted at roughly one-third of their pre-crash value. In the first week of January 1990, only a $100m. payment to suppliers staved off bankruptcy. On 15 January 1990, Allied–Federated filed for Chapter 11 bankruptcy in Cincinnati, Ohio, after a deadline was set on $2.3bn. of payments.

Campeau himself was ousted as chairman and chief executive of Campeau Corp. on 10 August 1990. The rest of the fallout from the Campeau affair was eminently predictable. The major winners were the previous owners of the companies where the price was bidded-up by the apparently endless availability of finance. Those who backed Campeau but ensured that their loans were secured on real estate assets probably found themselves left with good value for money. Among the losers, the promoters of junk finance were both direct and indirect losers in a market that had already seen gold turn to dross.

The position of the store-based assets is less certain. In many cases the trading names will survive. One source (Weberman, 1990) noted that Ralph's could be seen as Campeau's strongest asset. Its food-based cash flow could probably pull it out of its $1bn. debt. Finally, there were the jobs that disappeared as costs were cut at stores in order to increase asset values. Thousands of retail jobs ceased to exist as pruning took place.

Nor do Canadian disasters south of the border end with Campeau. We may note that Dylex Corp. has been seen as one of Canada's foremost retail segmentation specialists. It is excellent at its core business, but it is rather less than excellent at acquisitions in the USA. In 1984 Dylex spent $44.3m. on the purchase of Brooks ladies fashion stores. This firm proceeded into Chapter 11 bankruptcy in January 1987, along with another Dylex purchase – Foxmoor. Write-downs on US losses led to Dylex losing $77.8m. in 1989 and $60.7m. in the year ending 3 February 1990.

If, as I argue, the mercantilist/globalist dichotomy is at the root of the short-termist viewpoint, then no part of the UK/US political/economic empires should be safe. This is amply abetted by examination of events in Australia, upon which we have already touched. The primacy of capital is having no difficulty in leaving its mark there also. The saga of the collapse of the Fairfax empire in Australia is again one of management buy-out: the taking private at massive (AUS $2.6bn.) cost of a family firm. The disposals tied in to the financing coincided with the stock market collapse and were sufficient to cause the dismemberment of one of Australia's oldest companies. Kerry Packer who had wisely divested a great deal of his shares before the October 1987 crash, was on hand to collect, for cash, parts of this and the Alan Bond empire. Indeed, he repurchased from Bond the Channel Nine media empire that he himself had earlier sold to Bond – but at a fraction of the price Bond paid.

Discussion

It is clear that the MBO/LBO phenomenon has caused considerable turmoil, with ordinary workers the clearest victims. Certain of the issues that arise from this can be cast in the context of collective state provision. One reading of Hirsch (1978) supposes some kind of collectivity of demand that requires groups to ask from the state that which they cannot acquire as individuals. I am more persuaded by the alternative interpretations of Castells and others that the state is required to provide the infrastructure that private capital alone would not provide – to 'pick up the pieces', as it were. The costs of the negative externalities of private capital accumulation, most notably in the form of pollution, have generally been collectively borne. Taxation has neither sufficiently penalised the polluters nor, where tax has been collected at all, has it been redistributed in a way that compensates those who most suffer. Likewise, the state (i.e. the ordinary taxpayer) pays when workers lose their jobs after an LBO.

No raider enters the LBO fray without the expectation of profit. If the battle is costly, especially if the target corporation reacts to threat with a revaluation of its assets and gains some backing from existing shareholders, then the LBO may, at best, be of only marginal profitability. This reflects some of the later adventures of Robert Campeau. There are not many easy savings that can be made in the short term and in recessionary/high interest rate circumstances. Property sales are only profitable when ready buyers can be found. The one quick, easy saving is to slash the wages bill. There may be a provision for senior personnel (the ones allegedly at fault under the business efficiency scenario of LBO-ism) to continue their gilded lifestyle, but the ordinary worker may be forced out of employment with little prospect of a future job. It is at this point that society at large picks up the tab. The raider still extracts profit, but virtually directly at the expense of the taxpayer in general. If we fit this into our previous observations on the growing pool of unemployed and the resentment that they engender in the employed middle classes, we see the roots of a conflict that is started by neither but which negatively affects both. The working middle classes resent the burden of the unemployed in general and the antisocial underclass in particular, but they rarely question the wider process that may have brought this situation about. The well-cultivated concept of success through individual endeavour and nothing else blinds the voting classes to the structural problems of society. Supporters of LBO activity, especially in the USA, are not blind to the argument that society in general must pay for what the private corporation will not pay. Indeed, this one has been perversely inverted so that the argument becomes that the profound good that is wrought by LBOs is constrained by Federal regulation – hence society pays in lost efficiency. Yet again we see how labour takes the strain, and how the nature of labour has changed. Whilst the Japanese head for multi-skilled manufacturing work, the US and UK increasingly offer menial multi-tasking (filling the shelves, packing the groceries, sweeping the floor) as a substitute for Fordist routine repetition in work.

10

A TECHNOLOGY-DRIVEN CYCLE OF CHANGE

In drawing forth the various influences that are bringing about change in contemporary society it becomes evident that the interconnectedness of the process is profound. Changing ways of work influence spending power and thereby influence what is sold, and how. This in turn creates new demands for products, and so the cycle continues.

At this point, then, it is useful to pause and summarise the types of trends that are bringing about change. Because the process as we view it at any one time is circular, it is possible to break into it at any point and at any level. I have attempted to summarise the process in a diagram (Figure 10.1). Probably it is simplest to work from the outside into the centre. We may start with employment change which we have characterised as typically Japanese-motivated. This feeds into cost-cutting part-time working, loss of mass labour markets and polarised incomes. At the central, operating level, this implies a decline in mass markets and thus of mass merchandising. The next macro influence is demographic. The types of jobs that are on offer imply female work participation. This puts a real economic price on child-bearing and, alternatively, increases the possibility of dual income households ('dinkys'). The implication is that niche or segmented markets will rise to serve the newly affluent and child-free.

In this process there is still another stage, that of financial changes. Affluence (for the two-income household) having encouraged consumerism, there is a pressure on the balance of payments (BOP) from imports of finished goods – not least from Japan (which is where we started the cycle). Pressures increase to cut costs through outsourcing (itself affecting the BOP) and through more imports. Labour costs are cut, again through Japanese working practices, and the cycle is complete. The changes in financial markets make up the final third of the cycle.

We have now reached the point where the cycle of change can be seen to be operating in response to global pressures from the tensions and contradictions of mercantilism and globalism. Equally, labour has been set at centre stage of the retailing process. The changes in labour markets

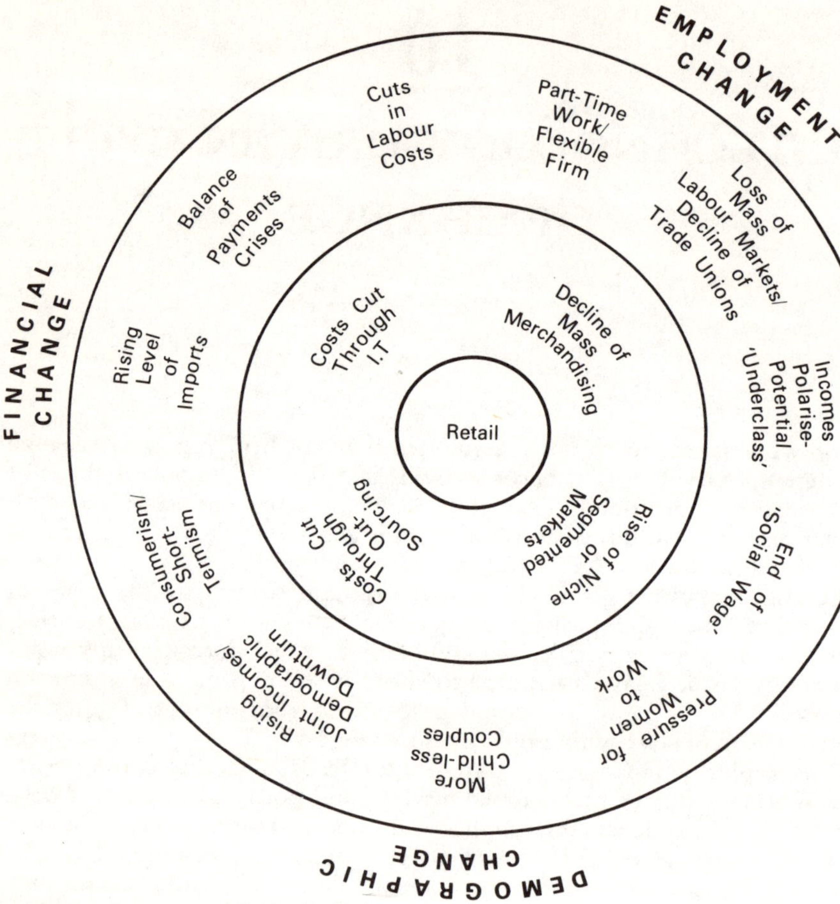

Figure 10.1 A cycle of change

are creating a new form of consumer. That consumer is, or has been encouraged to feel, more individualistic as the mass norms of spatially-fixed mass employment locations (coal mines/Fordist car factories) erode through job-shedding and labour flexibility.

Information technology

The next question must be: is the cycle rolling at a steady speed? Unquestionably, it is not. Change occurs at an ever-faster rate. The reason is the second part of Strange's conceptualism of IPE — technology. Technological change was the engine of the rise of Japan, but we may also trace its evolution in all other spheres. Let us first consider the ideal-typical Japanese concept of 'Just-in-Time'. The application of Just-in-Time (JIT) technology is arguably far simpler for industrial enterprises than for, say, retailing. Classically, one finds a single car plant to which JIT deliveries are required. The nature of the parts is known, the speed at which they must be delivered is a function of the speed of the assembly process (which ultimately can itself be seen as a function of consumer demand). What we should not lose sight of is the prime aim of JIT — to reduce stockholding costs or at least offload them on to the supplier. Retailing, on the other hand, tends to operate from many locations of differing sizes where stock requires replenishment at variable rates. Certain peak demands can be anticipated, but past sales do not always reflect future ones and stock availability has to be total and instantaneous. By comparison, few people buy a car 'off the shelf'. Retailers can aid their own transfer to JIT technology by standardising store sizes (the larger the better, within limits) and reorganising depot arrangements (McKinnon, 1986). (They can of course, ignore flexible processes altogether!)

The markets now scrutinise every move made by retailers and so profit is paramount. Profit is influenced by control of costs, one of which is stocks. The keys to JIT in retailing are good stock control: hence cost control via information technology and a delivery process that is free of bottlenecks. As advocates of Just-in-Time always point out, buffer stocks can hide production/delivery bottlenecks. Whilst buffer stocks represent a inventory holding cost, they also prevent out-of-stock situations (Just-in-Time becomes Just-in-Case).

The overall trend to emerge is that just as Japan, the USA and Germany are creating exclusionary power by becoming the only players in the expensive ultra-high-technologies of the future, so retailers can increase their power and profits by using retail IT as a barrier to exclude smaller players. How long such an advantage can last is a function of the falling unit costs and increasing sophistication of IT equipment.

Technological possibilities for IT-driven power-advantages may readily be identified. In-store technology could include video-wall systems and interactive video — the latter offering translation facilities for the foreign traveller. Then comes the 'smart card' which can hold records of transactions. Smart cards can store customer measurements, tastes and preferences in order to advise on purchasing at the next visit. Japanese 'stores of the future' demonstrate many applications of robotics, including the 'magic mirror' where different styles of clothing can be reflected back in an 'instant fitting room'. Satellite linking of stores facilitates stock transfer – and copying of rivals' best-selling styles.

Finally, the use of point-of-sale technology may be linked to stock reordering or to shelf-display/stocking systems. It is perfectly possible to organise stockholding without necessarily going into automatic stock reordering. By knowing simply how much space a product takes and the rate at which it sells, shelf-displays can be allocated space that minimises out-of-stocks. The market analysts constantly mark up the share price of companies that use IT well and mark down those that do not.

Technology, mercifully, is not without its pitfalls. Fotheringham (1988) showed how a well-modelled retail prediction can go adrift. One grocery store in his set failed, but not on operational grounds that would be predicted from size, or local area income. The store which failed did so because it had the wrong image for the area – like Fortnums in the Gorbals or Kwik-Save in Knightsbridge. That the inappropriateness of such store/location combinations is obvious to us merely reinforces the validity of brand/image concepts. What we really need to do, however, is to bring IT back to the central concept of the changing consumer.

Geodemographic models based on national censuses are now in widespread use: but why? The market area analyst who uses augmented geodemographic data to identify the likely source areas of shoppers has, again, a power/knowledge advantage over a rival who knows little about the types of individuals who live in the local area. The *Journal of the Market Research Society* (1989, Vol. 31, No. 1) devoted a whole issue to this topic. As Brown (1989) has noted, it was the machine-readable nature of the 1966 small area census statistics that gave the first theoretical/research impetus to geodemographic analysis as we have come to know it. R. J. Webber, working at the Centre for Environmental Studies, was engaged on research to discover how much data might be clustered in order to illustrate areas of deprivation in Liverpool – hardly a commercial application, but a crucial breakthrough. In the mid-1980s, spurred by the 1981 census and the availability of cheap, powerful computers and further refinements to cluster techniques, the typologies proliferated. CCN, part of Great Universal Stores (GUS), developed its MOSAIC model and augmented the census data with the Post Office address file and data from shopper surveys. Pinpoint developed Pin whilst CDMS (part of the Littlewoods organisation) began to use the Superprofiles system that started life as an ESRC research project. Brown (1989) noted how such systems can be used in retail site analysis, market research, credit referencing and target marketing.

IT adds power

We again have a technology that confers upon the user a marketing advantage over the rival who is operating 'blind' or by intuition – not that such systems are infallible (see Sayer, 1976). The results are as good as the data collection system, and some UK systems assume that the enumeration district (ED) has been assigned to its correct postcode area – there is not an exact overlap. Errors of inference that ascribe to the individual all the characteristics of the general area in which he or she lives are also possible (the so-called ecological fallacy). The bottom line is to move beyond simple census data and into an identification of customer types. That is, to identify individuals who will, it is assumed, have similar tastes and buying habits. Future developments in geodemographics will show more attention being paid to specific sub-sectors of the databases as Pinpoint's financial development, Fin Pin, presaged. Most retailers are attempting to exploit segmented markets, which readily implies segmented databases. What should be clear is that the more personalised or unique the technology-driven data, the more power advantage is conferred. Astute retailers recognise the fact that their first unique data source is information supplied by customers. The majority of business is repeat business. The more that is known about existing customers, the better.

At this point one can separate off one of the key functions of store credit cards. Whilst store cards (and bank cards) are part of the credit-driven economy, it is very much the case that use of a credit card is an information-giving exercise by the customer. Whilst the cash customer proffers only cash, the card customer offers a name and a link to the goods sold. The extent to which the retailer can access this information is a key to unlocking valuable data. Until recently, bank card purchases in stores may have been regarded as 'lost information'. The segment of customers using the store card may, too, be untypical of the general customer (or bank card user). The most favoured group in this respect has been M&S, whose store card is the only one accepted in the stores and thus all possible information is internalised. M&S had the power to exclude Visa and Access. This particular use of IT has also spun-off into the product ranges carried. Store credit cards permit much larger individual purchases and so Marks and Spencer have been able to carry bulkier goods. Good use of store-card information allows better customer targeting and the ability to offer add-on service such as financial services. In the USA 'smart' cards with customer loyalty bonuses are in use. As the customer market has fragmented, it has become important to know who shops where – and why. The retailers desperately need a link into the new consumers who are replacing the old mass markets.

EPOS

Nor is customer-based data the only aim. If one wished to identify an area of exceptionally rapid technological change in UK retailing, then the adoption of Electronics at Point of Sale (EPOS) would be the classic case. It is generally considered that the first supermarket checkout with a barcode scanner was a Marsh Store in 1974 in Troy, Ohio, USA. In just a few years the unusual has become the commonplace, as the power conferred by EPOS data capture has been realised. It is easy to neglect just how fast this change has been. To exemplify this, we can consider the literature from the mid 1980s when around 20 per cent of leading retailers used EPOS. Davies and Reynolds (1986, p. 3) noted that the advantages perceived by the retail trade included 'stock control, inter-company communications and delivery scheduling'. They later pointed out, with reference to EFTPOS (Electronic Fund Transfer at Point of Sale) (1986, p. 22), that 'whilst EFTPOS is an inevitable development they [retailers] can see little or no consumer demand for it'. Guy (1986, p. 1) noted 'EPOS, EFTPOS, private view data systems and remote shopping' as the main uses of IT in retailing, and went on to note that the overall impact of IT had been 'disappointing', stating (pp. 1–2): 'For example, EPOS systems involving scanners or laser wands are still exceptional among British grocery retailers, despite a history of experiments stretching well back into the 1970s'. Guy also stressed the significance of 'improving stock control within the store . . . but increasingly their linking together'.

The applications alluded to are now all too common in UK retailing — a vast change in just a few years. Also in 1986 most of the major multiples were in the process of installing systems for reading bar codes. Shoppers' Paradise had installed a system in all stores and were utilising a scanning system. IBM systems had been chosen by Tesco, Next, Mothercare and William Low.

This in itself was a major advance over the position of a few years before when there appeared to be many obstacles to EPOS. Dobbin (1985), for example, demonstrated that for Sir James Goldsmith's Food Giant chain, based in Maryland and a pioneer in 1975 of scanning in the USA, the removal of the price label from individual items was a major consumer rights battle that took six years to resolve and involved the Maryland state legislature. The group became involved with shelf-edge labelling problems and pioneered more informative self-edge data. The cost of adding scanning to over 100 stores was put at $25m. Approximately fifty times a week the shelf-edge label offered a different price than that held in the computer. More accurately, perhaps, a customer spotted this difference and, under a public relations exercise, claimed the item free. This practice of offering the item free was not uncommon, being noted, for example, by Ahlin (EPOS, 1985). How odd that Sir James Goldsmith went to the USA in search of more liberal market climates!

So well accepted is in-store technology that it is surprising to recall that operational problems for the early EPOS users came close to outweighing the anticipated cost savings. Labour savings at the item-pricing stage and less possibility for checkout fraud were the obvious plus points. The monitoring of stock levels came, for many, behind the ability to extend the range. It also took a while for stores with many checkout lanes to realise that faster checkouts could mean fewer checkouts and fewer workers.

The market for shelf-edge labelling systems in retailing was a classic example of technology forcing its effects down the line. We have already noted the substantial advantages of EPOS systems. Initially, the simple desire to do away with labelling of individual items and thus to save on labour costs seemed to be the prime motive. Then the realisation that speed of checkout and operator accuracy were adding to the benefits (and furthermore that stock flow could be handled) allowed the technology to take off. Not forgetting, of course, the enabling factors of virtually universal bar coding and the falling price of technology. At this point we can return to the shelf-edge label problem. We saw how, in countries such as the USA where consumer power is a major influence, such issues became significant. Even in the UK, some DIY operations in particular have received adverse publicity from price inconsistencies. Usually, these were instances where the system in use prioritised stock control over customer satisfaction.

The technology at point of sale was being undermined by human error at another point in the chain. It is reasonable to suggest that if EPOS pioneers had been told that they would eventually have to pay substantial sums for shelf-edge technology, then the growth of EPOS might have been stunted. The shelf-edge technologies are not trivial. Liquid-crystal displays are becoming more usual and shelf-edge technology can, in a large foodstore, outstrip the hardware costs of the POS. Control systems for price-changing are becoming ever more exotic, from radio controls to flickering of the overhead store lighting. Only once the advantages of EPOS technology in terms of checkout speed, stock control and payment were proven could one think in terms of exotic shelf-edge labels.

The adoption curve for EPOS technology mirrors classic patterns for the cumulative adoption of most techniques. The EPOS curve is, however, a very fast one. This implies that the adoption of EPOS at the ideal time is hard to plan. Being a laggard is worse than being an innovator. As we have seen, EPOS cuts 'shrinkage' by eliminating errors (or fraud) in ringing in prices at manual tills. Another advantage links through to exclusive power. Whilst price-cutting at one store can be replicated in minutes by a rival next door, certain other trends are harder to copy. Scanning systems cope very well with special multiple-purchase offers. They will discount the ninth package in an '9 for 8' offer, whatever order the packages come through the till. Such special package offers (where an extra item is linked into others at a special price) represent ways of seeking power advantage as they cannot quickly be copied. Where instances exist of companies that will use satellite technology to transmit images of products to suppliers so that the suppliers can instantly imitate them, the business of copy-catting is very significant indeed.

EFTPOS

We have seen that, only five years or so ago, there was general scepticism about the future for EFTPOS. Whilst the idea of Electronic Fund Transfer at Point of Sale had inherent benefits for the banks, the greatest stumbling-block was felt likely to be customer resistance (Sparks, 1984). It was pointed that there might be severe operational difficulties. With a cheque, the customer has a bank guarantee card, and at the point of sale the customer is virtually assured that the transaction will take place. The customer may then have to dash to the bank to ensure that there are covering funds, but there is a four-day period of grace before the cheque is presented. The fear about EFTPOS was that the card-based transaction would clear through the customer's account at once. Thus customers who did not always keep a surplus in their bank account would not use the card, or would have to keep a running tally of expenditures. With such drawbacks, stores might be reluctant to invest in the technology.

It is easy to see how power was exerted in the case of EFTPOS, and it parallels the Marks and Spencer case. Retailers appeared to be refusing EFTPOS: they needed to fit the new EFTPOS terminals, some doubted the security of proposed personal identification number (PIN) systems and also baulked at the costs where systems were on-line. The on-line EFTPOS UK system was launched at roughly the same time (December 1986) as the off-line Switch system. A built-in three-day delay for debits to accounts allayed some of the fears that had been expected from users. Problems with unauthorised or disputed uses of cards remain much the same as with credit cards. Whilst Marks and Spencer exerted its power over the use of cards in its stores, banks seeking to use EFTPOS found a Trojan Horse. J. Sainsbury, biased towards the affluent card-using south, were (like M&S) not allowing the use of Visa and Access. Once J. Sainsbury accepted Connect (Barclays' 1987 innovation) and Switch, then these became the only plastic in-store. As with the M&S card, it was a case of this plastic or no plastic — exclusionary power. Most retailers still accepting cheques as payment will confirm that there has been an increase in cheques returned by banks. Banks are entitled to do this if there is any small error on the cheque. It also happens to be a useful reminder of the benefits of EFTPOS — and of the power of banks. The problem of the customer with insufficient funds in the account to cover direct transfer was overcome by the built in delay before the EFTPOS account was presented. We recall that shopping should never be uncomfortable.

An end to consumer sovereignty?

Further benefits to the retailer from EPOS are closely related to DPP (Direct Product Profitability). A new line of, say, breakfast cereal can readily be assessed in terms of sales. Furthermore, the extent to which it genuinely increases all cereal sales can be separated out from any propensity to simply divert sales from other, possibly more profitable, cereal lines. Promotions on other price changes can equally rapidly be assessed. It is not difficult to see how this soon links into DPP. Once all parameters are known and a stable in-stock position is reached, it is a logical further step to look at real net margins. A manufacturer may offer the retailer a substantial margin on a product. But what if it is bulkier than a rival product offering lower mark-up? It will take up more shelf space, and more warehouse space. It may sell more slowly, with risks of passing sell-by dates; it may require special storage, such as cold rooms. In short, the Direct Product Profit may be lower than the rival. In a cycle of feedback, the consumer is soon only offered more of what sold before – hardly a golden age of consumerism.

It behoves manufacturers, already heavily pressed by the own-brands favoured by retailers, to promote the importance of variety. It is already abundantly clear that retailers are increasingly disinclined to stock new products from manufacturers and are renting out space on supermarket shelves. The immediate logical consequence will be to herald the demise of any third-or fourth-ranking product. It should also hasten the trend to own-label goods since most will inevitably show better net margins than branded goods. Manufacturers of branded goods, then, can be seen to be losing power to the major supermarket chains. This tendency has been exploited to good effect by the Kwik-Save operation in the UK. The policy of taking branded goods only (and preparedness to take the second-rank brand name if the market leader would not supply) has proven fruitful.

Electronic Data Interchange – EDI

All is not gloom, though, for the major manufacturers. Aside from offering variety and range, they tend to be, inevitably, large and powerful organisations. Many are preparing their own customer databases. As retailers push technology even further back down the chain, so the attractions of EDI loom larger. Why have a paperless store when ordering is still, relatively, in manual mode? EDI pushes new technology into retailer/supplier relations. Retailers, however, will want suppliers to bear as much as possible of the cost. This implies a degree of maturity on the part of the supplier. A backstreet supplier of occasional orders of items will not be participating in EDI. EDI could therefore help redress the retailer/supplier imbalance, but in favour of those suppliers big enough to participate in the retailers' schemes.

Manual stock ordering is inherently error-prone and subject to delays. Indeed, trade surveys all tend to show that some delay in delivery was regarded as normal. For a non-food operation the usual delay might be 7–10 days. We can contrast this with the Japanese industrial system where delivery times are often estimated in minutes.

EDI promises a better in-stock position, reductions in stockholding (the Japanese model) and better overall stock control. Buying times and buying procedures *per se* would be enhanced. Again, such a system could not be implemented without a show of power from the retail trade. Once major retailers demanded EDI links, suppliers were forced to follow suit. Crucially, too, a revolution in distribution was needed. The distribution element of total retail costs is low, and falling – but it is also a crucial link. As major retailers have tried to concentrate on cost-cutting and stockturn, so many have hived off the delivery/distribution function. The rise of private carriers in the wake of past general postal strikes in the UK has facilitated this hiving-off. It has also led to a greater concentration of power in the hands, not just of manufacturers, but also of the few major delivery firms that are large enough and efficient enough to cope with EDI. This may also be a source of the erosion of the relative power of retailers, especially the smaller ones. Such trends will probably accelerate after 1992 when there may be a handful of giant Euro-distributors.

EDI might even out power between retailer and supplier, partly offsetting the abolition in the UK in 1964 of Resale Price Maintenance that tipped the power balance in favour of the retailers. Small retailers have often complained that, especially when exaggerated by loss-leader pricing, some large retailers can sell items at a lower price than the small retailer can acquire them. The major retailers have had legendary purchasing power over the small supplier, being able to dictate terms at will. Under EDI, retailers can exercise power by excluding suppliers who are unwilling to invest in joining EDI networks. The problem for retailers may come if too few suppliers are pulled into the EDI net. The result would be a reduction of choice, and increased power for the suppliers who have joined EDI. It is in the retailer's long-term interests to facilitate a process whereby as many suppliers as possible join EDI. This would augment power in two ways. Once the supplier has invested in EDI technology, there will be a reluctance to be excluded from the network. Also, as more major retailers and suppliers join in, so the smaller retailers not in the net will find that the suppliers find it more difficult to supply them. Suppliers are likely to prefer to do all their business on the network. This would form an exclusionary power on the part of big retailers on EDI nets versus small retailers who are not. Clearly, the battlefield rests on the numbers lined up on either side of the EDI divide.

One sensitive area where EPOS and EFTPOS can lead to labour-cost improvements lies in monitoring of performance. The speed at which items pass over the scanner is easily measured and slow-performing checkout operators may be identified. J. Sainsbury stirred some debate in 1989 by suggesting that it had a minimum performance level for operators. The company also pointed out that this was not seen as a difficult target, and failure to perform to this level would not lead to dismissal. The implications for less scrupulous operators seeking power over employees is clear. Let us emphasise again that the central importance of applications of IT stems from the power that is offered to retailers to identify, segment, and target customers. If we can no longer assume a lumpen market for goods, then the retailer who can most accurately access the individuals who will buy has real power. It is to that type of power that we now turn.

11

THE BRAVE NEW CONSUMER

Arguments have been set out in the context of IPE, because of a belief that the mercantilist/globalist dichotomy is fundamental. As mercantilism has increasingly appeared to be the winner (if we are not all losers in the long run), so the contradictions of the Japanese ability to bury comparative advantage have come more to the fore. The crushing of unions in Japan, the acceptance of robotics (as long as the economy expands) and their export-orientation have become the envy of the world. Yet, as Marriner Eccles pointed out, producers need consumers, and Henry Ford's well-paid unionised workers were as good as any. But the eighties restructuring in much of the OECD sphere was fought out over the dying bodies of trade unions and basic wage rates. The mechanisms of change and restructuring clearly imply a new breed of consumer, and from this point on we need to discover the implications for the wider economy of the nature of the changing consumer – a consumer constantly to be analysed, moulded and remoulded.

Mass employment

To touch again upon the way in which flexibility has superseded mass labour, the erosion of mass employment in routine repetitive work is nowhere better exemplified than in the UK mining workforce. In 1921 there were over 1,200,000 men in the UK mining and quarrying industries: by 1990 coal employed fewer than 100,000 men – a 13-fold decrease. The pace of pit closures in the UK accelerated rapidly after the defeat of the National Union of Mineworkers. No sector more adequately mirrors the changing nature of union power between the 1970s and 1980s.

In 1974 Joe Gormley's National Union of Mineworkers (NUM) threw Edward Heath's Conservatives from power. As Hugo Young has argued (1989/90, pp. 367–75), Margaret Thatcher prepared the ground for a defeat from which the NUM would never recover. This example is just part of a general anti-union trend. Such trends – part of the inter-sectoral shift of employment that we have previously encountered – have profound implications for the class structure of society. Such changes have already been observed in marketing through psychographics. The present aim is not to pursue social class changes, but to discuss the implications of psychographics. Despite having no theoretical foundations, psychographics has become a growth industry: testimony to the employment implications of restructuring. The consumers have not gone away; they have polarised and they have changed.

Psychographics

For reasons just alluded to, the Registrar-General's definition of social classes has become increasingly permeable and more difficult to relate to any applied behavioural norms. Census-based geodemographic clusters are an obvious reaction to the rigidities (and small number) of social classes: but first, back to the decline of mass norms. As general rises in median living standards have taken place at the expense of an unemployed 'underclass', so we have seen that those with jobs have increasingly been able to express individuality through consumerism: through Hirsch's 'positional goods'. Psychographic analysis – of direct use to brand marketers seeking images with which to associate – has thus grown. The US-based (from Stanford University) classification of 'lifestyles and values' is perhaps best known, and includes tags such as:

Belongers
Achievers
Emulators
'I am me'
Survivors
Sustainers

This type of labelling is increasingly being bolted on to geodemographics, but one can most clearly see its relevance to individual product markets and to advertising. An image may be created for a product and targeted to one of these groups in an identifiable way: social classes are harder to appeal to. Market researchers are in constant search of the right mix of phrases that will quickly tell them that they have an 'achiever' or an 'emulator' responding. (In a sense, Hirsch argued that we are all emulating someone.) Geodemographics may permit some kind of locational fix on individuals (for example, the UK company NDL, most closely associated with product guarantees, conduct lifestyle appraisal that should permit the association between individual and product to be identified). Over the last two decades in particular, there has been a desire to find ways of expressing individuality – psychographics tap into this.

Attitude-based psychographics are difficult to relate directly to retail operations which cannot always be seen as 'brands'. The problem is far more acute for the mass merchandiser than for the niche or segment specialist. Indeed, there must be a clear link between the end of mass employment norms and the rise of 'this is me' feeding into a segmented retail market. Next is one of the better examples of a retail operation that struck a chord with a lifestyle group that had emerged but was alienated from mass-merchandisers.

This should sound a warning to dominant retail groups in the UK, many of whom have been mass-merchandisers. Power can be eroded in two ways. One is that where one's natural market is in decline (and this is equally well manifested through demographics as well as mass purchasing), then the whole customer base may melt away. A second, more likely outcome is that power will be lost through gradual chipping-away at the mass-market by the segmentors. In North America, where a diverse customer base long ago led to a great deal of segmentation, the market has proved difficult for European mass-marketers to penetrate: some have had to alter policy and pursue segmentation strategies.

Jones and Simmons (1987) graphically demonstrated the extent of segmentation in just one Canadian chain, the aforementioned Dylex. Small, segmented stores with a short life-span (and that were seen as replaceable when fashions changed) may restore some hoped-for diversity to UK high streets, even if the ownership power behind them remains oligopolistic. The fundamental purpose of the 'cycle of change' was to demonstrate a circularity. That is, one can enter the retail change debate at any level and from any perspective. Financial analysts, sociologists, anthropologists, geographers, political analysts and dozens more will all find it possible to leap into the cycle of change at some point. The only unacceptable perspective is one that claims retailing to the sole province of one discipline or, worse still, of one sub-sector of that discipline. One need only accept that, whatever one's perspective, research will inevitably lead off somewhere else.

One example of this is to consider the key demographic concern in the UK over the projected shortfall of young people in the 15–19-year-old age groups. This should be distinguished from a fall in the total workforce, which is far less likely in most cases. The older cohorts passing into retirement are more than matched, in most cases, by the supply of young persons. The problem is acute simply because the young have, or ought to have, advantages that the older existing workforce do not. They ought to be computer literate, they ought to be better educated all round than ever before. They ought to be. One cannot be certain that they will be, not least in those countries with a poor tradition of participation in higher education or where the education system itself is under strain. In 1991 it was revealed that the public's confidence in the state education system was lower in Britain than in any EC or Scandinavian country.

New social attitudes

On another level, we can analyse new behaviours under changed demographic patterns and see how these lead through into likely retail behaviour. To take a trivial example, the rise of the 'dinky' couple has been seen by some as being reflected in what can be described as executive pet owning. As a child substitute, the pet — especially a cat — may be favoured. The implication is that high-income couples will be prepared to lavish substantial amounts of money on the creature.

One phenomenon, then, that is inextricably linked to wider changes in industrial society is the working woman. Shevky and Bell (1956) postulated that industrial society *per se* would increase the proportion of women in the workforce. The industrial division of labour (pure Taylorism) would create demand for (largely clerical) working women. They envisaged this as employment for single, independent women.

The proportion of women in the workforce has certainly risen with time but, in the UK, has tended to be dominated by married women. This can be seen as an attempt to increase the total family income; as a financial pressure before child-rearing, or as female independence. It should not be seen outside of the context of the wider changes in society already outlined. The post-war trend of cost-cutting has led to labour substitution: a fall in the number of men in full-time work and an attendant rise in part-time female employment.

In contrast we can cast our minds back to physically-strenuous, 'male' work typified by the days when Britain had those 1 million (all male) miners slaving away underground. Male employment was, (where males and females were employed in the same industry), dominantly more highly paid, unionised and inflexible. Simplified working procedures, where robotics was not seen as the solution, led to routine assembly and servicing work. Women were to be preferred for their compliance, reliability and cheapness. The retail trade itself adopted just such labour strategies. Lack of reliable data on the smallest units makes analysis difficult but retail, too, can safely be seen as a labour-shedding industry in aggregate terms.

With women pressed into part-time work, especially where there is no full-time work for men, we immediately instigate a feedback loop. Part-time pay never approaches the level of the 'social' or family wage. Under such circumstances, children become the sort of economic liability that was presaged in the 'demographic transition theory'. Often, two wages are seen as necessary to keep the household solvent — again mitigating against childbearing. A worse irony comes when two incomes are needed to provide the income that will be needed to support a child, yet once the child is born, only one income is possible. Two incomes may bridge the cost gap where state health and education no longer offer acceptable standards. Here again, we hit a feedback loop. Fewer children means less sympathy for the state education system and a cycle of decline begins.

The cult of the individual

Recognition of the collapse of the mass market/mass consumption/mass employment triumvirate caused substantial political tremors in the troubled 1970s. For politicians the problem became one, partly, of social control. What would happen to the lumpen mass of workers if they became a lumpen mass of unemployed? This problem was severe, perhaps intolerably severe, for centre-left parties devoted to full employment at a time when full employment was no longer feasible. In this light, the rise of the Thatcher/Reagan axis was almost inevitable. The cult of the individual was indispensable. If individuals controlled their own destiny, then the state could hardly be blamed if they failed. Under centre-left formulations (and Carter in the US as much as Callaghan in the UK exemplified this), the state accepted blame for mass unemployment. The New Right merely portrayed failure as a series of personal failures. The need to replace the collapsing mass industries, wrecked by the new flexibility, led inevitably to the canonisation of the individual entrepreneur. It may be argued that in the very act of canonising the self-made man who has 'risen to the top' (i.e. become extremely rich) without benefit of formal education, the New Right has undermined its own precepts. The promotion of hard work above the need for educational qualifications has proven to be counter-productive. Far too many of those who are already idolised by disadvantaged and disaffected youth have achieved status by routes where a strong educational background has not been a factor and may even have been a disadvantage. Then add on the message from the New Right that anyone can 'make it' despite a poor background, and the slow but steady education-driven route begins to pall. Again, those who promote the ideal that anyone can make it never add the Hirsch caveat: 'but not all can make it'.

These same disaffected youth may have noticed that their own parents, often living in areas of high unemployment, do not seem to have achieved much status, whether they worked hard at school or not. With the profession of teaching further undermined by a general flight to private education and by government-led accusations of left-wing bias in the state system, respect for teachers and education has plummeted in many areas of the UK. The exhortation to work hard at school, in order to get on in life is still vital in Japan but, conversely, has an especially hollow ring in the UK of the 1990's. It may even be that the US/UK New Right perceived a need to create the entrepreneurial underpinning to large industries that the Japanese system created. It is just a pity that, unlike the Japanese, they failed to foster the large industries that the entrepreneurs were meant to underpin. In the event, the UK saw a rise of the self-employed (particularly the small entrepreneur) from 1.9 million in 1979 to 3.2 million in 1988. This regrettably failed to offset the 2.4 million jobs lost in the period 1979–85 and the massive rise in the number of unemployed. That over 90 per cent of small firms do not export and that the bulk do not deal in new technologies has not generally been seen as a problem.

Nor, for some, has the employment fall-out been perceived as problematical; in 1990 the Institute for Fiscal Studies noted that the numbers of people on Social Security in the UK rose from 2.6 million in 1979 to 4.3 million in 1987, with another 1.9 million families having an income below the social security safety net level. What does matter to the producers is how the individual consumes. The work of Hirsch suggests that the western consumer is on a treadmill that 'green' attitudes have done little to slow.

Admittedly, against the tide of consumerism it is possible to identify a rise in concern for conservation and the environment. It is equally noticeable that enthusiasm for such ideas is greater among the more advanced nations than among developing nations. The same schism applies within economies. The enthusiasm for the higher costs associated with greener products is far less marked among the poor, the sick and the unemployed. Only where green issues could be allied to good publicity has much progress been made.

This dichotomy between rich and poor is fundamental and has been reinforced by the New Right during the 1980s. That Thatcherism was highly selective in its beneficial effects was evidenced by Jenkins (1991). He demonstrated that in the decade 1978–89 the poorest 10 per cent of British society saw a fall in average weekly income from £48 to £42. The top 10 per cent in income terms, however, saw a rise from £492 to £745 (at 1986 prices). The pecking order for positional gains was clear – the top gained massively at the expense of the poor. Their assets rose in value even as their taxes fell precipitately. On the next rung, the upwardly-mobile aspirers in the entrepreneurial sector saw some gaining of ground on those at the top. However, their greatest success was to break free from those, the employed professional classes, with whom they had in the past been approximately equal in financial terms. From that point it was all 'look behind you'. The positional losers were encouraged not to bemoan their fate relative to the winners, but to look instead at the millions who had lost their jobs and thus their ability to make any positional statement at all. This was a further lever to erode wage-bargaining, spending power and, for a while, inflation. Under Thatcher, the top 10 per cent of UK society was keeping more income than the whole of the bottom 50 per cent.

Positional goods

Perhaps the greatest revolution in the UK in the eighties was the change in the nature of positional goods. Following from Hirsch, positional goods are those which are desirable and which can, potentially, be owned by *any* person, but not by *all*. The classic example of the positional treadmill is Napoleon's reference to every soldier carrying in his knapsack the baton of a Field Marshal. Theoretically at least, any soldier could become a Field Marshal; the problem is that not *all* soldiers can achieve this. The baton is an especially good analogy since the post of Field Marshal is defined in terms of the number of men under his direct command. For one person to succeed, a fixed number *must* fail. Interestingly, Adam Smith also made much the same point in noting that for every one rich man there must be several hundred poor men.

The essential point is that the system requires that all individuals should believe that they are, indeed, the potential Marshal or Porsche-owner. The continuing fight for status symbols is what inspires the effort that will, for most, be quite fruitless. It is entirely vital that the game not be given away too soon. Once individuals realise that their efforts are never going to achieve the success they crave, then motivation can die. The psychologist might recognise this as powerlessness or helplessness: the sociologist might diagnose anomie. Possibly, some failed aspirers will refuse to believe that they have failed and cope with the situation through denial. Lest this seem unduly pessimistic, in the light of advice for us all to prepare for many potentially exciting new career changes through our working lives, I can make two points. One is the preponderance of individuals (choosing, or forced, into mid-life career changes) who find they are too old at 30 or 40 to fit into a new career. The second is to recall again the sixties utopians who predicted a life of leisure for the masses as the machines did all the work. Yes, there is some job-sharing these days, but a high percentage of individuals would prefer to put in extra effort and take the other man's job, income and lifestyle.

To return to positional goods, a luxury limousine could not be so defined if everyone were to own one. The present-day family car has many features not present even in luxury cars of thirty years ago. Yet luxury cars still exist, for luxury has been redefined upwards to keep it beyond the financial means of the herd. A pure positional good, then, is a special level, or sub-set within a set. The luxury car is self-defining, as is the post of Field Marshal, whatever the pressures from below. The rich were forced into ever-more-exotic holiday locations as the masses first overwhelmed UK coastal resorts, then Mediterranean resorts and then planned their *sorties* into the Seychelles.

Embedded within Hirsch's work is the important notion that striving after goods may not only be futile, but that the goods themselves may be destroyed as they are devalued. Perhaps the classic example of destroying something by the act of attaining it is the desire of many urbanites to live in a quiet rural village. Such villages are defined in terms of not having been invaded by the new houses associated with an influx of strangers. What was desired is not what was gained, and it was the very act of gaining it that caused the destruction. In the work of Hirsch is the clear warning that the Thatcher/Reagan cult of the individual would set the majority on a fool's errand. However, since basic education (not the higher levels of education that Hirsch mentioned), basic health care and basic housing have become positional goods in the UK, the whole nature of the game has changed. The losers now lose in a much bigger way, and their offspring also lose. The wealth gap is now more clearly evident and reaffirms most of the old class boundaries, In some areas of the UK, those individuals whose quality of life was enhanced during the fifties, sixties and seventies are now liquidating their positional gains just in order to give their children no better an education, no better health care, than they themselves once received for free. Older money has reserves on which to draw and thus does not lose position. What has happened is that the treadmill has speeded up for those lower down the social hierarchy. Such matters were also touched on by Bourdieu.

Bourdieu (1984), in examining 'taste', provided data relating social origin and education to patronage of various types of furniture stores. More significantly for present purposes he wrote: 'This *petite bourgeoisie* of consumers, [which] means to acquire on credit, i.e. before its due time, the attributes of the legitimate lifestyles . . . is perfectly adapted to act as a transmission belt and pull into the race for consumption and competition those from whom it means to distinguish itself'. (Bourdieu, 1984, p. 365). Bourdieu thus reinforces both the primacy of consumption as a demand factor and the futility of mass competition for position. As Hirsch indicated, the great mass of consumers are like the donkey chasing the carrot or the hamster in its wheel. Rather like running down the up-escalator, the goal is always just beyond the reach of all but the fortunate few, whose very successes serve to speed up the escalator. What also speeds up the escalator is consumer credit, as Bourdieu clearly states.

Consumer credit

The 1980s, as I have suggested, saw new users of the debt sucked back by the financial markets from the disgraced Third World borrowers. These new corporate borrowers burdened themselves with huge amounts of debt. By June of 1990 the fabled fortunes of Donald Trump had gone into decline, as had those of Alan Bond. Massive debt burdens are never far from the minds of the big players. The 1970s was the decade that made the credit card and killed savings. The 1980s was the decade that killed short-term borrowing for the small man, and created the corporate mega-stars: a recipe for 'clogs to clogs in three decades', rather than three generations. Credit, Marx's fictitious capital, equally served to obscure the future in respect of retail change: could the consumers (consuming before their time) really afford what they bought?

Without the availability of credit, retail sales would of necessity be a far more accurate indicator of a strengthening or weakening economy. If individuals could genuinely not afford the items, based on their savings, then they could not purchase them. Conversely, any real sustained rise in consumer spending would be a clearer indicator of underlying growth. At the very least it would be a clearer indicator of a sustained desire to spend real disposable income with the retail sector. We can leave aside the tendency, in times of general affluence, for spending to go outside the retail sector and into holidays abroad or meals taken away from home. Retailers ought to seek to know if a given level of spending is real or sustainable, and this requires a conventional view of credit.

The Credit explosion

There are many possible measures of the increased availability of credit,

Table 11.1 Total outstanding consumer credit in the UK

Year end	*Outstanding credit (£m)*
1990	52,899
1989	48,427
1988	42,839
1987	36,829
1986	30,831
1985	25,994
1984	22,093
1983	19,251
1982	15,741
1981	14,513
1980	13,148
1979	10,564

Source: Highest annual estimate published in Central Statistical Office, *Monthly Digest of Statistics*, London, HMSO (to June 1991).

but the one chosen here is the level of consumer credit reported in the Monthly Digest of Statistics by the UK Central Statistical Office (CSO) (1980–89). No attempt is made to deflate the figures, which are presented as reported regularly. As shown in Table 11.1, the rise in outstanding credit is substantial and can be seen to have outstripped the performance of the economy in terms of economic growth. The percentage increases also outstrip the measures offered by either the Retail Price Index or the Tax and Price Index. Inevitably, most indicators are on an upward spiral, not least because of underlying inflationary pressures. The object here is not to seek correlations or causality between the credit explosion and other indicators, but merely to ask what the trends might mean for retailing. Discussion of the apparent relationship between aspects of economic performance may be found, if desired, in the Bank of England Quarterly Bulletin (e.g. 1988, pp. 4–5).

Table 11.1 indicates that outstanding consumer credit in Britain rose by more than 400 per cent between 1979 and 1988. Consumer credit is only one element of personal indebtedness, but there are signs that the UK is more closely following the US pattern of living by credit than would be the case in Japan or West Germany. Credit is an event more potent force in US retailing.

By 1991 there were over 1,000 million credit cards in circulation in the USA with outstanding credit in excess of $225,000 million. Culturally, one suspects, the stigma of debt is more ingrained in Japan and Germany. To raise a further issue, one may look at the savings ratio which is the level of personal savings expressed as a percentage of total disposable income. The whole issue of the trend of savings in various countries is both a vital and complex topic. One good source of comparative data is the OECD (Dean *et al.*, 1989). As Nigel Lawson found out in the context of the UK, figures on this subject are notoriously unreliable, as some analysts were attempting to point out at the time. However unreliable the figures, one has to accept them simply in order to make any kind of comparison between nations. The pattern, which might be seen as a mirror-image of credit indebtedness, seems to show Japan and West Germany having historically high values that are being maintained. The USA has had historically much lower savings levels which have eroded yet further, and the UK has moved from high savings to low. To illustrate: in 1987 the ratio was 15.1 per cent in Japan, 12.3 per cent in West Germany, 5.6 per cent in the UK and 3.9 per cent in the USA. Yet in 1982, the UK level had been 11.2 per cent and was to see a further fall to 4.4 per cent for 1988. This may start to suggest to us that some of the credit growth is real – that is, likely to be sustainable, in that individuals prefer spending over saving or will dig into savings to fund spending. We may be witnessing a structural change in how UK individuals deal with their finances. However, there are caveats. The US and UK entered the 1980s on a wave of import-boosting tax cuts for the rich.

Another underlying factor in the UK is likely to have been the general restructuring of financial operations dating roughly from 1986 copycatting the earlier US deregulation of S&Ls. What is significant is that building societies were permitted, from that date, to offer unsecured loans. General financial deregulation has led to intense competition between banks, building societies and other financial organisations to make loans. The rise in computing technology in the mid-1980s that led to the boom in geodemographic analysis also coincided with a boom in credit-referencing and substantial market demand for such services.

It is perfectly possible that more sophisticated techniques are offering far more accurate credit referencing than was hitherto possible. That is, those who were credit-worthy in the past may not have received the credit they sought. A simple case of market restructuring may have made credit more appropriately available. To exemplify, the number of Visa cards in circulation rose from 3.3 million in 1975 to 12.1 million in 1986. The figures for Access-type cards were 3.1 million and 9.8 million respectively (CSO, 1988). Euromonitor (1990) offered a figure of 12,100,000 Eurocard/Mastercards in use in the UK in 1988 as compared with 1,840,000 in France and only 835,000 in West Germany. This also symbolises the power of the UK financial system. An enabling factor in this growth has been the development of a system whereby issuers, for example building societies, acquire the right to supply Visa-type cards from the original licence-holder. The proliferation of cards by adjunct financial organisations has greatly accelerated card availability. The number of cards offered by retail stores has also increased phenomenally. After their store card launch in 1985, Marks and Spencer supplied 1 million cards in six months. The simple point to be made is that sheer availability may have brought a boom in credit usage. There are many good trading reasons, mostly related to market information, why retailers offer store cards. There is probably a ratchet effect, with the level of availability increasing total indebtedness. We should also note that, as repatriated loans also turned sour, the domestic credit lenders tightened up their loan criteria.

Credit and money supply

Dow and Saville (1988) offer further welcome balance to some of the strict monetarist credos in respect of money supply. Their focus is on the primacy of bank lending in the financial process. They observe:

> Much monetary analysis looks only at the preferences of final lenders, and sees the stock of money as determined solely by the preferences of those who hold financial assets. Financial assets, however, are other agents' debts. Money creation involves increases more or less equivalent in both bank loans and bank deposits; in our account, it is the bank lending that sets the pace . . . if the monetary authorities are to control monetary growth they must control bank lending. (Dow and Saville, 1988, p. 40).

This confirms their earlier basic point that banks are not some final repository of national spending power. They are not a variety of kindly uncle who will store money and take it out of circulation. Under the high real interest rates emphasised by Congdon (1988), there is every incentive for banks to lend and generate further bank profits. Whenever an individual home-owner is crippled by double-digit interest rates that he or she must pay, then someone is making profit at his/her expense as long as real interest rates prevail. High interest rates may be some kind of disincentive to what we can call discretionary borrowing, but they are a real incentive to lending. Never forget, either, that in the UK much financial repayment being made at high 1990 interest rates was on long-term loans contracted at much lower interest rates on offer as recently as 1987.

The type of false boom that can be facilitated by credit would include so-called 'distress borrowing' where households, squeezed by mortgage interest rates, may continue to maintain habitual spending patterns by using credit rather than cash. In other words, this is the easier adjustment as opposed to cutbacks in the household budget. Dow and Saville (1988) further suggest that interest rates have little effect on the saving habits of the majority. This finding echoes distress borrowing, reinforcing the reality that changes in personal habits, even when in financial distress, involve costly changes of financial direction. It is simpler just to carry on as before. Psychologically, the individual expects that something will turn up to save the day. Purchasing material goods is emotionally reassuring and reinforcing of one's 'worth' (McCann-Erickson, 1989). In practical terms, the potential saver/investor may have little knowledge of how to go about maximising savings. Unwillingness to take on long-term debt may have shaken some borrowing out of the mortgage market and into general consumer credit. Such adjustments might go some way towards explaining the continued rise of credit – a rise that has prompted such observations as: 'Increased credit facilities are influential in increasing consumption'. (Economist Intelligence Unit, June 1989, p. 15).

Only in February, 1990, was there any real sign of a slackening in the demand for credit in the UK. There can be little doubt that credit availability is a factor in retail performance, but it is not the only one. Retailing is also driven by wider market expectations, and expansion may be powered by a desire for market share or some other performance indicator. Likewise, competition will necessarily force retailers and developers into refurbishment schemes. It is clear that there are both distortions to the market and in the market. Judging the appropriate level of retail investment is becoming less and less easy.

Credit, then, operates at several levels – global, national and personal. Equally clearly, credit is not simply there as a consumption-facilitator (which is the simplest level at which we can view it). Indeed, we have barely made use of the realisation that the post-Bretton Woods world is awash with credit. Yet we have already chased that credit through the Third World and back to the corporate megastars. We clearly live in Veblen's vision of a world where fewer and fewer live by making goods and more and more live by making money.

Conflating credit and positional goods

Having already set up the proposition that footloose credit has sought to ground itself in real assets or at least real returns, we can firmly conflate the world of credit and the world of positional goods. This also helps us with a rather tricky point that flows from having mentioned that the UK savings ratio is in decline. It was possibly as a result of Chancellor Lawson's attacks on 'teenage scribblers' that 1988 saw a series of papers from the offices of market analysts seeking to demonstrate that the estimates of the savings ratio were grossly false, and further, that this error masked real potential to draw on assets – and thus to keep on spending. Indeed, Lawson himself (interviewed in September 1990) offered insights into this problem. He listed three elements of misjudgement during his reign as Chancellor. One of these was to have underestimated the strength of consumer demand and the capacity to go on borrowing even at high interest rates. Since another error had been to overreact to the October 1987 crash (with low interest rates), there can be no surprise at how staggeringly inflationary the period from the 1988 budget onwards was. Here we have the extreme instance of an inflation-fighting regime itself blatantly causing that inflation. In all probability the UK plunged into an exaggerated recession in 1991 through the government refusing to ease interest rates for fear of compounding its own error of 1988.

If we follow this through, we can see what a disaster UK government policy in the UK has been since 1987. Chancellor Lawson loosened fiscal policy in order to further advantage the wealthy, possibly believing that this was safe in that some consumers were short of spending power, and that therefore the effects on inflation and imports would not be too dire. The scribblers were busily pointing out that because official figures were so dreadful, the economy would be robust to this and spend on. There was thus a mini re-run of 1981 with the wealthy continuing to spend and eventually drawing down the wrath of continued high interest rates upon those least able to afford them.

That the country went on a spending spree simply should not have been a surprise. Clive Wolman, writing in the *Financial Times* began his budget analysis (entitled 'Dramatic gains for the rich') with the following words: 'The 1988 budget is one for the rich to a much greater extent than any of the Conservative Government's previous budgets . . . without any local or State income taxes . . . the marginal tax rates of high UK earners is now similar to their US counterparts'. Nor was tax-cutting the only means by which the rich were about to be rewarded. A doubling of tax allowances and a shelter for unearned income were on the horizon in the guise of independent taxation for women. The *FT* continued: 'independent taxation of husband and wife . . . may have been presented . . . as a blow for women's equality . . . when the symbolism is stripped away, the only substance . . . will be to benefit the wealthier and generally older married couples' (*Financial Times*, 16 March 1988).

So how does this help conflate credit and positional goods? We have already noted the British preoccupation with land as a symbol of wealth and other writers have, with justification, come to regard house property as a positional good. The consumer may have difficulty in understanding where and when to stop spending, but the positional status of the house (considered most recently by Thrift and Leyshon, 1990) is easy to comprehend. Furthermore, we have the suggestion by Hamnett *et al.* (1990) that the house is both a wealth store and a wealth source. What better policy in times of uncertainty than to store capital in a (usually) inflating asset that one can also live in? Successive house price shocks during the 1970s convinced many that the real economic divides in Britain were between those with a house as constantly-inflating asset, home and piggy-bank, and those without. We thus return again to the central advantage accruing to Margaret Thatcher from putting home-ownership at the summit of her 1979 general election agenda.

Now insert credit. With housing established as a positional good and with desirable inflation-proofing characteristics, the latent demand was clearly there. Mortgage credit made it possible to acquire today the positional good for which one would normally have had to wait until tomorrow. Credit, indeed, made it possible to obtain that which one would otherwise never have obtained at all. The further advantage for the lender, whose risks always appeared slim, is that this rooted credit in the ultimate tangible asset — property. If the borrower defaulted, the valuable resaleable item reverted to the lender. We should never allow ourselves to forget that the bulk of bank lending is secured on tangible assets. For the most part, in all economic sectors including housing, services and industry, this basically means land and little else. Small wonder that, in the finance-driven economics of the UK and USA we can find ready evidence of involvement with land. In the UK in 1990, banks were exposed to £40bn. of property sector loans.

Sale and leaseback

The position in the USA was, if anything, more grim. We have noted already that the UK and US contrast in their attitudes to land. The UK habit of by-passing industrial investment in order to get straight into prime land has a strong history. Legislation that, whatever its alleged intent, has had the effect of preserving land values has made this a safe policy. The ability of retailers to undertake sale and leaseback of expensive stores with financial institutions usually testifies to confidence in the long-term value of the land. Indeed, one of the opening statements in this book concerned the centrality of property in UK life. The links between retail and property have never been hard to find. The *rentier* existence is everywhere appealing. All property market analysts constantly monitor the three key rental sectors: retail; industrial; offices. The retailer seeking the prime high street site will usually pay most handsomely for the privilege. For investors, retail property dominated by the High Street will always have its appeal. If the great British shopper never stops shopping, then retailers will always be in shape to take rental increases. It is in new retail locations, however that the windfall gains are made. A piece of undeveloped land may have little intrinsic worth until the shop developer comes along. The value then rises enormously and the retailer may get to share in the windfall. Most commonly though, after fighting a few battles over true residual values, the lucrative part of new development comes when the pension funds and insurance companies are involved.

The retailer starts by proving that the new store is generating income, then indulges in sale and leaseback. The long-term value of the site is released to fund yet another new store and placate the analysts with growth. As long as the overall system does not permit of overdevelopment (and here the planning profession is most helpful), the land values form a stable investment. As Britain headed into the 1990 property collapse, the heavily-exposed UK banks began to worry. After all, around £180bn. of the total £205bn. outstanding loans in the UK were ultimately secured on property. As if to ram home the message of Campeau, the 1990 UK property downturn caught out the Burton group of retailers. They had begun several expensive new shop property schemes just in time for the downturn. In 1990, the group wrote off £120m. in property losses (declared profits were around £190m. and interest payments stood at close to £50m.). The Chief Executive soon left, groaning under the weight of an enormous golden handshake. Some months later, hundreds of ordinary employees were disposed of on rather less lucrative terms.

The USA, however, has usually regarded land as just one more ingredient in the equation of building profit. Even without planning restrictions, a multi-million-pound freestanding foodstore in the UK would probably be protected from next-door competition because rivals would not want to take on the substantial costs of building simply in order to split a market. In the USA, low land prices mean that it is easy to find competition nearby, and a retail property that trades well today could be demolished as redundant in a few years' time. It ill behoves anyone to become too heavily involved in land investment *per se*. Yet under deregulatory pressures, and with major tax incentives, many did – to disastrous effect. US banks between 1986 and 1989 exposed themselves to £247bn. of investment in land (about fifteen times the amount they loaned to industry). The central significance of land is evidenced by the fact that 1988 saw 2.8 million homes sold in the UK (with attendant mortgage finance) in comparison with 0.4 million in West Germany. Conversely, the Germans have invested hundreds of billions of pounds more in industrial plant than have the British. The latter appear to feel that property is the last thing that a borrower will give up – and this may well be true. With not just a house, but status, a positional good at stake, the borrower will sacrifice much before bearing the stigma of losing his/her home. This resistance is, of course, more evident in those social groupings where housing has always been a positional good – even before the credit/asset value factor became pre-eminent.

The peculiar status of housing as a positional good and as an inflation-proofer makes it especially attractive to the credit agencies. It is also especially attractive to them to encourage price inflation in this sector, which leads to bigger, more worthwhile loans. The idea of credit 'creating the consumer' is discussed at length by Shaoul (1990). Note, too, that pressure to get into the UK's home-ownership treadmill is a key pressure for high wages from the beginning of working life – very inflationary!

Everything about the British housing market makes it apparently easy prey for those wishing to extend safe, lucrative loans. The housing market also mirrors the general fate of borrowers and lenders in the 1980s. Those who were heavy borrowers seeking to get into this positional good found themselves crippled by high real interest rates. Those who already had the assets that were being chased and who possibly had no debt outstanding on their home were massively advantaged. If need be, the home could stand as security against a modest loan to take advantage of falling prices in consumer goods as recession shook out the economy. If a homeowner inherited (probably tax-free) the home of a parent, then this could be seen as an additional free source of spending power to fuel the spending booms so poorly predicted by a tax-cutting government. Quite simply, just as banks do not take money out of circulation but merely recycle it in a way that advantages investors, so housing is not a final repository, but an enduring source of spending power – for some.

Because we can see housing (and credit's role in the market) as a source of spending power, we are saved from having to delve too deeply into searching for the Black Economy or other less plausible sources of robust spending. It should hardly surprise us that Ball (1983) was able to write *The Political Economy of Owner Occupation*. Ball saw a cyclical, self-reinforcing process whereby high prices led to high receipts for the lending agencies, thus facilitating more big, inflationary loans. All too soon we return to Dow and Saville's strictures on uncontrolled lending – yet the 1980s saw the financial deregulation of those lending agencies devoted to the house market. The crucial advantage that accrues to credit organisations when they spot a positional good cannot be overstated. Such a good becomes a treadmill to higher, inflationary prices. In order to retain status as a positional good, scarcity must be maintained. Price is the simplest scarcity mechanism. Yet here are the lenders, prepared to loan to any aspirant chasing the positional good – and forcing it ever beyond the reach of the masses. Thus does credit find its natural home.

Retailers will have little trouble in identifying their positional goods. They can be created, for children, by media cartoon series (though the lifecycle of such goods is short). More enduring positional goods are not hard to identify – making all the more remarkable the soon-reversed decision by Porsche to produce a downmarket model when all the positional evidence was that profits lay the other way!

There is a natural tendency to presume that positional pressure for a satellite dish on every roof in some neighbourhoods (and no such dishes on any roof in others!) takes positional spending out of the sphere of most retailers. Surely it will just be the leading-edge consumer goods retailers who benefit most from the phenomenon? At this point we may note that UK food retailers have not so readily joined in the US price war. Instead, UK food retailers increased profit margins by moving away from basic food products into the more exotic items. Is putting an avocado in the shopping trolley 'saying something' about the purchaser, even if only to the checkout assistant? We are surely hitting the exact opposite of price-lining goods for the uncomfortable, uncertain customer who craved the comfort of self-service. This is an area that could be pursued further.

The particular status of the motor car

Finally, let us also consider the motor car – once itself a positional good. If we seek a talisman for the industrial decline of the UK, then it is readily provided by the car industry. At one point after World War Two, whilst the USA was building its own internal market, the UK was the world's biggest car exporter. In 1988 the UK car trade was £6.1bn. in deficit and comprised 55 per cent of the manufacturing trade deficit; clothing, building materials and consumer electronics also did their best.

One gut response to unacceptable figures is to denounce them as misleading. It is clear from the above that a de-industrialised/post-industrial Britain playing the Trojan Horse for foreign manufacturers seeking European markets is going to find its balance of payments accounts looking rather different. Already, though, there has been criticism of the balance of payments figures (much as the US BOP figures had to be treated with caution under its reserve currency rôle). This may be so, but Table 11.2 seems to tell a clear tale.

As the UK increasingly lost its capacity to manufacture cars, with

Table 11.2 UK balance of payments (non-oil visibles only) in £m.

1976	+ 18
1977	+ 487
1978	+ 442
1979	− 2718
1980	+ 1045
1981	+ 248
1982	− 2728
1983	− 8509
1984	− 12,269
1985	− 11,446
1986	− 13,555
1987	− 15,406
1988	− 23,875
1989	− 25,321

Source: Based on Central Statistical Office, *External Trade Statistics of the UK*, London, HMSO, Table A1 1990, 1986, 1984.

production falling from 1,556,000 in 1964 to 807,000 in 1986, the demand for them (fuelled by tax breaks for company cars) rose threefold between 1961 and 1987. On 1 August 1989 alone 500,000 new cars were registered. A 1990 Greenpeace report suggested that the UK taxpayer was subsidising company cars to the tune of £2.8bn. per annum. More than half of the new cars bought each year in the UK are company cars and the subsidies make a company car cheaper to use than public transport. Inevitably, the bias favours the wealthier sectors of society.

We yet again see how data can be treated at two levels. On the one hand, UK retailing reacts to the greater mobility that results from there being over 320 cars per 1,000 people in 1986. On the other hand, the trade deficit that results from high import penetration is accorded less significance. The increased level of car ownership is one post-war phenomenon with which most retailers have learned to live, and which some have exploited to profitable effect.

Until the demise of public transport in the UK, the car conformed to Veblen's model of conspicuous consumption. The car as status symbol has literally given way to the car as necessity. The minority without a car fail to support public transport sufficiently to generate income. The service then declines to the point where it becomes a drain on public resources. Transport deregulation in the UK has tended to exacerbate the polarisation between the profitable minority of routes (and times) and the unprofitable majority. Thus we see that the minority who lack cars nowadays are worse off than were the car-less majority of yesteryear who were able to use well-supported, viable, public transport systems.

That said, public transport has, in most advanced countries at least, been seen as a public service. More to the point, since modern capitalism requires a mobile workforce, there has been recognition of the totality of

Table 11.3 Motor vehicle production

Date	*USA*	*Canada*	*France*	*Germany*	*Italy*	*UK*	*Japan*
1913	485,000	14,976	45,000	20,388	6,760	34,000	
1939	3,588,889	155,426	182,000	180,200	68,834	402,000	
1953	7,349,123	486,049	497,348	490,046	174,320	834,275	49,778
1966	10,396,299	872,214	2,024,552	3,050,708	1,365,598	2,042,354	2,286,399
1985	11,652,743	1,933,381	3,016,106	4,445,920	1,572,907	1,311,256	12,271,095

the transport system. Public transport cannot match the flexibility of the private car, but it can reduce congestion, is more cost-efficient when viewed globally, and reduces pollution. A case can be made for fast, efficient, public transport, and many modern forward-thinking western cities have made that case with some success. There is, of course, a social implication in public transport investment. It pulls expenditure out of an area of potential direct benefit to the individual into an area of potential collective benefit. The countries where the New Right found greatest success with the cult of the individual are those with the most awful public transport systems. We can turn again to theories of social traps to explain the attractions of individualism, inefficiency, congestion and pollution. The example of a crowd panicking to escape a fire or similar catastrophe, with the attendant blocking of exists, is again apposite. It can be shown that orderly exiting would save more lives in total. Why, then, the panic? Not least this is because in the orderly scenario, more will survive, but those individuals closest to the source of the fire will almost certainly die. The panic situation is most often caused by those at risk trying to leapfrog the rush to the door at the expense of others. Collective action is more sensible for the general good, but far less attractive to each individual. Much the same applies to the driver on congested roads; public transport is the attractive solution, provided it is the other driver who abandons their use of the car.

This point is laboured precisely because the 1980s has been the decade of the re-emergence of the individual ego, the 'me' decade. Retailers in locations accessible only by car and fearing a mass exodus to public transport can rest assured that the egocentric decade will take a great deal of unlearning. Drivers may assuage guilt through catalytic converters or charitable giving, but giving up cars has a considerable way to go. For that reason, Table 11.3 is best seen as a talisman of the industrial decline of the UK and a key component of the imbalance in visible trade.

How fascinating it would be to travel back through time and ask Adam Smith just how it came about that Japan, with all its lack of resources and at great distance from markets, could achieve the transposition of fortunes with the UK in the period 1953–85.

The unequal consumer

As part of the dependent sector of the economy, retailing is at the mercy of overall spending levels – yet we have seen that wealth is by no means evenly distributed. The polarisation of the UK society between the 'haves' and 'have-nots' is a clear consequence of the changes seen in the 1980s since tax cuts have come to the fore. Inequality (though illustrated in many areas) is most evident in taxation and housing. In 1966 the marginal rate of UK tax for the top band of earners was 95 per cent: in 1989 the rate fell to 40 per cent. The difference was a staggering drop of 55 per cent. For the basic rate taxpayer in 1966 the tax rate was 35 per cent. By 1989 this had fallen to 25 per cent: altogether a far less significant fall than for the rich. When one bears in mind that VAT was virtually doubled by the incoming Thatcher administration of 1979 and that basic rates of other indirect taxes have not kept pace with rising prices, it is soon seen that the total tax burden of the basic rate taxpayer has changed hardly at all in over twenty years. The rich, however, have received massive tax cuts, whilst rewards to company directors have also shown substantial increases. The wealth gap between the very top and the very bottom of British society has, in the last decade, begun to widen again after decades of closing. In the Thatcher years, the top 1 per cent of society showed a staggering income rise of 80 per cent. For the bottom 10 per cent the figure was 0.1 per cent.

To return once again to housing, the differences were every bit as stark. By 1988 in parts of London £1 million would not buy a house. At the same time, the figures on homelessness stood at record levels. Of all areas of government expenditure, the housing budget was the one that suffered the greatest cuts in real terms. Again, shortages and price rises step up the treadmill. The £1 million house is the carrot: homelessness is the stick. The work of Hirsch gives the lie to the conception of the rise in personal financial liquidity as being in some way the province of the young City dealer. In fact, there is likely to have been little real movement of wealth between the various social classes. We can draw on Giddens' (1984) theory of class structuration to show not only that with permeable class boundaries such trends are inherently self-fulfilling, but also that financial accumulation merely creates upward pressures to further advantage the already advantaged, as predicted by Hirsch.

Housing as a form of unearned income usually provides assets far in excess of what might have been gained through paid employment. The greatest gains have gone to those who were able to acquire good-quality accommodation well before price inflation became a factor in the housing market. Leaving aside those in London who had, until 1989, benefited from owner-occupation across the board, we see that this singled out middle-class individuals who were in the housing market in the 1950s and 1960s. The likelihood that lower-income individuals will have gained massively from house-price inflation is lessened by two factors. First, these groups did not generally enter the housing market until after the first two major house-price inflations. Secondly, they are more prone to unemployment and more susceptible to mortgage interest rate inflation — both factors likely to force them back out of the housing market. Asset accumulation through housing, like other measures of wealth that are rarely accounted for under means-testing, act as a way of distorting perceptions of true available spending power — as we noted when discussing credit.

A potential underclass?

The homelessness problem is accentuated by the decline in the house rental market. Housing rental is common in, for example, West Germany or The Netherlands where only some 40 per cent of the population are owner-occupiers. One price for access to owner occupation in the UK is that the mortgage rate is changed frequently and by substantial amounts. This has an immediate spin-off into income available for other purchases. The real problems accumulate for those individuals where access to home-ownership is infeasible. By 1986 it was estimated that in the south-east and east of the UK over 30 per cent of households had an income too low to sustain house purchase at prices prevailing in those areas. This problem was said to afflict less than 5 per cent of households in areas such as the north and north-west (though housing quality factors must be taken into account). What, then, does this imply for British society? Socially, the UK, as some commentators have begun to note, has started to develop all the signs of having a significant underclass (Dahrendorf, 1987). The concept of the underclass was also raised by Hall who identified this clearly as a product of de-industrialisation, and added (Hall, 1986, p. 17), 'It just might be permanent . . . society, in self-defence, would react by retaining the underclass in their urban ghettos by aggressive policing.' Hall's fear was that the capitalist crisis might be coming true — that progress would substitute machinery for labour — but that machines (unlike labour) do not consume the products of their own work. For Hall, a more likely alternative to taxing the rich in order to give the poor some dignity and employment would be for the rich to 'pay for extra police to keep the problem away from their front door' Hall (1986, p. 20). At the same time, Hall saw Britain's progress in high-tech growth industries as 'lamentable'.

In the UK, the dramatic rise in homelessness among the young is a trend that has been increased by steps taken to avoid the much-reviled Poll Tax. The central rôle of the family unit in all its manifestations is breaking down. From the 1960s to the 1980s, the decline of the typical family of wedded parents with two offspring was marked. The whole lifestyle-marketing industry thrived on the rise of the 'dinky' phenomenon — 'Dual Income, No Kids Yet'. So where were the 'kids', if not parented (yet) by yuppy households? Increasingly, they were becoming the province of single mothers. By 1988, the number of households with dependents and headed by a lone mother reached 15 per cent of all families with children. From within these figures, there was a 25 per cent increase in unmarried mothers, a 20 per cent increase in divorced mothers, and a 50 per cent increase in separated mothers. The figure of 15 per cent of households with children having a lone mother status had risen from a level of 9 per cent in 1979. The lone father phenomenon (more classically a product of the death of a parent) was stable at 1 per cent – as in 1971. Overall, 27 per cent of births in 1988 took place outside marriage; in the city of Manchester the figure rose to 49 per cent.

In terms of the underclass notion, the fact that 20 per cent of unmarried women aged 18–49 were cohabiting is of less significance. The underclass phenomenon relates more clearly to a total inability or unwillingness to seek economic solutions to existing problems. Lone mothers have little capacity to escape drudgery. Cohabiting individuals without children have no dependents to constrain their economic opportunities. Exacerbated by the poverty trap, whereby up to 90 per cent of a marginal increase in income can be offset by loss of benefits, there is little incentive for lone mothers to seek work. Nor, since we have seen that mass labour is in terminal decline, is there much point for many people in looking. The only ray of hope is that the lone parent may loop back into the Third World syndrome where the child is seen as an economic asset. Abolition of wages council regulations for young people means that the exploitation of child labour is now feasible. This move (directly opposed in the USA by the Department of Labor) finds favour in the UK with certain right-wing thinkers. Certainly, the revisions brought in by the 1990 Employment Act changed the ground rules for 16–18-year-old workers. Once restricted to 48 hours' work per week, now 16–18-year-olds can work unlimited hours – and all night if required. The advent of central heating offsets the advantage that younger and smaller children can probably still fit inside chimneys.

The underclass, aside from being general barometers of the wider social condition, impact on retailing in many ways. They have few resources and therefore make poor customers for all but the most basic foodstore operators. Their *milieu* manifests itself in the sort of phenomenon that is occasionally covered in the press as a civic malaise. Ferdinand Mount (*The Times*, 2 February 1990) stated:

> But it is pointless to argue whether the degrading conditions create disgusting behaviour, or the other way about. Both have to be eradicated. And, in a curious way, I think both come ultimately from the same cause: the gradual erosion of civic pride in Britain, especially industrial England, over the past half-century . . .
>
> I am not sure, even now that inner-city regeneration is beginning to be a reality (as the National Audit Office's report yesterday confirmed), whether its importance is fully understood.

Mr. Mount's analysis – more enterprise needed – excludes the reality of an underclass that not only symbolises lack of 'civic pride' but is also quite powerless to alter its fate. The underclass is the lowest level of the polarised society. Non-food purchases are likely to be made from market stalls or from one of the burgeoning 'seconds' or 'cut price' operations that have begun to sense that here is a substantial market.

12

THE FUTURE FOR CAPITAL – AND CONSUMERS?

What, then, have we learned from the a consideration of IPE? Not least, it can be shown that associated with the two power bases of mercantilism and globalism are two extremes or the ideal-typical bank. The Japanese-style mercantilist bank hitches its fortunes to national economic output via manufacturing and it acts as a low-cost money wholesaler or facilitator. It thinks nationalistically and acts long-term, considering the future of the companies with which it is involved. By backing long-term winners, Japanese-style banks also seek to avoid inflation – and Japanese banks now number seven out of the ten largest in the world. Interestingly, some signs of a more balanced attitude from a UK bank emerged in October 1990 when National Westminster Bank began to hint that it would be advisable for banks to move more towards equity holdings in companies – the German model. In particular, the bank warned against risky lending, including that financed by junk. The suggestion that large companies, not small, should be the targets for equity-holding was reinforced by the Deutsche Bank rescue of Daimler Benz: in contrast, the high failure rate amongst smaller companies was noted. This suggests that National Westminster was thinking along the lines that it was in the national interest to save major corporations by boosting them, rather than spread risk among smaller companies. The second ideal-typical bank is the UK or US style of bank. These banks are far from being the hand-servants of industry. Industry in the national setting is just one of the myriad of possibilities for seeking the best returns wherever it may be found – a classic monetarist credo. The placement of finance, not industry, at the pinnacle of society means that there is no aversion to starving native industry of help, finance or expertise, especially when opportunities such as investment in Third World countries beckon. This shrewdest-of-shrewd investments has left many UK and US banks dead in the water. They are effectively insolvent. Only the illusion that Third World debt is actually worth something sustains their existence – that, and the helping hand of governments who cannot afford to see the banking system go under. This second type of bank is now reacting in one of two ways. One is to continue to attempt to exploit both borrowers and lenders; the other is to continue to gamble on wild pay-offs from the corporate megastars.

Does this, then, explain the comparative state of retail consumption and industrial production in the US and UK? We have clearly seen that it is inherently contradictory to expect to play a global financial role and support native industry to the extent that mercantilist nations can. What we probably see is that retailing is exalted (especially in the UK), largely because manufacturing industry offers so poor a contrast. Equally, whilst UK manufacturing essentially must attempt to compete in foreign markets, retailing has been content to feed off national income however derived: from empire, trade, export manufacturing or finance capital. That position has been further reinforced by the protection from over-competition that was offered by planning laws. The appropriateness to retailing of Japanese-style labour practices was obvious, and was assisted by factors of low unionisation and high female participation. Add to this the advantages conferred by the financial manipulation of the 1980s and it becomes easy to see why retailing has had an easier ride than manufacturing.

Nevertheless, in terms of the future need to develop the US and UK economies, manufacturing must still play a major role. To that extent, the greater academic attention traditionally paid to modelling and analysing that sector is fully justified. Conversely, a commonly-held belief that retailing does not rise above the mechanistic may have been reinforced by the general failure to produce a widely acceptable model of the activity (note the debate between Brown and Savitt, 1988).

Modelling change

Whatever model one ascribes to in analysing retail change, it remains clear that no retailer can stay aloof from the pressures of the market. Pressures either work directly from the economy or from rival retailers who are themselves equally pressured into growth or decline. This is the focus of retail strategy. It is perhaps here that retail models such as the 'wheel' have their value – for I do not deny that they have value. The models can function, as good models should, as a template for action, as Brown (1990) rightly pointed out.

If anything is clear, it is that there are subordinate and superordinate levels of power in the retail environment. Have we not seen that perhaps the most overweaning power (the one that took Safeway out of the market, shook it up and set it back down again) was financial power? How can explanations of changing consumer behaviour possibly ignore this? The pressure to agglomerate, merge, seek economies of scale and protect advantage (pressure that is initiated by the expectation of the financial markets) may go some way towards explaining the many cyclical or wave-like trends observed in retail change. What is certain is that, however much technological barriers can now be used to set up exclusionary power, new markets will still appear (Kirby, 1978).

The Markusen cycle

Since we have acceded to the primacy of the manufactured product, are there models that relate to growth, change and decline and from which we may draw analogies? There would appear to be several, one of particular relevance being the product cycle as described by Markusen (1985), in which she shows how:

> Four sequential profitability experiences, arising from disparate competitive conditions, dictate different responsive strategies. In initial innovative eras new industries can garner superprofits from the novelty of their commodity and the absence of immediate competition. While rates of return may be high, looming competitive pressures dictate further innovation plus intense organization building. A second era, of normal profits, corresponds to the competitive economic model and produces relatively conventional pressures to cut costs and move toward optimal scale production. A third era, sometimes pre-empting the second, is one in which market power, rather than innovative edge, permits greater-than-normal profitability, with distinct business strategies colouring industry performance. Such oligopolistic forms do not emerge in all industries but have characterised significant portions of the US industrial structure. A fourth era of profit squeeze results from renewed competition from outsiders or substitutes and produces pressures to rationalise and often to close down capacity. Bracketed by two stages of unrealised profit, an inventive, precommodity stage and a postsqueeze obsolescence stage, these areas are hypothesized to comprise the normal evolutionary history of an industry. (1985, p. 3)

Saturation

This does not operate perfectly analogously for retailing, for the simple reason that the nature of the retail industry casts it as an agency as much as a brand product. The obsolescence stage manifests itself, in retail, through the risk of market saturation. Not that there is no money to be made – just not enough growth to satisfy the investors. This latter point is worth emphasising as it is clear that many product brands pass through the stages that Markusen outlines. What is evident is that the latter substitute stages do apply to retail and thus reinforce the pressure for unique selling propositions. Unfettered financial market pressures do not allow of a no-grow situation. The Markusen model fits perfectly – for decline and disinvestment must result. Consumers can tire of a product, or advertising may draw them to a substitute. The markets are merciless on producers whose products no longer sell.

Saturated retail markets are anathema for investment; they will be dumped in favour of any alternative that offers better returns. The collapse since 15 August 1971 of any firm basis for monetary value has only compounded the problem. We should not, then, be surprised that

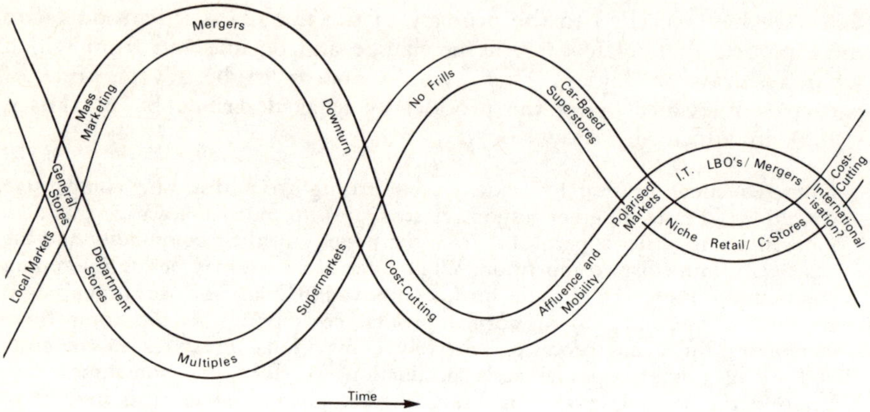

Figure 12.1 Factors driving change in retail formats

there have already been major reports on two retail topics of concern to UK analysts. One is Do-it-Yourself (DIY) – which has shown fast growth – the other food. Food is a natural cause for concern since the traditional view has been that growth is exclusively limited to population increase. As we have already seen, the food retailers have found other ways to extract growth via value-added own brands that match consumer lifestyles.

The escapology act for market saturation cannot, however, last forever. The unbundling phenomenon has already begun and population growth will continue to slow. UK food retailing, however, does have somewhere else to go. In the long run UK food retailers will have to look abroad, not least because foreign rivals who face the same no-growth pressures at home will themselves be looking abroad. If retailers do not want to internationalise, then they can choose stagnation and decline or be pushed by the analysts (see Hallsworth, 1990a, for an earlier version of some of these arguments). The retailer must seek a new frontier and, if costs have been cut and markets exploited as fully as possible in the UK, then the retailer must look abroad. We have already seen how the leveraging of the USA has assisted this process.

Putting together everything that has emerged from a consideration of the existing models of retail change and from the Markusen model, a preliminary attempt may be made at a form of process model that incorporates both financial and environmental pressure as explanatory variables of retail format change. To model two axes it seems fancifully appropriate to use an interlocking cycle (Figure 12.1). This model incorporates the commonly-held view that retail life-cycles are shortening. It is a speculative and far from comprehensive model, but brings about the necessary interface between what we may call process and response. The older formats from earlier eras will persist as a consequence of inertia and planning protection. Longest-lived of all will be the ubiquitous small shop – best equipped to serve the smallest of spatial markets.

Europe – the final frontier?

Saturation causes pressures to look beyond national frontiers, so 'Europe 1992' is likely to impact on UK retailing in several ways and the global connectivities of retailing will lead to knock-on effects in countries outside the EC. This is to be expected, for if the single market can be made to work, it comprises the greatest bloc of consumers in the developed world and some of the strongest and most competitive individual economies. The total retail market in Europe was worth more that £650bn. in 1988. The Ceccini report suggested that the single market of the twelve member states would gain benefits of 4.3–6.4 per cent of GDP with a maximum of ECU 258bn. at 1988 prices.

The Ceccini report

The most immediate policies to affect retailers will be the elimination of customs duties and the elimination of obstacles to free movement of persons, services and capital. Trade barriers were seen in the Ceccini report to be costing ECU 8–9bn., whilst the restrictions on production were costing ECU 57–71bn. The removal of physical trade barriers will clearly impinge on retailers, but other matters will have an effect and one such is the policy on competition. For example, companies that form cartels in order to stay out of each other's markets will, potentially, be prosecuted.

Article 85 of the EEC treaty prohibits practices that distort competition. This includes price-fixing, agreements on market shares or tie-in clauses. Specifically, Article 85 (1) may be infringed by share-acquisitions leading to market concentration. This applies to both horizontal agreements (as between retailers) and vertical agreements (retailer/supplier). The outcome, however, must have a perceptible effect on trade. The bottom line is that the agreement should not represent more than 5 per cent of the turnover of the market area where the agreement has effect. Clearly, the basic geographical definition of what constitutes the area affected makes a great deal of difference. Also, aggregate turnover affected should not exceed ECU 200m.

Naturally, a company may place any restrictions it likes upon the activities of its own subsidiaries and so one begins to see a merger imperative emerging there. To return to Ceccini, the greatest gains were predicted from market integration and the reductions of inefficiencies and monopolies which could be costed at ECU 62–107bn. One can perhaps see how small local monopolies and businesses impose inefficiency costs. The crucial question is where the better competition will come from. As widely predicted by the sceptics, US/Canada free trade simply meant that the bigger, more powerful, US companies serviced remote Canadian markets from their secure home base, at the expense of employment in Canada. It is reasonable to predict that removal of barriers in the EC will lead to small monopolistic firms being ousted by large monopolistic firms. Essentially, the whole thrust of Ceccini is that efficient companies will be the leading powers in the new market. Since the route to efficiency comes from economies of scale in the enlarged market, we can quickly deduce that Europe post-1992 will be a paradise for large, efficient companies operating in most, if not all, of the member states. Everything that we have covered in the earlier chapters of this book suggests that many corporations will take the M&A route to growth. The bottom line to market power in 'Europe 1992' reduces to this – who can buy, who can be bought and who is worth buying?

To demonstrate that the EC Commission is not totally anti-agreement/collaboration (a first route to market power), we may note that they also decided that eighteen types of agreements did not impinge upon competition. These included exchanges of opinion or experience, market research, joint R&D and use of production, storage and transport equipment. In the light of this, cross-national retail alliances (of which more below) such as the European Retail Alliance of Argyll (UK), Ahold (Netherlands) and Casino (France) have had to be careful to identify their purposes. Without doubt, however, as the cross-border restrictions fall, so manufacturers/distributors will see substantial cost savings. The retailers will need purchasing alliances in order to recoup lost market power. Restrictive practices which appeared to be beneficial might escape the wrath of the Commission. Examples extant include exclusive purchasing and distribution agreements.

Article 86, on the other hand, relates to undertakings already having a dominant position – an inevitable problem for a Community built from existing blocks. Here, concern lies with any abuse of such a dominant position. The concept of what is a dominant position is troublesome. No corporation in any commercial sector dominates all the markets. There is thus another question of geography to be resolved.

Another '1992 factor' is the harmonisation of laws: the clearest link to retail practice is the fact that two-tier VAT levies are in sight. This could affect consumer perceptions of retailers in those countries where steep rises or falls in the price of certain types of goods is set to take place. We may further note the potential for change in the areas of technological standards and policies in respect of IT. Here, the changes may take some time to work through the system.

The EC and labour

UK retailers will have noticed that they presently hold a middle ground between Europe and the USA in respect of staff costs. In the USA the deregulating influence of the Reagan years has reintroduced excessive working hours, reduced protection and security for workers, and exerted a downward pressure on labour costs. There are cost benefits accruing to UK retailers from the use of part-time labour: certain taxes are reduced. The fact that European retailers tend, in general, to pay higher wages can partly be laid at the door of payments in respect of the costs of statutory employee benefits and training. UK retailers should already have faced up to the reality that issues under the European Social Charter will benefit workers, and so employment costs after 1992 will inevitably rise.

The aim to harmonise working conditions within the community as an aid to the free movement of workers represents a trend diametrically opposed to the anti-worker, deregulatory experiences in the US under Reaganomics. As of early 1991, draft directives under articles 100, 100a and 118a of the Treaty of Rome gave some indications of likely future trends. A major thrust was to seek equality of treatment between full-time and part-time staff. We have already noted that it is the very differences that have generally existed between these two groups in the UK that has accelerated trends towards part-time working. Specifically, part-time workers (and their employers) in the UK have not in the past been obliged to make National Insurance contributions. Future EC directives seem set to eliminate such differences since every employee working more than eight hours per week would have to enjoy the same employment benefits. This would increase retailers' costs — the more so for retailers with a great percentage of part-timers. The part-timers are also likely to be eligible for costly redundancy payments and to gain more protection against unfair dismissal. Night workers — greatly increased in number in the US retail market under deregulation — would, in the EC, have yet greater protection. These proposals are all part of the Social Charter announced in 1989 and agreed by all member states bar one. It should hardly surprise us that the Thatcher government, aping the USA in so many other ways, should have made the UK the dissenting voice in arguing against greater rights for ordinary workers. The level playing-field analogy can, after all, only be taken so far. The UK can, however, only dissent within limits, so UK retailers will have to decide whether they can cope with masses of low-paid workers on eight-hour contracts, or whether to engender a new loyalty among the workforce and thereby aim for a more professional core of full-time workers.

Subsidy to industry

Finally, much is often made of the fact that EC member states are forbidden to offer direct subsidies to business. In many industries this is a vital prohibition as state intervention in key industries has a long history, and the more mercantilist the nation, the more subtle and pervasive that intervention.

Inevitably, then, how one defines aid is crucial – as we have been discovering. The mercantilist philosophy engenders a whole national attitude that reinforces native industry. The Japanese have, at various times, had to be urged to buy imported manufactured goods – against their natural inclinations. Governments that structure their taxation in such a way as to encourage collective effort, or which make strategic infrastructural investments are, in a very real sense, aiding industry. Governments that foster banking systems that are industry-serving rather than industry-using are aiding industry. Governments that do not indulge in tax-cutting that sucks in imports and fans inflation are aiding industry. Governments that protect their native industries by prohibitions on takeovers by foreign nationals are also aiding industry by offering stability and the chance for long-term planning.

Retail, '1992'

The concept of aiding industry is as vital for national economies seeking a place in the new Europe as it has been for mercantilist or globalist national economies outside defined trading blocs. The various factors that have protected UK retailing but sacrificed UK industry will be as prominent as before. The most obvious example is the influence of the Town and Country Planning legislation which has traditionally dampened retail competition (Hallsworth, 1990c). Retailers hoping to break into the UK retail market who seek new premises in new locations will face costly delays as before. Nor is this unique to the UK. The regulations surrounding 'Europe 1992' will have little effect upon the restrictive Belgian 'Padlock Law' that has offered secure and protected markets to existing retailers. Nor will the German construction laws and their regulations to restrict shop opening hours be affected. One could go on to list potentially even more restrictive policies in countries such as Italy.

Two areas of retail internationalisation suggest themselves in the context of the new Europe: one collaborative, one rather more combative.

Collaborative alliances

The first key international restructuring mode is via retail alliances, as outlined by Treadgold (1990). Mention has already been made of the European Retail Alliance (ERA), and it is important to put such moves into context. Perhaps the first and most obvious point to make is that the Argyll initiative in respect of ERA is the exception rather than the rule. UK retailers have so far fought shy of joining alliances, and this may be related to the fact that the borders issue is less immediate than it is, say, in the Benelux area where the new Euro-distributors could cross two or three countries in a single delivery. The physical barriers associated with having an island location will prevent overnight revolutions in supplier behaviour.

We have noted that because of EC proscription of cartels (counter to the Reagan mood in the USA), the alliances have to be careful to restrict the remit of their collaboration. Treadgold has identified several ways in which alliances might function. The ERA, being ambitious, falls into his widest category since it encompasses many points of common interest, cemented by a symbolic cross-shareholding. It is reasonable to state that this alliance is still developing and could concentrate on one – but probably more than one – of the more focused types of alliance that have so far emerged.

Probably the simplest of the single-track alliances is that which leads to new retail formats in unfamiliar markets. Several French retail chains have been significant in restructuring Spanish retailing by the introduction of hypermarkets. Spaniards seem to have adopted this large retail outlet with even more alacrity than the French did themselves. Treadgold has noted how alliances with local traders to develop French-style hypermarkets is also extending into Portugal. Furthermore, leading retail chains within mature European markets are also collaborating, whilst groups from outside the EC such as Ikea may benefit from working with an insider.

Characterised as a defensive response to '1992', there are also several purchasing-led alliances. This is to be expected, given the benefits likely to accrue to suppliers. Indeed, the speed with which these alliances are growing suggests that retailers are perhaps more aware of power-issues than is often assumed. Treadgold noted Eurogroupe (comprising GB-Inno-BM (GIB) of Belgium, Vendex of The Netherlands and Rewe Zentrale of Germany) as a purchasing alliance, adding that GIB also acted in concert with Paridoc of France.

Finally Treadgold identified skills-based alliances such as that whereby J. Sainsbury was assisted in the UK by GIB in setting up their Homebase DIY outlet. One might just as easily note the ubiquity of GIB in the field of alliances! This is a group with market dominance of some sectors of the protected but saturated Belgian market. From this base it can use its existing stores as cash cows to fund diversification or internationalisation.

From this brief consideration of collaboration in Europe it is possible to turn to more combative prospects. Classically, one can compete directly in foreign markets, or make portfolio investments.

Combative responses to 'Europe 1992'

The UK has already seen manifestations of both the combative responses to '1992' – direct competition and portfolio investment. The two clearest examples have come from Germany as Aldi are now trading in several locations in the UK, whilst Tenglemann used its US subsidiary A&P to mount an attack for control of Gateway.

We should not assume that either of these approaches is merely geared to the realities of '1992'. The pursuit of growth and new markets (as saturation bites) would be just as influential. However, we can argue that, as pan-European distributors force pan-European retail alliances, so there comes an increasing likelihood of the development of retail conglomerates that are as large as the EC cartel restrictions will permit. These will seek to be represented in most, if not all countries, and so pressure will grow.

The crux of the matter appears to focus on just how unique and/or transferable a retail format is. Aldi, for example, clearly believes that its 'box' style can be transferred to foreign markets, and is seeking a firm foothold in the UK. Groups such as Ikea, perhaps believing that their very large store format requires very large markets, have also sought to be represented in major centres in many countries.

Portfolio investment

Other groups may have a good deal of cash flow and market share from being proficient operators of more general retail modes, such as supermarkets. They, like Safeway/Argyll or J. Sainsbury may have a good image in the home market, but cannot be sure that their greatest asset – that image – will travel. Costs of setting-up in a foreign country may inhibit direct competitive ventures. These, then, are the chains that may use their stable home markets as a stepping-stone to portfolio investment in successful retailers abroad. J. Sainsbury seem to be operating in this way, but are looking to expand in the USA (via Shaws) rather than in Europe. A further example of this stratagem is the longstanding involvement of Delhaize–Le Lion of Belgium in the affairs of US group Food Lion. Delhaize probably believe that there is little that they can teach Food Lion about how to operate in its home-ballpark, the USA, but they can pump in cash for growth.

Albert Gubay, founder of Kwik-Save in the UK, has run operations on three continents (Lord *et al.*, 1988). Arguably, the 1979–83 US operations were his least successful (in a trading sense). It may be that his lack of local knowledge (he only later admitted to having discovered demographics) and his choice of an already saturated market (the Carolinas) make his experience atypical of other such ventures. Lord's US perspective was that the market there had tightened up, whilst there were still relatively easy pickings to be had in the UK (at the expense of Co-ops and independents).

What may be of most relevance is that Gubay's closest rivals were Food Lion. This group (previously trading as Food Town) were controlled as an investment by Delhaize–Le Lion from 1974. Lord's perception was that other impediments to success would be ethnocentrism (less likely in the case of Delhaize than Gubay), higher costs in terms of purpose-built as opposed to converted premises, and greater distribution costs.

The key appears to be whether or not the intending foreign rival perceives (rightly or wrongly) that there is anything to teach the locals, or if it is simply the case of buying into a market that has proved to be lucrative. The example of past efforts at retail internationalisation via direct competition through a specially-created subsidiary is not promising. It often turns out that it is the locals, attuned to their markets, who have a thing or two to teach. This, along with ever-shortening format lifespans, may be why US operators are so fond of franchising to franchisees with local knowledge.

It should come as no surprise that the position I expect to see evolving is one whereby the continental core of the EC market will give rise to retail powers to rival any in the world. These will increasingly seek new investment opportunities – which leads us back to mercantilism *vs* globalism. At root, the countries that will be bought up will be the ones that allow themselves to be bought up. We have spent much of this book identifying them.

Looking ahead

The overall balance of evidence is that deregulation in the USA has led to a plethora of largely unforeseen side-effects, most of which have impacted negatively on the labour force. Whilst in every way inclined to follow the US rôle model, Thatcherite UK governments have been drawn inexorably towards a far more mercantilist federal Europe with protectionist policies akin to those reserved (in the past) by the US for its internal markets. Yet neither the US nor the UK is now what it once was; one has lost its empire, the other is losing it. The right to dictate how the world economy should be run is the privilege of the strong. The USA is still a major influence at GATT negotiations, but only in respect of agriculture (the only sector that bears witness to the concept of comparative advantage). As power-blocs emerge, the UK has the chance to join in with a neo-mercantilist Europe – or become increasingly marginalised as it seeks to offer Euro-investors a cheap labour market. The USA could become more introverted and protectionist, if it can ever square its debts to Japan.

For retailers in the UK and USA the implications are severe: stronger foreign companies are likely to move in and take them over. The position of 'Europe 1992' means that there will be by 1997 – perhaps sooner – some mega retail powers. They may be preoccupied with serving the continental Euro-market in the first instance, but they will soon go shopping again in the USA and UK. Where will these mega-retailers come from? The most likely source is Germany. After 1992, German retailers will still remain protected and, whilst the federal structure inhibits too much expansion within the country, German retailers have not been averse to looking abroad. The Dutch may attempt to be predatory from another protected base. France, on the other hand, could face uncertainties. France has started to jump on the merger bandwagon and, though this is geared to competing on the European stage, may be preoccupied with restructuring. This could inhibit their already strong growth into Spain.

Japan is also likely to be a player in foreign retail markets. Though the status of retailing is less in Japan, and Japanese takeovers have rarely focused on this sector, the sector is nevertheless cash-rich. Of the two purchasable markets, the UK may eventually become prime, if only because an outsider perception of the recorded gross margins of UK retailers suggests a lucrative market (Wrigley, 1990). It may not occur to some non-UK retailers that such recorded profits can equally well spell a drain on reinvestment.

Structurally, the US and UK markets will continue to reflect the varied futures of the population. The off-price trend in the USA and its counterparts (the burgeoning cut-price/seconds market) will grow as more and more unemployed/unemployable individuals join the underclass and as the economies wilt under the burden of debt. Polarisation, then, will continue. The largest UK retailers may seek growth in the USA and become too large for Euro-takeover — but the second-rank retailers will be prime targets. That said, a UK (and, to an extent European) preoccupation with property values may cause them to misvalue US assets: they could over-purchase in the USA and face problems at home. Some European retail companies are following Aldi into the UK market direct, and so UK retailers could face a pincer movement. They could be outcompeted on cost at home whilst overspending on acquisitions abroad.

Costs

The key to costs will be technology. Proper use of EDI/EPOS/EFTPOS should allow retailers in the UK to retain cost-competitiveness. If this is allied to good store location information, the future looks bright. The worst prospect lies where neither problem is addressed. If a store chain fails to address the question of information technology, then it will lose competitiveness. The profound advantage of automatic stock reordering, direct product profitability and basic market information offered by IT will become the industry norm. The retailers who have little idea of their stock position, the rate of turnover of items and the profit margins on each good will fail to match up to the profit expectations of their judges in the market.

In effect, one can also achieve a measure of direct product profitability on retail sites. The retail chain that is expanding into new locations can quickly analyse, with a retail gravity model or location-allocation model, what profit might be expected from a store of a given size on a given site. It is soon feasible to work out how much one ought to bid for a site. The retailer lacking this information goes blind into the land-sale auction. This is a vital weakness in a development market like that of the UK where land prices are excessively high.

That said, as I have argued elsewhere (Hallsworth, 1987), it may be worthwhile to overbid for a real prime cornerstone site from which good trading will undercut a range of competitors. The issue of demographics is one that remains difficult to predict. We have seen how presently-observable trends are likely to be linked to the labour demands of the 1970s and 1980s. The well-paid manual, male, full-time, routine, blue-collar job may be in terminal decline. This suggests that market polarisation will continue. The underclass with its low spending power will continue to provide a ready market for low-quality off-price goods. Low-grade routine office or assembly work for women is also likely to be cost effective – and the retail trade is set to be a prime employer. As a low-cost labour market, the UK may be attractive to Japanese firms looking to penetrate European markets. The only possible counter-scenario to more of the same would be if the next wave of economic recessions sufficiently dented the confidence of white-collar workers about the future, as some suggest is now happening. It might then be possible to see a re-run of more egalitarian arguments from centre-left politicians in the UK and USA. However, deregulation and dispersal of state assets has gone so far that it is difficult to see much scope for major policy shifts – and in the context of both the UK and USA, the oil is running out. The return to the mass market remains an implausible out-turn.

If we take the technological arguments a little further, then one technology-driven retail possibility remains as yet unexplored – teleshopping. This has been facilitated in the USA by cable networks, a single currency and a common language. These necessary conditions are not yet met in the Euro-market. Even with satellite TV and the ECU, mass TV retailing will not easily create a viable market.

The central issue, however, remains the facilitating rôle of capital. Until the fall of the Berlin Wall it seemed likely that there would be continued re-runs of the October 1987 'crash' as footloose capital tried, and failed, to ground itself in the equity markets. The severely overheated Tokyo market did have a separate fall in 1989 because the worst excesses of capital grounding were to be found in the Japanese property market. With food retailers, in particular, demonstrating strong cash-flow characteristics, it is in some ways surprising that retail firms have only recently been seen as major buy-out propositions. This is a trend that must continue as capital searches the globe for tangible gains. This whole pattern is no new phenomenon, having been well chronicled by Harvey (1982). What has changed is the scale of finance and credit that productive enterprises are trying to keep afloat. I doubt if, as resources decline and battles over the carcass continue, the present greed/growth scenario can much longer be supported. Stock market crashes and economic recessions, polarised markets and the underclass phenomenon all seem too closely linked for comfort. This seems to call for a new set of criteria for the future – yet no prospect of a new agenda is in sight. Slower, more measured growth is likely to be the order of the day, but only after any growth at all is rendered difficult by the excesses we experience today, as the fight for positional goods intensifies.

EPILOGUE

The aim in writing this book was to explore the factors, internal but particularly external, that were driving changes in retail consumption patterns. Because influences seemed to be variable in scope and scale, the widest possible format for analysis – International Political Economy – was chosen. It is for the reader to decide if my adoption of this paradigm worked. My view remains that, though Regulation Theory certainly covers many of the same issues, the IPE approach is better equipped to explain away most of the apparently conflicting and contradictory changes that we have seen in OECD countries. I think here especially of the flip-over from the dominance of (ideal-typical) Fordism to (ideal-typical) Japanese flexibility. Both technological and financial pressures have been seen to have penalised Fordism on its own territory (the USA) and at a time of particular vulnerability.

I have argued that retail has been primarily affected by financial and technological change. These twin influences have also affected OECD societies in differing ways: ways that ultimately depended upon whether or not they were espousing broadly mercantilist trade structures. When the contradictions of capital that were inherent in the hegemonic stance taken by the USA in the post-war period blew apart, after the demise of Bretton Woods in 1971, then the mercantilist nations were best battened-down against the inflationary storm that ensued. The inflationary storm, when reversed by Volcker and Reagan, went on to damage badly both western waged labour and also Third World countries. The inherent advantages of neo-mercantilism were further exaggerated by technological developments that were sometimes – but not always – a product of processes naturally set in train by mercantilists in the pursuit of their own ends.

In the UK and the USA there emerges a picture of societies that have almost given up the fight for dominance in the field of the production of consumer goods, to which primacy must still be attached. Those societies elected governments that set in train a spending spree enabling millions to force up prices in the chase for positional status (and thereby push yet higher the position of the already-advantaged). There was an espousal of Laffer-curve philosophies that allowed certain clearly-defined sectors to get ahead, whilst structurally committing other groups within society to become worse off – often in both relative and absolute terms. I have identified this as predictable from the writings of Fred Hirsch. At the same time the governments manifestly failed to deal with the further contradictions that left their societies poorly placed to supply the goods that they had both encouraged and enabled their citizens to consume. This consumption-mania, coupled with production-aversion and especially unfavourable and historically well-entrenched financial regimes, led inexorably to astonishing disasters in the trade balance figures. The globalist perspectives of the UK and the USA in particular leave them in an impasse. They cannot break out of the inevitable cycle of decline without first facing the fact that the policies of the last decade have been a dangerous nonsense. However, such is the significance of these two societies as a sponge to soak up surplus Japanese production of consumer products that they have actually been further encouraged upon this 'rake's progress'. This fact, augmented by deregulated financial markets, enables them to endlessly draw in and then spend other people's capital. This ensures that the party can continue for a while yet. Under such conditions, retailing will continue to thrive whilst, as the bumper stickers declare, 'we are spending our childrens' inheritance'.

References and Bibliography

Aaronovitch, S. and Sawyer, M. (1975) *Big Business: Theoretical and Empirical Aspects of Concentration and Mergers in the United Kingdom*, London, Macmillan.

'A private eye's view: why Wall Street is rife with crime', *New York Times*, 15 February 1987, p. D2.

Accountancy (1988) editorial, February, p. 26.

Ackerman, K. B. and LaLonde, B. J. (1980) 'Making warehousing more efficient', *Harvard Business Review*, 58, 4, 2, pp. 94–102.

Agergard, E., Olsen, P. A. and Allpass, J. (1970) 'The interaction between retailing and the urban centre structure' *Environment and Planning* 2, pp. 55–71.

Aglieta, M. (1976) *Regulation et crises du capitalisme: L'experience des Etats-Unies*, Paris, Calman-Levy.

Aglieta, M. (1979) *A Theory of Capitalist Regulation: The US Experience*, London, New Left Books.

Ahlin, J. (1985) 'Scandinavian experience of scanning', *Proceedings EPOS '85*, Sixth European congress on automation in retailing.

Akehurst, G. P. (1983) 'Concentration in retail distribution: measurement and significance', *Service Industries Journal*, 3, pp. 161–79.

Alexander, N. (1989) 'The internal market of 1992', *Retail and Distribution Management*, January/February, pp. 13–15.

Ambrose, P. and Colenutt, B. (1975) *The Property Machine*, Harmondsworth, Penguin.

Amin, A. (1989) 'Flexible specialisation and small firms in Italy: myths and realities', *Antipode*, 21, 1, pp. 13–34.

Anders, G. (1987) 'Recapitalisations are a bonanza for some, but bondholders can take a terrific beating', *Wall Street Journal*, 1 June.

Applebaum, W. (1965) 'Can store location research be a science?', *Economic Geography*, 41. pp. 234–7.

Atkinson, J. (1984), 'Flexibility, uncertainty and manpower management', *Report 89, Institute of Manpower Studies*, Univesity of Sussex.

Bagehot, W. (1922), *Lombard Street: A Description of the Money Market*, New York, Arno Press.

Balogh, T. (1982) *The Irrelevance of Conventional Economics*, London, Weidenfeld.

Ball, M. (1983) *Housing Policy and Economic Power: The Political Economy of Owner Occupation*, London, Methuen.

Bank of England Quarterly Bulletin, various years.

Baran, P. and Sweezy, P. (1966) *Monopoly Capital*, New York, Monthly Review Press.

Bassett, K. and Short, J. (1980) *Housing and Residential Structure: Alternative Approaches*, London, Routledge & Kegan Paul.

Baudrillard, J. (1982) *For a Critique of the Political Economy of the Sign*, Paris, Gallimard.

Beaujeau-Garnier, J. and Delobez, A. (1979) *Geography of Marketing*, London, Longmans.

Bell, D. (1974) *The Coming of Post-Industrial Society*, London, Heinemann.

Bell, D. (1979) 'Communications technology – for better or for worse', *Harvard Business Review*, 57, pp. 20–45.

Bellew, P. A. (1984) 'Nordstrom strategy of coddling shoppers facing challenge in California expansion', *Wall Street Journal*, 10 May, p. 33.

Benedict, R. F. (1935) *Patterns of Culture*, London, Routledge.

Berry, L. L. (1979) 'The time-buying consumer', *Journal of Retailing*, Winter, pp. 58–69.

Berry, L. L. (1982) 'Retailing positioning strategies for the 1980s', *Business Horizons*, November–December, pp. 45–50.

Beynon, H. (1973) *Working for Ford*, Harmondsworth, Penguin.

Blackaby, F. (ed.) (1978) *De-industrialisation*, London, Heinemann.

Bluestone, B. and Harrison, B. T. (1982) *The De-industrialisation of America*, New York, Free Press.

Bolton Report (1971), *Committee of Inquiry into Small Firms*, Reports 1–18, London, HMSO.

Bourdieu, P. (1984), *Distinction: A Social Critique of the Judgement of Taste*, London, Routledge & Kegan Paul.

Bosworth, D. L. (ed.) (1983) *The Employment Consequences of Technological Change*, London, Macmillan.

Bowlby, S. R. (1979) 'Accessibility, mobility and shopping provision', in Goodall, B. and Kirby, A. (eds.) *Resources and Planning*, Oxford, Pergamon, pp. 293–324.

Breathnach, P. (1988) 'Uneven development and capitalist peripheralisation: the case of Ireland', *Antipode*, 20, 2, pp. 122–41.

Brittan, S. (1964) *The Treasury Under The Tories 1951–1964*, Harmondsworth Penguin.

Brown, B. (1988) *The Flight of International Capital*, London, Routledge.

Brown, C. J. F. (1980) 'Industrial policy and economic planning in Japan and France', *National Institute Economic Review*, No. 93, pp. 59–75.

Brown, P. (1989) 'Geodemographics: a review of recent developments and emerging issues', paper presented to 29th RSA European Congress, St John's College, Cambridge, August.

Brown, S. (1988) 'The wheel of the wheel of retailing', *International Journal of Retailing*, 3, 1, pp. 16–37.

Brown, S. (1990) 'The wheel of retailing: past and future', *Journal of Retailing*, 66, 2, pp. 143–9.

Brown, S. (1991) 'The wheel of retailing: retrospect and prospect', pp. 269–83 in *Proceedings: Sixth World Conference on Research in Distributive Trades*, The Hague, Netherlands, July.

Browning, P. (1986) *The Treasury and Economic Policy 1964–1985*, Harlow, Longmans.

Bruner, R. F. and Paine, L. S. (1988) 'Management buyouts and managerial ethics', *California Management Review*, 30, Winter. p. 89.

Buckingham, L. and Milner, M. (1989) 'Why headline-grabbing pay is often the tip of the corporate iceberg', *Guardian*, 1 July.

Bullen, K. (1988) 'Campeau is on a shopper's high', *Fortune*, 118, 4, pp. 70–73.
Calleo, D. P. (1976) 'The decline and rebuilding of an international economic system: some general considerations', in Calleo, D. P. (ed.) *Money and the Coming World Order*, New York, New York University Press.
Calleo, D. P. (1978) 'The historiography of the inter-war period: reconsiderations', in Rowland, B. M. (ed.) *The Balance of Power or Hegemony: The Interwar Monetary System*, New York, New York University Press.
Calleo, D. P. (1981) 'Inflation and American power', *Foreign Affairs*, 59, 4, Spring. 781–812.
Calleo, D. P. (ed.) (1982) *The Imperious Economy*, Cambridge, MA, Harvard University Press.
Calleo, D. P. and Strange, S. (1984) 'Money and world politics', in Strange, S. (ed.) *Paths to International Political Economy*, London, Allen & Unwin, pp. 91–125.
Calleo, D. P. (1987) *Beyond American Hegemony*, New York, Basic Books.
Camus, A. (1975) *The Fall*, Harmondsworth, Penguin.
Castells, M. (1977) *The Urban Question*, London, Edward Arnold.
Castells, M. (1978) *City, Class and Power*, London, Macmillan.
Ceccini, P. (1988) *The European Challenge, 1992: The Benefits of a Single Market*, Aldershot, Wildwood House.
Central Statistical Office (1984–1990) *External Trade Statistics of the UK*, London, HMSO.
Central Statistical Office (1980–1989), *Monthly Digest of Statistics*, London, HMSO.
Chain Store Age Executive (1986) 'Analysts cherry picking retail stocks', April, 48.
Channon, D. F. (1978) *The Service Industries: Strategy, Structure and Financial Performance*, London, Macmillan.
Channon, D. F. (1977) *British Banking Strategy and the International Challenge*, London, Macmillan
Clark, B. and Bolwell, L. (1968) 'Attractiveness as part of retail potential models', *Journal of the Royal Town Planning Institute*, 54, pp. 477–8.
Clark, D. (1985) *Post-Industrial America: A Geographical Perspective*, London, Methuen.
Clark, G. L. (1989) 'Remaking the map of corporate capitalism: the arbitrage economy of the 1990s', *Environment and Planning A*, 21, 997–1000.
Clark, G. L. (1991) 'Dimensions of global economic restructuring and the idea of decentralising labour relations in Australia', forthcoming in *Australian Geographical Studies*.
Clarke, W. M. (1965) *The City in the World Economy*, Harmondsworth, Penguin.
Clifford Chance (1989) *Takeovers and Mergers in Europe*, London, Clifford Chance.
Clutterbuck, D. (ed.) (1985) *New Patterns of Work*, Aldershot, Gower.
Coakley, J. and Harris, L. (1983) *The City of Capital*, Oxford, Blackwell.
Coelho, J. and Wilson, A. (1976) 'The optimum location and size for shopping centres', *Regional Studies*, 10, pp. 413–21.
Cohen, S. and Zysman, J. (1987) 'Why manufacturing matters: the myth of the post-industrial economy', *California Management Review*, 29, 3, Spring, pp. 9–10.
Cole, H. (1986) 'Retail planning permissions', *Proceedings Summer Annual Meeting PTRC*, Brighton.
Congdon, T. (1988) *The Debt Threat*, Oxford, Blackwell.
Cooke, T. (1988) *International Mergers and Acquisitions*, Oxford, Blackwell.
Corbridge, S. (1989) 'International money and the crisis of global Fordism', paper

presented to the annual conference of the Association of American Geographers, Baltimore, MD.
Corden, W. M. (1977), *Inflation, Exchange Rates in the World Economy*, London, Oxford University Press.
Cosh, A., Hughes, A. and Singh, A. (1990) *Takeovers and Short-Termism in the UK*, IPPR Industrial policy Paper No 3.
Curson, C. (1986) (ed.) *Flexible Patterns of Work*, London, IPM.
Dahrendorf, R. (1981) 'The politics of economic decline', *Political Studies*, XXIX, pp. 284–91.
Dahrendorf, R. (1987) 'The erosion of citizenship and its consequences for us all', *New Statesman*, 12 June.
Daniels, P. W. (1985) 'Producer services in the post-industrial space economy', in Martin, R. and Rowthorn, B. (eds.) *De-industrialisation and the British Space Economy*, London, Macmillan.
Davidson, K. (1985) *Mega-Mergers*, Cambridge, MA, Ballinger.
Davies, E. and Kay, J. (1990) 'Assessing corporate performance', *Business Strategy Review*, Summer, pp. 1–15.
Davies, R. L. (ed.) (1979) *Retail Planning in the European Community*, Farnborough, Saxon House.
Davies, R. L. (1984) *Retail and Commercial Planning*, London, Croom Helm.
Davies, R. L. and Reynolds, J. (1986) 'Technological change in retailing: the long-term implications', paper presented to Annual conference of the Institute of British Geographers, Reading, January.
Davis, W. (1970) *Merger Mania*, London, Constable.
Dawson, J. (1979) 'Retail trends in the EEC', in Davies, R. (ed.) *Retail Planning in the European Community*, Farnborough, Saxon House.
Dawson, J. A. (ed.) (1979) *The Marketing Environment*, London, Croom Helm.
Dawson, J. A. (ed.) (1980) *Retail Geography*, London, Croom Helm.
Dawson, J. A. and Sato, T. (1983) 'Controls over the development of retail stores in Japan', *Service Industries Journal*, 3, 2, pp. 136–45.
Dawson, J. A. (ed.) (1983a) *Shopping Centre Development*, London, Longman.
Dawson, J. A. (1983b) 'Independent retailing in Great Britain: dinosaur or chameleon?', *Retail and Distribution Management*, 11, pp. 29–32.
Dawson, J. A. and Kirby, D. A. (1979) *Small Scale Retailing in the UK*, Farnborough, Saxon House.
Deakin, B. M. and George, K. D. (1965) *Productivity Trends in the Service Industries, 1948–63*, London, Cambridge University Press.
Dean, A., Durrand, M., Fallon, J. and Hoeller, P. (1989) 'Saving trends and behaviour in OECD countries', *Working Paper No. 67*, Paris, OECD.
DeAngelo, H, DeAngelo, L. and Rice, E. M. (1984) 'Going private: minority freezeouts and stockholder wealth', *Journal of Law and Economics*, 27, p. 367.
De Cecco, M. (1974) *Money and Empire: The International Gold Standard*, Oxford, Blackwell.
De Vito, M. J. (1980) 'Retailing plays a key role in downtown renaissance', *Journal of Housing*, 37, pp. 197–200.
Dicken, P. (1971) 'Some aspects of the decision-making behaviour of business organisations', *Economic Geography*, 47, pp. 426–37.
Dicken, P. (1976) 'The multi-plant enterprise and geographic space', *Regional Studies*, x, 4, pp. 401–12.
Dicken, P. (1986) *Global Shift*, London, Harper & Row.
Dicken, P. and Lloyd, P. E. (1976) 'Geographical perspectives on United States investment in the United Kingdom', *Environment and Planning A*, VIII, pp. 685–705.

Dobbin, A. (1985) '100% scanning and the step towards item price removal', *Proceedings, EPOS '85*, Sixth European Congress on Automation in Retailing.

Dosi, G., Freeman, C., Nelson, R., Silverberg, G. and Soete, L. (eds.) (1988) *Technical Change and Economic Theory*, London, Frances Pinter.

Douglas, M. and Isherwood, B. (1979) *The World of Goods*, London, Allen Lane.

Dow, J. C. R. and Saville, I. D. (1988) *A Critique of Monetary Policy*, Clarendon, Oxford.

Drucker, P. F. (1986) 'To end the raiding roulette game', *Across the Board*, April, p. 39.

Duffy, G. and Giddy, I. H. (1978) *The International Money Market*, Englewood Cliffs, NJ, Prentice-Hall.

Dunning, J. H. and Norman, G. (1983) 'The theory of the multinational enterprise: an application to multinational office location', *Environment and Planning A*, 15, 675–92.

Economist Intelligence Unit (1989), *Retail Business*, June, p. 15.

Egan, D. (1983) 'The location of service outlets: an economic perspective', *Service Industries Journal*, 3, 180–90.

Elger, T. (1979) 'Valorisation and deskilling: a critique of Braverman', *Capital and Class*, 7, Spring, 58–99.

Estall, R. (1985) 'Stock control in manufacturing: the just-in-time system and its locational implications', *Area*, 17, 2, pp. 129–33.

Euromonitor (1990) *Consumer Europe 1990*, London, Euromonitor.

Fothergill, S. and Gudgin, G. (1978a) 'Long-term trends in the regional distribution of service activity in the UK', *Centre for Environmental Studies Working Note, 481*, London, CES.

Fothergill, S. and Gudgin, G. (1979) 'Regional employment change: a subregional explanation', *Progress in Planning*, 12, 3, pp. 155–219.

Fothergill, S. and Gudgin, G. (1982), *Unequal Growth: Urban and Regional Employment Change in the UK*, London, Heinemann.

Fotheringham, S. (1988) 'Market share analysis techniques', chapter 5 in Wrigley, N. (ed.) *Store Choice, Store Location and Market Analysis*, London, Routledge.

Friedman, M. (1968a) *Dollars and Deficits*, Englewood Cliffs, NJ, Prentice-Hall.

Friedman, M. (1968b) 'The role of monetary policy', *American Economic Review*, 58, pp. 1–17.

Friedman, M. (1970) 'The social responsibility of business is to increase its profits', *New York Times Magazine*, 13 September.

Froebel, F., Heinrichs, J. and Kreye, O. (1980) *The New International Division of Labour: Structural Unemployment in Industrialised Countries and Industrialisation in Developing Countries*, Cambridge, Cambridge University Press, Editions de la Maison des Sciences de l'Homme.

Galbraith, J. K. (1974) *The New Industrial State*, Harmondsworth, Penguin.

Galbraith, J. K. (1975) *The Money: Whence it Came, Where it Went*, London, André Deutsch.

Galbraith, J. K. (1984) *The Anatomy of Power*, London, Hamish Hamilton.

Gallagher, R. (1988) 'Changes set for Federated, Allied', *Chain-Store Age Executive*, 64, p. 5.

Gamble, A. (1981) *Britain in Decline: Economic Policy, Political Strategy and the British State*, London, Macmillan.

Gershuny, J. I. and Miles, I. D. (1983) *The New Service Economy*, London, Pinter Publishers.

Gershuny, J. (1978) *After Industrial Society? The Emerging Self-Service Economy*, London, Macmillan.

Gertler, M. (1989) 'Resurrecting flexibility', *Transactions, Institute of British Geographers*, 14, 1, pp. 109–12.

Greenfield, H. I. (1966) *Manpower and the Growth of Producer Services*, New York, Columbia Press.

Gibbs, R. (1980) *Industrial Policy in More Successful Economies: Japan*, NEDO, London, HMSO

Giddens, A. (1972) *Politics and Sociology in the Thought of Max Weber*, London, Macmillan.

Giddens, A. (1976) *New Rules of Sociological Method*, London, Hutchinson.

Giddens, A. (1984) *The Constitution of Society: Outline of the Theory of Structuration*, Cambridge, Polity.

Gilpin, R. (1975) *US Power and the Multinational Corporation*, New York, Basic Books.

Gist, R. (1971) *Marketing and Society*, New York, Holt, Reinhart & Winston.

Gough, T. J. (1975) 'The diversionary effects of institutional property investment', *Estates Gazette*, ccxxxv, 19 July, pp. 199–201.

Gow, I. (1988) 'Japan', chapter 2 in Handy, C. *et al.* (eds.) *Making Managers*, London, Pitman.

Gujerati, D. and Dors, L. (1972) 'Production and non-production workers in US manufacturing industries', *Industrial and Labour Relations Review*, 26, 660–69.

Greider, W. (1987) *Secrets of the Temple*, Touchstone Books, New York, Simon & Schuster.

Guy, C. M. (1977) 'A method of examining and evaluating the impact of major retail developments upon existing shops and their users', *Environment and Planning A*, 9, 491–504.

Guy, C. M. (1986) 'Information technology and retailing: the implications for analysis and forecasting', paper presented to ESRC workshop on Methods of Retail Analysis, Bristol, February.

Hall, P. (1986) 'From the unsocial city to the social city', *The Planner*, March, pp. 17–24.

Hall, P. and Markusen, A. (1985) *Silicon Landscapes*, Winchester, Mass., Allen & Unwin.

Hall, P., Thomas, R., and Drewett, R. (1973) *The Containment of Urban England*, 2 vols., London, Allen & Unwin.

Hall, S. and Jacques, M. (eds.) (1983) *The Politics of Thatcherism*, London, Lawrence & Wishart.

Hallsworth, A. G. (1986) 'Scanning: information technology and retail change', paper presented to IGU study group meeting, Barcelona, August.

Hallsworth, A. G. (1987a) 'Geography and nuclear war', paper presented to annual meeting of the Association of American Geographers, Portland, Oregon.

Hallsworth, A. G. (1987b) 'Some aspects of growth in the British DIY market', paper presented to IGU Colloquium, Liège, September.

Hallsworth, A. G. (1987c) 'Some welfare determinants of the impact of large-scale grocery stores', unpublished Ph.D. thesis, Portsmouth.

Hallsworth, A. G. (1988) *Regional Shopping Centres: Some Lessons From Canada*, London, Transport and Environmental Studies (TEST)

Hallsworth, A. G. (1989a) 'The service sector in Canada', pp. 382–8 in *The USA and Canada*, London, Europa.

Hallsworth, A. G. (1989b) 'Crime and prejudice', *Hillier Parker Property Briefing*, January 1989, p. 19.

Hallsworth, A. G. (1990a) 'The lure of the USA: some further reflections',

Environment and Planning A, 22, pp. 551–8.
Hallsworth, A. G. (1990b) 'More home thoughts from abroad', *Town and Country Planning*, 59, 2, pp. 51–3.
Hallsworth, A. G. (1991a) 'Who shops where: and why?', *International Journal of Retail and Distribution Management*, 19, 3, pp. 21–8.
Hallsworth, A. G. (1991b) 'The Campeau takeovers: the arbitrage economy in action', *Environment and Planning A*, 23, pp. 1217–23.
Hamnett, C., Harmer, M. and Williams, P. (1990) *Safe as Houses: Housing Inheritance in Britain*, London, Paul Chapman.
Handy, C. (1984) *The Future of Work*, Oxford, Blackwell.
Harrod, R. (1958) 'The possibility of economic satiety: use of economic growth for improving the quality of education and leisure' in *Problems of United States Economic Development*, New York, Committee for Economic Development, pp. 207–13.
Hart, I. (1984) Address to Institute of Chartered Surveyors, London (mimeo).
Hartwell, R. M. (1973) 'The service revolution: the growth of services in the modern economy 1750–1914', in Cipolla, C. M. (ed.) *The Fontana Economic History of Europe*, Vol. 3, London, Fontana, pp. 358–96.
Harvey, D. (1973) *Social Justice and the City*, London, Edward Arnold.
Harvey, D. (1982) *The Limits to Capital*, Oxford, Basil Blackwell.
Harvey, D. (1989), *The Condition of Postmodernity*, Oxford, Blackwell.
Hayes, H. and Abernathy, W. J. (1980) 'Managing our way to economic decline', *Harvard Business Review*, 58, 4, July–August, pp. 67–77.
Hays, H. (1981) 'Why Japanese factories work', *Harvard Business Review*, 59, 4, July–August, p. 57.
Hawkins, C. (1989) 'A desperate Campeau grabs a Canadian lifeline', *Business Week*, 3125, p. 44.
Henderson, J. (1989) *The Globalisation of High Technology Production*, London, Routledge.
Hendry, J. (1987) *Understanding Japanese Society*, Beckenham, Croom Helm.
Herlihy, D. (1987) 'Chinese walls and insider trading: how well does self-policing work?', *National Law Journal*, 18 May, p. 39.
Hillman, J. (1990) 'The importance of the street', *Town and Country Planning*, February, pp. 42–6.
Hirsch, F. (1977) *Social Limits to Growth*, London, Routledge.
Hirschmann, E. C., Stampfl, R. W. (1980) 'The roles of retailing in the diffusion of popular culture', *Journal of Retailing*, Spring, pp. 16–36.
Hirst, P. and Zeitlin, J. (1989) 'Flexible specialisation and the competitive failure', *Political Quarterly*, 60, 3, 164–78.
Hirst, P. and Zeitlin, J. (1990) 'Flexible specialisation vs post-fordism: theory evidence and policy implications', *Birkbeck Public policy working paper*, London, Birkbeck College.
Hirschorn, L. (1974) *Toward a Political Economy of the Service Society*, Berkeley, Calif., Institute of Urban and Regional Development.
Holmes, J. (1983) 'Industrial reorganisation, capital restructuring and locational change: an analysis of the Canadian automobile industry in the 1960s', *Economic Geography*, 59, pp. 251–71.
Hornik, J. and Feldman, L. (1982) 'Retailing implications of the do-it-yourself movement', *Retail and Distribution Management*, 10, 44–9.
Hudson, R. (1989) 'Labour market changes and new forms of work in old industrial regions: maybe flexibility for some but not flexible accumulation', *Environment and Planning B: Society and Space*, 7, pp. 5–30.

Huff, D. L. (1963) 'A probability analysis of shopping centre trade areas', *Land Economics*, 53, pp. 81–9.

Hume, D. (1752) *Essays: Of The Balance of Trade* in Green T. H. and Grose T. H. (1964) *David Hume: philosophical works*, Vol 3, Darmstadt, Scientia Verlag Aalen.

Hymer, S. (1972) 'The internationalisation of capital', *Journal of Economic Issues*, 6, 1, pp. 91–111.

Hymer, S. (1975) 'International politics and international economics: a radical approach', Chapter 14 in Lindberg L. N. *et al.* (eds.) *Stress and Contradiction in Modern Capitalism*, Lexington, MA, D. C. Heath.

Hymer, S. (1976) *The International Operations of National Firms*, Boston, MIT Press.

Ingham, G. (1984) *Capitalism Divided? The City and Industry in British Social Development*, London, Macmillan.

Janelle, D. G. (1968) 'Central place development in a time–space framework', *Professional Geographer*, 20, 1, pp. 5–10.

Jefferys, J. B., Knee, D. (1988) *The Policies of European Department Stores in the Past Decade*, Harlow, Longman.

Jenkins, C. and Sherman, B. (1979) *The Collaspe of Work*, Andover, Methuen.

Jenkins, S. P. (1991) 'Income inequality and living standards', *Fiscal Studies*, 12, 1, pp. 1–28.

Jessop, B. (1990) 'Regulation theories in retrospect and prospect', *Economy and Society*, 19, pp. 153–216.

Jones, K. and Simmons, J. (1987) *Location, Location, Location*, Agincourt, Methuen.

Kacker, M. (1985) *Transatlantic Trends in Retailing*, Westport, Quorum.

Kaldor, M., Sharp, M. and Walker, W. (1986) 'Industrial competitiveness and Britain's defence', *Lloyds Bank Review*, 162, pp. 31–49.

Kaldor, N. (1966) *Causes of the Slow Rate of Economic Growth in the UK*, London, Cambridge University Press.

Kay, W. (1985) 'How the City laid its foundations', *The Times*, 4 January.

Kaynack, E. (1976) 'A refined approach to the wheel of retailing', *European Journal of Marketing*, 13, 7, 237–45.

Keeble, D. (1976) *Industrial Location and Planning in the UK*, London, Methuen.

Keegan, W. (1990) *Observer*, 18 May.

Keynes, J. M. (1936) *The General Theory of Employment, Interest and Money*, New York, Harcourt Brace Jovanovich.

Kindleberger, C. (1976) 'Systems of international organisation', in Calleo, D. P. (ed.) *Money and the Coming World Order*, New York, New York University Press.

Kindleberger, C. P. (1973) *The World in Depression 1929–39*, London, Allen & Unwin.

Kindleberger, C. P. (1978) *Manias, Panics and Crashes*, London, Macmillan.

Kirby, D. (1976) 'The North American convenience store: implications for Britain', in Jones, P. and Oliphant, R. (eds.) *Local Shops: Problems and Prospects*, Reading, URPI.

Kolodziej, E. A. (1980) 'France and the arms trade', *International Affairs*, 56, 1, pp. 54–72.

Labich, K. (1990) 'The Reichmann's rare mis-step', *Fortune*, 121, 3, pp. 121–2.

Lakshmanan, T. R. and Hansen, W. G. (1965) 'A retail market potential model', *Journal of the American Institute of Planners*, 31, 134–43.

Lash, S. and Urry, J. (1987) *The End of Organized Capitalism*, Cambridge, Polity.

Lehrman, L. (1976) 'Creation of an international monetary order', in Calleo, D. P. (ed.) *Money and the Coming World Order*, New York, New York University Press.

Leigh, R. and North, D. (1978) 'Acquisitions in British industries: implications for regional development', Chapter 13 in Hamilton, F. E. I. (ed.) *Contemporary Industrialisation: Spatial Analysis and Regional Development*, London, Longmans.

Leigh, R. and North, D. J. (1978) 'Regional aspects of acquisition activity in British manufacturing industry', *Regional Studies*, 12, 227–45.

Lever, H. and Huhne, C. (1985) *Debt and Danger*, Harmondsworth, Penguin.

Lever, H. and Edwards, G. (1980a) 'Why Germany beats Britain', *Sunday Times*, 9 November.

Lever, H. and Edwards, G. (1980b) 'How to bank on Britain', *Sunday Times*, 16 November.

Levitt, T. (1976) 'The industrialisation of service', *Harvard Business Review*, September/October, 63–74.

Lewis, J. (1988) 'Employment matters', in Marshall, N., (ed.) *Services and Uneven Development*, Oxford, Oxford University Press.

Lewis, M. (1989) 'Retailing and global change', *Retail and Distribution Management*, November/December, pp. 19–20.

Lloyd, P. E. and Dicken, P. (1977) *Location in Space: A Theoretical Approach to Economic Geography*, London, Harper & Row.

Lord, J. D., Moran, W., Parker, A. J. and Sparks, L. (1988) 'Retailing on three continents', *International Journal of Retailing*, 3, 3 (whole issue).

Lovering, J. (1990) 'Fordism's unknown successor: a comment on Scott's theory of flexible accumulation', *International Journal of Urban and Regional Research*, 14, 159–74.

McCann Erickson (1989), *The New Generation*, London, McCann Erickson Research.

McKinnon, A. C. (1985) 'The distribution systems of supermarket chains', *Service Industries Journal*, 5, 226–38.

McKinnon, A. C. (1986) 'The physical distribution strategies of multiple retailers', *International Journal of Retailing*, 1, 2, pp. 49–63.

McNair, M. P. and May, E. (1976) *The Evolution of Retail Institutions in the USA*, Cambridge, MA, Marketing Sciences Institute.

McNair, M. P. and May, E. (1978) 'The next revolution of the retailing wheel', *Harvard Business Review*, S6, pp. 81–91.

Magowan, P. (1990) 'Won over by an LBO', *Across the Board*, 12 March, pp. 16–20.

Makin, P., Cooper, C. and Cox, C. (1989) *Managing People at Work*, London, Routledge.

Malecki, E. J. (1980a) 'Corporate organisation of R and D and the location of technological activities', *Regional Studies*, 14, pp. 219–34.

Malecki, E. J. (1980b) 'Science and technology in the American metropolitan system', in Brunn, S. and Wheeler, J. (eds.) *The American Metropolitan System: Present and Future*, New York, Wiley.

Markey, E. (1989) 'Takeover reform: a view from Congress', Chapter 11 in Hoffman, W. M. *et al.* (eds.) *The Ethics of Organisational Transformation*, Westport, Quorum.

Markusen, A. (1984) *The Politics of Regions*, New Jersey, Rowman & Allenheld.

Markusen, A. R. (1985) *Profit Cycles, Oligopoly and Regional Development*, Cambridge, MA, MIT Press.

Marquand, J. (1983) 'The changing distribution of service employment', in Goddard, J. B. and Champion, A. G. (eds.) *The Urban and Regional Transformation of Britain*, London, Methuen, pp. 99–134.

Marshall, J. N. (1982a) 'Linkages between manufacturing industry and business

services', *Environment and Planning A*, 14, pp. 1523–40.
Marshall, J. N., Damesick, P. and Wood, P. (1987) 'Understanding the location and role of producer services in the UK', *Environment and Planning A*, 19, 575–95.
Marshall, N. (1988), *Services and Uneven Development*, Oxford, Oxford, University Press.
Marwick, A. (1980) *Class: Image and Reality*, Glasgow, Collins.
Maslow, A. (1970) *Motivation and Personality*, New York, Harper & Row.
Mason, R. S. (1981) *Conspicuous Consumption: A Study of Exceptional Consumer Behaviour*, Farnborough, Gower.
Mason, T. and Weiner, E. (1990) 'Inside the Reichmann empire: why their gambles usually pay off', *Business Week*, 3143, pp. 32–6.
Massey, D. and Catalano, A. (1978) *Capital and Land*, London, Edward Arnold.
Massey, D. and Meegan, R. (1979) 'The geography of industrial reorganisation', *Progress in Planning*, 10, p. 3.
Massey, D. and Meegan, R. (1982) *The Anatomy of Job Loss*, London, Methuen.
Massey, D. (1984) *Spatial Divisions of Labour*, Basingstoke, Macmillan.
Mathias, P. (1967) *Retailing Revolution*, London, Longmans.
May, E. (1981) 'Product positioning and segmentation strategy: adaptable to retail stores?', Chapter 13 in Stampfl, R. W. and Hirschmann, E. C. (eds.) *Theory in Retailing: Traditional and Non-Traditional Sources*, Chicago, American Marketing Association.
Melman, S. (1970) *Pentagon Capitalism*, New York, McGraw-Hill.
Mendelsohn, S. (1980) *Money on the Move*, New York, McGraw-Hill.
Merritt, G. (1982) *World Out of Work*, London, Collins.
Miles, I. (1975) *The Poverty of Prediction*, Farnborough, Saxon House.
Mills, C. W. (1956) *The Power Elite*, New York, Oxford University Press.
Minchinton, W. (1969) *Mercantilism*, Boston, Heath & Co.
Mitroff, I. and Mason, R. (1981) *Creating a Dialectical Social Science*, Dordrecht, D. Reidel.
Mount, F. (1990), *The Times* 2 February 1990.
Munton, R. J. C. (1977) 'Financial institutions: their ownership of agricultural land in Britain', *Area*, 9, pp. 29–37.
Murray, F. (1987) 'Flexible specialisation in the third Italy', *Capital and Class*, 33, pp. 84–95.
Musani, Y. and George, F. (1987) *Focus on European Retailers – Banque Paribas Capital Markets*, London, Banque Paribas.
Myrdal, G. (1957) *Economic Theory and Underdeveloped Regions*, London, Duckworth.
Nakane, C. (1970) *Japanese Society*, Harmondsworth, Penguin.
Nakanijhi, M. (1981) 'Marketing developments in Japan', *Journal of Marketing*, 45, 3, pp. 206–8.
NEDO (1988) *Part-Time Working in the Distributive Trades*, London, HMSO.
Nelson, R. L. (1958) *The Selection of Retail Locations*, New York, Dodge.
Newton, L. (1989) 'Takeovers, makeovers and destruction: the ethics of corporate transformation', Chapter 3 in Hofman W. M. *et al.* (eds.) *The Ethics of Organisational Transformation*, Westport, Quorum.
Norris, S. (1989) 'The return of impact assessment', paper presented to 29th RSA European Conference, Cambridge.
Norton, R. D. and Rees, J. (1979) 'The product cycle and the spatial decentralisation of American manufacturing', *Regional Studies*, 13, 141–51.
Pahl, R. (1984) *Divisions of Labour*, Oxford, Blackwell.

Penny, N. and Broom, D. (1988) 'The Tesco approach to store location', Chapter 4 in Wrigley, N. (ed.) *Store Choice, Store Location and Market Analysis*, London, Routledge.

Perrons, D. (1981) 'The role of Ireland in the new international division of labour: a proposed framework for analysis', *Regional Studies*, xv, 2, pp. 81–100.

Petit, P. (1986) *Slow Growth and the Service Economy*, London, Pinter Publishers.

Piercy, N. (1984) 'The impact of new technology on services marketing', *Service Industries Journal*, 4, 193–204.

Piore, M. and Sabel, C. (1984) *The Second Industrial Divide*, New York, Basic Books.

Plender, J. (1982) *That's the Way the Money Goes: The Financial Institutions and the Nation's Savings*, London, André Deutsch.

Plender, J. (1990) 'Throw sand in the takeover machine', *Financial Times*, 24 July.

Porter, M. (1990) *The Competitive Advantage of Nations*, London, Macmillan.

Poynor, M. (1987) 'The changing consumer', in McFadyen, E. (ed.) *The Changing Face of British Retailing*, London, Newman Books, pp. 103–13.

Rajan, A. (1987) *Services: The Second Industrial Revolution?*, London, Butterworth.

Rees, G. (1969) *St Michael: a History of Marks and Spencer*, London, Weidenfeld & Nicolson.

Rees, J. (1979) 'Technological change and regional shifts in American manufacturing', *Professional Geographer*, 31, pp. 45–54.

Rees, J. (1979) 'Manufacturing headquarters in the post industrial context', *Economic Geography*, 54, 337–54.

Robertson, K. A. (1983) 'Downtown retail activity in large American cities 1954–77', *Geographical Review*, 73, 314–23.

Robinson-Patman Antidiscrimination Act, (1936), amended section 15: 13 *US Federal Code on Price Discrimination by Monopolies and Combines*, Washington, US Government.

Rogers, D. (1983) 'The changing pattern of American retailing', *Retail and Distribution Management*, 11, pp. 8–13.

Roosa, R. (1967) *The Dollar and World Liquidity*, New York, Random House.

Rowland, B. M. (ed.) (1978) *The Balance of Power or Hegemony: The Interwar Monetary System*, New York, New York University Press.

Rueff, J. (1972) *Monetary Sin of the West*, London, Macmillan.

Rybczynski, T. M. (1988) 'Financial systems and industrial restructuring', *National Westminster Bank Quarterly Review*, November, pp. 3–13.

Sabel, C. (1982) *Work and Politics: The Division of Labour in Industry*, Cambridge, Cambridge University Press.

Sampson, A. (1982) *The Changing Anatomy of Britain*, London, Hodder & Stoughton.

Santink, J. L. (1990) *Timothy Eaton and the Rise of his Department Store*, Toronto, University of Toronto Press.

Sargent, J. R. (1979) 'UK performance in services', in F. Blackaby (ed.) *De-industrialisation*, London: Heinemann.

Saunders, L. (1988) 'The Campeau coup and the May manoeuvre', *Forbes Magazine*, 142, 10, pp. 98–9.

Savitt, R. (1987) in Johnson, G. (ed.) *Business Strategy and Retailing*, Chichester, Wiley, pp. 117–32.

Savitt, R. (1988) 'Comment: the wheel of the wheel of retailing', *International Journal of Retailing*, 3, 1, pp. 38–40.

Sayer, A. (1976) 'A critique of urban modelling', *Progress in Planning*, 6, 3, pp. 187–254.

Scammell, W. M. (1975) *International Monetary Policy*, London, Macmillan.
Schiller, R. K. (1971) 'Location trends of specialist services', *Regional Studies*, 5, pp. 1–10.
Schiller, R. K. (1972) 'The measurement of attractiveness of shopping centres to middle class luxury consumers', *Regional Studies*, 6, pp. 291–7.
Schiller, R. K. (1977) 'What the census says about shops', *Chartered Surveyor*, 109, pp. 190–92.
Schmitt, H. O. (1979) 'Mercantilism: a modern argument', *The Manchester School*, June.
Schoenberger, E. (1989) 'Thinking about flexibility', *Transactions of the Institute of British Geographers*, 14, 1, pp. 98–108.
Schumpeter, J. (1939) *Business Cycles: A Theoretical, Historical and Statistical Analysis of the Capitalist Process*, New York, McGraw-Hill.
Scott, A. J. (1991) 'Flexible production systems: a reply to Lovering', *International Journal of Urban and Regional Research*, 15, pp. 130–34.
Scott, M. (1982) 'Mythology and misplaced pessimism: the real failure record of new small businesses' in Watkins, D. *et al.* (eds.) *Stimulating Small Firms*, Aldershot, Gower, pp. 220–44.
Sethi, S. and Bhalla, B. (1989) 'Demanagerialisation of US industry', Chapter 18 in Hoffman W. M. *et al.* (eds.) *The ethics of organisational transformation*, Westport, Quorum.
Shaw, G. K. (1988) *Keynesian Economics*, Aldershot, Edward Elgar.
Shaoul, M. (1990) 'The acrobat of desire: consumer credit and its linkages to modern consumerism', working paper, *School of Management*, UMIST, Manchester.
Shevky, E. and Bell, W. (1955) *Social Area Analysis*, Stanford, Stanford University Press.
Short, J. R. and Bassett, K. A. (1981) 'Housing policy and the inner city in the 1970s', *Transactions of the Institute of British Geographers*, New Series, 6, pp. 293–312.
Short, J. R. (1984) *The Urban Arena*, London, Macmillan.
Short, J. R. (1989) 'Yuppies, yuffies and the new urban order', *Transactions Institute of British Geographers*, 14, pp. 173–88.
Shrager, C. (1987) 'LBO case study: Safeway stores', *Buyouts and Acquisitions*, 5, 1, pp. 344–8.
Sigler, A. (1989) 'What is a corporation's responsibility in the U.S. today?' in Hoffman W. M. *et al.* (eds.) *The Ethics of Organisational Transformation*, Quorum, Westport, pp. 85–90.
Smith, L. and Jones, D. (eds.) (1981) *Deprivation, Participation and Community Action*, London, Routledge & Kegan Paul.
Smith, A. (1975) *The wealth of nations*, London, Dent.
Smith, A. (1980) *The Geopolitics of Information: How Western Culture Dominates the World*, London, Faber.
Smith, R. and Wynne, B. (1989) *Expert Evidence: Interpreting Science in the Law*, London, Routledge.
Solomon, R. (1977) *The International Monetary System, 1949–1976: An Insider's View*, New York, Harper & Row.
Soloway, S. (1985) 'The step towards 100% scanning and the benefits achieved', *Proceedings, EPOS '85*, Sixth European Congress in Automation in Retailing, London.
Sparks, L. (1981) 'A note upon retail employment and superstore development', *Service Industries Review*, 1, 3, pp. 44–60.

Sparks, L. (1984) 'Electronic funds transfer at point of sale: an overview', Institute for Retail Studies Working Paper No. 8406, University of Stirling.

Spence, N. A. and Frost, M. E. (1983) 'Urban employment change', in Goddard, J. B. and Champion, A. G. (eds.) *The Urban and Regional Transformation of Britain*, London, Meuthuen, pp. 71–98.

Spero, J. (1985) *The Politics of International Economic Relations*, London, Allen & Unwin.

Spink, F. H. (1981) 'Downtown malls: prospects, design, constraints', in Sternlieb, G. and Hughes, J. W. (eds.) *Shopping Centres: USA*, Rutgers, NJ, State University of New Jersey, Centre for Urban Policy Research, pp. 201–18.

Stampfl, R. W. and Hirschmann, E. C. (1981) *Theory in Retailing: Traditional and Non-Traditional Sources*, Chicago, American Marketing Association (AMA).

Steinberg, B. (1983) 'The mass market is splitting apart', *Fortune*, 28 November, pp. 76–80.

Stopford, J., Channon, D. and Constable, J. (1980) *Cases in Strategic Management*, London, John Wiley.

Strange, S. (1971), *Sterling and British Policy: A Political Study of an International Currency in Decline*, London: Oxford University Press.

Strange, S. (ed.) (1984) *Paths to International Policy Economy*, London, Allen & Unwin.

Strange, S. (1986) *Casino Capitalism*, Oxford, Blackwell.

Strange, S. (1988) *States and Markets*, London, Frances Pinter.

Tait, N. (1989) 'If you don't succeed, hone your method', *Financial Times*, 20 April, p. 33.

Taylor, M. J. and Thrift, N. (1982) 'Models of corporate development and the multinational corporations', in Taylor, M. J. and Thrift, N. (eds.) *The Geography of Multinationals*, London, Croom Helm, pp. 14–32.

Teitz, M. (1986) 'Towards a theory of urban policy facility location', *Papers of the Regional Science Association*, 13, pp. 35–51.

Terasaka, A. (1985) 'Recent trends of commercial environment and the study of commercial geography in Japan', paper presented to IGU study group conference, Sorbonne, Paris, June.

Tew, B. (1982) *Evolution of the International Monetary System, 1945–76*, London, Hutchinson.

Thirlwall, A. P. (1982) 'De-industrialisation in the United Kingdom', *Lloyds Bank Review*, 144, April, pp. 22–37.

Thomas, R. E. (1970) 'Change in the distribution systems of western industrialised economics', *British Journal of Marketing*, 4, pp. 62–9.

Thompson, E. P. (1970) *The Making of the English Working Class*, Harmondsworth, Penguin.

Thompson, E. P. (1978) *The Poverty of Theory and Other Essays*, London, Merlin.

Thompson, W. (1975) 'Internal and external factors in urban economics', in Friedmann J. and Alonso W. (eds.) *Regional Development and Planning: A Reader*, Cambridge, MA, MIT Press.

Thrift, N. and Leyshon, A. (1990) 'In the wake of money: the City of London and the accumulation of value', Working Paper No. 16, University of Bristol and SIRC Portsmouth.

Thurow, L. (1981) *The Zero-Sum Society*, Harmondsworth, Penguin.

Toffler, A. (1981) *The Third Wave*, New York, Bantam.

Tooze, R. (1984) 'Perspectives and theory: a consumer's guide' in Strange, S. (ed.) *Paths to International Political Economy*, London, George Allen & Unwin, pp. 1–22.

Touraine, A. (1971) *The Post-Industrial Society*, New York, Random House.
Townsend, A. R. (1981) 'Geographical perspectives on major job losses in the UK 1977–80', *Area*, 13, 1, pp. 31–38.
Townsend, A. R. (1986) 'Spatial aspects of the growth of part-time employment in Britain', *Regional Studies*, 20, pp. 313–30.
Treadgold, A. (1990) 'Retail alliances in Europe' in Sanghavi, N. and Treadgold, A. (eds.) *Developments in European Retailing*, Yeovil, Dower House, pp. 77–90.
Triffin, R. (1966) *The World Money Maze: National Currencies in International Payments*, New Haven, CT, Yale University Press.
Tse, K. (1985) *Marks and Spencer: Anatomy of Britain's Most Efficiently Managed Company*, Oxford, Pergamon.
Uncles, M. D. and Ehrenberg, A. S. C. (1990) 'The buying of packaged goods at US retail chains', *Journal of Retailing*, 66, 3, pp. 278–96.
US Securities and Exchange Commission (1989) *File no 33–1047*, fiscal year ended 30 December 1989.
Veblen, T. (1989) *The Theory of the Leisure Class*, New York, Random House.
Vernon, R. (1971) *Sovereignty at Bay: The Multinational Spread of United States Enterprises*, New York, Basic Books.
Vernon, R. (1977) *Storm Over the Multinationals: The Real Issues*, Cambridge, MA, Harvard University Press.
Waldman, C. (1978) *Strategies of International Mass Retailers*, New York, Praeger.
Wallerstein, I. (1974) *The Modern World System*, New York, Academic Press.
Wallerstein, I. (1979) *The Capitalist World Economy*, Cambridge, Cambridge University Press.
Wallerstein, I. (1980) 'The future of the world-economy' in Hopkins, T. K. and Wallerstein, I. (eds.) *Processes of the World-System*, Beverley Hills, Sage.
Walters, D. (1975) 'Physical distribution features of the UK food industry', *Retail and Distribution Management*, 3, pp. 42–7.
Walters, M. (1988) *How to make a killing in new issues*, London, Sidgwick & Jackson.
Wanniski, J. (1978) *The Way the World Works*, New York, Basic Books.
Waters, C. D. J. (1984) 'Is UK manufacturing industry really overstocked?', *International Journal of Physical Distribution and Materials Management*, 14, 5, pp. 5–10.
Weber, M. (1948) *Essays in Sociology*, trans. and ed. Gerth, H. and Wright Mills, C., London, Routledge & Kegan Paul.
Weber, M. (1950) *The Protestant Ethic and the Spirit of Capitalism*, New York, Schrager.
Weber, M. (1968) *Economy and Society*, trans. Fischoff, E., New York, Bedminster.
Weitzel, W., Schwartzkopf, A. and Peach, E. (1989) 'The influence of employee perceptions of customer service on retail store sales', *Journal of Retailing*, 65, 1, pp. 27–39.
Wells, L. T. (ed.) (1972) *The Product Life Cycle and International Trade*, Cambridge, MA, Harvard University Press.
Wells, J. D. and Imber, J. C. (1977) 'The home and export peformance of United Kingdom industries', *Economic Trends*, 286, pp. 78–81.
Wiener, M. (1981) *English Culture and the Decline of the Industrial Spirit 1850–1980*, Cambridge, Cambridge University Press.
Williams, R. (1984) 'The International Political Economy of technology', Chapter 5 in Strange, S. (ed.) *Paths to International Political Economy*, London, Allen & Unwin.
Wilson, C. (1965) *England's Apprenticeship*, London, Longmans.
Wilson, A. G. (1976) 'Retailers' profits and consumers' welfare in a spatial

interaction shopping model', in Masser, I. (ed.) *Theory and Practice in Regional Science*, London, Pion, pp. 42–59.

Wilson Report (1980) *Committee to Review the Functioning of Financial Institutions*, Cmnd 7939, London HMSO.

Wintzer, F. W. (1985) 'The future of off-price retailing', *Retail Control*, January, pp. 21–3.

Wolferen, K. van (1989) *The Enigma of Japanese Power*, London, Macmillan.

Wolman, C. (1988) 'Dramatic gains for the rich', *Financial Times*, 16 March, p. 25.

Wolpert, J. (1964) 'The decision process in spatial context', *Annals of the Association of American Geographers*, 64, pp. 537–8.

Woronoff, J. C. (1984) *Japan's Commercial Empire*, Armonk, M. E. Sharpe.

Wrigley, N. (1987) 'The concentration of capital in UK grocery retailing', *Environment and Planning A*, 19, pp. 1283–8.

Wrigley, N. (1988) 'Retail restructuring and retail analysis' in *Store Choice, Store Location and Market Analysis*, Wrigley, N. (ed.), London, Routledge, pp. 3–34.

Wrigley, N. (1989) 'The lure of the USA: further reflections on the internationalisation of British grocery retailing capital', *Environment and Planning A*, 21, 283–8.

Wrigley, N. (1990) 'Retail restructuring in the UK', paper presented to Fulbright Colloquium, Miskin Manor, Wales, December.

Wrong, D. H. L. (1979) *Power: its Forms, Bases and Uses*, Oxford, Blackwell.

Wynne, B. (1982) *Rationality and Ritual*, Chalfont St Giles, British Society for the History of Science.

Yeager, L. B. (1966) *International Monetary Relations*, New York, Harper & Row.

Young, H. (1989/90) *One of Us*, London, Macmillan/Pan.

Zysman, J. (1983) *Governments, Markets and Growth*, New York, Cornell University Press.

Index